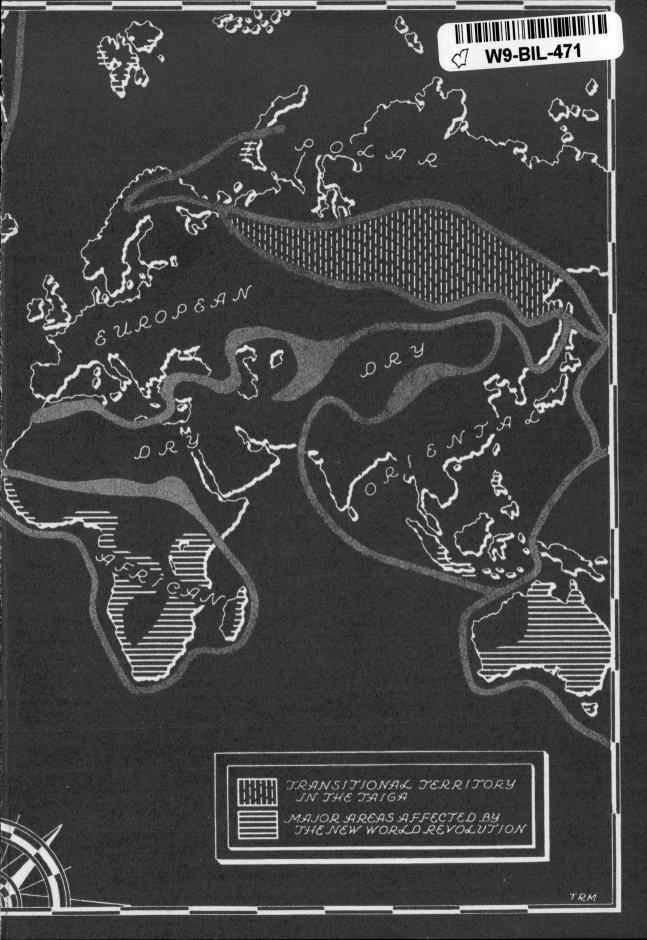

TRANSITIONAL TERRITORY
IN THE TAIGA

MAJOR AREAS AFFECTED BY
THE NEW WORLD REVOLUTION

POLAR

EUROPEAN

DRY

DRY

ORIENTAL

AFRICAN

TRM

Brief Edition

CULTURE WORLDS

Brief Edition

CULTURE

WORLDS

RICHARD JOEL RUSSELL
FRED BOWERMAN KNIFFEN

Professors of Geography, Louisiana State University

EVELYN LORD PRUITT

Head, Geography Branch, Office of Naval Research

New York THE MACMILLAN COMPANY

Library of Congress catalog card number: 61–5508

The Macmillan Company, New York
Brett-Macmillan Ltd., Galt, Ontario

Printed in the United States of America

This book is an abridged and revised edition of *Culture Worlds* by Richard Joel Russell and Fred Bowerman Kniffen, copyright 1951 by The Macmillan Company.

Foreword

More than twenty years have elapsed since the Culture Worlds approach to geography at the first-year level was initiated at Louisiana State University. During roughly the first half of that time students were furnished with syllabus outlines that evolved gradually into the textbook used for the rest of the period. The advantage of starting the curriculum with a comprehensive regional course is satisfactory in all ways. Students enjoy the subject, the faculty respect it and give it high priority in the curricula of all colleges, and an excellent background is provided for students who continue with other courses in geography. Students unable to continue retain a valuable understanding of the earth's parts and peoples.

Although CULTURE WORLDS has been adopted widely as a textbook, its most common use has been as a text for a one-semester courses, a use not recommended by its authors. To meet the need for presenting the major themes and pertinent content of CULTURE WORLDS in a text suitable in length and content for a one-semester course, the authors turned to Miss Evelyn L. Pruitt, Head of the Geography Branch of the Office of Naval Research, with the request that she undertake the preparation of a brief, revised edition. Miss Pruitt's capable editing of the *Professional Geographer* and familiarity with world-wide geographical problems suggested her as an ideal choice for the assignment. The original authors agree that she has succeeded admirably.

The decade since CULTURE WORLDS appeared has been unmatched in population growth and political change. Emendations and corrections of the original edition halfway through the decade served to some extent in keeping information current but could not have anticipated happenings in Africa nor the many name changes and boundary shifts occurring elsewhere. In a sense these are details, far outweighed by events over a long history that are responsible for the world's cultural landscapes, but any textbook must be kept up to date insofar as possible. This Brief Edition attempts seriously to present accurate data current at the time of going to press.

CULTURE WORLDS was written with the idea in mind that all students would be required to own a reasonably good atlas. Its many maps made no pretense of including all places mentioned in the text, though care was taken to use customary spellings of place names and to include only those to be found in the better student atlases. In the Brief Edition the maps have been revised not only to bring them up to date but also to cover all places mentioned in the text. Cartographic revision has been directed by Philip B. Larimore, Jr., to whom the authors are indebted. New maps have been added to show population densities and other information not included in the original edition. There has been a notable increase in the number of photographs.

The Brief Edition contains almost precisely half of the number of lines of text of the original edition for sections other than the American World, which remains at approximately its original length. Though completely rewritten, the text retains much of the style, wording, and essential content of CULTURE WORLDS. Condensation results from omission of detail and content not regarded as essential for one-semester treatment. Many guide lines for the revision were furnished by persons who were kind enough to send us criticisms of the original edition. We hope that suggestions for further improvement may be forthcoming.

RICHARD JOEL RUSSELL
FRED BOWERMAN KNIFFEN
EVELYN LORD PRUITT

Baton Rouge and Washington

Before we prefent you the matters of fact
it is fit to offer to your view the State whereon they were acted:
for as Geographie without Hiftorie feemeth a carkaffe without motions;
fo Hiftorie without Geographie,
wandereth as a Vagrant without certaine habitation.

JOHN SMITH—*The Generall Hiftorie of Virginia, New England, and the Summer Ifles*

Contents

PACIFIC WORLD

AMERICAN WORLD

Maps

CULTURE WORLDS

Home of El Molo people, Kenya
[*British Information Service*]

1. Culture Worlds

Because we live in the European culture world we accept the *culture traits*, the ways of living and thinking, of that world and consider them reasonable and logical, but we are mistaken if we think that all the inhabitants of the earth would find our cultural patterns acceptable. We live in houses, own land, and recognize certain lines as boundaries between individual properties, states, and countries. Our houses have glass windows, hinged doors, and rooms for such special uses as sleeping, eating, preparation of food, entertaining, and recreation. These habitations are served by definite systems of streets, roads, sidewalks, or other avenues of transportation. Closely spaced groups of houses and other buildings form villages, towns, and cities. At least the more important of these are served by water supply systems, sewers, and such public utilities as gas and electricity. These culture traits seem elementary and commonplace to us, but to the peoples of large parts of the earth they would be novel, unworkable, amusing, or beyond belief.

We are self-sufficient to only a very limited degree. Most of us would perish promptly if turned loose without clothing or implements of any kind in territory teeming with fish, abounding in game, and richly endowed with vegetable fibers and edible plants. We require the services of many groups of people just to make and sell ordinary garments, and a huge crew is needed to feed an urban dweller. To many of the

1

earth's inhabitants who are highly self-sufficient, these complications appear ridiculous, but we live in an extremely specialized *culture world*.

People in the European culture world normally make livings by performing highly specialized tasks. The services of many experts are likely to be available to us every day. In any city, town, or large village we expect to find barbers, doctors, lawyers, clergymen, educators, plumbers, and other specialists. We expect to be able to purchase meat, vegetables, utensils of all sorts, and all necessities of life. We assume the presence of "modern" conveniences to be perfectly normal. Many people in other culture worlds would regard such culture traits as strange, antireligious, or impracticable.

All these things we accept and expect simply because we were raised in this particular culture world. No one is born with any prejudices about culture traits, nor with any special adaptability toward those which are characteristic of one individual culture world. The things we grow up with become the normal things and the ways we use them become the natural ways. The things and ways of other peoples are strange in proportion to the degree of contrast with ours. At our next meal we expect to use such utensils as knife, fork, spoon, plate, glass, or salt shaker, but over a quarter of the world's population anticipates the use of chopsticks and bowls. And so would we, had we been raised in the Orient. Had we lived a number of generations ago, even in the European culture world, we would not have used knives and forks, nor worn the kinds of clothing we now wear. This is because cultures are dynamic, always in a state of modification, evolution, and substitution. Any individual culture trait has its place in time as well as its identification with place or people. As cultures change, culture traits may spread far beyond the world in which they originate. Acceptance of culture traits by even a large group of people does not mean that populations are incorporated automatically into the originating culture world. European clothing, for example, has been widely adopted, but the mere fact that such clothing is worn by many Japanese, for instance, does not mean that they are part of the European culture world, for the Japanese have a whole array of other culture traits that are entirely different from those of the European world. People are regarded as having the same culture only when all or most of their culture traits are essentially similar.

The culture of the United States is almost purely of European origin. In the main it developed in northwestern Europe. From the English we have taken our guiding principles of morals and ethics, most of our basic design for living, the fundamental parts of our legal code, our complicated language, and our awkward system of weights and measures. We have modified many English culture traits and will change others in the future. There are today many cultural contrasts between England and the United States, but as compared with other peoples the kinship is very close. We feel very much at home in England, but find many things that seem curious. We observe many examples of what we consider strange conduct, we are confronted with an environment that seems old-fashioned and inefficient, and we probably dislike the way food is prepared; but we see that in general the English live very much as we do, enjoy the things we enjoy, and that they tolerate our cultural differences about as well as we tolerate theirs. Far different and to

Tea ceremony, Japan
[*Consulate General of Japan, N.Y.*]

us far more difficult to understand are the ways of eastern Europeans. Culture traits of the Arabs or of other peoples beyond the confines of the European culture world are so foreign that many seem incomprehensible.

Tracing the ancestry of our own culture brings us first to the British Isles, which, by the time the earliest English colonists were leaving for America, had already undergone a tremendous *cultural evolution*. When Caesar reached southern Britain in the first century B.C. he found a group of barbarians who painted their bodies blue, and who were extremely backward in the ways of civilization as measured by Roman standards. Between that time and the colonization of America the English people had changed not only culturally but physically. Only in part were they descended from the Mediterranean and Alpine Britons known to Caesar. The main stock had become Nordic as a result of invasions from the continent. The culture that evolved in Great Britain blended elements brought in by various Germanic tribes, such as Angles and Saxons, and by Scandinavians, and it drew heavily from the French. These peoples from the continent came from cultures that had similarly undergone considerable change. Some five thousand years ago Europeans might be considered barbarians in comparison with the peoples of Mesopotamia and parts of Africa who stood far higher on the scale of civilization. In those places flourishing kingdoms existed where people were engaged in specialized tasks, where architecture and science had made progress, and where written records were being kept. It took many centuries before equivalent cultural advancement reached any part of Europe. From northwestern Europe, then, we find that our culture paths lead to the eastern Mediterranean, Egypt, Mesopotamia, and India, crossing parts of three culture worlds.

The cultural evolution of man was slow. He probably originated somewhere in the tropics, and at a very early time is known to have lived in Java, Africa, and eastern Asia. By some such time as half a million years ago men were inhabiting many parts of south and east Africa, Europe, and western Asia. During most of man's early experience he depended on stones, bones, and wood as hard implements. After many thousands of years he discovered that advantageous shapes could be obtained by chipping, and later he found that stones could be made into desired shapes by grinding and polishing. When peoples of the Near East discovered the use of metals, less than eight thousand years ago, a *cultural revolution* was initiated. It started with copper, and later man found that a mixture of tin and copper produced bronze, an alloy harder than either and hence more useful. Slowly came the use of iron, steel, and other metals. These were tremendous forward strides and long intervals of time passed between them; still longer intervals were required for the knowledge of these discoveries to become widespread. Cultural changes associated with even the most important discoveries were localized for long periods. Even today there are some very backward peoples in this world according to our standards, for culture traits spread slowly.

Geographers are interested in culture traits and cultures in general because they provide a rational and fundamental basis for dividing the earth's surface into its most significant parts. Peoples who are closest akin culturally tend to modify landscapes in similar ways so that they live in places that physically resemble their homelands, and they alter the landscapes in ways to which they are accustomed. New Zealand today looks far more like England than would have been the case if its dominant European population had been French.

Geography is the study of the earth's surface. It is concerned very much with man because he is the most active agent in changing the earth's surface today. Man upsets balances of nature both deliberately and unintentionally. He remodels landscapes to serve his needs, almost at will. In the earliest times, primitive peoples made few changes in the landscape. Once man had learned to use fire as a weapon against undesirable vegetation or as an aid in hunting animals, an era of landscape modification began. Grasslands expanded at the expense of forests. Forces of nature capable of removing surface soil or cutting ravines began to enjoy accelerated activity. With further cultural advancement man's effect on landscape became more profound. He dug canals, removed vast quantities of coal, iron, and other materials from the earth, built roads, constructed dams and huge buildings, and in innumerable other ways altered the earth's surface. The *natural landscapes* of the earth with their topographic, hydrographic, vegetational, and other forms have been converted nearly everywhere into complex *cultural landscapes* with new forms that vary according to the culture groups who have produced them.

MAJOR CULTURE GROUPS

The geographer is extremely interested in the fact that a culture boundary crosses Africa from the mouth of the Senegal River to Khartoum in Sudan and southeast to the mouth of the Juba River. On the north are peoples mainly of Caucasoid racial stock who follow nomadic pursuits, living in tents and moving with flocks, or who live crowded together in oases. To the south are mainly Negroid peoples who live in small huts and houses, who depend largely on primitive agriculture involving the use of crude hoes. Languages, religious beliefs, codes of morals, possessions, and practically all other culture traits differ fundamentally on opposing sides of this boundary. The major culture group to the north is Arabian, and to the south it is Negroid. The location of this boundary is a result of neither chance nor political decision. In the main it follows a significant climatic boundary which marks the change from vast areas of dry climates, grassy steppes, and barren deserts on the north to the humid climates on the south where tropical savannas with rank, tall grass, or rain forest with densely spaced trees, prevail. The Arabian peoples understand how to live in dry regions, while the Negroid peoples understand ways of life in territory where the vegetation is altogether too luxuriant by Arabian standards of usefulness.

The contrast between Arabian and Negroid parts of Africa is so striking that it deserves recognition as a cultural boundary of the *first order*. There are relatively few first order divisions between cultures, and they separate the main groupings of mankind's *culture worlds*.

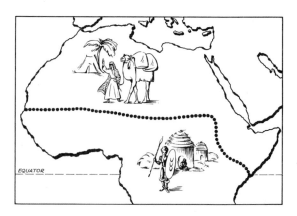

Boundary between culture worlds

Each culture world, of course, contains within it some variety of peoples and culture traits, but these local variations are minor in contrast to the dominant characteristics that unify each culture world, and are quite insignificant in comparison with the differences that exist between culture worlds. To distinguish local differences within a culture world, there are divisions of the *second order*, each of which is a *culture realm*. Within each realm there may be smaller units, *culture regions*.

EUROPEAN WORLD

European culture is noted for aggressiveness. Europeans, since the dawn of history, have gone to distant lands as tradesmen, soldiers, and colonizers. With them has gone the notion that their own culture traits are "right," all others being "wrong," barbaric, or of low order. Many Europeans have felt the duty of spreading European culture and "enlightenment" among foreign or "less fortunate" peoples. Rarely does the European question the superiority of his own culture traits, and he tends to judge the "progress" of non-European cultures by the degree to which they accept his culture traits. What are some of the outstanding traits of this aggressive and self-confident culture?

Field agriculture is a characteristic of the European World. Each field belongs to someone, and its size is large in comparison with fields in many parts of the world. Crop raising involves the use of such implements as metal plows, cultivators, harrows, and harvesters, many of which are powered mechanically. A large part of the food required by the entire population comes from the fields, but the proportion of persons engaged in agriculture is rather small and tends to diminish as time goes on. Places are considered "backward" where more than half the population is rural and agricultural. "Progressive" places require fewer than one quarter of the people to till the land. Just as an example, rice is grown both in the United States and Japan, but in the United States where it is planted and dusted by airplane, and harvested and threshed by machine, it takes only seven man-hours to grow one acre, while in Japan it takes 900 man-hours of hand labor.

Industrialization is an outstanding trait of European culture. Accompanying it is a marked degree of *urbanization*, or growth of large cities. There were a few large cities in the Ancient Mediterranean world, such as Athens, Carthage, and Rome, and today there are some huge cities of non-European origin, but the great cities of the European World are different from any of these. A large European World city is not only a concentration of people, a market on a grand scale, but it is a product of a highly developed technology, a place where raw materials are

Field agriculture, Austria
[*Austrian Information Service*]

converted into manufactured products rapidly and in enormous quantities. Industrialization is comparatively new, and with it came many specialized fields of activity, new occupations, and a steady increase in vocational opportunities.

No other culture world comes close to the European in technological development and specialization. European culture expects and demands that people specialize, that they become doctors, lawyers, educators, bankers, merchandizers, and the like, and in our particular segment of the European world we go even farther, and expect to be able to call upon the services of people who are expert in just a tiny part of one field of specialization. There was a time not too far back when barbers were called upon to act as surgeons, but now we demand not only a highly trained surgeon, we expect one who is expert in a particular field of surgery. Such specialization has arisen as a consequence of industrialization and urbanization. It is least developed in rural areas, where professional people, like general stores, still cater to a wide variety of needs.

The aggressive European World, with such culture traits as field agriculture, industrialization, urbanization, and a high degree of occupational specialization, is characterized by the things and ways that seem most ordinary to us. But it should be remembered that these are by no means common throughout the world, and that to a degree these and other culture traits vary within the European World. These internal variations are the basis for distinguishing secondary divisions: Northwestern Europe Realm, Eastern Europe Realm, and Mediterranean Realm.

ORIENTAL WORLD

More than 4,000 years ago a distinctive culture had advanced far toward its present condition in parts of northern China. The culture spread southward into the Red Basin of Szechwan and beyond. The spread was resisted by primitive, possibly Caucasoid, inhabitants of eastern Asia. Mongoloid peoples gradually pushed back the walls of "barbarism"

Dry steppe landscape, Israel

[*Israel Office of Information*]

and spread their culture over much of southeastern Asia. A culture world was developed in China and it spread widely, bringing "progress" and "enlightenment" to backward places, but the enlightenment was a Chinese brand, not our own.

The Indus Valley of western India witnessed another important cultural development in extremely remote times. Spreading to the upper Ganges Valley, this culture became centered in one of the world's most productive regions and so felt the attack of many successive waves of invaders, plunderers, and colonizers. The evolving culture of India resembled that of the Chinese somewhat more closely than that of Europeans. These basic similarities continue to the present day, and justify the inclusion of the Indian Realm in the Oriental World in a position equal to the Chinese Realm. Somewhat distinct from either of these Realms, yet drawing on both of them, is the culture exhibited in the garlands of islands that drape the southeastern Asian coast. This cultural subdivision of the Oriental World is called Malayan Realm.

The distinctions between realms are subordinate to the unifying cultural characteristics displayed throughout southern and eastern Asia that place all this territory in the Oriental World. Everywhere there is the tradition of a very old civilization, one that predates the European civilization, making the Orientals feel spiritually and culturally superior. Rooted deep in their culture are many traits that are completely incomprehensible to a European, such as the willingness to accept an arbitrarily assigned place in a hierarchy of rank, as in the caste system, the lack of value placed on the individual and even on his life, the whole complicated business of "saving face," and what constitutes "honor." Although within the Oriental World there is great diversity of religions, languages, and social organizations, this diversity itself is a unifying element.

DRY WORLD

Between the European and Oriental worlds is the largest and broadest belt of arid climates on earth. This belt reaches from the Atlantic coast of northern Africa to the Great Khingan Mountains bordering western Manchuria near the Pacific. Within it are many individual deserts, some of vast dimensions. The *deserts* are territories of extreme aridity, with broad surfaces too dry to support enough grass to permit a grazing economy. Marginal to the deserts are less arid *steppes*, too dry for forest growth but wet enough to support grasses. The grass is bunchy and scattered along the arid borders of the steppe, and taller and more abundant along the borders of *humid climates*, where precipitation is ample to allow forest growth. The Dry World not only has served as a barrier between peoples in culture worlds of the humid climates on either side, but has developed a significant culture of its own.

Dry World peoples are typically nomadic, or else they dwell in more or less congested oases. To survive under conditions that most of the earth's inhabitants would consider intolerable, it was essential that they develop ways of life quite different from those of well-watered lands. They did this along the lines of herding, oasis agriculture, and banditry, characteristics that are equally common in the Arab-Berber Realm of north Africa and Arabia where the problem is one of dryness and heat, and in the Turko-Mongolian Realm where drought combines with cold.

AFRICAN WORLD

To the south of Dry World Africa is the home of most Negroid peoples. Isolated from European cultures by broad, inhospitable deserts and inhabiting lands only partially suited to adaptation of Dry World culture traits, African World peoples have solved problems of living and have developed cultures along lines strikingly unlike those of peoples to the north. By European standards the culture is primitive, being dominated by simple gathering and hunting, pastoral nomadism, and hoe agriculture. This "dark" and mysterious part of Africa, once it was "discovered" by Europeans, offered a rich prize, a source of slaves and raw materials, and lands which could be incorporated into European empires. Although colonial status is now fast disappearing from the African World, the cultural imprint of Europeans is still very evident in the exploitation of resources and in political organization, especially in the dominantly European south Africa.

POLAR WORLD

The *taiga*, a broad, monotonous forest, separates territory inhabited by Europeans and Orientals from a belt of *tundra*, or treeless land along the shores of the Arctic Ocean. The inhabitants are Mongoloids who have learned to live in the tundra mainly at the expense of animals. The severe climate precludes agriculture, but allows reindeer herding, typical of the Eurasian Realm, and the hunting of seal and caribou and fishing, characteristic of the American Realm. Isolation and uniqueness of culture traits distinguish the inhabitants of the Arctic territories as a culture world quite unlike any other.

No similar development occurred in the Southern Hemisphere. The Antarctic continent was too remote and too hostile environmentally to be habitable. The scattered islands in the southern ocean are still mainly uninhabited, although occasionally visited by whalers.

AMERICAN WORLD

When Columbus took part in a period of exploration known as the Voyages of Discovery, he found peoples who were mistakenly identified as Indians on the assumption that the lands they inhabited were part of Asia. These peoples were racially Mongoloid, but they had arrived in America at such an early time that all trace of an Asian cultural heritage had disappeared. In the Americas they evolved many distinct cultures. The highly developed civilizations of the Mexican and Andean plateaus compared favorably with any contemporaneous European culture and in some respects were superior. Indians had domesticated a long list of plants and animals which were adopted by the Europeans when they arrived, and which have become basic elements in American life. Just as the Indians had developed a diversity of cultures in the many different kinds of natural landscapes they inhabited, so did the arriving Europeans. Diversity, then, is a recognized characteristic of the cultures of the American World, cultures which in a small way incorporate Indian contributions, but which stem mainly from Europe. Distinctions within the American World rest primarily on the origins of the Europeans who settled the Americas and put their imprint on the landscape. To the north, French and English ties help to identify the Anglo-American Realm, while to the south the Latin-American Realm shows evidence of Spanish and Portuguese influence.

PACIFIC WORLD

The continent of Australia and the many islands to its immediate north and dotting the Pacific Ocean may be regarded as a single culture world whose roots are largely in the Malayan Realm of the Oriental World, but with an overprint of cultures of the European World. Australia long remained remote, and together with adjacent islands, was inhabited by some of the world's most primitive peoples whose cultural development involved simple hunting and gathering in Australia, and fishing and limited agriculture in the islands. Material wealth was meager and cultural attainments were few, yet among the inhabitants of the Pacific World there were widespread and highly developed skills, such as seamanship and navigation. On the basis both of primitive cultures and of modern development as a result largely of European impacts, four subdivisions are apparent: Australian and New Zealand Realm, Polynesian Realm, Melanesian Realm, and Micronesian Realm.

NEW WORLD REVOLUTION

From the beginning of the 16th century, Europeans have embarked on waves of domination, conquest, and colonization on a scale such as the world had never before experienced. There had been many important early migrations and conquests; armies had moved thousands of miles on errands of subjugation and plunder, uninhabited territories had been appropriated by peoples in search of new homes, but all such events are insignificant when compared with the happenings that followed the Voyages of Discovery. Possessing superior ships, more effective arms, and a feeling of righteousness in their will to spread religion and culture, as well as to establish new avenues of trade, Europeans initiated with extraordinary vigor an attempt to dominate the entire world, once they discovered how vast and varied it is. This entire movement is the *New World Revolution*, and it is still in progress.

New World includes those parts of the earth that have experienced the introduction of European World cultures at the expense of cultures already present. The typical pattern of New World Revolution is illustrated by the Americas, where Europeans have succeeded in displacing or exterminating original American World cultures over vast areas. The pattern is also exhibited in South Africa, Australia and New Zealand, and on many islands in the Pacific World.

Europeans used their own values in appraising foreign lands, and promptly took over parts they considered most desirable. In many cases native peoples or cultures were exterminated, as in Tasmania, Australia, and most of the United States. In other cases there was considerable assimilation and mixing of peoples and cultures, as in much of Middle and South America and many parts of Polynesia. Isolated remnants of old cultures commonly remained after the contest between Europeans and natives, and examples are seen in many Indian groups in the Americas that remain almost untouched by European culture today.

The older, well-established cultures of the Oriental and Dry worlds have proved extremely resistant to New World influences. Much Dry World territory is hostile from a physical standpoint and escapes European inroads for the same reason that much of the Polar World remains untouched. The culture traits of the Oriental World are held by such vast hordes that Europeans have made little headway in displacing them. Many Orientals feel about the same contempt, pity, and superiority toward the European that the latter feels toward primitive savages. European culture has managed to establish only a few island outposts in the Oriental World, such as Hongkong and Shanghai, but the influence is restricted and hardly felt in the back country, or hinterland.

In South Africa the domination of Europeans has developed according to typical New World patterns and has reached nearly to completion in extensive areas. In other parts of the African World the Revolution is still very much in progress; European ways are being adopted, but European control is being thrown off in a surge of nationalism and independence.

Russians were pioneers in the New World

Children dancing, Transvaal
[*South African Information Service*]

movement. A *Siberian Wedge* of European culture was pushed across Asia to the Pacific, and temporary outposts were established at an early date along the western coast of North America. Today no other people surpass their activity in thrusting cultures and influence into foreign culture worlds. The Dry World boundary has been pushed back notable distances in central Asia and the hostile taiga is being crossed. Deep inroads are affecting the Soviet segment of the Polar World.

THESIS

Individual assemblages of people possess characteristic culture traits that enable social scientists to group peoples according to their cultures. The broadest of these groupings are culture worlds. Seven of these are so distinctive that they form an excellent basis for introducing students to the field of geography. These broadest divisions of the earth are the European, Dry, African, Oriental, Polar, Pacific, and American worlds. Each has subordinate realms and regions. The pattern of life in each culture world has come about through a long and complicated series of events and experiences which have left their imprint on the landscape. Within the last few centuries the European World has undergone amazing expansion, a movement recognized as the New World Revolution.

The primary interest of the geographer is in the earth as it exists today. He seeks to understand and explain its surface. In most places he finds man, knowingly or unawares, changing the face of the earth. The type of changes varies in accordance with the culture group concerned, for the forms of the cultural landscape are a complex expression of man's culture, superposed upon or replacing the forms of the natural landscape. Each culture world has its own characteristic culture traits and its own typical cultural landscape. An entrance into the field of geography can best be made through a study of these culture worlds.

POLAR WORLD

Arctic landscape, Greenland
[*U.S. Army photograph*]

2. *Polar World*

NATURAL LANDSCAPES

The Polar World is physically and culturally the least complex of the seven culture worlds. Economically it is simple because the activities of its inhabitants are restricted by the severity of the environment. There is little possibility for these people beyond eking out a primitive existence by hunting, fishing and a little reindeer herding. It is no wonder that this population is sparsely distributed. In the Polar World, it is nature, rather than man, that dominates the scene. And to anyone except the inhabitants, nature presents a hostile array of cold, ice, and treeless lands. Life here is simple and direct. Basic needs are supplied by the things close at hand and the choice is strictly limited.

Restricted and direct as Polar World material

cultures seem, there are many local differences in this Arctic fringe extending from northern Norway across Eurasia and North America to eastern Greenland. The ways men fish, use caribou, or make weapons, for example, vary from place to place. This diversity in culture traits splits the Polar World into two main realms, each including many significant culture regions.

The boundaries of the Polar World are cultural and its extent is determined by the geographical distribution of a general way of life. In North America, the boundary is between Eskimo and Indian. Across Eurasia the demarcation may be between such peoples as the Lapps and Europeans, or between tundra dwellers of the Siberian coasts and the forest tribes to the south. The Asian boundary is

13

really a zone of taiga, or boreal forests, to some extent invaded by Polar World peoples and, in recent years, by Europeans in large numbers. It is a wide transition zone between the Polar World and the Siberian Wedge of the European World.

Realms of the Polar World

Although these boundaries are cultural, they correspond in general to natural boundaries. The southern limit of the Polar World is approximately the northern edge of forest growth. Roughly speaking, forests can grow as far north as the July isotherm of 50°F. This isotherm is a line connecting adjacent places where the average temperature during July is 50°. North of the line and on land at higher elevations, the average temperature is cooler and the area is treeless tundra. To the south and on lower land it is warmer and here is found the taiga forest. July is the warmest month of the year in Arctic regions.

The Polar World is chiefly a cultural development of the tundra, but in places it spreads beyond the tundra, and all tundra does not fall within its limits. Iceland, for example, is certainly a region of tundra vegetation and climate, all months of the year being cooler than 50°F., but in no sense is it part of the

Polar World. Its first settlers were European and its culture has remained European since it was established over a thousand years ago. On the other hand, the Aleutian Islands, where climatic conditions are a little less severe, are inhabited by Eskimolike Aleuts whose culture is distinctly that of the Polar World. The influence of European culture has been slight on polar or subpolar regions, despite the fact that outposts of the European World are fairly numerous and have been for several centuries. Furs, whaling, minerals, and scientific exploration have attracted Europeans, but only to a few localities. There they staunchly cling to their European ways of life as much as possible. Nor do they convert many Polar World inhabitants, very few of whom have become permanently incorporated into the European, or any other, culture world.

LANDFORMS

The Polar World stretches along the borders of the Arctic Ocean in a circular belt mainly north of the Arctic Circle. The Arctic shoreline is extremely irregular. Many peninsulas jut poleward, such as Boothia in Canada and Taimyr in Siberia. The Canadian sector is covered with many islands, large and small. To the east is the large island of Greenland. Between Greenland and Europe, where the sea is relatively shallow, Iceland, Jan Mayen, Svalbard (Spitsbergen), and other islands rise above the submerged continental platform. North of Eurasia lie such detached continental fragments as Novaya Zemlya, Northern Land, New Siberian Islands, and Wrangel Island. The bays and seas along the borders of the Arctic Ocean all have local names, such as Barents Sea and Beaufort Sea. The White Sea and the Gulf of Ob mark prominent indentations of the coast. The greatest indentation is Hudson Bay, a shallow continental sea whose southern shores lie outside the Polar World.

The Arctic Ocean is connected with both the Pacific and the Atlantic. The Pacific connection is the narrow opening at Bering Strait. Here the Asian and American peninsulas lie only 36 miles apart. In the geologic past this has served as an important *land bridge* used by man and many animals and plants as they migrated between the two major land masses. No such simple bridge spanned the many connections between the Arctic and Atlantic oceans. The broad passageways between Labrador and Greenland, Greenland and Iceland, and Iceland and the British Isles or Scandinavia have been more effective barriers. Even though in the distant past some of these gaps have been closed by land links enabling plants and animals to migrate at least between northern Europe and Greenland, no primitive man ever crossed this bridge.

The land fringing the Arctic Ocean is mainly flat. In fact, most of the land of the Polar World consists of coastal lowlands or low plateaus with mountains occurring only here and there along the southern border or in scattered areas as on the coasts of Greenland, Labrador, and eastern Baffin Land. Many Polar lands are new, made up of recently deposited alluvial deltas and plains, which account in part for the general flatness. Old-rock areas are flattened because here the processes of weathering and removal of debris work at high speed. Rocks are exposed to the elements with little or no protective soil cover. Changes in temperature, the prying action of ice being formed in crevices, chemical attack by waters carrying organic acids, and similar processes shatter the rocks. During the summer, the fragmental debris above the impermeable permanently frozen ground becomes saturated and slides down hill at a rapid rate, thus tending to level the terrain.

Permanently frozen ground underlies most of the Polar World. Water, unable to penetrate it, remains on or near the surface, forming the innumerable lakes and bogs that characterize the lowlands. The typical stream crossing the tundra is sluggish and wanders aimlessly among the shallow ponds. Streams become active only during the season of thaw when most of the land is surfaced with ooze. There are, however, a number of large, north-flowing rivers that empty into the Arctic Ocean, but they originate well south of the Polar World. The Mackenzie, Ob, Yenisei, Lena and others have served as routes of European World penetration, but

what is of more importance to the inhabitants of the Polar World, these rivers bring driftwood from the forested regions to the treeless Arctic shores. They also bring spring floods. The fact that summer warmth thaws their headwaters before the downstream parts are released from their frozen winter state causes widespread innundation that effectively prohibits surface travel.

A number of interesting landforms is found in the Arctic and subarctic regions. Slopes are commonly *striped*, as if giant rakes had been drawn down them. This banded effect is caused by the varying downslope speed of rock fragments. In fast moving bands, the rocks stand on edge while there is no particular orientation to the rocks in bands of slower movement. Very fast-moving bands, called *rock streams*, lead to *talus* accumulations resembling the piles of rock rubble found beneath steep slopes in milder climates. *Polygonal ground* is a common occurrence. This pattern is formed either by hexagonal rings of stones shoved to the surface by *frost action* or by somewhat circular depressions or trenches lying above buried ice wedges. On the flatter surfaces the pattern is fairly regular while on the slopes it becomes elongated down hill.

The resident of the Polar World is acutely aware of these different kinds of surfaces because he usually travels on foot. He would group all Arctic surfaces in three classes: (1) ice-free land, mainly rather flat tundra but in some places steeper and rocky; (2) ice-covered land, or inland ice; and (3) the sea, varying from a water to an ice surface.

CLIMATE

Far more than any other natural factor, climate shapes the Arctic scene. Man, animals, plants, landforms and drainage are all responsive to its dominance. But though Arctic climate is rigorous, it has few record-holders among its elements. For example, the coldest place in the Northern Hemisphere lies south of the Arctic Circle, near Oimekon in northeast Siberia where the summers are quite warm. In matters of snowfall the Arctic records fall far short of those in much lower latitudes, as in the mountains of Washington and California. Although fog, storms, and cloudiness are common in the Arctic, they are considerably worse in areas outside the Polar World. The Arctic does have the lowest mean annual temperatures in the Northern Hemisphere. This means that persistently, day after day, the average temperature is lower than elsewhere, but it does not imply extremely cold winters. Cool summers help to hold the averages down. The range between summer and winter temperatures is not as great as in more "temperate" climates where the very high summer temperatures tend to balance the severe winter cold.

The short cool summers that characterize the Arctic are also periods of continuous daylight. The amount of *insolation*, or radiant energy received from the sun, is relatively large, but the sun's rays come in at a low angle and have to penetrate great thicknesses of air where heat is lost from reflection by clouds and absorption by atmospheric moisture, so when the sunlight reaches the earth's surface it does little to raise the temperature. Most of this solar energy is spent in melting the ice and evaporating the water. Nor does the long daylight period mean good visibility. Fog is prevalent in spring and summer, shrouding much of the coast and lowlands.

Winter is a period of semi-darkness. The length of the *winter night* varies. At the North Pole the sun fails to appear for six months. The period is shorter toward the south and at the Arctic Circle the sun fails to appear only one day a year. The lack of sunshine is somewhat balanced by the long periods of bright moonlight, enhanced by the snow and ice reflecting light from the stars, the aurora, and the moon. Winter is also the period of greatest heat loss by radiation. Occasionally some warmed air mass from the south drifts into the Arctic borderlands, but its warming effect is local and temporary. Usually when summer ends the temperature drops to low levels and stays there.

Cool summers and cold winters are common to the whole Polar World, but local differences exist in relation to the three major types of surfaces. Ice-covered land, such as interior Green-

land, has cold summers and cold winters. The July isotherm of 32° F. rings the icecap, showing that all interior places have average temperatures below freezing even in the warmest month. These are lands of "perpetual frost," lands without summer. Here, "rivers" are the slow creep of glacial ice. The extensive ice cover of the central Arctic Ocean acts like ice-covered land in reducing summer temperatures. Along the sea ice margins where leads of open water exist, summer temperatures are a little higher, but winter is still cold. Open water helps to modify the temperatures, thus, coastal and island areas tend to have less extreme temperatures.

The contrasts between summer and winter increase with distance from the sea or from massive land ice. At these interior locations, individual summer days may be oppressively hot. A maximum of 100° F. has been recorded north of the Arctic Circle and maximums above 80° are not unusual for these interior stations. Winter may bring extreme cold. Verkhoyansk is a good example of the ranges of temperature exhibited by interior stations. Located in the taiga of northeast Siberia, more than 250 miles inland, it was long considered the winter cold pole of the Northern Hemisphere. Here there is nearly a 120° F. range between the average July temperature of almost 60° and the average January temperature of —58.9°. Between the highest and lowest temperatures ever recorded for this station the range is almost 180°!

The peoples of the Polar World have learned to get along with the climate. They avoid the cold summers of inland ice, rarely venture far out onto the sea ice and stay most of the time on the tundra. Low temperatures of themselves are not unbearable. Even at temperatures of —60° F., if the air is still and dry, polar peoples go about their normal activities. But if the wind is blowing and the air is moist, even if the temperature is much higher, every living thing will seek shelter from the blizzard's blast.

Winter is a time of festivity and visiting among Polar World peoples. To the European it is a spectacular season, during which he may experience such novelties as hearing the tinkling

Eskimo children viewing Eskimo handicrafts, Arctic Canada
[*National Film Board of Canada*]

clatter of his frozen breath or sharp sounds which may have carried over 10 miles, and being able to see great distances, even up to 100 miles under special conditions. He will be fascinated by the overhead display of sun dogs, aurora borealis, and myriads of bright stars. The long winter period of darkness, however, will probably lose its novelty and bring mental depression to the European.

Though winter is severe, summer may be less comfortable. Its arrival is accompanied by lashing storms and icy blasts far more biting than the intense cold of winter. Dense fogs are very apt to form along the coasts and remain for long periods. Much more annoying, however, to man and beast alike are the clouds of hungry insects that bedevil the tundra summer.

Most Arctic regions have scant precipitation. If the yearly rainfall and snowfall is measured in water equivalents, it amounts to less than 10 inches, typical of a desert or arid steppe climate. Even this small amount of precipitation is sufficient in the Arctic to keep much of the ground wet and boggy, partly because underground drainage is prevented by the underlying frozen ground, and partly because water evaporates very slowly when cold. Cold air has little capacity to hold water vapor. Snow that falls at low temperatures is fine ice needles, dry and hard, and easily whisked about by the wind. Drifts quickly form in every sheltered

place and some in more protected ravines are able to persist through the brief summer. These little accumulations are bright white patches on the black or dark gray tundra surface.

Masses of cold, dry, heavy air pile up over the Arctic, particularly in the winter. These air masses act as barriers to invasions of southern air and are largely responsible for the meagerness of the precipitation. The northernmost islands and parts of northern Greenland are essentially ice free because they are overlain by dry air so much of the time. Even during the Ice Age these northernmost lands remained ice free. The dryness of the air is a boon to aviation. Icing is a serious problem only around the Arctic margins. Of much more concern are the navigation problems posed by fog, cloudiness, and the eccentric operation of the compass in the vicinity of the geographic and magnetic poles.

Invasions of warmer and moist air occur mainly at the northern ends of the two great oceans causing bad weather conditions, heavy precipitation, and serious hazards of aircraft icing. This is a common experience around the Aleutian Islands. Similar conditions occur along the North Atlantic. The only Arctic territory with sufficiently heavy snowfall to accumulate large masses of land ice lies between Baffin Land and Novaya Zemlya. Similar climatic patterns existed during the Ice Age, for this region served as the center from which the great continental icecaps spread.

ICE ACCUMULATIONS

Of the three main types of surface in the Polar World, only the tundra remains free at all times of a surficial mantle of ice.

Extensive areas of ice-covered land occur near the Atlantic-Arctic openings, and are results of heavy precipitation and cool summers. In fact, land ice areas tend to preserve themselves by creating their own cold climates. In the case of the large icecap on Greenland, the low temperature effects may be widespread, carried by winds to areas hundreds of miles away. In the Polar World, only Greenland has a true icecap—a turtle-back mass so thick it obscures most of the bedrock topography. The central parts of the ice mass are relatively flat at elevations of 8000 to 10,000 feet, with only minor surface irregularities such as low, parallel ridges of hard, crystalline snow. The outer edges are steep and marked by huge cracks and crevasses in the slowly outward-moving ice. In a zone about fifty miles wide along the ice margins are *nunataks*, mountain peaks of solid rock that rise through the ice. Between the icecap and the shore is a narrow rocky band crossed by numerous glaciers, or ice streams. When these ice tongues reach the sea, blocks break off. These detached blocks, or *icebergs*, some of enormous size, are carried south by winds and currents. A few even reach the North Atlantic shipping lanes before they melt. The ice covers found on other Arctic islands, such as Svalbard, Franz Joseph Land, and Novaya Zemlya, are neither extensive nor thick enough to be considered true icecaps.

Ice on the polar seas is different from land ice. It results from the freezing of saline ocean water, whereas land ice comes from snow, a solid form of fresh water. In a typical winter, Arctic sea ice may grow to a depth of 5 to 6 feet. Even in the summer some new ice may be added on the bottom of the layer. A second year may add a couple more feet, but 8 feet is about the maximum thickness of undisturbed sea ice or *floe ice* because at that depth the ice

acts as sufficient insulator to prevent growth by freezing at the bottom. Sea ice does not remain undisturbed very long. Tides, winds, currents, and sea swells keep the floes in motion. They are driven together to form *pack ice* or are pushed against the shore. The ice buckles, becomes ridged and rafted, and is often piled 30 to 40 feet high, with ridges rising as high as 100 feet. Conflicting movements or the release of pressure open large cracks, or *leads*, which may freeze over or be closed by a shift in the pack ice. An intermittent lead exists between the pack ice of the central Arctic Ocean and the solid stationary winter ice along the coast. The coastal ice makes a fine 4 to 8 mile wide winter highway for sledges. Ice reaches maximum thickness in April or May before it begins to waste. As it melts, pools form on the surface and travel is difficult.

In winter about 90 per cent of the Arctic Ocean is ice-covered, and even in summer about three fourths of it have heavy pack ice. Open water is always an intermittent occurrence, although for a month or so during summer it may be more persistent along the coasts of the continents, allowing limited coastal shipping.

VEGETATION

In the rigorous climate of the Polar World very few plants are able to survive, and these mostly on the tundra. Only the lowly alga manages to grow on the icecap and sea ice. However, despite the aridity, inadequate soil, frozen subsoil, and short growing season, tundra vegetation in summer is luxuriant. Innumerable flowering plants burst into bloom and complete a hasty life cycle between June and August in these Arctic meadows. In other ways also these plants show adaptations to the environment. For example, many have leathery, waxy or woolly leaves to preserve moisture, much like desert plants; others have greatly developed subterranean stems and roots that spread in the shallow lateral layer above the frozen ground. All of the plants are low, some even prostrate to avoid the winds and seek the protection of the ground, where they absorb maximum amounts of heat while the sun shines, and radiate a minimum of heat at night or when dry winds blow. The few hardy trees, such as birch, willow, alder, and mountain ash, that have pushed north of the taiga, grow as scraggly bushes, close to the ground. Grass is abundant in the meadows, though it often is in clumps and tussocks. There are numerous lichens and mosses in the colder, more exposed areas, and aquatic and semiaquatic plants in the bogs and water-logged areas. Tundra plants all grow very slowly, so the size of the plant is not an indication of its age—a very small plant may be 10 to 20 years old. Plant growth is favored on south slopes and in protective depressions.

Toward the coasts and around the land ice, the number of species is reduced, the individual plants grow farther apart, and mosses and lichens become more prevalent than grasses and flowering annuals. The summerless, ice-mantled lands are almost completely without vegetation because none of the higher forms of plants can survive. The colorful Arctic meadows in bloom seem remote from these drab icy lands where only sporadically do algae redden snowbanks or pools of summer melt-water lying on the flat ice surfaces.

ANIMAL LIFE

Ice-covered lands have almost no animal life, while the tundra and the sea support faunas rich in individuals though limited in the number of distinct species.

The cold waters of the polar seas teem with animal populations far denser than those of tropical waters. The basis of this population is *plankton*, an assemblage of minute plants, mainly algae and diatoms, and microscopic animals, *protozoans*. Plankton provides food for crustaceans, shell fish and small fish, and all combine to provide food for the larger animals, such as whales, seals, and walruses. The polar bear lives mainly at the expense of seals, and is followed in his perambulations around the edges of the sea ice by the Arctic fox who scavenges after him. Open summer seas invite countless waterfowl who nest on shore and feast on the abundant insects or the plentiful food in the shallow waters. The most important fishing banks of the

Polar World lie off the coast of Labrador and along the Murman Coast northeast of Scandinavia. These furnish the European World with great quantities of cod, halibut, and salmon. These plankton "meadows" also attract whales and seals.

What plankton is to sea life, tundra vegetation is to the land animals of the Polar World. Edibility and abundance are the prime controls in land-animal density. The numbers and varieties of both plants and animals are greatest in the inner tundra and least along the cold coasts or near ice-covered lands. Although limited in species and individuals, the animal community is a vital, almost exclusive, basis of life for many Polar World peoples. Depending directly on plant resources are the herbivores: lemming, hare, and migrating herds of caribou, reindeer, and musk-oxen. Indirectly dependent are the carnivores: fox, ermine, wolf, and wolverine. Together they move north in the summer with the land birds, such as ptarmigan, owl, and snow bunting, and the ducks, geese, gulls, and other waterfowl. And who could overlook the countless insects: mosquitoes, flies, bees, moths, and butterflies. Herbivores harvest the vegetation; carnivores prey on the herbivores; flies and mosquitoes feast on both to make the short summer a time of torment. Largely independent of this intimate relationship is the abundance of freshwater fish in lakes and streams, a basic item in the diet.

Animals exhibit many adaptations to polar life. Some have a protective winter camouflage of white fur or feathers. All animals that stay in the north add a protective layer of fat, and often fur or feathers thicken to ward off the cold. A few animals spend the winter in hibernation. But summer's end finds many animals migrating south, some of the birds to winter in the tropics, caribou to seek protection in the taiga, and the wolf slinking behind his chief source of food, the caribou.

To man, the most important land animal is the caribou, or reindeer. It provides fine meat and excellent skins for winter clothing. When domesticated, it is used to pull sleds and as a riding animal. Among the Lapps it is milked, so it fulfills functions of both horses and cattle.

POLAR WORLD CULTURES

For man to live in this harsh and demanding land, facetiously said to have only two seasons—winter and July, he must possess skill, ingenuity, and resourcefulness. Native ways of life seem primitive, on a barely subsistence level, yet in detail they display inventiveness in utilizing what little nature offers, and above all, a deep appreciation and keen knowledge of the unbenevolent environment. To some extent this primitive level may be blamed on *cultural heritage* which provided no background of knowledge or techniques concerning the use of some of the natural resources, as coal and iron. Use of these sources of power and metal, commonplace among Europeans and Orientals, only relatively recently became known to the peoples of the Polar World, living as they do in isolation, cut off from other culture worlds by the broad taiga. Within their isolated world, however, Polar World peoples share many com-

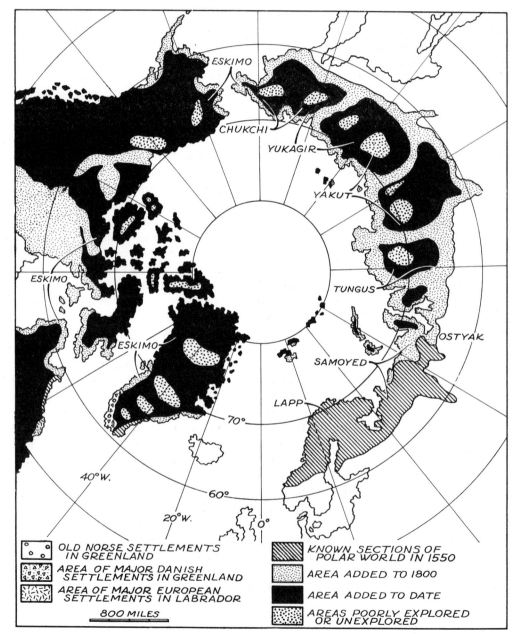

Polar World Peoples and European exploration

ESKIMO

CHUKCHI

YUKAGIR

YAKUT

ESKIMO

TUNGUS

OSTYAK

ESKIMO

SAMOYED

LAPP

70°

40°W.

60°

20°W.

0°

□ OLD NORSE SETTLEMENTS IN GREENLAND

AREA OF MAJOR DANISH SETTLEMENTS IN GREENLAND

AREA OF MAJOR EUROPEAN SETTLEMENTS IN LABRADOR

800 MILES

KNOWN SECTIONS OF POLAR WORLD IN 1550

AREA ADDED TO 1800

AREA ADDED TO DATE

AREAS POORLY EXPLORED OR UNEXPLORED

mon traits and practices. This general uniformity comes in part from the limited range of opportunities for different ways of life, and in part from the diffusion, or spread of culture traits from one group to the next. Surprisingly enough, new ideas travel rather fast among this scattered population, probably because of their winter delight in going a'visiting.

All the Polar World peoples depend heavily upon animals and make little use of plants for food and fiber. They all dress about alike, use similar shelters, make about the same tools and weapons, and universally use the sledge for travel. These happy, good-natured people are untroubled by complex political and economic organizations. They live in a simple tribal society, sharing good times and bad, cheerfully working together in small groups. They have no large settlements or cities. As hunters and herders, they move about in small bands, following the game or seeking better grazing. This nomadic way of life can support only sparse population.

Another unifying trait of Polar World peoples is that most of them look alike. Practically all have darkly pigmented skin and coarse, straight black hair, common to the Mongoloid or "yellow race." This racial unity, however, is not coupled with unity of language, for they speak a wide variety of tongues, particularly in the Eurasian realm.

But language is not the only difference found among Polar World peoples. Despite the many broad similarities in ways of life, there are several other marked differences which separate peoples into various culture groups occupying individual culture regions. The most pronounced difference divides the Polar World into two main culture realms, Eurasian and American. This outstanding distinction is that the peoples of the Eurasian realm are mainly hunters of land animals and herders of reindeer, while those of the American realm are mainly hunters of sea mammals. The way of life of Eurasian peoples takes them inland, whereas the American realm peoples congregate along coasts. Of course, there are some exceptions to this general difference, and they help to show that it is human choice, rather than significant

environmental contrasts, that distinguish these culture realms.

EURASIAN REALM

The Eurasian realm extends along the tundra from north-central Norway to easternmost Siberia. Scattered along this enormous territory are several loosely organized tribes or groups, such as Lapp, Samoyed, Ostyak, Tungus, Yakut, Yukagir, and Chukchi, many with distinct and complicated languages. But in all they number less than 30,000 people. Most of these tribes avoid the cold, foggy coasts. They migrate between their summer homes of frequently moved skin tents in the central tundra to their winter dwellings, solidly covered pits dug in the ground at the protective edges of the taiga. Here they gather roots, tubers and berries, and collect wood which they use to make tools and implements. Long sledge journeys are undertaken both in summer and winter, the runners sliding with equal ease over mossy tundra or snow and frozen ground.

The most distinctive culture trait of Eurasian tribes is the breeding and use of reindeer. Well-adapted to the tundra, this animal is an important and mobile source of food and clothing. It is even used as a draft and riding animal. Many of the practices used with the reindeer were borrowed from the horse-and-cattle-using peoples to the south. Of course, the treatment and use of reindeer differ in various parts of the Eurasian realm. The Lapps, who have done most to domesticate the animal, depend upon reindeer cows for fresh milk, and treat the animals with gentleness much as Europeans treat cattle. To the east, among the tribes of central Eurasia, reindeer are used as transport animals and as aids in hunting the wild caribou. Still farther east, half-wild reindeer are held loosely in large herds, mainly as a source of flesh and skins when needed. The seasonal migration of Eurasian realm tribes is largely governed by the movements of reindeer herds from open tundra in summer to the protective forests along streams or the taiga border where they winter. Thus people and animals follow the instinctive migration pattern of the wild caribou.

AMERICAN REALM

The American realm, the land of the Eskimo, laps over into easternmost Siberia and extends to Labrador and Greenland. Here dwell some 30,000 Eskimo who speak only one main language and share a common culture. Because they are primarily hunters and fishermen they live in small groups scattered along the coasts, not only of the mainland, but on some of the islands of the polar sea. One rugged, isolated group, living at Etah, Greenland, on the shore of Smith Sound, has the distinction of being the northernmost people in the world. In establishing themselves along the coasts, the Eskimos are in sharp contrast with the Eurasian tribes who seek more inland sites. Another marked difference is that the Eskimos have no domesticated animals other than the dog. The life of the Eskimo is primarily dependent upon the things he can obtain from the sea, and of these, the seal, in all its varieties from smallest to the giant walrus, is the most important. It provides food, oil, skin, bone, and ivory. To reap this harvest, the Eskimo must stay where the seal is—on the chilly coasts. Only seasonally does he venture inland to hunt caribou, primarily to get skins for clothing.

Like all hunters, Eskimo are nomadic, their yearly cycle of activities being prescribed by seasonal changes and the availability of game. The long, cold Arctic night drives them into their warm and comfortable houses of sod or stone, clustered in little temporary villages. Hunting is an individual matter, frequently interrupted by long spells of bad weather and unfavorable ice conditions. Much of the time indoors is spend in sleeping and in eating large quantities of fat, frozen, and sometimes rotten, raw meat. For the Eskimo, this is far from a dreary season. In winter they delight in sports, ceremonies, and sociability. It is not unusual to sledge hundreds of miles merely to visit some friends or relatives. On these journeys, the Eskimo answer to the motel is the speedily constructed snow house.

Spring bustles with more serious activities. The appearance of seals, walruses, and whales in the open sea initiates the main hunting season. Waterfowl arrive, and their eggs offer welcome variety to a rather monotonous diet. At the onset of summer, the solid winter dwellings are abandoned in favor of easily moved skin tents. Villagers scatter to gather driftwood or dig fossil ivory from the frozen ground. Small parties travel inland for caribou or musk-ox. By fall, the Eskimo may be a long way from where he spent the previous Arctic night. Unconcerned, he prepares a new house, and looks forward in great anticipation to the long dark season with its freedom from insects and its bright social prospects.

That the Eskimo have been able to create a reasonably comfortable way of life in this austere environment is evidence of their ingenuity. There was little in the cultural heritage brought from their original homes in northeast Asia to guide the Eskimo in solving the problems involved in living along the edge of the polar sea. They had to devise new tools and procedures to meet their needs. They developed the kayak and umiak, skin-covered boats admirably suited to use in polar seas, and perfected a versatile oil-burning stone lamp. Their discovery of the principle of the vaulted dome, as used in building snow houses, entitles them to high praise for inventive genius.

EUROPEAN CONTACTS

Stories of a land where the sun shone at midnight and other equally unbelieved accounts of the Polar World began to circulate in Europe after Pytheas of Massilia made his daring northern journey in about 325 B.C. to a place he called Thule. Sadly enough, his discoveries were discredited, and for over a thousand years after his death, knowledge of the "frigid zone" was more fantasy than fact. It was not until about the eighth century A.D. that European World culture began making sporadic inroads into the Polar World. An Irish colony was attempted in Iceland, followed by Scandinavians under Eric the Red and his son Leif who moved to southern Greenland to set up settlements used as headquarters for explorations that eventually took them to mainland North America. Sometime during the fifteenth cen-

**Port Radium Mill,
Great Bear Lake**
[*George Hunter*]

tury contact was lost with these little Greenland colonies of transplanted European World culture, and when someone thought to look for them a couple of hundred years later, only Eskimo of somewhat mixed blood could be found where the Norse settlements had been.

While Europeans were searching for routes to the Orient, they found the way blocked by newly "discovered" America which forced them into the Polar World. Even after it was determined that a Northeast Passage and a Northwest Passage existed, it was not until 1878–1879 that the first ship passage along the northern coast of Eurasia was completed by Nördenskiold's "Vega." The Northwest Passage was not conquered until 1903–1906 when Amundsen's "Göja" made the journey.

European interest in the North has always been intermittent and marked by waves of enthusiasm, which in turn have brought explorers, missionaries, traders, trappers, miners, adventurers, scientists, fishermen, and even exiles to various parts of the Arctic. Almost all of these people were motivated by the possibilities of quick personal gains of money or fame. These European contacts, even though temporary, brought unwelcome changes to the natives. Lethal diseases were introduced. With the gun came the inevitable depletion of game. The new goods introduced created tastes that undermined native independence.

Not all European contacts are destructive.

In Greenland, for example, Mongoloids and Caucasoids have mixed to produce a Greenlander culture, a blend of European and Polar World elements. Polar World low stone and turf houses appear among the European World wooden churches, schools and trading posts. In southern villages there are cattle and even small gardens of hardy vegetables. European culture traits, such as the use of tobacco and coffee and newspaper reading, are part of Greenland's mixed culture. The dog sled and kayak, however, remain the principal tools of existence, and seal hunting is still the primary basis of life. Fortunately for the Greenlander, the Danish administration is both enlightened and protective.

Permanent European settlements in the Arctic are few, and all depend upon support from the outside. In the American realm, the tiny and widely separated settlements are usually sites of trading posts, missions, fishing stations, and defense installations. The recently constructed network of radar stations across northern North America not only introduced many outsiders to the Arctic, but the maintenance of these DEW line (Distant Early Warning) sites may require small semipermanent staffs to settle in these isolated places.

In recent years a number of permanent European towns and cities have been established in the Eurasian realm of the Polar World. Most are located at or near river mouths where they serve as trans-shipping points of commerce mainly of non-Arctic origin. Murmansk, the largest and most populous Arctic port, has an ice-free harbor although at 68°50′ N. it is well within the Polar World. In winter when more southerly Russian ports are ice bound, Murmansk enjoys a lively traffic made possible by the warming affects of the tag ends of the Gulf Stream which find their way past North Cape. But this port, like other Arctic ports and coastal stations in the Soviet Union, must be maintained by supplies from the outside, despite enthusiastic efforts toward self-sufficiency, such as growing vegetables in greenhouses. More success has been achieved in meeting the problems of fuel deficiencies in this cold but coal-less region. Numerous hydro-electric power stations have been installed to serve ports and mines, and to encourage the growth of industry.

EUROPEAN EXPLOITATION

Europeans have rarely come to the Arctic with the intention of staying. That a few of them have stayed, as in the settlements in Greenland, Labrador, and along the Soviet coasts, does not change the general rule that most people in the *factories* or trading posts, mining camps, administrative posts, and fishing or whaling centers feel their residence is only temporary. Their purpose is to exploit the natural resources as quickly as possible and return home. A typical story is that of whaling and sealing which flourished for a while, produced enormous revenues, engaged thousands of men, then rapidly declined. During the big era of whaling in the nineteenth century, Americans and British realized over a billion dollars. The depletion of whales and seals, coupled with the loss of markets for whale bone and oil and seal hides and oil, almost brought these activities to an end. They left little mark on the Polar landscape other than a native population decimated by disease.

In the nick of time, the northern fur seal of Bering Sea was saved from extinction by the imposition of government regulations which limited the catch. Other fur-bearing animals have not been so lucky. Furs of land animals have long attracted trappers to Polar lands. At least 20 centuries before the Voyages of Discovery, these furs were prized in the eastern Mediterranean. In recent centuries the demand of Chinese markets brought Russian trappers and traders across Siberia and into Alaska, while the European market sent Englishmen to Hudson Bay and Russians to Arctic Eurasia.

Fur traffic established the oldest Arctic trade routes. One extended overland across the southern edge of the tundra of European Russia. Cossack leaders opened Siberian rivers to traffic in the seventeenth century to bring furs and fossil ivory from the tundra. Sea routes to Taimyr Peninsula have been used by traders for centuries. Important companies were founded on the fur trade. The Russian-American Company, organized in 1788, controlled the fur trade of the Aleutians and parts of Alaska, prospering on profits from the now nearly extinct sea otter. The Hudson's Bay Company began operations in 1670 and still continues its hold on the Canadian Arctic, where today the catch is mainly Arctic fox.

Minerals have attracted their share of outsiders to the Polar World. Rich gold placer deposits found in 1899 near Nome, Alaska, brought an influx of 12,000 hopefuls. Seven years later, production reached $7,500,000, then declined sharply. Today, Nome has only about 2,000 people. At Ivigtut in southwest Greenland, a Danish mining community is busily working the world's richest deposits of cryolite, a mineral used in smelting aluminum. Like Nome, Ivigtut may fade when the supply of cryolite or the demand for it comes to an end. Normally only highly concentrated or extremely valuable minerals can be commercially exploited in the Arctic because of the cost of transportation to distant markets. Coal in Svalbard is an exception because it is located near the coasts and available to cheap water transportation. Coal mining began commercially on the western island of Svalbard in 1905 and has proved to be a boon to the mineral-poor mother country, Norway. Svalbard contains not only large deposits of near-anthracite coal, but also commercial quantities of gypsum, asbestos, iron ore, marble, and possibly, petroleum.

A new era of prospecting and mining with

the aid of the airplane was started in the nine-teen-thirties. These new methods uncovered valuable pitchblende deposits, sources of radium and uranium, in eastern Great Bear Lake district, Canada.

Many important mineral deposits of the Polar World now occupy the uncertain position of being discovered but as yet unexploited. These include great quantities of petroleum and coal in Alaska, copper and iron in Canada, anthracite and copper in Novaya Zemlya, and placer gold in the Chukotski Peninsula of eastern Siberia. Rapid strides in invention and discovery may make it quite unnecessary to go to the Polar World for many bulky minerals, but it is comforting in an age of rapid mineral exploitation to know that a few supplies exist.

Europeans have invaded the Polar World for many reasons. Furs and whales were early attractions. Today, fish and minerals are leading products. Scientific curiosity brings increasing numbers into the Arctic. The International Geophysical Year (1958–59) was responsible for an unprecedented influx of scientists bent on measuring and recording as much information as possible about the weather, aurora, geomagnetic and electronic disturbances, sea ice, Arctic Ocean currents and bottom topography, and numerous other physical aspects of the Arctic. These scientists supplemented the few American and numerous Soviet meteorologists and geophysicists manning northern outposts who have been observing conditions in this weather-exporting region to improve forecasting in the more temperate areas. It is known that Arctic atmospheric changes affect weather conditions throughout the lands to the south. The five main Soviet observatories and dozens of polar stations are also concerned with sea ice conditions in connection with the shipping activities along the north sea route. The American sector of the Arctic has lagged far behind the Soviet sector in scientific observation and investigation.

Initiation in late 1954 of commercial passenger flights across the Polar World emphasized the truism that the shortest distances between important Northern Hemisphere centers lie along routes crossing the Arctic. Attention was again focused on the Arctic and its

Eskimo visiting Aklavik, Mackenzie River delta
[*George Hunter*]

strategic importance to the two great world powers: the United States and the Soviet Union, who eye each other uneasily across this cold expanse. Peripheral lands have gained importance as military and commercial air base sites. The Arctic Ocean is no longer considered a natural barrier in defense planning. Flights across it are routine, and in 1957 a United States Navy submarine sailed under the ice to the vicinity of the North Pole.

All these activities, however, are entirely the doings of non-Polar World peoples, and are little concerned with the natives. The Polar World native has cheerfully accepted an outside religion, and tools, weapons, and foods which seem better than his own. In turn, he has paid a severe price for European contacts in terms of dwindling game supply, exposure to new diseases, and dependence on items that his environment cannot supply. He cannot adopt European culture entirely because his milieu does not permit sedentary agriculture which is basic to European ways of life. As he replaces his Polar World culture traits with those from the European World he becomes less self-sufficient and more dependent on people and things outside his control. This trend poses serious social problems for the peoples of the Polar World and for the peoples of the European World who must assume the responsibility.

EUROPEAN WORLD

Alpine landscape, Switzerland
[*Swiss National Tourist Office*]

3. Europe: Small but Diverse

Where does Europe end and Asia begin? This is hard to say because Europe, Asia, and Africa are really one landmass. The Mediterranean Sea nicely defines Europe's southern border, but the Asian border offers no such distinctive physical marker. For convenience, the Ural Mountains, Caspian Sea, and the Caucasus Range are generally accepted as the dividing features, but this leaves the boundary line from the Urals to the Caspian a matter of arbitrary choice, and here, as throughout its length, the boundary has shifted back and forth historically.

Europe's eastern boundary, however, is unimportant culturally. European World culture has spread across the Urals, and extends as a wedge across Siberia to the Pacific. The Mediterranean was equally ineffective as a barrier to the spread of European culture to the better watered parts of North Africa. In fact, the New World Revolution has seen the introduction and adoption of European ways of life across all oceans.

29

SIZE AND SHAPE

In area, Europe is exceeded by all other continents except Australia. In shape, it is extremely irregular and ranks with Australia as leading other continents in length of exterior sea coast in proportion to total land area. Europe's shape is so irregular that very little of its western part lies over 300 miles from an exterior coast. Only in mid-Soviet Russia does any considerable land lie more than 500 miles from ocean-connected seas, and no place lies as much as 1,000 miles inland.

The long coastline is a great asset. It helped develop cultural unity, and stimulated commercial and political activity. It allows extensive use of cheap water transport and minimum use of costly overland hauls. Nearness to the sea means milder climates while the coasts favor fishing and maritime enterprises.

MOUNTAINS AND HIGHLANDS

Across southern Europe stretches the highland system that extends to eastern China and southeast Asia. This great mountain barrier lies between the European Plain and the Mediterranean peninsulas. The western end of this east-west barrier is Cape Finisterre, the sea end of the Cantabrian Mountains. East of the Cantabrians rise the high, rough Pyrenees, of which it is said that the best way to cross them is to go around their ends, the routes used by the main railroads and highways.

A break exists in the mountain barrier across southern France where the Cévennes and Massif Central (Central Plateau) are like a plug that fails on both sides to fill an opening. West of the plug is the gateway of Toulouse (or Carcassonne), an easy pass between the Mediterranean and lowlands along the Bay of Biscay.

Mountains and gateways of Europe

Pyrenees landscape, France
[*French Embassy, Press and Information Division*]

East of the plug, the Rhone Corridor leads northward to the Rhine Valley and to Paris and the North Sea lowlands. Roads, highways, and canals go through these gaps which have always allowed free movement of peoples and goods across France. The spread northward of Mediterranean culture traits was mainly through these breaches.

Alpine ranges cut off the Italian Peninsula from the rest of Europe, and are an effective cultural barrier. They are high, with many elevations in excess of 12,000 feet. Mt. Blanc, the highest peak in western Europe, rises to 15,781 feet, and lies in France a short distance south of Switzerland. Many Swiss peaks are above 13,000 feet and Monte Rosa reaches 15,217. The valleys are deep and steep. The Alps have a fishhook shape with the shank pointed east toward Vienna. The barb of the hook lies along the Ligurian coast of Italy and the bend swings through the Maritime Alps to Switzerland. Trans-Alpine crossings go through high, narrow passes or long tunnels. The Alps are mainly north of 45° N. and thus the timberline is fairly low, emphasizing the ruggedness

of the land looming above it. Hence, the term *alpine* is used to describe lofty regions.

Many separate ranges and highlands extend southeastward from the Alps. A major trend is along the highlands of Yugoslavia and the Pindus Mountains of Greece to Crete. The Balkan Mountains, south of the Wallachian Plain of the lower Danube, form a second major trend. Between these main mountain trends lie several fingerlike ranges stretching toward the Aegean.

South of the great mountain barrier are the Mediterranean lands of Europe, three large peninsulas whose rugged terrain inhibited land travel and encouraged use of the sea. The Iberian Peninsula, south of the Cantabrians and Pyrenees, is mainly a high, dissected plateau, the Meseta. The plateau is broken by east-west trending ranges rising several thousand feet above it and by deep valleys. In their lower parts the valleys broaden into important plains such as the Plain of Aragon in Catalonia south of the Pyrenees, the broad Andalusian Plain of southwest Spain, and the Tejo (Tagus) River plains of Portugal. Here and there fringing the plateau are small, productive coastal plains. Along the Italian Peninsula extend the Apennines, from the Alps to Sicily. Unlike a central backbone, the Apennines swing from the west coast to the Adriatic coast about halfway down the peninsula, then back to the west coast to become the "toe." Italy's most extensive lowland is the Po Valley. The Grecian Peninsula is very irregular both in outline and relief. Lowland areas are small and are mainly in the northeast. Deep indentations of the coast mark former valleys that were *drowned* (flooded) by the rise of encroaching seas. Former hills have become islands, and old ridges are now chains of islands, such as Ionia and the Cyclades.

North of the great east-west mountain barrier are broad plateaus and uplands extending through eastern France to southern Belgium and through southern Germany. Here the Rhine dissects the plateau, leaving relatively flat residual highlands.

The main uplands of central Europe are north of the Eastern Alps. The Bohemian Forest, Ore Mountains, Sudetes, and Bohemian-Moravian Highlands surround and isolate Bohemia, the basin in which the main headwaters of the Elbe gather. West of Bohemia, between the Bohemian Forest and the Eastern Alps of Tirol, is the Bavarian Basin, headwaters of the Danube. East of Bohemia is the arc of the Car-

pathians. These ranges are low where they join the Alps near Vienna, and rise as they swing around the northern and east sides of Alföld, the Plain of Hungary. Through central Rumania the Carpathians trend almost north-south. Here they abut against the eastern end of the Transylvanian Alps, the great east-west range that separates the plain of Wallachia from the Muresul (Maros) Valley of Transylvania. The Transylvanian Alps extend westward to the Iron Gate of the Danube.

CULTURAL EFFECTS OF HIGHLANDS

Mountains and lofty highlands are generally cultural barriers. They are sparsely inhabited and tend to separate more populous areas. People on one side of the barrier commonly differ in race, language, religion, economy, and other culture traits from those on the other side. The great east-west highland system of Europe acts as such a barrier, separating the distinctive Mediterranean culture realm from the culture realms of Northwestern and Eastern Europe. The barrier, however, has gaps in it which have enabled some cultural diffusion. It also offers refuge sites where small groups of peoples, such as the Basques in the western Pyrenees, preserve interesting old cultures, cling to ancient languages, and maintain individuality even from

Rhine Gorge landscape
[*German Tourist Information Office*]

Group of Alpines
[*Swiss National Tourist Office*]

neighbors in nearby valleys. The east-west mountain barrier is also the habitat of a distinct racial stock, the Alpines. Though Alpine peoples are not confined to the mountains, and in fact, these sturdy, broad-headed peoples are found in every part of the continent, they are particularly numerous in the highlands between more Nordic peoples of the northern plains and the Mediterraneans of the peninsulas to the south.

The larger and more attractive plains and basins within the mountain barrier have been sought-after prizes. Sometimes the invaders moved on, other times they remained and their stocks and cultures blended with those already there. Thus came the Romans to Wallachia, bringing a language that has changed less during 20 centuries in becoming Rumanian than has the language at home in becoming Italian. Germanic invaders crossed or by-passed the Alps to occupy such places as the Po Valley. Some went past the Pyrenees to settle in Spain and north Africa. Invaders from remote places, such as the Asian Huns, Magyars, and Turks, still retain some of their old culture traits despite long residence in Europe. Most invading groups became absorbed by the peoples in the basins of central Europe.

Toward the eastern end of the mountain barrier, especially in the area between Vienna and the Black Sea, cultures have clashed and mixed to a degree hardly equalled elsewhere. Here are the most confused patterns of distribution of such traits as language, religion, dress, house types, and ways of living.

EUROPEAN PLAIN

The great European Plain lies north of the east-west mountain barrier and is one of the most productive and densely settled areas on earth. It starts on the French side of the Pyrenees and in western Ireland and extends eastward to the Urals. The width expands abruptly just east of the Carpathians, so that the plain spreads from the Arctic Ocean to the Black Sea. This vast lowland is studded with hills, especially in the west. Some are remnants of old mountains worn down by processes of degradation and erosion. Others are more recent glacial deposits.

The Ice Age is extremely significant in the geography of the European Plain. At that time, great ice caps covered large parts of the northern continents. Ice covered all of Scandinavia, the British Isles as far south as London, and the European Plain from the Netherlands eastward to central Russia. Many mountains to the south had individual ice caps. The thickest ice was over Scandinavia, Finland, and northwest Russia. This massive, slow-moving ice scoured many basins in solid rock and carried away most soil and loose materials. This debris even-

European Plain landscape, Scotland
[*British Information Service*]

(*opposite*) **Northwestern Highlands landscape, Lake District, England**
[*British Information Services*]

tually reached the ice margins to be deposited as *moraines*. The ice margins advanced when the main cap thickened, and retreated when the ice supply was insufficient to overcome melting. Moraines are thus spread widely over the plain, many as high ridges marking places where the margin halted for a relatively long time, and others as irregular low ground where the ice retreat was faster.

Morainal ridges have long dictated the routes across the European Plain because they rise above the frequently flooded lowlands. Early man located his trails on them, and today they shape the road patterns. These ridges also divert many north-flowing rivers to the west, especially in Germany. The Elbe is typical. After it reaches the plain south of Berlin, it travels alternately along short courses northward across morainal ridges and longer courses westward in valleys between moraines. Several of these intra-

morainal valleys serve more than one stream. These streams have been connected by easily built, low-cost canals. The cultural unification of the western part of the European Plain is in many ways indebted to the morainal trends.

During the Ice Age there were several *glacial stages* of ice accumulation and *interglacial stages* of ice retreat. The water for the vast ice caps came from the oceans, which were thus lowered more than 400 feet below their present levels. Each interglacial stage saw a return of water to the oceans and a rise of sea level. During glacial stages the European Plain extended farther west, the British Isles were connected with the mainland, and most of the North Sea was a lowland plain. Ancient man could then walk freely between England and France. The melting of continental ice during waning glacial stages drowned the coasts. People living on the coasts were driven upslope, but since it took thousands of years for the ice to melt and raise the seas, the migration was so slow probably no one was aware of it.

NORTH SEA CULTURE FOCUS

Though the drowning of the western European Plain created most of the North Sea, the Baltic, and other arms of the sea, and flooded many ancient land routes, peoples continued to communicate. Man learned to use boats at a very early date and had no difficulty in sailing along coasts or across narrow seas. The ancients thus "coasted" far beyond the limits of the eastern Mediterranean to all shores of the Black Sea, along the shores of Asia to Ceylon, westward past Gibraltar to Britain, the Canaries, and around Africa. They sailed freely along the North Sea shores and across the Baltic. The widespread use of boats had much to do with the unification of cultures around the Mediterranean, and around the North Sea.

Several of Europe's more important rivers lead to the North Sea, and for untold centuries peoples gravitated down these valleys toward the sea coast. There culture traits were exchanged and so blended that regardless of the racial origins of any group, all North Sea peoples came to resemble each other more closely than they resembled peoples of distant lands. The North Sea served as a culture focus in the evolution of the distinctive culture of Northwestern Europe.

The focal attraction of the Baltic has been less than that of the North Sea, partly because its comparatively fresh waters freeze more readily and block winter sea communications, and partly because the similarities of products along its various shores made commerce, barter, and plunder fairly unprofitable. Though Swedes and others have crossed the Baltic for conquest or trade, contacts between peoples were generally less frequent than around the North Sea. Culture traits were less blended and remained more localized. The Baltic, thus, has had only a secondary influence in the cultural evolution of Northwestern Europe.

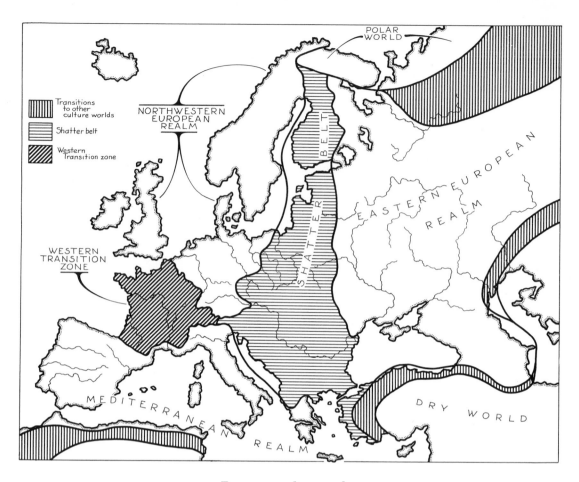

European culture realms

EASTERN EUROPE

The expanded plain in eastern Europe differs from the western plain. Marine influences are only marginal. Rivers, instead of leading to a common focus, flow radially outward from the low Valdai Hills northwest of Moscow. South-flowing rivers lead to the nearly land-locked Black Sea, rivers flowing northwest end in the seasonally ice-locked eastern Baltic, while the many north-flowing rivers lead to the cold Barents Sea of the Arctic. Even the great Volga leads down a blind alley to the Caspian which is without ocean connections and is 92 feet below sea level. Because of these unattractive outlets of their rivers, the Russians have long sought control of more useful coasts. In particular, they have tried to gain mastery of the narrow connection leading from the Mediter-

ranean to their most important coast on the Black Sea. Alien peoples also flank the Baltic. Though unsuccessful in their efforts, the Russians were considerably unified by their common "urge to the sea."

Although summer overland movement was always difficult across the muddy flats of eastern Europe, winter with its frozen ground and ice-covered streams made communications easy. Goods were traded and contacts made during this season when people were less busy with agriculture. Sled transportation and long, cold winters helped to unify culturally peoples of the eastern part of the plain, much as the use of boats blended cultures around the North Sea. A rather homogeneous culture, unlike that of Northwestern Europe, evolved on the plains of Russia.

SUMMARY OF CULTURE REALMS

South of the great east-west mountain barrier on the rugged peninsulas of the Mediterranean, people developed cultural unification, and this Mediterranean culture constitutes one of the realms of the European World. North of the barrier the great European Plain is divided by the contrast in physical conditions between the partially submerged western part and the broad eastern part. Around the focus of the North Sea, and secondarily along the Baltic, the Northwestern European culture realm developed. On the extensive eastern flats evolved the culture realm of Eastern Europe. Between these realms are transitional zones of clashing cultures.

MARGINAL HIGHLANDS

Having little to do with shaping European cultures are three main highland areas: the Northwestern Highlands of Scandinavia, Scotland, and Ireland; the Urals, between the plains of Europe and Siberia; and the Caucasus of Europe's southeast border.

The Northwestern Highlands are of negative cultural significance, with environments hostile to European culture traits. But they offer refuges for peoples who resisted European ways, such as the Celtic tribes of Scotland and Ireland, and the Lapps of Norway. The Urals, with their gentle slopes and many low passes, have let peoples cross them at will for thousands of years. In recent times, European culture has spread east, almost unobstructed by the mountains. In contrast is the Caucasus Range, a part of the east-west mountain barrier, containing the highest peaks and deepest valleys in Europe. Elbrus rises to 18,480 feet and ten or more peaks rise above 15,000 feet. Passes are few and difficult. Peoples deep in valleys have long remained isolated. These conditions favor sharp cultural differences and make the area a hodge-podge of culture traits. Diversification is also favored by location in the transitional zone between European and Dry Worlds, the flatter, better-watered places tending to be European while the more arid areas are better suited to Dry World nomads.

CLIMATIC ASPECTS

All of Europe lies north of the latitude of Memphis, Tennessee. In fact, in terms of similar latitude, Europe occupies the same band as that between Durham, North Carolina and Point Barrow, Alaska. But for all its high latitude, Europe enjoys relatively mild temperatures, and almost everywhere has adequate precipitation. It is favored above other continents in having almost no uninhabitable deserts, Arctic wastes, or plateaus too high to allow normal human activities, and it is entirely free from tropical heat. There are few parts with too much rain for efficient agriculture.

Europe's climates are like those of western parts of other continents in similar latitudes. Coastal Norway climatically resembles coastal Alaska and southern Chile. Climates through France to the Iberian Peninsula are like those from British Columbia to Southern California, or from southern to central Chile. Northeastern European Russia resembles northwestern Canada along the Mackenzie River, but there is no Southern Hemisphere counterpart because South America tapers too much to develop a similar continental climate. Southeastern Europe is the climatic equivalent of the more arid parts of Utah and parts of Patagonia. The relative positions of similar climates are the same in Europe as in North America, but their inland extent differs because in western North America the north-south mountains crowd the climatic regions into a coastal belt while the uninterrupted lowlands of Europe allow a broad eastward spread of climates. European climates also tend to be a little milder than their American latitude equivalents because the North Atlantic is favored by the warming influence of the Gulf Stream.

METEOROLOGICAL PROCESSES

Air that stays some time over the North Atlantic becomes relatively warm and moist, and when it moves as wind the warmth and moisture are carried along. The moisture is invisible in the form of gas, water vapor. When this air is forced upward by topographic slopes or rises above the surface of a warm place, it expands and expansion causes cooling. Then condensation and cloudiness occur if the air contains sufficient water vapor. Air that rises over hot deserts is often too dry to form clouds. Air is seldom motionless, but moves at varying speeds in response to *pressure gradients* that force it from places where the pressure is high toward places where pressure is low. Pressure gradients may force it up slopes of mountains, in which case it cools, or downslope, where compression results in heating. Cooling favors condensation and heating favors evaporation. Suppose, for example, that during summer the eastern European Plain has been sufficiently heated to cause a drop in pressure far below that over the North Atlantic. Air then starts to move down the pressure gradient from the ocean toward Russia. Some of the air reaches Norway where it is forced abruptly upward by the mountains causing its water vapor to condense and form clouds. If these clouds are dense and thick, many cloud particles will unite, becoming raindrops if the temperature is above freezing, or snowflakes if below. As the air flows down the slopes of Sweden, it is heated, clouds evaporate, and skies become clear. Moving east across the lower, flatter country, the air is likely to remain clear and dry until it reaches a place where the pressure is low enough to have attracted winds from other directions. Here some of the air is forced up to produce general cloudiness.

Sometimes warmer, lighter air is forced upward over masses of cold, heavy air, such as a polar air mass. All air masses are important shapers of climate. An air mass is simply a large volume of air having fairly uniform temperature, moisture, and weight characteristics that differ from those of surrounding volumes of air. An air mass lying over a large surface of relatively warm water, such as the North Atlantic, is likely to be warm and moist. Air over continental interiors, on the other hand, tends to be dry. If the continental area is cold, the air becomes cold, and therefore, heavy. Air over hot areas tends to be hot and light. The characteristics of an air mass depend mainly on the nature of the surface below it. Thus air over interior Asia becomes very dry, cold, and heavy

in winter and dry, warm, and light in summer. The main air masses may be classified as polar (cold and heavy) or tropical (warm and light); marine or oceanic (wet) and continental (dry). Temperatures and weights of oceanic air masses are rather uniform because large water surfaces are not subject to great temperature changes. Continental air masses are subject to greater seasonal extremes in temperature and weight.

One air mass does not readily mix with another. The boundary surfaces between air masses are called *fronts* and they move with the air masses over the earth's surface. Fronts are sharp and well defined between contrasting air masses, but indistinct between similar air masses. Abrupt changes in weather take place along sharply defined fronts.

The weather and climates of Europe depend upon invasions of polar continental air from Siberia and marine air from the North Atlantic with the front between these air masses being pushed back and forth across the continent. Winds from the Siberian polar continental air mass leave it with great force and regularity during the cold season. Many times during the year the Siberian air wedges its heavy way under the marine air and produces cloudiness and precipitation. But, unlike the conditions in the United States where the polar continental air mass from Canada is in such sharp contrast with the tropical maritime air from the Gulf and Caribbean that the front is ordinarily well defined, the North Atlantic air is less hot and wet so that fronts in Europe are less distinct. The intensity of European storms is therefore likely to be less, and tornadoes are almost unknown. In summer, when Siberian air is warmer and lighter, continental pressures are lowered and marine air becomes widespread over Europe.

The location of the frontal zones of storminess and precipitation varies with the season, being farther south in winter and in higher latitudes in summer. That is why most of the rain in southern Europe falls in winter. This is especially true of the Mediterranean which reaps little or no summer rain because it is south of the zone of fronts. North of the east-west mountain barrier most of the rain falls in summer because there is more oceanic air over the continent at that season with abundant moisture to be condensed and precipitated whenever fronts pass, or other disturbances force air upward. Southeasternmost Europe has difficulty getting any precipitation. In winter it is ordinarily covered by polar Siberian air and is thus dry. In summer it lies south of the zone where fronts are common, and like the Mediterranean, it stays dry. At any season it lies too far from the sea to benefit from oceanic air. The Caucasus Mountains, however, rise high enough to wring moisture from even the dry air.

PRECIPITATION AND TEMPERATURES

The Atlantic Ocean is the source of almost all the moisture that reaches the continent, and thus western Europe gets the most precipitation and eastern Europe the least. In most of the western highlands and along some windward slopes of the Alps, precipitation is excessive, amounting in places to over 60 inches per year. The proportion falling in winter increases toward the south, but these very wet places can expect rain in every month. In extreme contrast are the arid lowlands of the Caspian and the dry region along the Arctic coast east of Norway.

Mediterranean Europe is a land of winter rain. It rains in Northwestern Europe in all seasons with some snow in winter. Eastern Europe has mainly summer rains, and remains dry with little snow in winter. Highlands everywhere get more rain and snow than nearby lowlands.

The west coast of Europe has mild temperatures because it commonly lies under North Atlantic air. During July the average temperature at North Cape is about 50° F. (10° C.). Temperatures rise toward the south, those in southwest Portugal being about 70° F. (21° C.). Winter temperatures are also mild. In January it is necessary to go north to the Lofoten Islands at about 68° N. to find an average temperature as low as that of New York City (40°40′ N.). The temperature-ameliorating marine influence fails to reach eastern Europe where summers are really hot and winters bitterly cold. In summer the temperatures of European lowlands are arranged in easterly trending belts, warmer in the south and cooler in the north or in highlands. The winter temperature pattern is quite different. The belts trend north-south with warmer temperatures in the west and the coldest in the east.

The January isotherm of 32° F. (0° C.) is a critical geographic boundary because it is used as a marker between the milder climates found on its warmer side and the more severe climates on its colder side. Its course across Europe is shown on the map of climates. Along this line occurs a temperature equal to the freezing point of water for the average of all hours of all January days. Winters are considered mild if the coldest month has a temperature averaging above 32° F. The British Isles, westernmost Germany, the Low Countries, western France, Mediterranean lowlands, and a very narrow strip of southern Russia are in this category. Snow is uncommon, but when it occurs it is the "wet" variety with large flakes that cling to everything and delightfully transform the landscape into winter beauty. In these mild conditions, problems of keeping men and livestock warm are relatively simple. Houses need little insulation and fuel supply is of only moderate concern. Streams do not freeze and harbors remain open. Where summers are warm enough, citrus, grapes, and olives may be grown, as well as many other plants unable to survive severe freezes. Quite different are winters in other parts of Europe where severity increases with distance from the January 32° F. isotherm. In the northeastern part of the continent the average January temperature is below 0° F. (−17.8° C.).

The isotherm of 50° F. (10° C.) for the warmest month is another significant line. In general it marks the poleward limit of forest growth and the southern border of tundra climates. On the cold side of this line dwell the Polar World peoples.

CLIMATES

Temperature and precipitation characteristics are combined to define climatic types, or climates. By this process, Europe may be divided into the following distinctive climates:

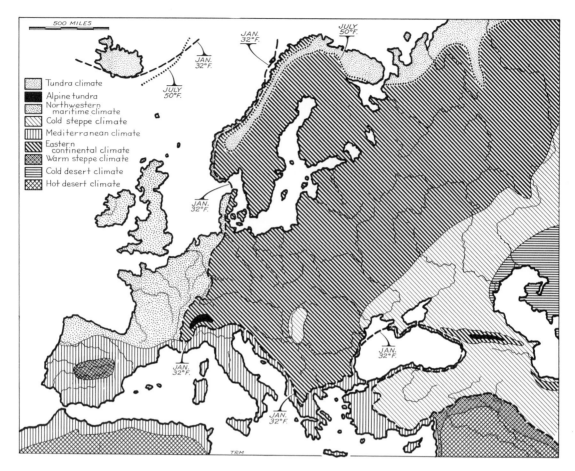

Europe: climates

1. *Tundra climate*, characterized by an average of less than 50° F. for the warmest month, occurs along the Arctic coast. Its summers are too cool for tree growth or field agriculture. The typical vegetation is low shrubs, quick-growing summer annuals and grass, moss, lichens, and other lowly forms of plants.

Alpine tundra appears above certain critical elevations varying from near sea level in the Arctic to about 12,000 feet in middle latitudes. The main contrast between alpine and sub-polar tundra is with regard to length of day at various seasons, an effect of latitude. Midwinter does not bring periods of continuous darkness to the alpine tundra localities in the Alps or Caucasus. There is less forcing of plant growth by long days of continuous sunshine in midsummer.

2. *Northwestern maritime climate*, with adequate precipitation at all seasons and all monthly temperatures above 32° F. with that of the warmest month above 50° F., is typical of a narrow coastal belt of Norway, western Denmark, the British Isles, and most of France. Forest originally covered extensive areas. Plants are abundant, agriculture prospers, and landscapes are green at most seasons.

3. *Eastern continental climate*, with most of its precipitation in summer, its coldest month below 32° F. and its warmest month above 50° F., is most typical of central European Russia, but exists in milder form west to Norway and Germany and southwest to the Alps. Winter in the east is extremely cold, and the landscape turns from green to drab gray. Spring and fall are short, but the hot summer brings a return of green landscapes and plants grow vigorously.

4. *Mediterranean climate*, characterized by tem-

peratures like those of the northwestern maritime climate but with hotter summers and with precipitation concentrated in winter, occurs mainly around the Mediterranean Sea, particularly in lowlands. Landscapes become green in late winter and spring, but by summer the drought has turned the vegetation brown.

5. *Steppe climate*, transitional between humid and desert regions, is somewhat deficient in precipitation, ordinarily receiving less than 20 inches annually. Europe has two types of steppe climate. *Cold steppe*, with temperatures below 32° F. during the coldest month, occurs in an extensive, broad belt across the plains of southern Russia. Here the annual precipitation is between 10 and 16 inches. A similar climate is found in the Alföld of Hungary. *Warm steppe*, with coldest month temperatures above 32° F., occurs in parts of the Spanish Meseta and some of the lowlands of Greece.

6. *Desert climate*, characterized by extreme aridity, occurs only in the lowlands north and east of the Caspian. This is a cold desert with January well below 32° F. The vegetation is mostly low shrubs, widely spaced.

CULTURE AND CLIMATE

Europeans shun the tundra and desert areas because they present environments too hostile and demanding for their ways of life. To make a living from land where field agriculture is impossible, Europeans would have to adopt different culture traits, a concession they are unwilling to make. Of course, the prospects of trade, exploitation of mineral deposits, scientific research, and spreading a religious gospel send Europeans into any kind of land, but rarely as permanent inhabitants. So the tundra and deserts are left to the peoples of the Polar and Dry Worlds. In the past the aridity and the grassland vegetation of the steppes also have kept away Europeans, who were skeptical of the the value of non-forested lands. These prejudices have disappeared in the last century or so. Now the steppes of Europe are almost completely Europeanized, and extensively used to produce cereal crops in the more humid parts and as grazing lands toward the arid borders.

Three of the main climates may be identified roughly with the three culture realms of the European World. Northwestern Europe is largely the region of northwestern maritime climate. Mediterranean Europe is intimately related to the area of Mediterranean climate. Eastern Europe centers in the territory of eastern continental climate.

Transitions between climates are more or less paralleled by culture transitions. The zone between northwestern maritime and eastern continental climates is broad because it occurs across a flat territory. Germany, in the midst of this zone, is transitional in culture. The transitions northward from Mediterranean to other climates are typically abrupt, taking place up the slopes of mountains. Here cultural transitions are also sharply defined.

VEGETATION

The distribution patterns of vegetation and climates are closely associated, and frequently the boundary lines of one are defined in terms of the other. Thus the area of tundra vegetation coincides with that of tundra climate, the boundary line of the July isotherm of 50° F. having been selected because of its botanical significance as the general northern limit of tree growth. This general system is also applied to the other treeless areas, places of desert and steppe climates, but in these cases, aridity dictates both the type of climate and the types of vegetation.

Between the tundra and arid zones, things are not as simple because the intermediate climates are all generally capable of supporting forests, but the nature of the forests differs and these differences seem to ignore climatic boundaries. Man is another complication. Most maps showing the distribution of forest types attempt to portray conditions as they were prior to man's arrival. They leave out the vast areas that man has cleared to use for crops, cities, airports, and the like. So although the maps show forests covering extensive areas, in Europe today forests actually are more or less confined to the slopes or rough areas, and are largely a feature of the *cultural landscape*, the natural landscape as modi-

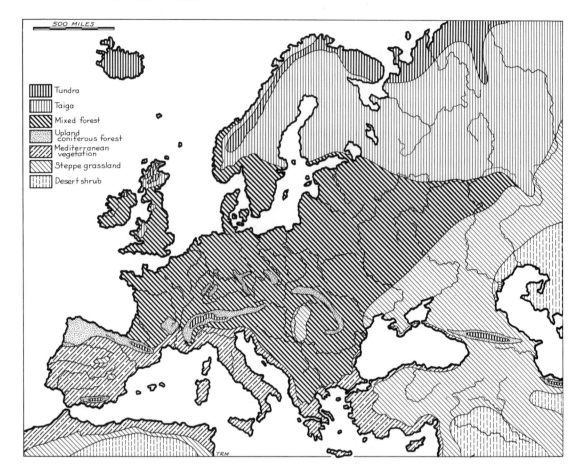

Europe: vegetation

fied by man. The surviving forests of Europe are mainly of three kinds: (1) taiga, (2) mixed deciduous-evergreen, and (3) dwarfed.

The *taiga* is the northern forest, and is mainly conifers such as spruce, fir, larch, and pine, all with needlelike narrow leaves. The stands of conifers are widespread and dense. They are of commercial importance because trees that grow slowly under cold conditions produce strong, durable lumber. Here and there among the conifers, particularly in the wet places as along streams and lakes, are deciduous, broad-leaved trees, trees that shed their leaves in the cold season. Toward the tundra border all trees are stunted.

The Eurasian taiga belt extends from the coast of Norway to the Pacific. This evergreen

belt has been a wide cultural barrier believed to be unsuited for settlement by both Europeans and peoples of the Polar World. Europeans have slowly invaded it as they cleared the forests to extend their fields northward toward the northern limit of cereal crops which is about in the middle of the belt. Taiga-like forests occur below the treeline of mountains south of the taiga zone. In these southerly coniferous forests, trees grow more rapidly and to larger size.

Southward from the taiga the conifers become intermingled with more and more broadleaf trees in the wide belt of *mixed forests*. This dense forest originally covered most of the European plain, but today only residual patches remain. These patches are mainly "second growth," trees that filled in after the virgin forests were cut down. The broadleaf deciduous trees, such as oak, elm, ash, linden, and maple, were especially dominant in the western areas and on lowlands and places of better soil. Conifers were mainly on uplands and better drained soils.

The transition between the taiga and mixed forest is broad in many places, especially across plains. The boundaries on the map are attempts to indicate the general center of the transition zone. The transition to the south of the mixed forest in Europe is ordinarily narrow, occurring along slopes of the east-west mountain barrier.

In the Mediterranean region, forests grow only under most favorable conditions, as on the moist lowlands along streams and on some uplands. Oak, pine, and laurel are common, with willow, poplar, and sycamore along streams.

The *dwarf forest* is characteristic of lower elevations in the Mediterranean realm. This shrubbery is variously called *maquis, makis,* or *macchia,* and in Mediterraneanlike Southern California, *chaparral.* It is rarely over six feet in height and consists of such plants as laurel, arbutus, heath, rockroses, and broom. In dense stands it blankets north slopes of hills and spreads over other places that cannot support larger trees or are not quite dry enough to be grassy barrens.

Plants in a Mediterranean climate must survive extreme drought and heat each summer. By late spring the grassy hillsides are turned a toasty brown. The shrubs cling to life by means of a number of special adaptations, such as having leaves that are small, leathery, oily, and sometimes hairy to reduce moisture loss. Many seeds are protected by thick layers of flesh, often oily as in the olive. The stunted size of plants also cuts moisture loss because total plant surface is smaller. Stunted plants are typical of all hostile environments, not only the summer-parched Mediterranean, but the deserts and tundra as well.

In the transition between forest of any type and arid regions, one of the first signs is the appearance of scattered "prairies," or grasslands of limited size, surrounded by forests. This blends into scattered trees surrounded by continuous grasslands, a *park landscape.* The proportion of grass increases toward the steppe

Coniferous forest and treeline, Bavarian Alps [*U.S.D.A.*]

where it is the dominant cover. Strips of *gallery forest*, mainly poplars, willows, and cottonwoods, extend far into the grasslands along the streams. In moist places there are groves of trees. Beyond the gallery forests and groves are the extensive grasslands of the steppe.

Park landscapes occur in many Mediterranean lowlands and in the wide transition south of the deciduous forest of the Soviet Union to the steppes north of the Black Sea. Long arms of gallery forest extend down the Russian rivers. Beyond the grasslands are the low-shrub deserts flanking the Caspian.

EUROPEANS

All living men, all members of the species *homo sapiens*, can be classified in many ways, according to their racial group, language, religion, nationality, or other characteristics. On any basis, Europeans present diversities and mixtures. These human complexities, however, are ones of detail which diminish when viewed from a little distance and, just as with the complexities of the physical landscape, broad general patterns emerge.

Before getting down to details on Europeans, it is necessary to digress to include background information on all men everywhere. Classifying all mankind according to inherited physical characteristics, such as body height, ratio between head width and length, kind of hair, or blood composition, produces three major divisions or *racial groups*: Caucasoid, Mongoloid, and Negroid.

Caucasoids vary in skin pigmentation from pinkish-white, or florid, to dark olive, and black. Hair is relatively abundant on face and body, that on the head varying from straight to curly. Their noses are fairly narrow, high and projecting, and lips are thin. High foreheads, well developed chins, small teeth, and inconspicuous cheekbones are typical. They have heads of all shapes. Caucasoids, inhabiting most of Europe, have also moved into practically all other lands. Archaic Caucasoids are found in India, Ceylon, Australia, and islands along the east coast of Asia as far as Kamchatka.

Mongoloids have yellowish-light-brown pig-

Group of Nordics, Sweden
[*Swedish Travel Information Bureau*]

mentation. They have sparse straight black hair, low noses, and medium-thick lips. Their cheekbones are prominent, and so are their upper front teeth which commonly project forward. A fold of skin extends across the upper eyelid and inner angle of the eye giving a slant-eyed effect. Foreheads are medium height and rounded; heads are ordinarily wide. Mongoloids inhabit most of Asia, the Polar World, and a large part of the Americas.

Negroids are characterized by skin pigmentation varying from black to brown or yellow-brown. They have little body hair, that on the head being usually kinky and sometimes in spaced tufts. Their ears are small, noses wide with broad, flat nostrils, and lips thick. Heads are long in proportion to width. Negroids inhabit most of Africa south of the Dry World, a few live farther north, and many occupy islands extending eastward through the Indian Ocean, East Indies, and into the western Pacific.

RACES

Some of the more significant races in the Caucasoid division are:

Mediterraneans, who are generally brunet or olive-skinned, with dark brown or black hair, brown eyes, long heads, oval faces, and medium stature (5 feet 4 inches average) with slender bodies during youth tending to develop obesity in middle age. They are characteristic of the borders of the Mediterranean Sea, are numerous in the British Isles, and have spread into eastern Africa and southwestern Asia.

Nordics, who may have been derived from Mediterraneans through long ages of depigmentation, are generally pinkish in complexion, with blond, light-brown, or red hair, eyes of blue or gray, long to medium wide heads, and rather tall stature (5 feet 8 inches average) with slender bodies, long necks, and rather flat chests. They are characteristic of Scandinavia, Iceland, the British Isles, and Low Countries, and extend east along the European Plain into Russia.

Alpines, who are somewhat darker than Nordics, with chestnut-brown to black hair, broad, high heads, abundant body hair, and stocky bodies of medium stature (5 feet 5 inches average) with short, thick necks, broad shoulders, and thick chests. They are most numerous along the highland belt from France to Asia Minor, with large numbers in Russia and Siberia.

Dinarics, who resemble Alpines, with even higher and rounder heads, long, deep faces, prominent noses often convex, and of taller stature (5 feet 8 inches average) with very long legs and rather short arms. They center in the Eastern Alps and southeast toward Greece.

East Baltics, who are lightly pigmented in skin, hair and eyes, with round heads rather

Europe: races

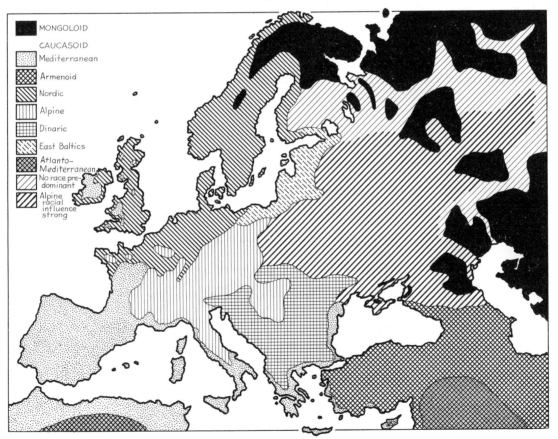

MONGOLOID

CAUCASOID
Mediterranean
Armenoid
Nordic
Alpine
Dinaric
East Baltics
Atlanto-Mediterranean
No race predominant
Alpine racial influence strong

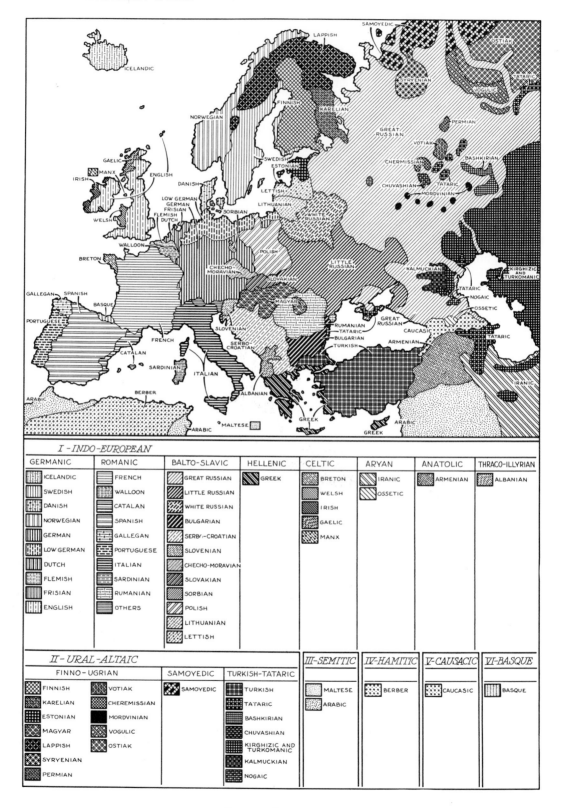

Europe: languages

flat in back, broad, high foreheads, fairly prominent cheekbones, concave noses and prominent nostrils, and medium stature (5 feet 4 inches average) with thickset, broad-shouldered bodies. They flank the eastern shores of the Baltic Sea.

There is a rough correlation between Europe's three culture realms and racial distribution. In general, Nordics are predominant in Northwestern Europe and Mediterraneans are predominant in Mediterranean Europe. Eastern Europe is more complicated racially, with Alpine and Nordic elements in close contact with other peoples, many of whom are Mongoloids.

LINGUISTIC GROUPS

Language is wholly a cultural matter. Individuals commonly learn the language of their parents or the language spoken locally. It has nothing to do with their race.

An enormous number of languages exists, possibly 4,000. They are commonly grouped into families, two being especially important in Europe.

Indo-European languages cover most of Europe and include the majority of its common tongues. *Germanic* languages are spoken by most people in the Northwestern culture realm, *Romanic* by most people in the Mediterranean realm, and *Slavic* by most people in the Eastern realm.

Ural-Altaic is the language family of second importance in Europe and is characteristic of northernmost Eurasia and has spread into Europe. Many minor Ural-Altaic languages are spoken in the eastern part of Europe. Two main centers lie to the west: one east of the Gulf of Bothnia and the eastern Baltic, the other in lowlands between the Carpathians and the Danube.

The other language families are of minor importance in Europe. Of the Semitic languages which are mainly non-European with Arabic dominant, only one, Maltese, exists in Europe on the small island of Malta. Caucasic, with a wide variety of languages, is found mainly in the Caucasus. Basque is a remnant survival at the west end of the Pyrenees. Its vocabulary and structure are unique.

RELIGIOUS GROUPS

The European World is predominantly Christian. Nordic, Germanic-speaking Northwestern Europe is the main European stronghold of Protestantism. Romanic-speaking Mediterranean Europe is predominantly Roman Catholic. Mixed-Alpine, Slavic-speaking Eastern Europe is Greek Catholic, either Eastern or Orthodox. The main religious groupings may be thus roughly identified with the main culture realms. But there are many exceptions among individuals and among rather large groups, such as the Roman Catholics of Ireland. Albania and other places once overrun by Turks remain outposts of Mohammedanism. Judaism is in all parts of Europe, especially in cities and along the western margins of the Eastern culture realm.

NATIONAL GROUPS

Social evolution beyond the family and tribal group developed into feudal organizations in many parts of Europe. People inclined to stay in one place and adopt agriculture as their economy, gathered rather naturally into groups centered around the home or land of the headman. Differentiation into ruling and serf classes followed. Most feudal holdings were small and agrarian, but little industries developed in some, and others found themselves advantageously on trade routes. Feudal units were in the control of hands that might turn to plunder, political aggrandizement, or the lust for increased size. Successful lords often built elaborate castles, which might be surrounded by walled towns sheltering considerable populations. Some of these grew to city-states, ripe for the later development of nationalism.

Political organization centered around the ruler. He was usually intent on defense against aggression or bent on conquest. It awaited the Romans to develop a political organization at all comparable to those of today and to expand territorial rule on an effective basis. The Roman Empire provided the model that the European World has followed. It was to enforce Pax Romana that the concept of "divine mission"

48

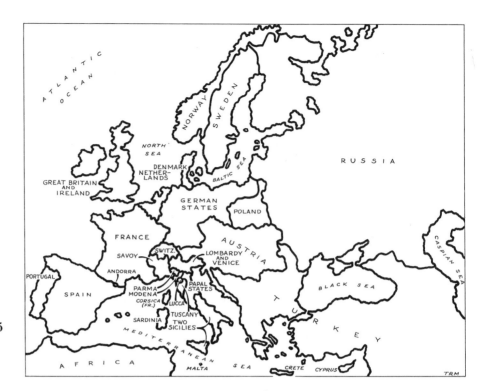

Europe, 1815

Europe, 1914

Europe, 1960

entered politics. The boundaries of the Empire long stood as bulwarks against barbarism. Though Germanic bands ended Roman domination after 378 A.D., Europeans having tasted the glory of empire never afterward gave up the hope of creating government on a grand, extensive scale.

A type of modern nationalism came into being with the Commercial Revolution and the associated Voyages of Discovery. Successful commerce had created a wealthy middle class who actively aided the monarchs in the overthrow of the feudal system. This strengthened the position of the monarchs and reduced the power of the minor lords. The movement started in England under Henry VII in 1485 and by the end of the Tudor period in 1603, England had become a nationalistic state in the modern sense. One by one, from the fifteenth to eighteenth centuries, the nations of Europe emerged from feudalism: Portugal, Spain, the Netherlands, France, Sweden, Russia, Prussia, Poland, until by the end of the eighteenth century most of Europe was a quiltwork of nationalistic powers.

New problems soon arose to vex the great monarchs. Their early allies, the wealthy merchant middle class, grew even more prosperous as technological advances developed into the Industrial Revolution, and they began to aspire to the political power held by the monarchs. They were joined by the lower classes as a tide of self-assertion swept many monarchs off their thrones. The English beheaded their king (1649) and experimented with middle class rule. The French launched their revolution (1789). These movements were signs of the growing importance of the "common people" in whose hands the nationalism of more recent times has developed. Through the nineteenth century these movements forged new independent states: Belgium, Greece, Luxemburg, Serbia, Montenegro, Rumania, Norway, Bulgaria, and Albania, to bring the map of Europe to its 1914 status on the eve of World War I. Out of this war came such countries as Finland and the Baltic States, Czechoslovakia, and modern Hungary.

The map was ever-changing; new nations, new boundaries, and equally as important, new meaning for boundaries both old and new. In earlier times, boundaries had been hazy, ineffective lines, but they gradually took on characteristics of barriers, hindering trade and diffusion of culture traits. A significant milestone in the development of boundary importance was the adoption of conscription laws, started in France and rapidly spreading to other countries. These required men to defend or fight for their own country. Nationalism, thus, became an armed force, and boundaries took on their present meaning. Today they are true breaks with real military, political, and cultural significance. Changes in laws, legal tender, language, gauges of railroads, and many other barriers emphasize each line between nations. Movement of goods is often obstructed by high tariff walls.

Nationalism is essentially a new cultural control. Though it cannot change racial inheritance, it goes far in forcing people to adopt certain languages, religions, and other culture traits. The influence of nationalism has been so profound that it is now possible to organize an outline of the culture distribution of Europe and many other parts of the world according to political units, such as individual nations.

In the Northwestern culture realm are: the British Isles, divided nationally into the United Kingdom and Ireland; the Scandinavian lands of Norway, Sweden, Denmark, and Iceland; the Low Countries, Netherlands and Belgium; and,

Symbol of Nationalism, Brandenburg Gate, Berlin

[*German Tourist Information Office*]

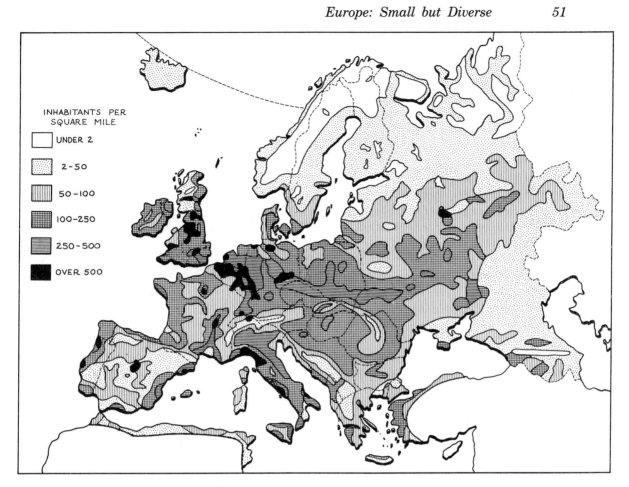

Europe: population density

in Central Europe, much of Germany. In the Eastern Realm is most of the European and Siberian territory of the old Russian Empire. In the Mediterranean Realm are: Greece, Italy, Spain, and Portugal. Between these main culture realms are transitional zones, of which a *Shatter Belt* extending south from Finland to northern Greece is the most complex in regard to nationalities. Most of it lies along the zone of clash between Northwestern and Eastern culture realms. Farther to the west, France and Switzerland occupy a transitional position between Northwestern and Mediterranean culture realms, forming a mild western Shatter Belt.

NORTHWESTERN
EUROPEAN REALM

London
[British Information Services]

4. The British Isles

Within the Northwestern European Culture Realm the British Isles are a distinctive and unified region, yet they possess considerable diversity. The climate, typically mild and maritime, includes significant contrasts in rainfall and temperature. Most of the surface is part of the European Plain, yet little of it is flat, some of it is uplands, and the Northwestern Highlands reach Scotland and parts of Ireland. The population is predominantly Nordic, but with considerable Mediterranean and Alpine admixture. A Germanic language is almost universal, but with strong residues of Celtic-speaking peoples. The Protestant religion dominates except in Ireland which is intensely Roman Catholic. Industrialism is highly advanced and population is mainly urban, yet rural life persists, some of it in rather primitive form. To the east lies the main focus of Northwestern European culture, the North Sea, yet Mediterranean influences are potent.

The British Isles form a barrier between the North Atlantic and the North Sea, consisting of about 5,500 islands and rocks. Great Britain is the largest (89,000 square miles), and Ireland is second (32,000 square miles). All the others combined are less than 500 square miles. Altogether the total area equals that of New Mexico, yet it supports over 54 million people, more than any other country in Europe except Germany and the Soviet Union.

The people of the British Isles enjoy an equable climate because winds from the North Atlantic bring about the same air temperature at all seasons. In winter, coastal Ireland has about the same temperature as the Mediter-

ranean coast of France, but the winds cool slightly as they go east and London is about 6° cooler, with a January average of 38.5° F. Winds in summer warm as they travel east, bringing average July temperatures somewhat above 60° to much of southeastern Ireland and all but the northwesternmost part of Great Britain. The temperature rarely climbs to 80° anywhere in the islands.

Winds from the North Atlantic also bring moisture, in excessive amounts to the west coasts and mountains. Fog and drizzle occur day after day, particularly in winter. Rain is abundant in all months, but especially in the fall when crops are ready to harvest. Western lowlands annually receive 30 to 40 inches or more and the mountains commonly get over 100 inches. The eastern areas, lying in the "rain shadow" of the mountains, are drier. They generally receive less than 25 inches a year. London, for example, has an annual precipitation of 24 inches. Most of this is rain. Snow rarely falls on the lowlands although London

may have a few flurries each year, and they are slightly more frequent farther north. Only the higher mountains are snow-covered for several weeks or months in winter, and all the snow disappears in summer.

This climate favored the growth of extensive forests which covered much of the area when man arrived on the scene. Deciduous trees grow on the lowlands, pine and birch on the uplands, with broad grassy areas on the lowland clay soils and scrubby growth on the sandy lands. Broad marshes, called *fens*, exist along the coasts, especially north of the Thames Estuary. Extensive wet *bogs* of grass and sedge cover much of central Ireland. Above the tree line, which is rather low because essentially all of Great Britain lies north of 50° N., are tundralike *moors* of low shrubby heather and small tufted plants. The tiny heather blossoms turn the gray moors to purple in late summer. On many of the damp uplands and in undrained lowlands, there are extensive deposits of *peat*.

Animals were abundant in prehistoric British

(*opposite*)
Lake District landscape
[*British Information Services*]

West coast of Ireland
[*Irish Tourist Office*]

Isles, but man has caused many changes. Many of the animals, such as the wolf, brown bear, boar, beaver, and Irish elk, are gone entirely, and others, such as the fox, otter, and badger, manage to survive in numbers only in protected areas. Britain has few snakes, and only one poisonous variety. Ireland has none. Many small creatures have benefited by man's presence for he makes an easy food supply available and has reduced their natural enemies. Foremost among these is the rat, always one of man's closest, if unwelcome, companions.

CULTURAL SUCCESSION

When the vast Ice Age glaciers pushed to their southernmost point, they covered almost all of Great Britain north of London, thus denying to earliest man the area north of the Thames. As the glaciers waned and waxed, and the ice margins moved north and south, man kept pace. It should surprise no one that man could live so close to enormous areas of ice; many men have, and some still do, as in Greenland. Man in England may well have pre-dated the ice if the stone flakes, called "Ipswichian flakes," found on the coasts north of the Thames are really signs of man's industry some million years ago, as some people believe.

During Neolithic times, long after the ice had retreated, the British Isles were overrun by Mediterraneans, probably the megolith builders and farmers, who arrived to find primitive farming already underway as early as 2000–3000 B.C. There were more invasions, and by the sixth century B.C., Celtic peoples with Alpine characteristics had all but replaced the Mediterraneans. These Celtic Britons were considered primitive, and so reported by Pytheas in the fourth century B.C. although he found them mining metals, tilling the soil, and brewing beer. Tin mined by Celts in Cornwall had already found its way to the centers of Mediterranean Civilization.

Roman conquerors arrived in A.D. 43 to sub-

British Isles: index map

jugate the people and exploit the resources for the benefit of their homeland. But while so doing, they incidentally benefited Britain, for they built roads, established Roman law and order, and stimulated cultural progress. After the 400 years of Roman rule, Britain was considerably better off than the unconquered areas in Scotland, Wales, and Cornwall.

During and after the collapse of the Roman Empire, the British Isles were invaded time and again. Germanic-speaking tribes of Frisians, Jutes, Saxons, Angles, and other Nordics spread into the area, coming mainly as settlers and colonizers. By the end of the eighth century much of England had become an Anglo-Saxon land. The Nordics brought new culture traits, altered the old Roman place names, and divided England into 40 counties, or shires. With St. Augustine in about 600 came the reestab-

lishment of the Christianity which had gained a precarious foothold in the time of the Romans, but had long since disappeared.

Then new flavors were added. Norwegians and Danes began to plunder and then to colonize the British Isles. Unification of Great Britain came about under the Danish King Knut (1016–1025) whose reign marked the only period in history when all peoples facing the North Sea focal area were unified politically. His capital was Winchester.

William the Conqueror (1066) was the last successful military invader of the British Isles, and with him came a strong French influence. For the second time, law and order of the Roman type reached England, but now it was imposed, not on primitive Celts but on Germanic peoples, who appeared uncouth and backward to the invading Normans. The various governments of England and Wales were welded into a bond that has remained permanent. French words were introduced, and the language gradually unified into an archaic type of English, despite the fact that until 1363 French was the official language of the country. Between the thirteenth and sixteenth centuries a culture was being shaped that became distinctively English. This was the culture of "Elder England."

During and after the sixteenth century, British influences steadily grew, but this was a new role. Up through the Middle Ages Britain was a primitive outpost on the fringe of Europe. It was ignored, invaded, and dominated, but never considered very important, except as a producer of limited amounts of wool and food for the use of more advanced mainland people. It was not until 1546 that anyone bothered to map England. Few would have predicted at this point in history that eventually more than 200 million people would speak English as their native tongue or that Great Britain as a political power was destined to control some 14 million square miles, nearly one quarter of the earth's land surface and 500 million people, nearly one quarter of the earth's population; or that its people would rule the seas and own over one quarter of the world's transportation facilities.

Proximity to the continent benefited Britain in many ways. Each invasion brought cultural enrichment and added important human elements for the building of a new nation. Alpines and Nordics combined ethical and moral codes into a social order that attracted peoples from other lands. England became a refuge from oppression, a haven of freedom and fair play. Once the English were powerful enough to protect their shores, their insularity brought peace. Invasions of England were thwarted in 1588, 1805, 1914, and 1940. The 21 miles of water between England and the mainland offered a security that even Air Age warfare failed to destroy. The position of England allowed it to borrow what it chose from the continent, maintain its own identity, and stand aloof from most serious conflicts on the mainland. This advantage is rapidly vanishing in a world of jet transport and missile warfare.

The first signs of empire appeared during the reign of Queen Elizabeth (d. 1603), for it was then that British seamen, having acquired the art of tacking or sailing almost into the wind, were becoming masters of the sea. This superiority of British seamanship, dramatically demonstrated in the defeat of the Spanish Armada in 1588 which ended Spain's hopes of ruling the islands, was a boon to the commercial interests. Several important trading companies were organized to engage in overseas commerce. Thus started a Commercial Revolution that eventually established the Empire. Its growth was not entirely deliberate. The flag followed the trader, innocently as a rule, but positively.

ELDER ENGLAND

Elder England, the attractive agricultural region of southeastern Great Britain, is the area where English culture was nurtured. Here the English language was evolved and from here English cultural influences spread not only throughout the British Isles, but also, by way of London and the Commercial Revolution, to many other parts of the world. It is a region of geologically young rocks, many of which help form its fertile soils. The western boundary of the young rock region and of Elder England, extends from Portland Isle on the south coast of Dorset to Scarborough on the coast of York. Along the boundary are outcrops of a resistant rock—called oolite (*oo*, egg; *lithos*, rock) because it is composed of little spherical particles that resemble fish eggs—which form a discontinuous ridge bearing such local names as Cotswolds, Northampton Upland, and North York Moors.

Minor folding of the young rocks, plus the fact that some layers are far more resistant to erosion than others, gives southeastern England topographic diversity. London basin, along the lower Thames, follows a major downfold. Chalk rocks and layers of sandstone stand as ridges, while belts of clay generally locate valleys. Agricultural values and population densities are low on the oolitic and chalk uplands, in contrast to the densely settled, fertile lowlands and *vales*.

Between the Thames Valley and the Channel coast is a minor uparched fold. Along its eroded, troughlike crest lies a hilly section called the Weald, a name derived from the German *wald*, meaning wood or forest. Local place names, such as the Forge and Cinder Hill, recall the fact that the Weald once possessed iron ore and forests, and was the original industrial core of Great Britain. The local forests were consumed and iron smelting died out in 1830. The central clay lowlands and sandy hills of the Weald were poorly suited to agriculture, and have remained sparsely settled and backward.

On either side of the Weald are the vales of Kent (north) and Sussex (south). Beyond these rise chalk hills, some exceeding 1,000 feet, with bare brows, steep slopes, and short-grass cover. These parallel ridges, North Downs and South Downs, were used by early Saxons for sheep raising. The area became an exporter of wool until the local demand for meat so increased that the Downs began to specialize in sheep for mutton, their chief use today. In the Downs the population density is low, only two per square mile, quite different from nearby rural lowlands that support 200 to 300 on each square mile. Lands similar to the Weald and Downs lie to the north of the Thames Valley, but the ridges are lower and the vales are wider.

A prominent feature on the east coast between the counties of Norfolk and Lincoln, is The Wash, a broad shallow indentation, once important for its ports. When ships increased in size and draft, most of these shallow ports fell into disuse, a few surviving as bases for small fishing and pleasure craft. The Fenlands, behind The Wash, were originally marsh, too wet for use and subject to flooding. As early as 1628 Dutch engineers started drainage projects and these have been continued with the result that a large tract of productive agricultural land has been added to Elder England.

The Humber Estuary lies upcoast from The Wash. The many branches of the Humber have been used as important avenues of transportation and communication. A southerly branch, the Trent, leads far toward Bristol Channel and Liverpool Bay on the west coast. From the Trent many easy passes lead to the Thames

Valley. Northern branches lead through the Vale of York, which arose as a secondary nucleus of older English culture. York was the Roman capital, and remained the largest town in England for more than ten centuries. Today it is the ecclesiastical capital of northern England.

The primary *nucleus* or *cradle area* of English culture lay in and around London Basin. Angles, Saxons, and Jutes blended to form the dominant population. The export of wool from this area aroused the first interest in commercial enterprise. The Thames Valley had a favored location with regard to the Commercial Revolution that centered around the North Sea on whose shores developed some of the world's greatest seaports. The Thames Valley lay not only in the heart of a productive region but led downstream to an estuary capable of becoming the world's leading seaport. The Thames is responsible for the existence and the importance of London.

Linn-dun (fortified hill above a lagoon) was a focal point even in Celtic times. The value of the site was recognized by the Romans who built a bridge across the river and roads radiating spokelike from their Londinium. It soon became one of the five largest cities north of the Alps, with a population of 15,000 before the Roman legions departed. During the Middle Ages the population increased in London, and it was enclosed by a wall. The old walled town is still the "City of London," though it contains only a small fraction of the County of London, or Greater London. The City of London has never been the political capital of Britain, an honor held by its sister City of Westminster.

The great trading companies organized in the fifteenth and later centuries, established London as the home office for foreign commerce. The city soon dominated all English trade and was the world's chief money market. The number of ship arrivals and departures increased enormously, as did the port facilities to accommodate them, spreading for miles down the Thames. Many of the ships from the Orient or the Americas had cargoes destined for the continent, and used London as a transfer point, the cargoes being then sent by ferry across the

North Sea. Ports on the continent prospered much according to their proximity to London. Absence of excessive tides and winter ice were advantages denied several other harbors that might have threatened London's supremacy.

The growth of London expanded the suburbs, but tended to empty the "City." The "outer ring" of suburbs, playing the role of dormitory for the fast-growing population, brought the size of Greater London to 693 square miles. Here live almost eight and one half million people, one fifth of England's total population. Although manufacturing and industry always remained subordinate to finance, commerce, and politics, any city of over eight million people requires many manufacturing establishments. Those of London spread widely, many being located in towns beyond the "outer ring."

The problems of feeding and caring for such a huge population are extremely complicated.

Essex has become a great dairy farm. Vegetables pour in from all over southern England and the Channel Islands. But the British Isles are no longer able to feed London and other English cities. So, Denmark sends large quantities of butter, bacon, and cheese; from the Southern Hemisphere come meat, cereals, and fruit; and in fact, about every corner of the globe is a contributor of one thing or another. This demands a highly developed distributing system, for foods must get to a population that in some areas has a density of over 200,000 per square mile, as in the east end of the city where the poor districts are concentrated. To many a cockney, the familiar landscape is mainly squalid, low houses strung in endless rows along narrow streets congested by foot and vehicular traffic, amid which are many small shops laden with cheap goods, and near which are large warehouses and dingy manufacturing plants. He has an escape, however, not always available

British Isles: physical features

to his counterparts in other, similar urban areas, for nearby will be one of the more than 50 parks in the city offering a grassy retreat from his drab surroundings. He has thus a distinct advantage over laborers in the great manufacturing centers west of the Pennines.

THE WEST

The earliest penetration of the English into the West came about when the lands of Elder England became so valuable as farms that the sheep were crowded out. Sheep raised for wool or cattle for hides had to be grazed in more remote places, and so these activities were shoved west and north, across the oolitic escarpment, and into the moors and lowlands of the West. This area had been the stronghold of the Celts, but as the English gradually took over the better grazing lands, the Celts retreated to isolated refuges in the Pennines and the uplands of Wales.

The Pennine Chain is the topographic backbone of England. It extends from the low Cheviot Hills of southern Scotland southward to the Midland Gap. Its summits rarely exceed 2,000 feet, and it is crossed by several low passes which usefully serve as routes for rail and highway transportation. The original forest cover is gone, and today 95 per cent of the barren uplands of the Pennines is in pasturage, grassland, or moor.

West of the northern Pennines is the Cumbrian Dome, or Lake District, culminating in Scafell (3,200 feet). The more or less radial valleys, leading to peripheral lowlands, were scoured by ice during the Ice Age. Their sheer sides and rather flat, meadow-studded floors are so picturesque that the area has become one of England's most popular resorts. Above the valleys the lofty crags are frequently obscured by clouds, and throughout the District rainfall is so excessive that much of the upland is even too wet for grazing.

The Pennines lose their identity southward, where uplands spread into the relatively low Midland Plateau. Midland Gap, between the

Snowdonia, Wales
[*British Information Services*]

southern end of the Pennines and the higher plateau of Wales, offers easy access to the plains along the Irish Sea, both from the lowlands of Elder England and those of the Severn to the south. South of the Midland Gap, and covering most of Wales, is a plateau of old rock trenched by glacial valleys. Above 1,000 feet much of it is treeless and rugged. On the boulder-strewn uplands are extensive tracts of wet peat. The area around Snowdon (3,560 feet) in the northwest, is the rainiest in Europe. Although it is almost 700 years since the English conquered Wales, the Celtic Welsh have managed to retain their individuality and their language, an especially remarkable feat in view of the effects of the Industrial Revolution and its forerunners.

Orient, the realization that an important pair of continents lay to the west, and the start of the Commercial Revolution. England was found to occupy the world's most central position, with London approximately in the center of the land hemisphere, the half of the earth that contains seven eighths of all land. This gave London marked and early advantages in the competition for sea-borne trade.

Plymouth and other Devon ports soon arose as challengers, but were outdistanced by Bristol whose west coast position favored trade with the West Indies and America. Also, Bristol was only a short and easy haul from the London Basin. During the seventeenth century Bristol enjoyed a practical monopoly on the West Indian sugar-rum-tobacco trade. In payment for these American commodities went crude cloth to west Africa to be traded for slaves who were transported to the West Indies and America. Bristol's importance, however, declined rapidly when steamships began to supplant sailing vessels. It is ironical that Bristol in 1838 was the port of departure for the first steamer to cross the Atlantic, because its harbor was soon found to be inadequate for the larger ships. West Indian trade gravitated to Liverpool, Glasgow, and other ports with deeper water.

Liverpool had a particular advantage with regard to the British textile industry. In the sixteenth century people along the margins of the Pennines were learning how to spin thread and weave cloth, making use of local wool and the ready source of power offered by the Pennine streams. Toward the end of the century, cotton from the eastern Mediterranean Levant first reached London, and then had the long and expensive journey to the weavers. Liverpool was much closer, and soon took over the service of import and export for the industry.

Liverpool was just a small fishing center in the twelfth century, inhabited mainly by non-English. Trade with Ireland boosted the population slightly, but the real impetus came when sugar, rum, tobacco, and cotton began reaching its wharves. Immigrants from Ireland and Scotland poured in to make livings out of Liverpool's increasing commerce. Population

COMMERCIAL REVOLUTION

The last few centuries have witnessed cultural revolutions that completely upset old values. The first of these was the Commercial Revolution, closely associated with the Voyages of Discovery. Others followed. Among their geographical effects is the fact that, except for London, the great population centers of England now lie in the West.

In the fifteenth century, Great Britain was considered by Europe to be of little significance. The great centers of cultural enlightenment, commercial activity, and financial stability were in Italy, Spain, France, and beyond the Mediterranean. Toward the end of that century came the earliest of the Voyages of Discovery, the opening of a sea route around Africa to the

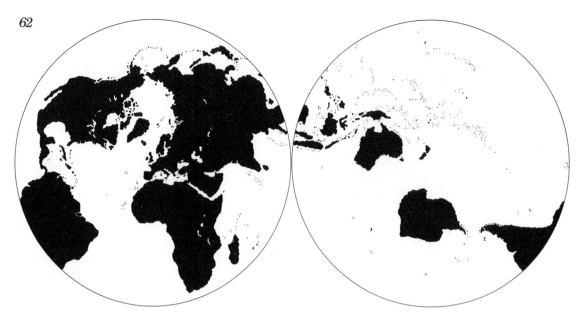

Land and water hemispheres

increased from 5,000 in 1700 to 35,000 in 1775. During this time, it became the leading center for slave trade. Over 300,000 Negroes crossed the Atlantic in ships of Liverpool registry between 1783 and 1793. Liverpool became wealthy and by the middle of the eighteenth century had displaced Bristol as second port in England. Despite its relatively late start, the port rose to the position of handling one fifth of all English imports, one third of all exports, and three quarters of the American cotton trade. Its wharfage grew to a length of over 77 miles.

These ports of the West, beyond the limits of Elder England, grew to a size which threatened the commercial leadership of London. Elder England began to devote most of its energy to serving London. Merchants and financiers of the West, growing more opulent than the old landed aristocracy, demanded greater political recognition. Conservative Elder England began losing ground to the uncultured West. New products and new prosperity called for larger population, and immigrants were welcomed from Ireland, Scotland, and the Continent. New skills were brought in to become the basis of another cultural revolution, along industrial lines.

INDUSTRIAL REVOLUTION

The first manufactured exports of England were chiefly textiles. Primitive industrial villages sprang up along the lower slopes of the Pennines where water wheels could be built. People gradually developed skill in producing thread and cloth, and new mechanical inventions, such as the flying shuttle, spinning jenny, and spinning mule, increased the speed while reducing costs of manufacture. The villages on the west side of the Pennines found with the coming of cotton that they had a real asset in their continual dampness—the moist air kept cotton threads from snapping during manufacturing. Lancashire rose to supremacy in the cotton industry, while districts east of the mountains specialized in woolens.

A rudimentary iron industry, begun in the forests of the Weald, soon moved on to better fuel supplies in Midland Gap and along the eastern side of the Pennines. Before 1600 the forges of smithies were busily consuming the Forest of Arden, near what is now Birmingham. Men around Northhampton, just to the east, learned that local trees yielded useful tanbark, and established a leather industry. These beginnings of the Industrial Revolution had a sad effect on British landscape. Deforestation proceeded at a rate unequalled elsewhere in Europe. Today only 4 per cent of England is forest covered. As British trees disappeared, industry turned to coal and gained momentum.

Even in pre-Roman times, Britons were gathering lumps of coal for fuel. By the thirteenth century, they were exporting small quantities of "sea coal" collected along the shore of northeast England. In this vicinity, around Newcastle, actual mining was started some 200–300 years later. These extensive coal beds were used by industry only in a limited way until the early eighteenth century when the process for making coke was discovered. Coal, subjected to this process of slow distillation, yielded a fuel which produced very high temperatures needed in making steel. Coal gained a new value, and mines began to open near Birmingham and in southern Wales. Vast coal deposits were located along both sides of the Pennines. In time it was found that Great Britain had one of the richest coal reserves in Europe.

The importance of Britain's richest geological endowment was not realized until after the invention of the steam engine in the late seventeen-hundreds. In general, the places that started local industries based on water power or fuel from nearby forests turned out to be near coal deposits. They were mainly places of little value in the days of Elder England. But values changed, and in the industrial age, the good soil and moderate rainfall of southeastern England were no longer factors of primary importance. The phenomenal growth of English cities in the nineteenth century occurred where soils were poor, wetness excessive, but coal present. England led the world in coal production and in iron and steel manufacturing until about 1900 when leadership in these activities passed to the United States.

Birmingham

[*British Information Services*]

The Industrial Revolution went hand in hand with an Agricultural Revolution, and both profoundly changed the English pattern of life. Cities and their industries attracted rural people in large numbers, and fewer people were needed on the farms. The pressure to grow food at home was lessened because the sale of industrial products abroad more than paid for increasingly large food imports. New agricultural practices led to a shift in emphasis from small, individually owned and worked farms to large estates using mechanized methods to produce food at lower costs. Properties increased in size, so that today nearly 90 per cent of Great Britain is in the hands of large owners. Such an owner is likely to be a London business man, who employs a staff of highly trained managers to run the farm worked by hired laborers. This system is rapidly spreading through most of the European World. The most specialized farming of all is in the Soviet Union, where the land belongs to the state and practically every phase of agriculture is undertaken by specially trained persons.

THE INDUSTRIAL WEST

Quite unlike Elder England, with its agricultural tradition, its landed gentry, and its conservatism, the West is a cultural product of industrialism, concerned primarily with increasing its profits and expanding its trade. These economic and social contrasts are seen in the landscape. The parks of London have few western equivalents. Western towns are shabby, grimy, and congested. Yet despite the drabness, lack of intellectual appeal, and disinterest in the welfare of the workers, the West attracted enormous numbers of people to swell its growing cities.

Lancashire has grown into a population knot of over five million and one of the most congested industrial districts on earth. Though split into many individual towns and cities, buildings are practically continuous for miles in any direction from the center of Manchester. From a small start in the woolen industry, Lancashire early switched to cotton, and today over 90 per cent of all British cotton spindles

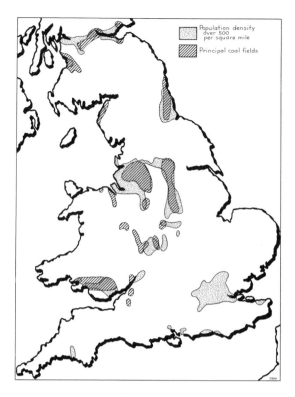

England:
coal fields and population density

are within 50 miles of Manchester and over 80 per cent are within 18 miles. Practically none are within the city itself where rents and land values are high. It serves as the nerve center of the industry, with its offices, wholesale houses, distributors and makers of machinery, and warehouses.

Liverpool was the cotton supply center for Manchester, but it suffered from extraordinarily high tides, a 26-foot rise and fall twice a day. This difficulty was to some extent alleviated by building floating docks which, with the ships along them, went up and down with the tide. But Manchester demanded a port of its own, so in 1894 the Manchester Ship Canal was completed, using five locks to overcome the 60-foot drop between the city and the sea. An artificial harbor was created to let this expanding city become a seaport. The population of Manchester and its suburbs grew to 2.5 million.

The **Black Country,** second in rank among the industrial districts of England, lies just south of the Pennines and about equidistant from Manchester, London, and Bristol, with easy communications to each. Here is Birmingham, a typical product of the Industrial Revolution. With a present population well over one million, it has recently snatched from Glasgow the rank of second largest city in the British Isles.

The presence of deposits of iron ore and coal gave Birmingham a natural lead in the iron industry. As manufacturing increased so did the pall of smoke that constantly filled the air. People began calling the district, Black Country, a name appropriate also to the acres of derelict land left after the removal of coal and iron. By the time the local iron and coal supplies had been exhausted, the area held enough skilled artisans to warrant import of raw materials if sufficiently high-priced products could be turned out. Industry then turned to a variety of brass and precious-metal products, heavier industries going into chemicals and glass. Birmingham boasts of having over a thousand different industries engaged in making everything from pins to steam rollers. The twentieth century has seen many of its workers turn to making automobiles, electrical goods, office machines, and rubber goods. Though it became the center of a great canal system in the eighteenth century, Birmingham has suffered from inland location. High transportation costs also favored particular concentration on high-value wares.

The industrial history of Coventry, about 15 miles southeast, is like that of Birmingham,

except that it started as a woolen center. Textile activities were ultimately eclipsed by metal industries, and Coventry came to produce such products as bicycles, automobiles, sewing machines, radios, and plastics. Its importance as an automobile manufacturing center brought it especially heavy German air attacks during World War II.

Between the Black Country and Manchester is the urban mass around Stoke on Trent in northern Staffordshire, known as the Potteries. This ugly area of hundreds of blackened bottle-shaped kilns, and equally blackened streets of crowded little brick houses, is the center of Britain's important pottery industry.

West Riding, in Yorkshire, is another great conurbation, with over two million people, and an average population density over 3,000 per square mile. Sheffield, long famous for its fine cutlery, turns out 14 per cent of all British steel, much of it in such finished products as railway wheels, axles, armor plate, guns, knives, files, scissors, and machinery. Leeds, farther north, retains its original textile interests, specializing in woolens. Like the other textile cities of West

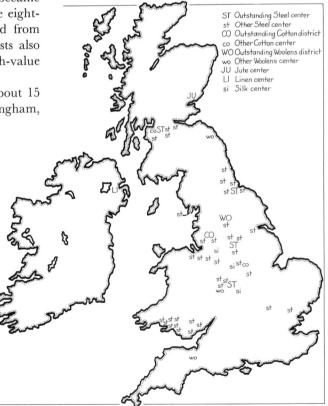

British Isles: manufacturing centers

ST Outstanding Steel center
st Other Steel center
CO Outstanding Cotton district
co Other Cotton center
WO Outstanding Woolens district
wo Other Woolens center
JU Jute center
LI Linen center
si Silk center

(*opposite*) **Village in Wales**
[*British Information Services*]

Wool factory, Yorkshire
[*British Information Services*]

as an outlet for wares manufactured in West Riding and other industrial centers east of the Pennines. It is also the center of a very large seed-crushing and oil-extracting industry, and the base for a large fleet of North Sea fishing trawlers.

Many small fishing ports line the English shore of the North Sea. Of the 30,000 craft that normally ply these waters, about two thirds are British. The incomes of about a million people depend on them. Grimsby, the world's greatest fishing port, sends out as many as 300 cars of fish per day on special trains to London, Birmingham, Manchester, Liverpool, and even Scotland.

Ports toward the Thames, of which Dover is the closest to the continent, are used both as resorts and as harbors for small continental steamers. South coast ports serve both resort and London outport functions, but only Portsmouth and Plymouth, important naval bases, have populations in excess of 200,000.

WALES AND CORNWALL

Wales was mainly a land of poverty and sheep for many centuries. In the sixteenth century it began to export small amounts of lead, copper, and silver, but its greatest mineral resource, coal, had to await development during the Industrial Revolution. The belt of coal near the south coast encouraged the establishment of heavy industries, particularly iron and steel.

Swansea developed as a great smelting center and metal-working town. Its fumes have killed trees for miles around, but despite this blight, it has long been a favorite British resort. Cardiff, with 80 per cent of its exports being coal, developed industrially as one of the centers of Welsh steel production. A large share of the total population of Wales lives within 30 miles of Cardiff, in the centers of heavy industry.

Riding, Leeds also has other industries. Typically, men work in machine shops and heavy industry while women and children tend machines that spin or weave.

Between the Black Country and West Riding are many smaller industrial centers, each tending to specialize in a particular product. In open spaces between all these sprawling, gloomy, industrial conurbations, the green and tidy countryside is used mainly for cattle raising and dairying.

Newcastle lies about as far north of the West Riding industrial center as the latter lies north of the Black Country. It has been exporting coal since the fourteenth century. Even in recent years coal accounted for over half of the value and 95 per cent of the weight of its exports. Returning colliers brought bulky, cheap cargoes, such as chalk, salt, and pyrite, which formed the basis of the chemical industry established in Newcastle and other Tyne ports. There is also considerable shipbuilding and repairing, along both the Tyne and the Tees. Over 800,000 people now live in the Tyneside district, less than half of whom reside in Newcastle itself.

Hull, with its docks extending down the Humber, is the important east coast complement to Liverpool. It serves mainly as an importer of foods from across the North Sea, and

Numerous resort towns along the northern and western coasts of Wales attract many tourists and serve as playgrounds for the English. The barren interior of Wales, furnishing domestic water to Liverpool and Birmingham, is intensively used for raising sheep. Cattle are numerous to the east, and near the eastern border; apples, berries, and other fruits are produced for English markets.

Cornwall, the southwestern point of England, resembles Wales in many ways, but is less rugged. Since the Bronze Age it has been a producer of tin, though in recent years the low price of imported tin has made most local mining unprofitable. The cool yet frost-free climate of Cornwall allows it to supply London markets with a variety of garden vegetables and flowers, and the Cornish pastures provide a surplus of butter, cheese, milk, and geese. The general lack of resources handicaps Cornwall in an industrial age. It is gradually losing population, in spite of the tourist attraction of its picturesque coastal villages.

SCOTLAND

Scotland is a land of conspicuous topographic grain. The highlands, lowlands, main valleys, estuaries, island chains, and long segments of the coasts trend in a general northeast direction. This topographic grain follows the geologic pattern; practically all belts of rock outcrop and major fault lines have this orientation.

The topography may be divided into three main parts: Southern Uplands along the English border of the same ancient rocks as the Pennines; Midlands or Central Valley of younger rocks; and Highlands to the north composed of extremely ancient rocks that have undergone folding, crumpling, and chemical alteration during their complicated geological history. The Hebrides, Orkney, and Shetland islands are summits of now-detached and partially submerged portions of the Highlands.

The **Southern Uplands** and the Cheviot Hills were a barrier zone between Elder England and the cultural nucleus of modern Scotland in the Midlands. Frequent battles waged back and forth across this "border" country which now is peacefully devoted to sheep and cattle raising. Precipitation is excessive, especially in the west. The slightly drier eastern valleys are more useful and provide better pasturage. The Valley of Tweed is the most eastern and most populous large lowland, long famous for its woolens from Cheviot breeds of sheep. In more recent years this region has prospered as a supplier of milk to cities.

The **Scottish Midlands** is a low belt between the firths of Clyde and Forth. These estuaries are less than 30 miles apart at their heads. Little truly flat land occurs. Rainfall is excessive, especially in the west, so that much land is doomed to raise oats, a cereal defined by Samuel Johnson as being food for horses in England and for men in Scotland. The lowlands widen eastward and rainfall decreases enough to permit wheat raising. The fertile lands around the Firth of Forth became Elder Scotland, and Edinburgh rose to prominence in this good soil region just as London did in Elder England.

The **Highlands** are divided into northern and southern parts by Glen More and its terminal estuaries. Glen More, following a fault line, or fracture in the earth's crust, is very straight and narrow, and has been deepened by glacial action and stream erosion. North of it are the Northwest Highlands, a direct continuation of the highlands of Scandinavia, which they resemble in geologic history, glacial sculpture, climate, vegetation, poverty of natural resources except water power, and population. This area emerged from the Ice Age with rocky, barren surfaces that today remain almost unchanged. Many of the deep, steep-walled valleys scoured by ice, were filled with water when the ice retreated, becoming landlocked lakes or fiords. Loch Morar, in western Inverness, is the deepest lake in the British Isles, having been sounded to a depth of 1,070 feet.

The Hebrides, to the west, are a small-scale replica of the Northwest Highlands. Northward are the partially agricultural Orkneys, and still farther north are the rugged Shetlands, a region of pony pastures and fishing bases. The Shetland and Orkney islands were convenient stepping stones during the centuries of Scandinavian migration to the British Isles.

Just south of Glen More are the Southern Highlands, or Grampians, with their highest peaks close to the glen. Ben Nevis (4,406 feet) is the highest peak in Great Britain. A considerable part of this gently rolling, dissected plateau is above 3,000 feet, but only half a dozen summits reach 4,000 feet. In its wooded vales arose the many clans of Highland Scot-

land. Toward the east are better agricultural lands and, along the coast, excellent bases for North Sea fishing, such as Aberdeen, Scotland's third largest city.

The Scotia of Roman times was inhabited by warlike Picts of Alpine stock. By the fifth century, Celtic Scots began arriving from northeast Ireland, bringing Christianity with them. From the south came an Anglo-Saxon influence, which had gradually crept north along the east coast of England, across the Valley of Tweed, and into the agricultural eastern part of the Central Lowlands. These Germanic settlements prospered, and ultimately political power fell into Anglo-Saxon hands. The culture that developed among the Germanic peoples was in many ways similar to that of the English and gradually spread to the Celts, who, more and more, were becoming the inhabitants of the Highlands. Roman Catholicism long remained the prevailing religion both in the Highlands and the Central Valley.

Strong rivalries between the Germanic Scots and Germanic English led to a long series of border wars and eventually the establishment in the thirteenth century of a boundary between England and Scotland. Border raids continued, however, until the countries were combined under a single crown in 1603, though the Parliaments were not united for another hundred years.

The impact of the Industrial Revolution was felt with about the same force in Scotland as in England, as is shown by the fact that the population is now over 77 per cent urban as compared with England's 80 per cent. The Highlands, with 60 per cent of the area, have only 10 per cent of the population. The main results of the Industrial Revolution are seen in the Midlands.

Edinburgh, like London, started primarily as an agricultural nucleus. It soon became the educational, financial, and political center of Elder Scotland. Although local coal deposits exist and for a while use was made of nearby ore deposits to establish Edinburgh as an important iron producing town, industrialization has not proceeded far in the direction of heavy industries. The main manufactures are simply those required by a capital and educational center of almost a half million people.

Glasgow resembles the cities of western England in being a product of the Industrial Revolution. It started on fertile volcanic soils as an agricultural center, but its growth to a population of over one million stems from the Commercial Revolution when it entered into active trade with the West Indies and the Americas. Cheap labor, capable of weaving

could be started in Glasgow. These now dominate the city. Glasgow builds bridges, locomotives, pipes, heavy machinery, and is foremost in shipbuilding. Some tobacco and cotton manufacturing and sugar refining remain as heritages of earlier days, and many other industries have been established, which together with the heavy industires, make the Glasgow landscape as ugly and dirty as that of the worst industrial cities of England.

Grampians landscape
[*British Information Services*]

coarse textiles suitable for Africa, gave Glasgow textile mills their start and provided an economic advantage over the English textile mills. Sugar, rum, and tobacco were imported in increasing amounts, and by 1775 Glasgow was receiving over half the tobacco arriving at European ports. The Clyde was deepened so ocean-going ships could come some 18 miles upstream to the port, and wharfage was increased along with prosperity.

About two thirds of all Scottish coal is near Glasgow, but it was not used in any considerable amount until long after Manchester, Birmingham, and other English cities had developed world-wide manufacturing fame. It was not until the middle of the nineteenth century, when methods were perfected for using the difficult-to-smelt Scottish iron ore, that heavy industries

Although the largest population increases have been urban, particularly in Lanarkshire, rural population has grown during the last century both in the lowlands and highlands. Farming has been intensified. Lowland rural landscapes are English in pattern; irregular hedgerows outline fields of wheat, oats, barley, turnips, potatoes, and clover. On the higher slopes and moors, sheep graze, to provide wool for Scottish and English mills, or to be driven to the lowlands where they are fattened on turnips and sold as mutton.

The Industrial Revolution brought little change to the Northwest Highlands. People here must supplement their meager farm earnings with income from fishing and home industries, such as weaving and spinning. There is some tourist trade in summer. Whisky distilling is an important industry in small villages, especially along the west coast north of the Firth of Clyde. Peat smoke is used to produce the distinctive flavor of Scotch whisky, most of which is sold to blenders and exporters in Glasgow.

IRELAND

The topography of Ireland is much like a saucer. Mountains and highlands rim the extensive limestone Central Plain or Lowland, except for a gap along the Irish Sea. Of these marginal highlands, those in the northwest are least favored by nature, for they are wild, rugged, excessively wet, and largely waste. Tucked in among the northern highlands is the Lough Neagh depression, which resembles the Central Lowlands of Scotland. Its good agricultural land supports a dense population. Elsewhere in Ireland, especially in the Central Plain, agriculture is problematic because of the wet and capricious climate.

Excessive wetness promotes the name, Emerald Isle, for its widespread cover of grass and moss makes the landscape typically green. Much of the surface drainage has been blocked by glacial moraines, and many of the resultant lakes have been filled with peat. Peat bogs cover about 15 per cent of the area, and in some places are quite thick. Drainage nearly everywhere is ineffective. The typical Irish river is only in a defined channel when it is not spreading out to form a lake or losing its identity crossing a bog or marsh. Most of this irregular drainage leads to the Shannon, the longest stream in the British Isles.

When Celts from Great Britain first reached Ireland they encountered Mediterraneans in a Stone Age of cultural development. Celts soon dominated and settled in the better parts of the Central Lowland. These were the original Scots. As population grew, the spread was northeastward into the relatively good region of Ulster. St. Patrick brought Christianity to Ireland in the middle of the fifth century. Monasteries were soon established at many points in the Scottish territory. Scholarship advanced rapidly, and surpassed by a wide margin that of Great Britain.

Danes and Norwegians came in the ninth century, followed in the twelfth century by the start of a great immigration of English which lasted until the end of the sixteenth century. Many of the English, who made Dublin their stronghold, moved into the rural sections, where some became an Anglo-Irish aristocracy. As a class, they adopted Irish ways and became culturally Irish, in contrast with those who remained in and near Dublin. To these intensely English people, the Gaels and other inhabitants of Ireland seemed crude and primitive. The sixteenth century also saw the arrival of Scottish immigrants driven from home by poor economic conditions. By the end of the sixteenth century, only one sixth of Ireland remained in truly Irish hands.

The Irish long toiled for foreign landlords. They kept their native tongue and remained steadfastly Roman Catholic. Their foreign masters, the English and Scots, adopted Protestantism. Fires of deep resentment burned in Irish breasts toward the Protestants in the northeast and the English everywhere. Finally, about five sixths of Ireland, 26 of its 32 counties, became a Republic in 1919 and was granted dominion status within the British Empire in 1921, with the name Eire. The boundary, still fought over, was unsatisfactory both to the Protestant north and Catholic south. Strong resentment against the British was shown by the Constitution of 1937 in its complete rejection of any Empire connection.

Neither the Commercial nor the Industrial revolutions had much effect on Ireland, which has remained primarily agricultural. Unlike the industrialized countries, its population is 50 per cent rural and has not increased significantly in the last 50 years. Immigration and the introduction of the "Irish" potato raised the population to some 8.5 million by 1846. Disaster struck in that year when the Irish famine caused so many deaths that emigration assumed panic aspects. By 1850 the population had been reduced to 4 million. About 90 per cent of the Irish emigrants went to the United States, where today the population of Irish extraction is over four times that of Ireland.

After 1900, Ireland's population slowly in-

**West coast
of Ireland,
Clifden**
[*Irish
Tourist Office*]

creased to its present 4.4 million. Three million of these live in Eire, and the other 1.4 million live in Northern Ireland which is only one fifth the size of Eire. Most of Northern Ireland's population is concentrated along the valley of Lagan, the sides of Lough Neagh, the River Bann, and in and around Belfast where over one third of the people live.

Belfast, like London and Edinburgh, was first an agricultural nucleus. The surrounding region of volcanic soils had great fertility and, for Ireland, the rainfall was moderate. By the eighteenth century Ireland was growing a great deal of flax and most of it went to Belfast to be made into linen cloth. Flax growing declined but the mills of Belfast continued to operate on imports from Belgium, Latvia, and elsewhere. Belfast's increase in population from 15,000 in 1800 to nearly a half million today is due chiefly

to industrial activity. Its 800,000 spindles are tended by some 60,000 persons, predominantly women and children, while men build ships and engage in other heavy industries. Some 10 per cent of all British tonnage originates on the ways of Belfast.

Londonderry, or Derry, at the head of Lough Foyle on the north coast, is the second largest city in Northern Ireland. This old walled city of long and turbulent history has become a miniature Belfast. Some ships are built, but textiles are the principal activity. The main specialization is in shirts, which are cut in shops and sewn in the homes of some 40,000 rural women, a system of piecework common in Northwestern Europe.

Dubh-linn (black pool) was an old settlement near the mouth of the Liffey River. During the thirteenth century many Bristol colonists arrived, and Dublin soon became a prosperous English agricultural center, for the soils were good and rainfall moderate. Its population grew and by the nineteenth century had far exceeded that of Belfast: in 1822 Dublin had 186,000 and Belfast, 39,000. Dublin still leads, with a population slightly over a half million, but the margin is small.

Dublin, which prefers to be called Baile Atha Cliath in its revival of the Celtic language, resembles London and Edinburgh not only in agricultural background, but also in subsequent development. It is primarily a political, commercial, financial, educational, and cultural center. Trade has been almost exclusively with English ports. Goods destined for Ireland are first taken to England, then transferred to smaller ships bound for Irish ports. Although

Dublin

[*Bord Failte Eireann*]

today some non-British trade is conducted, 75 per cent of all imports and 90 per cent of all exports are still with Great Britain.

The lateness of the Industrial Revolution in Eire is shown by the fact that only about one fifth of the population is urban. Landscapes have changed much less during the last three centuries than elsewhere in the British Isles, or in Northwestern Europe generally. Here and there appears some landmark of modern times, such as the important airport at Shannon, or the transatlantic cable landing on the island of Valentia. Though tourists in increasing numbers flock to the scenic Lakes of Killarney, Blarney Castle, and the many other picturesque Irish attractions, they bring very few changes. In general, the landscapes, especially in the uplands that rim the Central Plain, are much as they were many decades ago.

Poverty has remained chronic in the soggy Central Plain. It is estimated that a family can eke out a living on 30 acres of drained land, but two thirds of all farms are smaller then that and over half are smaller than 15 acres. Sixty per cent of Ireland is owned by fewer than 15,000 people. The Government has taken strenuous measures toward more equable distribution of land and improvement of rural conditions, but the acreage of plowed land has continued to decrease and pasturage increase. The greatest problem of the farmer is excessive water, and each year is a gamble, for too much rain may make harvesting impossible. In 1949 a land rehabilitation project was started to reclaim 4 million acres of unproductive land, and the Turf Board busily continues to drain the bogs that cover one seventh of the country.

Along the coasts, the many excellent harbors are used only by a few fishermen. Although the indentations of Sligo, Clew, Galway, and Shannon appear to be the equivalent of Bristol, and the railroads radiate from Dublin to these potential trade centers, there is little rail or port traffic. The hinterland has little to offer in the way of either agriculture or industry, so both imports and exports are very minor. Galway, the convenient outlet for the Central Plain, directly west of Dublin, supports only some 21,000 people. Limerick, at the head of

the Shannon estuary, is the leading west coast city, but has a population only just over 50,000. Its agricultural manufactures, such as flour, bacon, butter, and condensed milk, are exported to Scotland and England. Surprisingly, little cheese is made in Ireland. Limerick gets cheap hydroelectric power from the rapids of the Shannon below Killaloe, harnessed in 1950. Cork, on the south coast, comes closest to being a small Irish equivalent of Bristol. Its population is engaged chiefly in agricultural processing and export trade. Modern industrialization shows up in its tanneries, breweries, shipyards, and a Ford factory. Waterford, farther east and closer to Dublin, has a good harbor, some fair coal, and is making considerable commercial and industrial progress.

OTHER ISLANDS

Most of the other islands of the British group are small and culturally insignificant. A few rise above that category.

The Isle of Man, in the northern part of the Irish Sea, is a detached fragment of the Southern Uplands of Scotland about thirty miles long and ten wide. It is occupied by over 55,000 Manxmen, who raise sheep on the slopes and oats in the lowlands. The main sources of revenue, however, come from herring and mackerel, and from a lively summer resort trade.

The Channel Islands are really not part of the British group. They lie near the coast of France and are culturally French, but politically and economically English. The British lost Normandy in 1204 but retained the islands off its coast. Jersey and Guernsey share about equally the 75 square-mile area and the 106,000 population of the Channel Islands. In this mild climate, the French inhabitants on their small farms produce the first potatoes, many fruits, and luxury vegetables that reach the London market each spring. All economic ties are northward, and there is little contact with nearby France. More and more English are spending their holidays on these islands, but bringing little change in the French culture.

Fiord landscape, western Norway
[*Norwegian Information Service*]

5. Scandinavian Lands

Norway, Sweden, Denmark, and Iceland, together with Svalbard and a few other northern islands form a significant region in the Northwestern European culture realm. Iceland, Svalbard, and the northern islands are included because despite their Arctic physical characteristics, they are culturally European. Excluded are the lands occupied by the Lapps, Polar World peoples living in the higher parts of the Scandinavian Peninsula.

PHYSICAL GEOGRAPHY

The high latitude of the Scandinavian Peninsula, about the same as that of Alaska, means long summer days and long winter nights. At North Cape, for example, the summer day lasts from mid-May to the end of July, and the polar night drags on for three months after its start in late November. The duration of "days" and "nights" is less toward the south. The shortest summer nights and winter days are about five hours long in southern Sweden. These differences in the amounts of winter and summer sunshine promote climates with pronounced seasonal extremes. Only a narrow belt along the Norwegian coast, as far north as the Lofoten Islands, feels the moderating influences of the warmer winds from the Atlantic, whose waters, even as they round North Cape, never freeze. Short distances inland, climates become more continental in their annual temperature range characteristics.

The whole west coast of Norway receives heavy precipitation. At Bergen, where over 200 days a year are rainy, the annual average

Gentle eastward slopes landscape
[*Swedish National Travel Office*]

is 84 inches. Places higher along the west-facing slopes may receive 200 inches. The eastward slopes toward the Gulf of Bothnia, however, have much less precipitation. At Stockholm the annual average is only 22 inches, and parts of eastern Sweden have less than 15 inches.

The Scandinavian Peninsula is mainly a tableland about 3,000 feet high in the south, with an abrupt west face, and tilting gently northward and more steeply eastward. Its undulated surface is broken by occasional peaks such as those in southwest Norway where Mt. Galdhöpig and Glitterlind reach over 8,000 feet to mark the highest elevations in the Northwestern Highlands. Fjelds (fields) of snow and ice cover large tracts in this mountainous section of Norway and give rise to glaciers that extend short distances down the valleys.

Physically the Scandinavian Peninsula has four main parts: barren highlands, rugged westward slopes, gentle eastward slopes, and southern and eastern plains.

Barren highlands, composed like those of Scotland of very old rocks, have little soil, excessive rainfall, and cool summers. Everywhere there is evidence of Ice Age erosion: ice-polished surfaces with their many scratches, or *glacial striae*, made by hard rocks dragged across them by the ice; basins scooped out of the bedrock; and steep-walled, ice-scoured valleys leading to the sea where their submerged ends are called *fiords* (fjords). The apparent newness of this erosion makes the Ice Age, during which ice lay ten miles thick over what is now the Gulf of Bothnia, seem less remote. Much of the area is above a timber line that lies at about 1,600 feet in southern Norway and at about 300 feet in northern parts. Patchy stands of scraggly birch, aspen, and alders give way to wet tundra whose dark surface is broken here and there by glaring white fjelds.

Rugged westward slopes exhibit Norway's most magnificent scenery of steep-walled valleys and fiords cutting deeply into the highlands. The longest fiords, Sogne and Hardanger, measure over 100 miles. The sheer walls rise in some cases more than 3,000 feet, and plunge steeply below water level for several hundred feet. From the little lowland flats at fiord heads, step-like valleys lead to the high plateau, or *vidda*. The rocky treads of these steps, on which nestle little lakes, are separated by abrupt risers, hard to climb. From the many hanging valleys, streams plunge as waterfalls and cascades into the fiords. Most of the fiord-head lowlands are isolated in their steep-walled enclosures, but a few have been connected by rail or highway with the uplands.

Across the mouth of almost every fiord there is a shallow *sill*. While these shoals tend to break the force of storm waves and thus keep the fiord waters calm, they are a hazard to navigation. In fact, these apparently fine natural harbors are little used, being handicapped also by their winding shape, the prevalence of dense fog, and the lack of suitable bottom for anchorage. Only a few have been developed as seaports. Mostly the little harbors at fiord heads serve the few people in the limited lowland area.

The coast of Norway is strewn with some 150,000 islands. Most are small and low with irregular outlines, but some are high and large, like the Lofotens which rise to over 4,000 feet. The little islands, or *skerries*, tend to protect the mainland from storm waves, and form in their lee a protected route used by coastal steamers.

Gentle eastward slopes extend across Sweden to the Gulf of Bothnia. Down these slopes flow many large rivers, for in Scandinavia, as in England, main streams flow eastward. The upper ends of Swedish streams are glaciated, and the steep-walled valleys lead to long, narrow lakes that lie above morainal dams formed when the retreating ice halted for long periods. These lakes regulate stream flow, so Swedish rivers have no severe floods. The slopes of Sweden are covered by taiga.

Southern and eastern plains extend in a wide belt across Denmark, southern Sweden, and along the lower slopes flanking the Gulf of Bothnia. The plains blend gradually into the slopes with no distinct boundary. In southern Sweden, the lowlands are noted for the vast lakes, such as Väner (2,150 square miles) and Vätter (730 square miles). The lowlands along

Oslo Fiord and the Glommen or central valley of southeast Norway resemble the Swedish lake district.

Skane (pronounced skōne, Latinized as Scania, hence the English Scandinavia) is the southernmost tip of Sweden. Its rocks are like the chalk of England and France, but they are covered irregularly with glacial deposits. Here, in a region of moderate precipitation, is the best agricultural land of Sweden. This area is very similar to Denmark.

CULTURAL BACKGROUND

Pushing northward close to the retreating ice front, the tundra-hunters reached Scandinavia about 7000 B.C. to settle along the fiords of central Norway and scatter over the Baltic shores. By 2500 B.C. farmer colonists were arriving from the south to settle the attractive rolling plains of Denmark and southern Sweden. With the advantage of comparatively long, warm summers and fairly dry harvest seasons, the peoples of Sweden began grain cultivation long before it was attempted in Norway.

A truly Nordic culture began to take shape, and within it there was a gradual differentiation of such groups as Goths, Jutes, Angles, and Swedes. Goths gained a stronghold in Skane and Götaland. Angles occupied most of Denmark and were replaced by Danes when they moved to England. Central Svealand was held by Swedes. Remote as these Scandinavian settlements were, trade contacts existed with Mediterranean centers. During the Bronze Age, highly prized amber from the southeastern Baltic went south by way of the Elbe, Oder, and Vistula. By the third century B.C. traders from Skane had found their way to the Black Sea, and Mediterranean gold was being brought back to Sweden.

Swedes began to eye the developing lands of the Goths to the south of Lake Vätter, and in the sixth century managed to conquer the area, bringing political unity to southeast Scandinavia. Political unity did not mean peace, and for years religious conflicts continued between the Christianized Goths and pagan Swedes. It did, however, provide a basis of strength for aggressive expansion in another direction—

east. Slavs from central Europe had pushed west across the German plain and harassed the ancient trade routes to the Mediterranean. The tide turned in the ninth century when Germanic-speaking peoples began to drive the Slavs back. Active in this drive was Rurik, from Sweden, whose deep penetrations into the lands across the Baltic brought under his rule a vast territory extending up the basin of the Dvina into the upper reaches of the Volga. The name Russia stems from Rurik's followers, known as Routsi, from whence came Rus, Rusi, and the anglicized Russia. Rurik's son Igor extended the frontiers to Kiev, and then vainly attacked the wealthiest, most important city in Europe, Constantinople. Others of Rurik's descendants retained some power in Russia until the end of the twelfth century.

While the Swedes were focusing their attention on the Baltic, the Danes and Norwegians, looking always toward the sea, had become well known and feared as Viking pirates and plunderers. The Norsemen undertook legitimate trade and colonization only after 850 when Harold the Fairhair became undisputed king of Norway. This was the time of Norse colonization of Iceland and, later, Greenland. The adventures of these years of exploration, conquest, and emigration are told in the famous Sagas of the Vikings.

During this time the Germans were expanding their lands and by the middle of the twelfth century had established their first Baltic stronghold at Lübeck, just south of Danish territory. They founded other ports along the south shore of the Baltic, and a merchant colony at Visby on Gottland, just off the eastern shore of Sweden. Visby became a great center for trade with places east of the Baltic, and in general Baltic trade flourished and prospered.

Sweden was unable to compete with this German trade. The aggressiveness of Rurik's time seems to have faded out. One reason may have been the deterioration of the weather. Evidence indicates that winters during the thirteenth and fourteenth centuries were more severe than those of previous centuries. It is improbable that the Viking settlements on Iceland and Greenland would have been made if the weather had been as cold as it is today. The fact that contact with these settlements dwindled in the twelfth and thirteenth centuries points to a worsening of ice conditions on the intervening seas. These less favorable climatic conditions meant increased difficulty in gaining a living from the land and left little time for exploration and conquest. Another important factor in slowing the pace was the Black Death, a plague that ravaged and weakened Sweden in the mid-fourteenth century.

It was the Danes who arose to threaten German supremacy in the Baltic. By the end of the fourteenth century the Scandinavian lands had been unified by the Danish "Sea Queen" Margaret under the Treaty of Kalmar. This forced a decline in German activities, and the Hanseatic League of German commercial cities began to dissolve. It was dealt a final blow by the Swedish King Gustavus Vasa, who dissolved the Union of Kalmar and broke all Hansard power in 1523. The League died soon after the Voyages of Discovery turned attention to the New World.

Although the Danes entered Baltic trade in only a minor way, they occupied a commanding position with regard to sea traffic between the North Sea and the Baltic Sea. Very much like the Greeks in the Aegean, the Danes could dominate and control traffic through the complex waterways in the "Aegean of the Baltic." The wide passage from the North Sea, called Skagerrak, bends sharply around the north tip of Jutland to become the narrower and sheltered Kattegat between Denmark and Sweden. From the Kattegat, three main channels divide the islands of eastern Denmark. On the west is the narrow and treacherous Little Belt. In the middle is the Great Belt with a few harbors and many shoals. To the east is The Sound, a relatively deep, straight and safe channel, offering the best commercial route from Skagerrak to the Baltic. On the theory that The Sound, only three miles wide at one place, was really a Danish river, Danes began in the fourteen-thirties to collect tolls on all passing ships. This practice continued until the mid-nineteenth century. The Danes were powerful enough to keep English and Norwegian fishermen out of

Norwegian waters in 1410 and later banned them from Icelandic waters. These acts may well have contributed to the discovery of America by Columbus. Bristol fishermen were sent farther afield, and with them went many Italians, including Columbus.

The seventeenth century saw Sweden again on the rise. Conquests to the east and south created an empire of 350,000 square miles with three million population. In the middle of the century, when Sweden gained the east shore of The Sound, she controlled all of Finland, Estonia, Latvia, parts of Lithuania, and large sections of coastal Germany, including the important North Sea port of Bremen and centers to the east in Pomerania. Swedish decline, however, was rapid. Defeat by the Russians in 1709 was quickly followed by the end of Swedish domination of the Baltic. Soon Finland was lost to Russia and then the strategic Aland Islands at the mouth of the Gulf of Bothnia.

The Danes also were faced with difficulties. In the nineteenth century the British pushed the Danes aside in the trade with Sweden, Denmark lost control of The Sound, and Schleswig was snatched by Prussia. Denmark lost not only valuable agricultural lands but also the important overland trade route between the North Sea and the Baltic.

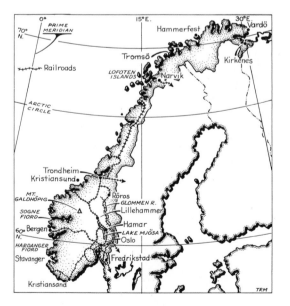

Norway: index map

Conquests, expansion and declines, and intense rivalries have marked the development of the Scandinavian lands. Although no one would say that today all old animosities have been erased, the formation of the Nordic Council in 1953 might well be interpreted as a recognition of the existing high degree of cultural unity. The Council, made up of parliamentary delegates from Denmark, Norway, Sweden, and Iceland, advises on broad and basic Scandinavian issues such as economic development, capital investment policies, and administrative matters. Other examples of cultural unity are seen in the high regard for education in all Scandinavian countries, the early development of cooperatives in these countries, and their work as pioneers in social welfare programs. Traditional differences show up. Denmark and Norway, always looking west, are members of NATO (North Atlantic Treaty Organization) while Sweden still looks toward the Baltic.

NORWAY

Norway is a true Viking country and its outlook has always been west toward the sea. One sixth of its population lives on islands along the coasts, and in one way or another, about 17 per cent of the adult male population takes to the sea. Thousands of Norwegian fishing craft ply the rich waters of their western coast, while the numerous merchant ships of Norwegian registry busily keep Norway in a prominent position in maritime trade. Receipts from shipping and the export of timber, fish, and chemicals help pay for Norway's imports of foods and raw materials.

It is not always by choice that Norwegians take to the sea; many are forced to it because of the poor opportunities for making a living at home. Agricultural land is extremely limited, being something less than 4 per cent of the country. Only about 20 per cent is forested, and three fourths of the country is waste or poor pasturage. Small wonder, then, that Norway is more sparsely populated than any other European country, and that Norwegians by the thousands emigrate to other lands. Limited as the agricultural land is, over one third of the

population ekes out a subsistence from farming. Needless to say, farms are small, usually less than 5 acres. The main crops are cereals. Oats lead the list, being able to withstand wetness. Then comes barley, the crop that needs only a short growing season to mature its grain. Wheat, in third place, is a high energy crop, but its demand for good soil and climate essentially restricts its production to the small lowland area near Oslo. The "poverty crop," rye, able to endure poor soils in cold climates, is grown only where other cereals fail. Where grain does not mature, it is cut green and dried as hay. Other hays, like timothy and clover, are grown on the wet uplands. To supplement the cereals, potatoes are grown, mostly on the sandy coasts. Few Norwegian meals are served without these little starchy tubers.

Benchlands above the fiords and better parts of the uplands are used as hayfields and communal pastures, and are essential to the livelihood of the small farms in the valleys below. Nothing less than absolute necessity would make worthwhile the great efforts needed to harvest this hay. Several times each summer, the grass is cut by hand and strung along special fences to dry. Cured hay is stored in *saetter*, little log-cabin-type huts that dot the landscape above the timber line and are clustered in highlands immediately above inhabited valleys. When the uplands are snow covered in winter, hay from

the saetter is sledded to cables that lead to barns in the valleys below, and is sent down this aerial transport in small loads. Such is the basis of Norwegian dairying. That these tedious efforts are important is shown by the fact that dairy products, poultry, and hogs provide more revenue than all cereal crops combined.

Farmers usually augment their incomes by fishing or working at nonagricultural jobs for part of the year. Despite the great number of Norwegian fishermen, less than 10 per cent depend entirely on fishing for income, and many of the rest are farmer-fishermen. Even Norwegian cows become fish-eaters when prolonged winters exhaust the supply of stored hay. Fishing starts in March in southern Norway and follows the cod northward until midsummer. While the Norwegian farmer takes

and the rest is used in paper manufacture, forest industries, and other factories.

Mining is a minor occupation. Only small amounts of copper, silver, nickel, and iron are obtained, and remoteness and inadequate transport facilities make mining difficult and unprofitable. Norway's greatest metallurgical industry depends on imported aluminum ores and the plants are located in delightfully clean villages scattered along the sides of fiords.

Communications have always been difficult in Norway. The highway system is best developed around Oslo Fiord, with many branches eastward to Sweden, westward into Telemark and along the coast to Stavanger, and northward to Trondheim via the main routes through Osterdal and Gudbrandsdal. Almost all Norwegian roads are liberally dotted with ferry

readily to the sea, he lacks enthusiasm for the woods. Most logging is done by Finns. The forests produce timber, lumber, and huge quantities of pulp wood.

Partly to make up for lack of coal, Norway has harnessed about one fifth of its water power. These hydroelectric resources come from the combination of excessive precipitation and rugged relief. And Norway makes the most of this resource, having the highest per capita consumption of electricity in the world. About half the electric power goes into Norwegian homes, some 40 per cent is used by the electrochemical and electrometallurgical industries,

crossings. Even between Norway's two largest cities, Oslo and Bergen, there is no continuous overland road. North of Trondheim, a single main road leads all the way to Vardö and Kirkenes in Finnmark, tying together the little local road networks around such centers as Narvik and Tromsö. Oslo is also the center of the railroad system. Trunk lines run east to Stockholm, southeast to Skane which has ferry connections to Europe, west to Bergen, and north past Trondheim almost to Bodö. Railroad construction is difficult over Norway's rough and broken terrain where numerous tunnels are required.

Oslo

[Norwegian Information Service]

Express steamers are the heart of the transport system. It takes a week for the trip from Oslo to Kirkenes, but the frequent schedules allow daily stops at the principal towns, and calls every other day at most minor ports. Almost every settlement, however remote, has some connection to the express routes and is dependent upon them for mail, provisions, and passenger service.

Although the Industrial Revolution has changed Norway in many ways, the trends toward urbanization and industrialization are minor compared with those in England. Life still centers along the coasts where cities must of necessity remain small. The limited natural resources cannot support large factories and huge population centers.

URBANIZATION

By no stretch of the imagination can Norway be considered highly urbanized. In this, it is in sharp contrast with other countries in the Northwestern European culture realm. Of the few cities in Norway, only four have over 40,000 population. Even the capital and largest city, Oslo, can attract only slightly more than 10 per cent of the population. This very limited urbanization is to be expected in view of the large number of Norwegians engaged in agriculture and because of the nature of Norwegian industries—scattered, and in locations that are unattractive to, or prohibit, city growth.

Oslo, with a population of 460,000, is in the midst of Norway's best lowlands and largest wheat-producing area. Near the site of the present city, an original Oslo had been founded in the eleventh century, and then in the seventeenth century Kristiania was founded on the present site of Oslo. The two were close and one name was used for both. Since Kristiania had been used during the days of Swedish control, it was hastily dropped after 1905 in favor of the older name. Aside from its important functions as capital, Oslo serves mainly as a seaport, handling half of Norway's imports and a large fraction of the exports.

Bergen, with over 115,000 population, has a much older tradition than Oslo. It was an important local capital prior to the Hanse period, and long the leading post in Norway for those Baltic merchants. Until about 1800 it was Norway's largest town. Bergen's harbor is one of the best in Scandinavia, being both deep and protected, but it lacks hinterland. It serves scattered hydroelectric and fishing industries. Its active trade with the Americas and Europe includes large imports of South American bauxite and exports of pulp. Stavanger has over 50,000 population and boasts the largest brisling and herring trade in the world. From its 70 canneries come most of the Norwegian sardines that reach the United States. Trondheim, Norway's third largest city, has almost 60,000 population. Located in the midst of the best lowlands on the west coast, this important port reaps benefits from this highly productive area and its diversified activities in dairying, fishing, lumbering, and mining. Ship connections with points in northern Norway and direct rail ties with Sweden promote a bustling commercial trade activity in the port, in addi-

tion to its function as a main naval base. Narvik, east of the Lofotens, with its ice-free harbor, serves as an outlet for Swedish iron ore brought in over the electric railroad from Kiruna and Gällivare. To the north Tromsö is the center of trade with Svalbard and other Arctic points. The 4,000 inhabitants of Hammerfest take pride in living in the northernmost city in the world, and busy themselves with fishing and marketing reindeer hides and other Arctic products from the surrounding tundra. Kirkenes is about the end of the road in Finnmark and just a stone's throw from the U.S.S.R. border.

SWEDEN

Sweden contrasts with Norway in its eastward outlook and physical endowments. It has a lot of good agricultural land and less than one third of the country is classed as unreclaimable. Most of Sweden has moderate rainfall, simplifying the problems of drying hay and harvesting crops. Widespread forests and valuable mineral deposits are also important Swedish assets.

Skane, part of the European plain, is low and fertile. Götaland contains large areas of productive farm land and a commercially impor-

Hammerfest
[*Norwegian Information Service*]

tant maritime coast. Agriculture is more limited in stony Svealand with its patches of moraine and strips of valley alluvium. North of Svealand, the forest and mineral resources have proved extremely valuable. The large rivers that cross northern Sweden serve as transportation routes, particularly for the rafting of timber, and as sources of electric power. In Upper Norrland, Sweden reaches into the part of the Polar World inhabited by Lapps. Rich ore deposits in Swedish Lapland have given rise to important mining centers and a railway network with connections to Narvik, Stockholm, and the Finnish railroads. Sweden's position as a leading commercial nation is based largely on the mineral resources of its northern, barren lands.

The Industrial Revolution brought many changes to Sweden, but not the growth of great factories. Sweden's first industrial importance was as a source of raw materials, especially for England. So important to the British were the Swedish timber products and ores that they sent one naval expedition after another to battle the Danes for control of The Sound.

Sweden's early mineral trade depended on copper, silver and lead, but mainly iron. By 1730 the mines of Dannemora, just north of Stockholm, supplied over one third of Europe's malleable iron and half of the pig iron, most of which went to England. Swedes got so busy exploiting their natural resources that by the latter part of the eighteenth century, they no longer fed themselves and had to import large quantities of rye from Riga.

To free themselves of the necessity of having their products go through The Sound, the Swedes built the Göta Canal, completed in 1832. This was no small undertaking. Seventy locks are used to raise boats a total of 300 feet along the 240 miles of waterway across Svealand's lakes and picturesque landscape. The canal, still busy commercially, attracts a heavy tourist trade.

The number of Swedes engaged in industry has steadily increased. Currently, over 40 per cent of the working population is industrially employed, mainly in mining, metal, and textile industries. The agricultural population has declined to about 20 per cent. One out of every three Swedes now lives in a city.

URBANIZATION

Stockholm, located on the shores and islands of Lake Malar and connected to the sea by its many complex inlets, was founded as a defendable military stronghold in 1157. It gained by being close to the early Swedish cultural centers at Birka, Sigtuna, and Uppsala. It has been the political capital for seven centuries. Stockholm's assets of an excellent harbor thoroughly protected from storm waves, proximity to extensive forests and the earliest exploited copper and iron deposits, and a rather central position in the "Baltic Lake" and on easy routes to Göteborg and Trondheim, gave it both an early start and a continuing advantage as a com-

Sweden: index map

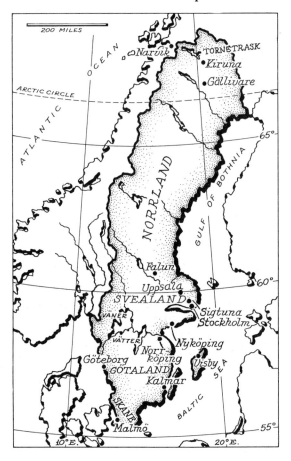

Stockholm

[*Swedish National Tourist Office*]

mercial center. The "Venice of the North" is considered Europe's cleanest, most modern city. Much of its modernization is due to prosperity that arose during World War I when, as a neutral, Sweden profited by sales of iron, steel, and other wares to both sides. A goodly number of the one million people in metropolitan Stockholm belong to consumers cooperatives, popular throughout Sweden.

Göteborg is one of the earliest examples of city planning and location by deliberate design. The site was picked to give Sweden a commercial outlet free of Danish interference. It prospered for 200 years after its founding in 1619, then went into a slump because of competition from Copenhagen. The twentieth century again brought prosperity. Its west-coast position favors overseas trade and now in total tonnage it exceeds Stockholm. It is Sweden's largest shipbuilding center, and second largest city, with almost 400,000 population. Malmö is the Swedish complement of Copenhagen. With over 200,000 population, it ranks as third city

of Sweden and first of Skane. Its many food-processing plants reflect its old agricultural interests, not overshadowed by newer shipyard activities. Of more importance to the commerce of the city, however, is the ferry connection with Copenhagen.

Much of Sweden's recent urbanization has taken the form of small manufacturing centers, especially in the belt between Stockholm and Göteborg. Here are found important producers of cotton textiles, matches, small machinery, and other goods. To the north are centers of mining and lumbering, served by Bothnian ports in the summer. In the winter, when the Gulf is frozen, products must be moved by rail.

ECONOMIC POSITION

Despite efficient practices and extensive use of available agricultural lands in Skane and Svealand, Sweden must import large quantities of wheat, rye, and other foods. Agricultural trends in recent years tend to de-emphasize wheat in favor of stock raising and dairying, with sugar beets supplementing income from hay, barley, and oats. North of Svealand, farmers combine summer agriculture with winter forest occupations. North of the agricultural lands of Svealand, and generally north of Falun, lies the taiga, forests of spruce, pine, and fir, covering roughly half of Sweden. The trees are slow growing. It takes from 80 years in south Sweden to over 100 years in the north for a conifer to reach a size usable for lumber. This slow growth means premium lumber, strong, easily worked, and less likely to warp. Birch, plentiful in the taiga, is in great demand, especially for furniture. Heavy snows make logging easy, and the numerous rivers provide cheap transportation, logs being floated to the 60 ports where the lumber mills and pulp factories are located. Paper, pulp, lumber, and other forest products account for two fifths of Sweden's exports. Increasing amounts of wood are being used in manufacture at home, then exported in every form from matches to furniture.

Mining supplies about one fourth of Sweden's exports. Starting with the exceptionally pure iron ore found at Dannemora, mining development spread first to the west through south-central Sweden, then north to the Lapland deposits found in 1894. Mines near Gällivare and Kiruna are connected by an electric railroad with Lulea on the Gulf of Bothnia for summer export, and with Narvik for year-round export. Swedish ore, considerably purer than most iron, goes mainly to Germany, with some to England and other countries. About 80 per cent is exported as ore and enables Sweden to lead the world in iron ore exports. The ore kept at home goes largely into Swedish steel, famous for its excellence.

Sweden has developed about one fourth of its hydroelectric power. The main development has been along the Dal and Göta rivers in the south while only a few of the many lakes and rivers of Norrland have been harnessed to provide power for local lumbering and railroads. The limited quantities of oil shale being exploited in southern Sweden fail to meet the needs, and coal and oil are imported.

DENMARK

Denmark is the smallest of the Scandinavian countries, less than one tenth of the size of Sweden. Its 16,576 square miles are broken up into the peninsula of Jutland, the large islands of Fyn (Funen) and Sealand (Zealand, Sjaelland), and some 500 small islands, about 100 of which are inhabited. The land is low, most of it under 200 feet and none above 500 feet. The general flatness is relieved here and there by the rolling surfaces of moraines. Western Jutland has poor sandy soil, with stony and barren areas. In many places moraines block the drainage and form bogs which are now being reclaimed and used as productive agriculture lands. Eastern Jutland and the larger islands resemble Skane as relatively good crop lands.

Denmark's main asset is its strategic position in relation to all of northwest Europe, and at the gates of the Baltic. Another asset is political permanence. Danes have maintained their own culture and government on Sealand since at least the sixth century: a record in Europe. The country lacks coal and other minerals. The immense agricultural productivity of Denmark stems directly from the Danish ability to make the best use of their meager soil resources. With ingenuity and intelligence, the Danes shifted from grain production, when their European markets were lost to North American grain exports, to their now famous production of bacon, eggs, and butter. These breakfast products form 60 per cent of Denmark's export trade.

Denmark has achieved agricultural preeminence only in the last few decades. Danes now lead the world in the export of butter, and are second only to the United States in the export of bacon. Two thirds of Denmark's food exports go to Great Britain.

Almost half the Danish population is urban and only one third is agricultural, but 75 per cent of the country is under cultivation. This high percentage and the rapid rise in agricultural activities are due largely to the cooperative movement among farmers. Close to half the population belongs to cooperative societies. Co-ops handle about 95 per cent of the marketing of all farm products, supply most needs of

Denmark: index map

the farmer, and conduct large urban trade. They have improved farming methods, increased the quality of farm products, assisted in land reclamation, streamlined merchandizing, and been influential in getting laws passed to benefit farmers.

Danish agriculture is intensive and most of the farms are small, over half being under 13 acres. The farms are operated by their owners who gain large-scale production and purchasing power through the cooperatives. This kind of farming is profitable, and so rural districts are gaining in population—a unique situation.

Though the country is primarily agricultural today, it still has vestiges of its Viking past. The retention of Bornholm in the Baltic, islands in the North Atlantic, and Greenland is a heritage from Viking expeditions. Museums are crowded with Viking artifacts and the vast Viking fortification uncovered at Trelleborg is a reminder

of the great military strength once mustered by a Danish king.

COPENHAGEN

Kobenhavn, "merchant's haven," on the site of a prehistoric fishing and trading village, considers Bishop Absalon its twelfth-century founder, when it became a fort against Slavic aggression. The fifteenth century saw it become the political and cultural center of Denmark, a status it still holds.

The city owes its commercial supremacy to a number of factors: its favorable position on The Sound and on world ocean trade routes; the fifteenth-century decline of Hanse power and later the decline of Dutch commercial power; and above all, the vigor of the merchants who overcame ravages of the plague and two costly fires in the eighteenth century, and bombard-

Danish farm
[Arne u Franken]

ment, occupation, and blockade by the English in the early nineteenth century followed by bankruptcy of the State. When it was apparent that the construction of the Kiel Canal might divert traffic from Copenhagen, the Danes shrewdly borrowed a German practice and established a *free port*. Here imports could enter, be unloaded, stored, repacked, manufactured, and re-exported, all without customs duties. Needless to say, this attractive system brought, and continues to bring, seaborne trade from all parts of the world to add to the prosperity and cosmopolitan flavor of Copenhagen. Like other great trade centers, its population increased enormously in the last century. From about 100,000 in 1800, metropolitan Copenhagen has grown to well over one million. It contains about one fourth of the total population of Denmark.

In this small agricultural country, without minerals and power, it is surprising to find Copenhagen engaged in so much industry. Of course, most of it has to do with processing foodstuffs, such as butter, bacon, and cheese. But next in importance is the manufacturing of exportable items that require skillful work and few raw materials, such as special marine machinery and diesel engines, dairy equipment, and scores of household items like the renowned Royal Copenhagen porcelain of Bornholm clay, and Danish silver. Of importance also is ship building and repair. Electric power for much of this industry and for domestic use comes by cable from Sweden.

Though nowhere near as big as Copenhagen, there are other Danish commercial centers. Aarhus, with over 150,000 population, serves as a focal point for Jutland trade. To the north, Aalborg, famous for its Akvavit (schnaps) distilleries, conducts the largest trade of any Danish provincial port. In the heart of the garden island of Fyn, Odense has become a commercial and craft center, has doubled its population in the past 25 years, and is Denmark's third largest city.

ICELAND

Celtic monks from Ireland were the first settlers of Iceland, followed closely by Norwegians and Danes, some 20,000 between A.D. 870 and 930. Soon the British arrived, and by the end of the eleventh century, Iceland's population was 77,000. The Black Death in 1202 killed one third of the population, and this, coupled with worsening climatic conditions, stunted its population growth. Since the tragic setback in the late eighteenth century when disease and volcanic catastrophies killed 20 per cent of the inhabitants, the population has increased sporadically to a present 170,000.

Iceland has been a republic since the founding of the Althing (Parliament) in 930, the oldest parliamentary assembly in the world. But it has not always been independent. It joined Norway in 1263 and both were incorporated into Denmark in 1381. When Norway left Denmark in 1814, Icelanders elected the Danish King as their own, but the two nations had no real political affiliations. Denmark recognized Iceland's sovereignty in 1918 and in 1944 Iceland broke off all ties with the King.

The language of Iceland is essentially the Norwegian of 1,000 years ago. It is the language of the Eddas and Sagas. Whereas the other Scandinavian countries modified and simplified the Old Norse language into the different forms they now use, Iceland has clung to its ancient language. This may have been due to the island's isolation brought on by increasing cold and storminess in the North Atlantic which reduced contact with Europe.

For 75 years prior to 1850 there was only one

regularly scheduled mail per year between Iceland and Denmark, and none to any other land. Regular steamship service began in 1858, but after 25 years the modest schedule was only seven trips to Copenhagen a year. The situation is now somewhat improved. Iceland has its own steamship line, and although it has few good harbors, its ports are regularly visited by Icelandic and other ships. Iceland also has its own airline.

Iceland is barren and naturally treeless. Much of the interior is covered by fresh volcanic ash and has little plant life. To the south, where volcanic peaks reach 7,000 feet and an extensive plateau rises over 3,000 feet, precipitation is heavy enough to support several small icecaps. The southeast coast is particularly scenic, with its high mountains and well-fed streams. Most of the northern portions of the island have little precipitation and are deserts of aridity as well as cold. The southwest is the only part really suitable for agriculture and habitation.

Agriculturally, Iceland makes little splash in the world. Only 65,000 acres of its almost 40,000 square miles of area are under cultivation, producing mainly potatoes, turnips, and hay. The growing season is short, even fast-growing barley at times fails to mature, and hay curing is handicapped by frequent rains. A few sturdy garden vegetables, root crops, and a little flax are grown. An added difficulty is the problem of keeping the field flat. As in other sub-arctic lands, cultivation produces hummocks, probably caused by frost action accentuated when the surface is plowed. Despite all these troubles, about 35 per cent of the population is agricultural, though for the most part occupied in sheep raising.

The fishing industry is particularly important. Though fish exporting to England got off to an early start, the industry only really began to flourish after 1900 with the introduction of improved methods. Fishing now provides a living for one fifth of the population and helps to stabilize the commerce of the country. About 90 per cent of the catch is cod, which goes frozen to England, or salted to France and Mediterranean countries.

Reykjavik, the capital, has a population of about 70,000 and is the only real city. Its buildings and homes are heated by natural hot water piped in from nearby springs. Aside from a small tourist trade, the city's main interests are commercial and political, the commerce being almost totally concerned with fish.

Hydroelectric development is in its infancy. The country has, however, launched a program of economic development, evidenced by the completion in 1954 of a $7,000,000 ammonium nitrate factory near Reykjavik.

Long ages of isolation ended with the establishment of air routes. Iceland's location on the northern transatlantic air routes brings increasing visitors. It will be interesting to see if this change will alter the cultural pattern of a people who have been remote for so long. Iceland has no army, no forts, no navy, and no illiteracy. But it also has no railroads, few roads, and very little industrialization.

ARCTIC ISLANDS

Jan Mayen, Svalbard and Bear Island are possessions of Norway. Only Svalbard (Spitzbergen) is significant. It was discovered in 1194, forgotten, rediscovered by Barents in 1596, and first used as an important whaling base. Now, its coal, iron, and other minerals are being mined for Norway's benefit. The mining has been conducted by Russians. Partly for that reason but mainly for strategic reasons, the Soviet Union has announced intentions of active participation in Svalbard's affairs.

Viking Exploration

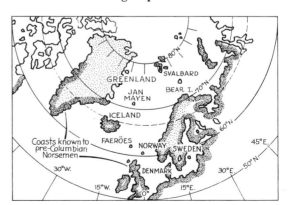

**Village
near Utrecht,
Loenen**
[*Hans Sibbelee*]

6. *Low Countries*

The Netherlands and Belgium are the gift of the Rhine, Meuse, and Schelde which built a productive compound delta along the North Sea. Accessibility has favored commercial leadership. Climate and soil conditions permit a dense agricultural population, and the hinterlands have provided raw materials for industry. Although they are only slightly larger than West Virginia, the Low Countries rank high in world significance.

PHYSICAL BACKGROUND

Along the North Sea coast of the Netherlands are broad sandy beaches leading to irregular dunes. Behind the dune belt is a strip of low, coastal plain considered by Netherland standards as high and firm. Here are many of leading towns and cities, such as Alkmaar, Haarlem, The Hague ('s Gravenhage), Leiden, and Delft. This is the nucleus of Holland, a term used for the Netherlands as a whole because it is the most important part of the country.

In central Holland is a low area around the shallow Ijselmeer, formerly the Zuider Zee. Almost one quarter of the Netherlands is below sea level, and even more of it is below the level of high tides. Much of this territory has been made into useful *polders*, areas surrounded by dikes and drained by pumps.

East of Ijselmeer is a higher rolling land similar to Jutland. Much of it is sandy and gravelly, useful only as pasture. The bogs and low places contain peat. Only in the extreme southeast is there high, well-drained land. Far below its surface are the coal deposits of Limburg.

Belgium is similar, but more diversified. From its short stretch of coast, only 62 miles, to the inner edge of the polder belt, is less than 10 miles. Very little land is below sea level. In the northeast is the relatively barren *Campine*, like the lands of eastern Netherlands, but between it and the polders is a broad agricultural belt of rolling lands dissected by small tributaries of the Schelde. In the southeast rises the Ardennes Plateau, cut by many valleys. The Ardennes contains rocks similar to those of the Pennines, with limited amounts of metal ores. Northwest of the plateau, the valleys of the Sambre and Meuse mark the coal belt and Belgium's industrial region.

CULTURAL BACKGROUND

Celtic and Germanic tribes, such as the Belgae, were occupying most of the Low Countries at the time of the Roman Conquest. The Romans, slightly appalled by the damp Netherlands, kept to the low alluvial ridges along the sides of the Rhine, avoiding the marshes. They built their villages on this relatively dry, firm land. Ruins of these villages are now about 15 feet below sea level, because this whole region, like delta lands everywhere, is slowly sinking.

Roman control of the Low Countries lasted for five centuries. It was most positive in Belgium and less firm in the frontier beyond the Rhine. As in England, the Romans introduced law and order, established towns, and built roads. When the Romans withdrew, Nordic pressures from the north and northeast increased. Invading Germanic tribes brought the feudal system, and by the ninth century the land was divided into counties and duchies under Teutonic rulers. Alpines were driven into the marshes and southeast uplands, Saxons marched down the Rhine, but Frisians, from

Low Countries: index map

the north coast of the Netherlands, became the most powerful group of all.

A Frisian stronghold was established at Dordrecht, a site which controlled the Rhine mouth and the Maas or lower Meuse. A toll was promptly levied on all passing trade to and from Cologne, Aachen, Liege, and other upstream points. This was not taken calmly by the upstream nobility, but efforts to stop the practice were fruitless against the Frisian count's well-protected stronghold in the low, marshy country. Dordrecht became headquarters of the counts of Holland, who so prospered from control of Rhine and Maas trade that they extended their power northward along the coast, establishing the cradle area of Dutch culture. During the Middle Ages the Dutch developed industrial skills and greatly expanded their commercial interests and their territory, spreading south into Flanders.

Flemish people in western and northern Belgium became known for their textiles, and developed a lively trade with England. Bruges for several centuries was ranked as Europe's most important center of cloth manufacturing. Ghent, a short distance inland, rose with Bruges. Its chief concern was with Rhine trade, which was developed along easy overland routes that by-passed Dordrecht and the treacherous Rhine mouths. For over two centuries Ghent fairly monopolized commerce between central Europe and the North Sea. Ghent was connected to Bruges by a canal, but both towns began to decline when their small rivers shoaled and trade was deflected to other routes. By the end of the fifteenth century their greatness was a thing of the past.

At this time, Antwerp, on the Schelde, rose to overshadow Bruges as a trade center. Its main import was wool. It also served Brussels, a short distance inland, and grew as Brussels became the industrial hearth of central Belgium. The rise of Antwerp and the decline of Bruges favored the Dutch who held the low islands of Zeeland astride the Schelde channels. Tolls were collected on all Schelde trade, a practice ended only in 1863 by the purchase of Dutch rights.

Dutch commerce was growing, despite the fact that the country had come under the political control of Spain. When the herring disappeared from The Sound and Lübeck began to decline, fishing activities moved into the North Sea, giving the Dutch a chance to engage in it. They helped the decline of Lübeck by breaking its monopoly on salt trade with countries to the north. Dutch Baltic trade increased and so did its traffic with western and southern Europe. The greatest stimulus to Dutch trade, however, followed the arrival of the first cargo of spices at Lisbon, in 1503, via Cape of Good Hope. Dutch merchants promptly became distributors of Lisbon goods to peoples in northwestern Europe. After Spain incorporated Portugal, Portuguese commerce was practically wrecked, so the Dutch gladly took over and carried goods from the Far East in their own ships.

The independence from Spain of the seven northern provinces of the Netherlands was achieved in 1579. Secession was proclaimed on religious grounds. The new government im-

mediately adopted a policy of religious tolerance, and the persecuted from many lands flocked to Holland. These immigrants brought many skills. Holland rapidly became the greatest commercial power in Europe.

The Dutch East India Company was founded in 1602. The Portuguese soon vanished from the seas and the Dutch dominated East Indian trade, laying foundations for their colonial empire.

Belgium, on the other hand, was slow to prosper. It passed from Spain to Austria, became part of revolutionary France, and after the fall of Napoleon, was merged with the Dutch provinces. Independence was not gained until 1831 when it became a constitutional monarchy. Lying across favored routes between Germany and France, Belgium had the misfortune to become the "Battleground of Europe," and the scene of conflicts such as Waterloo, Ramillies, and the invasions of 1914 and 1940. The disadvantages of foreign control and late rise of nationalism are still reflected by

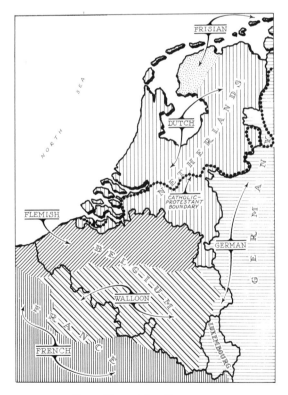

Low Countries: languages

its limited colonial power. While Dutch colonies spread around the globe, the sole possession of Belgium was a mineral-rich chunk of equatorial Africa, the Belgium Congo. But the empire of the Dutch is shrinking. In 1949 they relinquished sovereignty over the Netherlands Indies, and five years later raised Surinam and the Netherlands Antilles to equal status with Holland, with complete internal autonomy and a voice in the government of the Kingdom of the Netherlands.

Loss of colonies, vivid recollections of devastating wars, and the prospects of trade advantages, promote the interest of the Low Countries in unions of European nations. After World War II they joined Luxembourg in the Benelux commercial project. Continuing this support of supranational unions, Belgium, the Netherlands, and Luxembourg in 1957 joined with France, West Germany, and Italy in Euratom, a plan for peaceful development of atomic energy, and in Euromarket, a plan to create a common European market which ultimately will allow free movement of goods and people. These may be steps toward a United States of Europe, a prospect enthusiastically entertained by the Low Countries.

PEOPLES

The peoples of the Low Countries are racially similar, mainly Nordic, but divided on language and religion. Nationalism depended originally on religious contrasts, still apparent today. The Netherlands is mainly Protestant and Belgium is almost totally Roman Catholic.

Within the Netherlands the main linguistic contrast lies between Frisian-speaking people and Dutch. Frisian, an old Germanic tongue, is spoken by the inhabitants of islands along the north coast and in areas east of Ijselmeer, but Dutch is the dominant language of the country. Dutch is comparatively new and an offshoot of Flemish, the Germanic language spoken in northern Belgium.

East-west across Belgium, at about Brussels, is the boundary between Germanic Flemish to the north and Romanic Walloon to the south. Flemish is about as old as English and developed in the lowlands around Bruges and Ghent. It spread north across Zeeland into Holland, where it replaced Frisian, and slowly changed into Dutch. Walloon is a variant of French. The Flemish, in general, are the farmers and business people, while the Walloon-speaking people are the industrialists who dominate the economic and political life of the country. Walloon is the official language, but French is spoken in the urban centers. An additional, but slight, linguistic complication arises from the fact that the eastern boundaries of both countries are so drawn that a fringe of German-speaking people is included.

Place names in Belgium reflect the two tongues. Antwerp, for example, is really the English name. In Flemish it is Antwerpen and in Walloon it is Anvers. Brussels is really either Brussel (Flemish) or Bruxelles (Walloon). Ghent (English) is Gent (Flemish) or Gand (Walloon). The Flemish Brugge, Luik, and Ieper are better known under their Walloon names, Bruges, Liege, and Ypres.

RECLAMATION

Although today the mention of Holland generates mental pictures of a land mainly below sea level, it has not always been quite as low as it is now. In Roman times the marshes were sufficient to stymie the Legions' progress north of the Rhine, but Lake Flevo, in the center of the low land, was small. The Frisian Islands were large and high compared to their present condition. General flooding dates only from about the fourth century.

The whole region has been undergoing subsidence, or lowering of land elevation in relation to sea level, at a rate of one foot per century. This lowering was probably not too noticeable to the villagers because their settlements were along the edges of the rivers, places regularly supplied with alluvium and built up by the Rhine. The Frisian Islanders faced more tragic problems. With the Rhine courses shifting southward, their islands were deprived of the renewing effects of alluviation. Usable land diminished, both as a result of wave erosion and of general subsidence. Dry land became wet

Canal village,
Dokkum,
Netherlands
[*Heybroek*]

marshes that were gradually taken over by the sea. Houses rose on stilts, and cattle learned to graze between high tides.

By the thirteenth century the subsidence allowed North Sea waves to roll past the Frisian Islands and across the marshes into Lake Flevo. Erosion was rapid and in about 200 years Lake Flevo had become the extensive Zuider Zee. Though the land loss was serious, this new sea provided the Hollanders a degree of protection much like that offered by the North Sea, so about the time when they were attaining commercial prominence, their region became more difficult to invade.

Widespread diking in Holland started in the thirteenth century. Earlier dikes or earth ridges were little local affairs to hold back flood waters or the sea. These newer efforts were for reclamation rather than simple protection. Since dikes keep water in as well as out, the diked lands were drained by ditches, and the ditches emptied by pumping. Windmills to supply power for pumping appeared in increasing numbers in the Dutch landscape. Diking and recovery of agricultural lands spread eastward. About 40 per cent of the Netherlands became polder land enclosed by dikes. Cultural landscapes were revolutionized. The most ambitious reclamation project was begun in 1927, to add 800 square miles of useful land. A dike was strung across the entrance of the Zuider Zee, making it into a lake, Ijselmeer. Piece by piece

the lake is being made into polders, and used for crops and pasture. Meanwhile, the old Zuider Zee fishermen have had to move to the North Sea coast, or become farmers.

Holland was not only invaded by the Germans during World War II, but also by the sea when the dikes were cut to flood some 600 square miles of polders. The end of the war saw the Dutch busily rebuilding dikes, draining polders, and planting crops on soils that seemed only mildly affected by the saline incursions. They experienced one of their most severe floods in 1953 when storm waves of the North Sea broke through dikes in southern Holland to inundate one sixth of the country. Again, dike repairs were rapid and recovery prompt.

Not content with recovering lands from the sea, the Dutch are also improving the soils in eastern Netherlands, much as the Danes are doing in Jutland. This effort has increased the agricultural population in the eastern area, but the population is still much less dense than in the low polder country of western Holland where almost half the country's population is compressed into two ninths of the country's area.

INDUSTRIAL AND COMMERCIAL DEVELOPMENTS

The Industrial Revolution found the Netherlands without coal or other sources of power.

Windmills, long used for pumping, grinding flour, and small-scale manufacturing, could not compete with engines. From industrial leadership in the seventeenth century, a decline relative to England, France, and Belgium reduced the Netherlands to a fairly low industrial rating. The Dutch then turned with vigor to intensive agricultural development, greater emphasis on commerce, careful exploitation of their meager resources, and specialization in products of the Dutch colonies.

Amsterdam, favored by its site near the mouths of the Rhine, and by river, canal, and harbor development, became the largest and most active port on the Rhine Delta in the seventeenth century. Increase in size of ships made its Zuider Zee location a handicap, but this was overcome by the dredging of a deep, North Sea Canal westward to Ijmuiden. Like London, the city retains supremacy in population and control of colonial trade.

Rotterdam, on the Lek, gradually passed Amsterdam commercially, and now vies with Antwerp and Hamburg for the title of "busiest port" on the European mainland. A canal to the North Sea overcame the difficulty of shoaling channels, allowing the port to become a main transshipping point for the Rhine Valley.

Inland communications in the Netherlands are quite unusual, consisting of over 2,000 miles of railroads, some 3,000 miles of roads, and almost 5,000 miles of canals. Rotterdam is the center of canal trade and headquarters of Dutch barges that move goods throughout the Netherlands and along the Rhine, Meuse, and other streams.

Dutch commercial progress has been supported by a substantial agricultural program. About two thirds of the area is under cultivation or in pasture. Rye and oats are rivals for first place among crops, followed by wheat, barley, flax, sugar beets, and potatoes. No other country has such a great density of cattle, despite heavy losses in World War II. Although the number is declining, about 20 per cent of the population is engaged in agriculture. Farms are small, over half with areas under 10 acres. There is little or no mechanization. Cultivation is by hoe, typically wielded by a horticulturist who gives attention to each plant. In spite of intensified farming, one quarter of the imports are foods to feed the fast-growing population. Much of the cultivated land produces expensive flowers and bulbs, rather than low-cost foods. This great industry centers in the sandy lands around Haarlem and Alkmaar.

INDUSTRIAL REVOLUTION

About 40 per cent of the Netherlanders depend for livelihood on manufacturing. Industry has developed in three main directions: (1) agricultural, (2) processing of colonial products, and (3) making goods that require great skill but few bulky raw materials.

Butter and cheese are foremost among agricultural manufactures, especially in the northern half of the country. Closely related is the margarine industry, which now uses instead of animal fats imported oils of tropical plants. An exportable surplus of sugar is refined from local beets and crude sugar from tropical cane. Distilleries dot the landscape, making commercial alcohol from potatoes and Holland gin from

Amsterdam
[Cas Oorthuys]

rye. Dutch breweries refresh the world with their products from barley and other grains.

Colonial imports made Amsterdam and other Dutch cities centers of cocoa, chocolate, cigarette, cigar, and soap production. Of special fame and profit is diamond cutting in Amsterdam. The drab uncut stones brought from South Africa are very difficult to cut and polish because of their hardness. The techniques of using one diamond to cut or polish another diamond were developed in Amsterdam, which maintained a tight monopoly over the industry until 1940 when fears of German occupation moved many of the craftsmen to New York. After World War II, some of the diamond craftsmen returned to Amsterdam, some stayed in New York, and a few went to Palestine. These are now the three main centers of diamond cutting, with a fourth developing in Brazil.

The textile industry is widely scattered, with centers in Utrecht (linens), Tilburg (linens and woolens), and Breda (rayons). Cotton industry is centered along the German border north of the Rhine. The ceramic industries of Delft and Gouda have long been famous. Eindhoven is the leading center for radio and electric supplies.

The discovery of the deep but valuable coal deposits in the province of Limburg made Heerlen the chief coal-mining center of the country. An extremely progressive development plan not only produces 90 per cent of the coal needed by the Netherlands, but provides attractive houses for the miners, in contrast to the squalidness of most coal-producing areas. Another valuable resource, developed only since 1943, is petroleum. The northeast Netherlands fields now produce one fourth the domestic oil requirements.

URBANIZATION

Unlike other countries of Northwestern Europe, the 11 million Netherlanders are not heavily concentrated in cities. The average population density of over 800 per square mile is equivalent to England's, but only three cities are of any great size, a growth attained mainly in the last century. Amsterdam, serving as capital and commercial center, has a population approaching 900,000. Rotterdam, chief seaport, has grown to over 700,000, while The Hague, as seat of government, is over 600,000.

Only a few other Dutch cities have populations in excess of 100,000. Among these are Utrecht, a trade city on the main east-west and north-south crossroads, and Haarlem, the bulb center. These and other minor industrial centers account for only a fraction of the population, which is almost 60 per cent rural.

BELGIAN FLANDERS

People on the northern plain of Belgium took an early lead in textile manufacturing, art, and architecture. Proximity to wool-exporting England helped the Flemish cities of Bruges, Ghent, and Ypres to become leading commercial centers of northwestern Europe as early as the Middle Ages. Antwerp attained special greatness as a Hanseatic depot and still retains Germanic commercial ties. From Flanders the Dutch adopted their language and many skills as well. Flemish artisans taught the English to manufacture their own textiles.

Behind the straight, sandy coast of Flanders, with its little resort towns and termini for small steamers, is the horticultural belt. Here are raised flowers and bulbs for export, and garden vegetables, in part for English markets. The main agricultural belt lies to the south, centering in the Schelde basin along low valleys that converge toward Antwerp. The extremely dense rural population lives on farms averaging only 4 acres. These tiny plots produce enormous yields of sugar beets, potatoes, rye, wheat, oats, barley, flax, and tobacco. The farm landscape is dotted with breweries, distilleries, sugar refineries, and other factories for processing agricultural products.

Ghent, Tournai (Doornik), and Couranti (Kortryk) are centers of textile manufacturing, specializing in woolens and linens. Most mills are located along the streams of western Belgium which provide pure water for retting flax. Skilled artisans specialize in such expensive items as tapestries, lace, and carpets. Cotton is a minor item.

Rotterdam
[*Netherlands Information Service*]

Both of Belgium's great cities are in Flanders, although Brussels, the capital, is French speaking. As a political and manufacturing center, Brussels contains some 1.3 million people. Its port activities are minor, but it is the hub of a railway network denser than that of any other nation. Antwerp, with its vast artificial harbor connected by locks to the Schelde River, is one of the continent's leading ports. It has prospered as a distributing center for Congo imports: first, ivory; later, rubber and diamonds; and more recently, oils, copper, radium, and other minerals. The city's population of nearly 800,000 plus an even larger number of people in nearby towns, is engaged in port activities and various sorts of food processing and manufacturing.

Ghent is a nucleus of some 400,000 people and the center of the weaving industry. The Terneuzen Canal to the North Sea brings in needed raw cotton, and fosters minor port activities.

SOUTHERN BELGIUM

Southern Belgium is in sharp contrast to Flanders in language and landscape, and is more akin to industrialized parts of France. South of Brussels new crops appear, factory chimneys are more abundant, as are ugly pyramids of mine refuse. One of Europe's most highly industrialized areas lies along the valleys of the Sambre and Meuse. At the east end is Liege, developed on the basis of local coal and nearby iron, lead, and zinc in the Ardennes. West of Liege is a belt of industrial cities, such as Namur, Charleroi, Mons, and a host of smaller centers.

Local fuel and ore supplies have dwindled and no longer meet the demand, so metals are imported from many sources, while the German Ruhr provides excellent coal. The costs of these imports caused Belgian industry, like that of Birmingham and Sheffield, to turn to making more expensive wares, such as instruments, guns, hardware, and machinery. About three quarters of the product is exported. Pottery, cement, and glass are other important sources of Belgian income.

Though the Ardennes has furnished metals to Belgian industry, it is rural and quite unlike other parts of the Low Countries. Its picturesque valleys and forested slopes attract many visitors who supplement the area's main income from agriculture and sheep raising.

LUXEMBOURG

The 999 square miles that comprise Luxembourg lie half in the Ardennes and half in the Lorraine Plateau, divided by the Sauer (Sure) and its tributaries. Along the slopes of these valleys which lead to the Moselle are pear, apple, and plum orchards, and vineyards. In the valley bottoms are small farms, producing barley, oats, sugar beets, and potatoes. One third of Luxembourg's 300,000 population is agricultural.

This little Grand Duchy, only eight tenths the size of Rhode Island, has had a stormy history. Luxembourg, together with Alsace, Lorraine, and Saar was part of the ninth-century Lotharingia, or Middle Kingdom of Europe, a state extending north from the Rhone Valley to Friesland. Luxembourg became a separate country in 1867 by virtue of the Treaty of London which guaranteed its integrity and neutrality. Unarmed neutrality was abandoned in 1948 after Germany had overrun the country in two World Wars. Luxembourg, like the Low Countries, has sought economic and defense unions with European and other countries. It is a member of UN, NATO, Council of Europe, European Coal and Steel Community, Western European Union, Euratom, and Euromarket. Many of these associations are viewed by Luxembourg as means of promoting its important pig iron and steel industries. These industries are based on the iron deposits around Esch which extend into Lorraine, the prize much fought over by Germany and France.

Bavarian landscape
[*German Tourist Information Office*]

7. *Germany*

Germans make a distinction between *Deutsches Reich*, or Germany in the political sense as defined by boundaries, and *Deutschland*, a territory including most of Central Europe wherever German is the common language. German ambitions to make Deutschland a political actuality were almost realized just before World War II, which shattered them. Within the German-speaking core of Central Europe, which is approximately the Germany of 1938, Nordics are dominant, particularly in the north,

with some Alpines in the south. The culture is that of Northwestern Europe. Eastward from the core, cultures become complex, shading off into the Shatter Belt, a zone of political instability between Teuton and Slav. Southward and Southwestward it shades off into Mediterranean cultures.

As in other European countries, Germany's boundaries have been highly mobile, shifting about as land was acquired or lost. From its extensive holdings in the time of the Empire,

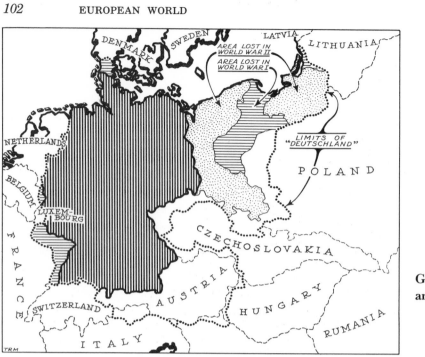

**Germany, 1950,
and Deutschland**

and again on the eve of World War II, it has shrunk to its present area of about 144,000 square miles (about the size of North and South Dakota), and has a population of slightly over 70 million (about 40 per cent that of the United States). Today Germany is split into two parts, west and east.

Germany has tremendous resources. Its mineral wealth includes deposits of fine coal and many kinds of metals and salts. A wide variety of soils and climates permits bountiful and diverse crops ranging from Scandinavian to Mediterranean types. It has extensive forests. Climates vary from continental, with long, bleak winters, in the east, to practically maritime types in the west. Annual precipitation is sufficient for the needs of agriculture and is excessive only in a few highlands, limiting their use to forests and pasture.

Germany's greatest handicaps have been cultural for it lacked ethnic or religious unity. There was no cradle of culture, such as that in Elder England and in other western European countries, to provide a focus for cultural development. The Germanic tribes that roamed the area in ancient times provided no core. By the Middle Ages they had divided themselves into

a most complex group of fiercely warring states. Medieval traditions and customs hung on and stifled political and economic development, making Germany's participation negligible in the early phases of Europe's Commercial and Industrial revolutions.

PHYSICAL AND CULTURAL LANDSCAPES

Germany may be divided into three topographic units: (1) the north German plain, (2) the central belt of uplands, and (3) the southern belt of mountains.

NORTH GERMAN PLAIN

The **north German plain** has three parts: (1) morainal heights along the Baltic, (2) the central depression, and (3) the southern foothill zone. Open in either direction, and part of the European Plain, this northern section of Germany has served as a wide corridor for migration of plants, animals, and peoples.

The **morainal heights** are a more or less continuous belt of highlands, rising about 1,000 feet. They flank the Baltic in an arc from the

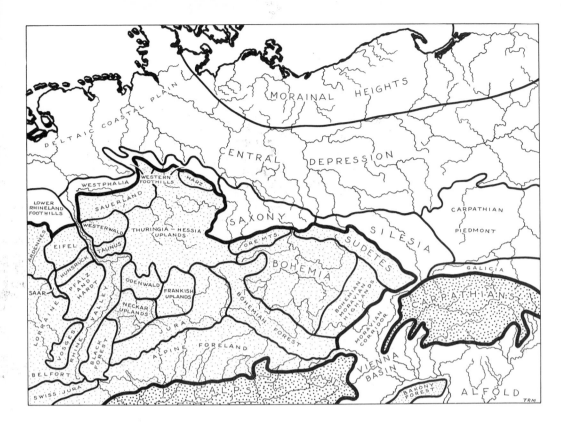

Vistula to Denmark, and mark a long halt in the last retreat of the vast continental glaciers. The surface is uneven, covered with gravels and sands, and dotted with hundreds of lakes. Many of the basins are meadowlands or marsh, and some contain peat. The area is characterized by poor agricultural lands and sterile soils that can produce only rye and potatoes, or support livestock. Coniferous forests cover the slopes. Population is sparse and land holdings necessarily are large.

The Oder River is a boundary between the two most distinctive coasts along the morainal heights. East of it, shores are smooth and sandy, with numerous bars and lagoons. Baltic waters are shallow and ports exist only at river mouths, and are closed by ice for two or more months in winter. West of the Oder, shores are indented by many inlets making harbors more plentiful. Ice is less of a problem. Lübeck, for example, is open most of the winter and with the aid of ice-breakers serves as an all-year port. Lands in the west are more productive, growing a variety of cereals and large quantities of sugar beets. The only place east of the Oder where wheat, beets,

and tobacco are grown intensively is the Vistula Delta.

The **central depression,** south of the morainal heights, is a broad belt extending from Poland to the North Sea coast. Although elevations of 500 feet are common, much of it is low, marshy land rimmed on the south by the foothills of central Germany. Its surface, like that of the morainal heights, is a product of Fennoscandian ice which reached the southern border of the central depression. Many streams in the central depression are deflected by the morainal ridges and forced to flow toward the west into the North Sea rather than the Baltic. Much of the land is subject to flooding or in need of drainage, making it of little agricultural or economic importance. Cities sought the higher lands, along the immediate sides of streams, and despite the unlikely surroundings, here Berlin grew to giant size. The best land lies in the extreme west where a variety of crops is easily grown, and rural population density is fairly high.

The **southern foothill zone** is the most important part of the north German plain. Population is densely concentrated in cities and on the excellent soils that flank the uplands to the south. The foothill zone includes Silesia and Saxony.

Silesia, a promontory of Germanic culture jutting into Slavic territory, extends along the Oder Valley and upslope into the Sudetes. Its lowland and terrace soils are very fertile. In Upper Silesia is one of Europe's best coal deposits, near rich bodies of iron, zinc, lead, and other ores. This fortunate combination of resources gave rise to a thriving industrial region, handicapped in recent years, first being divided among Germany, Poland, and Czechoslovakia by the Treaty of Versailles, and after World War II, being mainly under Polish administration.

Saxony, lying largely in the foothills of the Ore Mountains, has less fertile soils than Silesia, but milder winters. Agricultural productivity is higher and population denser than in any other equivalent area in Europe. A small coalfield east of Zwickau supplies about 4 per cent of Germany's output and supports an industrial region that surpasses Upper Silesia.

Silesia and Saxony culturally overlap topographic divisions of central Europe. Silesia extends well into the upper parts of the Sudetes, and Saxony reaches the summits of the mineral-rich Ore Mountains. The main centers of population, of course, lie in the lowlands of the foothill zone. Cultural penetration into the uplands was a natural consequence of broad valleys that extend into the mountains.

UPLANDS

The uplands of central Europe are extremely diversified in topography. Surrounding Bohemia are the well-defined Sudetes, Ore Mountains, and Bohemian Forest, distinct ranges with linear summits. To the west are many irregular upland masses separated by wide valleys. The whole area is composed of old, hard rocks, and most of it escaped glaciation during the Ice Age. Population is concentrated along the valley flats below the forested slopes that lead to upland pastures.

The Sudetes differ appreciably from the Ore Mountains. Forest products and wool come

Black Forest landscape
[German Tourist Information Office]

from the sparsely populated Sudetes, and many towns along the lower elevations specialize in textiles. In contrast, the Ore Mountains have great mineral wealth as well as abundant china clay and some coal. Rich deposits of potash and other salts became the basis for Germany's outstanding chemical industry. Silver mining brought a considerable population during the Middle Ages, and when the ore was exhausted the people either remained to develop domestic industries or followed the downslope shifting of heavier industrial activity toward the coal of Karl Marx Stadt (Chemnitz) and Zwickau. Although Saxony spreads from the foothills into the uplands, there are enormous contrasts between sophisticated, china-producing Dresden, an old royal residence and art center, grimy Karl Marx Stadt and other hives of industrial activity, and the rural highlands of the Ore Mountains where culture remains primitive and Slavic speech is common.

Westward from Saxony and the Ore Mountains is a broad upland region, including the

Thuringian Plateau and numerous individually named hills. This region contains many basins and valleys, all with a fairly dense agricultural population. In the western part, along both sides of the deep Rhine Gorge, is a sparsely populated cluster of hills and plateaus cut by narrow, frequently deep, valleys. Particularly in the Thuringian Plateau, industries tend to specialize in high-value products, using local sands to produce optical goods and deposits of clay to make porcelain, and capitalizing on the fortuitous combination of lignite from Halle and salts from Stassfurt to establish a chemical industry devoted to making drugs, dyes, and explosives, and many bulk products, such as fertilizers.

On the northern flank of this hill and plateau region is Westphalia and the rich *Ruhr Valley*. The Ruhr coal field normally accounts for three quarters of all German output, and since coal underlies most of the Westphalian plain, the reserves are truly enormous. In this small area, some 50 miles long and less than that wide, live 6 million people mainly engaged in producing coal, iron and steel. About half of these people live in the great conurbation that includes Duisburg, the busy Rhine port at the mouth of the valley, Mülheim, Essen, Gelsenkirchen, Bochum, and Dortmund. This center of heavy industry was repeatedly bombed during World War II, but has more than recovered its prewar status and now supplies 93 per cent of the coal and 80 per cent of the steel produced in West Germany.

South of the Ruhr is the Wupper Valley, where textiles are a specialty, as they are in places west of the Rhine: Aachen (woolens), Krefeld (silks), and München-Gladbach (cotton)—all on the Westphalian plain. Near the mouth of the Wupper is the Rhine port of Düsseldorf, the financial and commercial center for Westphalia.

The **Rhine,** the most important thoroughfare through the uplands, has two distinct parts. The Rhine Gorge, from Bingen to Bonn, is a deep cleft through the Rhine Highlands. Ancient castles and some modern buildings dot the summits on either side of the river. The south-facing slopes along the right bank are completely planted with grapes, introduced in the fourteenth century and the source of the excellent dry Rhine wines. Rapids near Bingen were an early obstacle to navigation, but these have been removed and the Rhine has become Europe's busiest river. Highways and railroads flank both sides of the river, and dodge in and out of tunnels because of the narrowness of the gorge. Each little bench of flat land is used for farms or villages. Cologne (Köln, Roman Colonia) became an important trade center in ancient times because of its position at the mouth of the Rhine Gorge and at the convergence of routes across the plains from Flanders and the Rhine Delta. Wool from the uplands started a textile industry during the Middle Ages, and nearby coal brought a great diversity of industries in modern times.

Above the Gorge the course of the Rhine is through different country both culturally and physically. The Rhine Gorge and all of the upland regions so far described are often regarded as central Germany. Culturally much of it is transitional between the extremes of Prussia and Bavaria, between the Protestant north and Roman Catholic south, and between a predominantly Nordic and a predominantly Alpine population. As a linguistic belt, it lies between the regions of old Low German and High German. Southern Germany is mainly uplands and extends into the Alps, but in the west it is crossed by the low corridor of the Rhine Valley. Upstream from Wiesbaden the Rhine Valley is a broad, straight lowland about 160 miles long and 15 to 25 miles wide. The flanking mountains rise about 4,500 feet above the 500-foot elevation of the nearly flat valley floor. The Rhine Valley soils are excellent and the climate favorable for diversified agriculture, including fruits, cereals, tobacco, and hops. Vineyards cover the foothills and magnificent forests cover the upper slopes.

In ancient times the Rhine was a formidable barrier between Latin and Teuton, its swampy margins encouraging armies and colonists to stay on their own sides. The Mediterraneans established their colonies along the western terraces and foothills, high and dry above the marshy valley bottom, just as the Teutons did on the east side. Two main lines of villages grew up, each on the outer edges of the Valley, a pattern that has survived. Later on, Germanic tribes crossed from the east and settled in and along the Vosges to become the basic Nordic population of Alsace. Lorraine was settled by Germanic Franks who centered in Cologne and Aachen. Both regions are claimed as part of Deutschland and Central Europe by Germans, although local traditions are largely Latin and French has been the dominant tongue since about A.D. 1000. In this respect and others, the Rhine Valley retains much of its old Lotharingian "route-state" and "dividing-kingdom" heritage, with a history of being attached to and separated from both Germany and France. After World War I, Alsace, Lorraine and a strip of the Valley went to France, but a plebiscite in 1935 returned the Saar to Germany. After World War II the Saar went to France, but is now back in Germany. Life in a route state is both prosperous and uncertain.

The Rhine Valley prospers as the intersection of many routes. Main roads and passes lead south to Switzerland, Italy and the Mediterranean, and westward to France. The Rhine Gorge leads northwestward to the Low Countries and North Sea. Easy passes from Frankfurt-am-Main lead to northern Germany, and other passes lead eastward to the Danube, Vienna, and Istanbul. Frankfurt-am-Main is one of the main focal points in the German railroad system, and like other cities in the Valley, it combines commerce with industry.

Considerably less populated than the Rhine Valley are the mountains and dissected plateaus between the Rhine and the Alps. People in the Black Forest must supplement their farm income by engaging in home industries, such as making clocks, jewelry, and wood carvings. The higher parts of the Jura plateau are used for pastures, and agriculture is confined to the valleys, with their small towns busily producing high-priced specialties. Stuttgart, the main city in western Jura, is a center of book manufacturing and electrical equipment, while Nürnberg, to the northeast, goes in for metal, glass, and wooden wares.

Sloping down from the Eastern Alps is the Alpine Foreland, a plateau strewn with boulders, gravels, and sterile sands left by the icecaps of the Alps during the Ice Age. Only rye, oats, and barley can be grown, and most of the land is used as pasture to support the main activity of dairying. The Romans thought the area so unattractive that they rushed through it, establishing forts and settlements only at nodal points, as at Augsburg on the Lech, which long remained the leading trade, religious, and political center of the Foreland. Munich (München), on the Isar in the center of the Foreland, was a rather late development. By the seventeenth century it had become a beautiful medieval town, but its rise as leading city of southern Germany came in the nineteenth century. Isar water power, hard water well suited to brewing, and central position in a railroad network were factors favoring its expansion. Hydroelectric developments along the Alpine slopes have aided the industrial growth of many Bavarian cities.

SOUTHERN MOUNTAINS

Only a small fraction of the Alpine region of central Europe lies in Germany, a narrow strip along southern Bavaria. Most of this rugged Tirolean section lies in Austria, and exhibits culture traits that reflect its transitional position between Northwestern and Eastern Europe. Within their isolated valleys, inhabitants of the Eastern Alps maintain highly localized culture traits, such as individuality in dress and dialects. Household crafts supplement the meager incomes from agriculture, dairying, and lumbering.

CULTURAL SUCCESSION

When Germanic-speaking peoples arrived in about 2000 B.C., they found much of Germany settled by Celts living in scattered habitations, as a *dispersed* population, rather than in the *nucleated* villages preferred by Germanic peoples. Tribes of Germanic-speaking Nordics, the Angles, Saxons, Frisians, Jutes, Goths, Vandals, Burgundians, and Franks, spread across and beyond the north German plain and into the

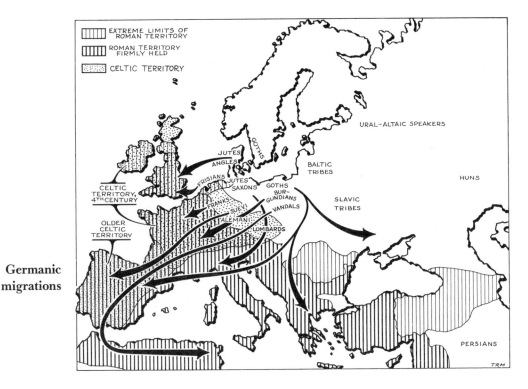

Germanic migrations

Map legend:
- EXTREME LIMITS OF ROMAN TERRITORY
- ROMAN TERRITORY FIRMLY HELD
- CELTIC TERRITORY

Map labels: JUTES, ANGLES, FRISIANS, JUTES SAXONS, GOTHS, BALTIC TRIBES, URAL-ALTAIC SPEAKERS, HUNS, CELTIC TERRITORY, 4TH CENTURY, FRANKS, SUEVI, ALEMANI, GOTHS BURGUNDIANS, VANDALS, SLAVIC TRIBES, OLDER CELTIC TERRITORY, LOMBARDS, PERSIANS, T.R.M.

uplands, establishing their nucleated settlements from the Vistula to the Rhine and from the Baltic to the Danube. Further migrations were effectively hindered during Roman times. The growing and warring population of central Europe remained outside the cultural influences of Rome, learning nothing of the Roman ideas of political organization, law, and religion that sparked the national development of states to the west. Roman control, however, did serve to hem in the Nordics. When the control faltered as Rome declined, a wave of Germanic tribes poured across western and southern Europe, bringing a culture so different from that of Mediterranean peoples that their coming, at the start of the fifth century, marks the beginnings of Europe's Dark Ages. Even before Rome collapsed, these Germanic peoples had a firm grip on much of France, and on parts of Italy and Iberia, and were making their presence felt from southern England to northern Africa and as far east as the Black Sea.

With these Germanic peoples came no concept of nation, either in the Roman or the modern sense. Their idea of government was something of a tribal affair, suited to mobility. In feudal times it was adapted to nucleated villages clustered about castles where rulers maintained strongholds. The main political result of the Germanic migrations was the establishment of tiny political units. These evolved into the intricate feudal system that characterized medieval Europe.

The Roman ideal of Empire, of organization, peace and justice, was not entirely lost on the Germanic mind. A Teutonic imitation of it took form under Charlemagne, a Frank, crowned in 800 as Emperor of what was to become the Holy Roman Empire: commonly characterized as neither Holy, Roman, nor Empire. It was a loosely bound, ever-changing confederation of generally powerless states, most of which were very small in area and in population. It was bumbling and ineffective, but it hung on during ten centuries of political struggles which were as confused and complex as the world has ever witnessed.

During all this turmoil, cultural changes were taking place. Trade and other contacts across the Alps considerably Latinized the southern Germans. Under Empire auspices, Christianity became widespread among Germanic-speaking peoples, although concepts of nationalism made little headway. During this period also, peoples

Frankfurt-am-Main
[*German Tourist Information Office*]

from the east were leaving their mark on the cultural landscape, for soon after the Germanic tribes started moving south and west, increasing numbers of Alpines and Mongoloids, speaking strange Slavic tongues, began pushing across the eastern Teutonic border. A trickle soon became a Slavic flood, shoving the German frontier westward from the Vistula to the Elbe. Slavs surrounded and displaced Teutonic villages, and established new villages of their own characteristic pattern, which tended to be circular around a central field for livestock.

Slavic invasions continued for about three centuries, until the Teutons started a series of drives eastward, beginning in the ninth century. The *Drang nach Osten* (drive eastward) lasted some 400 years. The marches were not continuous nor was warfare general as the Teuton-Slav frontier was slowly shifted eastward. The idea of pioneering, or developing new territory, was strong during the whole period. Many Slavs were absorbed and Germanized. Nordic characteristics were diluted, as blond east Baltics and swarthy Alpines came under Germanic influences.

But while Slavs were becoming Germanized in the east, the Germanic-speaking Nordics who had settled in the west were becoming Latinized. Franks in the Ardennes, Vosges, and lands to the west were discarding Germanic tongues, and giving up their Teutonic culture so thoroughly that their name was to be given to the nation that has done the most to advance the culture of Mediterraneans into northwestern Europe. West of the Rhine, Teutonism was on the decline, while along the Baltic it was spreading, hand in hand with commerce.

COMMERCIAL RISE

Commercial enterprise was an old trait among some Germanic groups. Early traders found that a market for their Baltic amber existed in Mediterranean lands. Between 1800 and 1000 B.C. this fossil resin was carried up the Elbe, along the valleys and over the mountains to Brenner Pass, and into northern Italy. Furs and leather also moved along the ancient "amber route." Later amber routes led along

the Oder and Danube to Byzantium (Istanbul). Germanic migrations broadened the base of German trade, and increased the exchange between central Europe and the Mediterranean. During feudal days, large warehouses were built, protected by walls and moats. Villages and trade centers were likely to be walled, especially in southern Germany. The period left its mark on the landscape, in remnants of walls and old gates, and in irregular, narrow streets in the parts of towns that lay within the original walls.

Germans along the Baltic developed a trade of their own, independent of Holy Roman Empire activities. Seaports were established, mainly in the twelfth and thirteenth centuries, but Scandinavian raids and pirating were constant hazards to commerce. Several Baltic ports formed an association in 1256 for purposes of protection and of clearing the Baltic of pirates. The objectives soon shifted to commercial development and trade monopoly. Thus began the Hanseatic League.

The League grew, and commerce flourished, particularly in Lübeck, its headquarters, and in Cologne and Hamburg. Hanse depots were established in foreign lands, all the way from London to Trondheim and east to Novgorod-the-Great, not far from Leningrad. Hanse ports still have a distinctive atmosphere. Most of them retain tall warehouses, with vertical lines of doors marking their half dozen or so floors into which goods were hoisted. Though the League declined after the fifteenth century and lost its significance during the Commercial Revolution, the main interests of Hanse ports have remained commercial.

Another Germanic movement along the Baltic, also independent of the Holy Roman Empire, was that of the Order of Teutonic Knights. From their center on the east flank of the Vistula Delta, Teutonic Knights spread their control east and north along the Baltic. Königsberg (Kaliningrad) was established in 1255 as a stronghold and a center for the Germanization of East Baltic and other peoples over a wide area that later became East Prussia.

It would seem that with the *Drang nach Osten*,

the rise of Hanse trade, the establishment of political control in the northeast by the Order of Teutonic Knights, and trade and cultural achievements in Holy Roman Empire lands, Germany was about to attain leadership among European nations. Such was not the case. The Reformation caused sharp cleavages within the Holy Roman Empire, and states once united became enemies. Germany's most crushing blow came with the Thirty Years' War, a bitter conflict between small states. When it died down into a "peace of exhaustion" with the Treaty of Westphalia in 1648, three fourths of Germany's population had been lost, the land had been thoroughly plundered by armies, trade was crippled, and the solid middle classes were gone. The Empire fell apart. The early phases of the Commercial Revolution came and went while there was no true German nation to participate. No German name appears in the chronicles of exploration. A destitute land, without colonies or sea power, having even lost its Baltic and North Sea ports to Sweden, Germany had little to contribute to the beginnings of the Industrial Revolution.

RISE OF GERMANY

The modern unification of Germany started from a base of 368 separate political units. The relics of feudalism began to disappear as state after state joined one or another of the various Prussian customs unions. Trade was encouraged through the removal of numerous state tariff walls. Prussian military skill regained the German coasts from Sweden, conquered Silesia, and added part of Poland to the growing Prussian Union. By 1864 Prussia felt ready to war on Denmark, a highly successful venture that led to the acquisition of Schleswig and Holstein. Though this brought on a war with Austria, it resulted in the formation in 1867 of the Prussian-dominated North German Confederation, which included most German states, but excluded Austria.

Germany as a modern nation dates only from the Franco-Prussian War, which started in 1870 and ended the following year. The German states united against France, even the southern states, which had stayed out of the Confederation, joining Prussia. A new nation arose and with victory came the acquisition of Alsace and part of Lorraine. The King of Prussia was chosen to head the political union, and according to best Holy Roman Empire tradition, was given the title of Emperor (Kaiser, Caesar).

With new-found union and peace, Germany also was introduced to the Industrial Revolution, which was already well under way in other western European lands. An intense purposefulness, plus the advantages of a late start, made possible a rapid rise. Germany was saved the trouble of going through the slow evolution from water wheel to steam engine, and started its Industrial Revolution with techniques and equipment acquired from its more advanced neighbors.

Germany's possession of some of the finest coal deposits in Europe and a variety of metals spurred its industrialization. Needs soon outran local resources of iron and other metals, which therefore had to be supplemented by huge imports. Peat and lignite deposits formed the basis of an important chemical industry. As Germany rose to pre-eminence in the chemical field, it also became leader in chemical research and discoveries. Local fuels and hydroelectric resources provided all but one main source of power, petroleum, which was imported from overseas. At its industrial zenith, Germany was the leading European producer of iron and steel goods, first in the manufacture of metalwares, first in the production of chemical products, and second as a consumer of raw cotton. Over 12 million people were engaged in manufacturing, about one third of them in textile industries.

Heavy demands were made on German agriculture to feed the growing industrial population. Using the same kind of scientific zeal that had promoted industrial development, the farmers obtained enormously increased yields. Some 90 per cent of all land was brought into agricultural use, to enable Germany to produce most of the food it needed. About one third of the population remained rural.

By 1914, Germany was surpassed only by Great Britain and the United States in the value of its foreign trade. Colonies had been picked up in Africa and the Pacific, and were being diligently developed. Germany was at the peak of its industrial and commercial activity at the start of World War I. But increasing ambitions to incorporate all Deutschland into the Deutsches Reich brought on destruction in 1918.

The sting of defeat, territorial losses that included all colonies and much of the Lotharingian Corridor as well as less-Germanized lands in the east, and industrial and commercial losses that reduced activities to less than half their prewar level, led to resentment and a new determination to assume world leadership. This culminated in the outbreak of World War II, 1939-45, a war that ended in the collapse of Germany, with some 7 million Germans killed, industry crippled, and commerce at a standstill.

POSTWAR DEVELOPMENT

The division of Germany into four zones of occupation, and more important, the establishment in 1949 of the Federal Republic of Germany (West Germany) and the German Democratic Republic (East Germany), introduced cultural complications. Slavic control now extends farther west than it did at the height of Slavic invasions in the eighth and ninth centuries. East Germany, with its 42,000 square miles and some 20 million population, may be lost to the Northwestern European culture realm. In all likelihood it will be incorporated into the Shatter Belt, the zone of confused peoples, linguistic chaos, and political instability that has long flanked northern Germany on the east. Lands east of the Oder-Neisse line, annexed by Poland, face this fate most certainly.

Within East Germany lie over half the arable lands of prewar Germany, allowing the country to be almost self-sufficient in food. It has valuable deposits of lignite, potash and salts which support a large chemical industry centered in Saxony. Loss of the Silesian coal and mineral district to Poland, leaves East Germany without the basic ingredients to support heavy industry. Although the drab industrial centers along the flanks of the Ore Mountains, such as Karl Marx Stadt and Zwickau, are again busily producing textiles, and the great cities of Saxony, Leipzig and Dresden, are once more turning out large quantities of electric goods, ceramics and many other products, East Germany as a whole suffers from poor economic conditions.

Quite different is the situation in West Germany. The 54 million or more people living

Munich
[*German Tourist
Information Office*]

in this resource-rich 96 thousand-square-mile country, are basking in a prosperity that well exceeds prewar levels. Production has risen to more than twice that of 1936.

West Germany's greatest asset is the Ruhr, now wholly recovered from the heavy war damage. The Federal Republic leads western Europe in steel production, and is fourth in the world in the production of finished steel, mainly a Ruhr contribution.

Economic recovery is not based on heavy industry alone. West Germany is a world leader in the export of machinery, coming from such industrial centers as rebuilt Cologne whose three quarters of a million people combine the manufacturing of machinery with Rhine and Ruhr trade activities and production of textiles and luxury items. Frankfurt-am-Main, about the same size as Cologne, is a contributor of machinery and chemicals, in addition to being a great commercial center for the Rhine Valley. Bonn, although overshadowed in size and industry by its giant neighbor, Cologne, combines manufacturing with its functions as present capital of West Germany. The astounding industrial recovery of the Ruhr benefited its Rhine ports of Duisburg and Düsseldorf, which rapidly expanded their trade and shipbuilding activities. A spectacular recovery has also been made in the German merchant fleet. It has now reached three quarters of its prewar tonnage, and is actively engaged in the effort to recover prewar trade levels and expand foreign markets for German products.

These efforts have also aided Hamburg, Germany's second largest city, with a population of almost 2 million. This vast artificial harbor, carved out of the marshes along the Elbe, is a main interchange point between seagoing ships and the barges and boats that ply the intricate and far-reaching network of rivers and canals. The damage sustained during the war provided an opportunity to improve and modernize facilities, particularly in its three main industries, shipbuilding, oil refining, and machine construction. Supplementing these are a host of other manufacturing and processing activities. Most of the harbor is a *free port*, a status which stimulates commerce through the device of not charging customs on cargoes that are stored, processed, and re-exported. Considerably more than half of Hamburg's traffic is inbound, consisting of foods, fuels, and raw materials for Germany's growing population and rapidly expanding industries.

With the objective of improving its economic status even more, West Germany became a member of the European Coal and Steel Community (Schuman Plan) whereby it, and the other members, Belgium, Netherlands, Luxembourg, France, and Italy, agreed to remove tariff barriers and import quotas on coal and steel, thus abolishing political frontiers to link these two basic industries. An expansion of this idea is Euromarket, of which West Germany is a member. Here the objectives, to be realized over a 17-year period, are to set aside old tariffs, to establish uniform tariffs for imports of foreign goods, and to stimulate free flow of goods, workers, and raw materials. West Germany's position in these unions with other western European countries will be enhanced by its recent acquisition of the Saar, the important coal, iron, and steel producing area which was united politically with the Republic in 1957, and economically in 1960.

The most awkward result of the war is the situation in Germany's greatest city, Berlin. Located in the midst of Soviet-oriented East Germany, less than half of the city belongs to that country, although that part has been named capital. The major part of the city is under Tripartite Government (France, Great Britain, United States), and is definitely in the western camp. Every day thousands of workers cross the boundary to get to their jobs, and every year thousands remain on the western side as refugees. The magnitude of the exodus from East Germany filled many West Berliners and West Germans with alarm and despondency, but as things have turned out, the expanding economy of West Germany is absorbing most of the refugees.

As a great conurbation of some 4 million people, Berlin is a leading industrial, commercial, and transportation center. Like the other big cities of Germany, its spurt of growth came late in the nineteenth century, long after the cities of England, France, and the Low Countries had attained considerable size. The political privileges which it enjoyed by the favor of kings of Prussia, and as capital of the Empire, favored the early years of this town on the Spree. Road and railroad networks were designed around Berlin, as a hub; commerce and trade were funneled through it. A nearby canal between the Oder and Elbe brought in needed resources which were absent locally. As industries flourished, Stettin, the outport, was called on to provide more and more materials of overseas origin. By World War II Berlin had attained a high position among world industrial centers. Despite heavy damage during the war, the commercial and manufacturing activities have largely recovered, although political complications handicap efforts to regain its former position.

Munich in many ways is the counterpart of Berlin in southern Germany. It developed along similar lines, and, like Berlin, is the hub of a transportation network that favors commerce and industry. Unlike Berlin, Munich's industrialization had the advantage of nearby sources of electric power in the Alps. Most of the war damage has been repaired, and the million people in Germany's third largest city are striving to make it again a great center of art and industry.

The re-establishment of prewar patterns in the cultural landscapes of Germany is thus progressing, though the Slavic influences may well leave some mark on the eastern sections. Eventual unity of East and West Germany may weaken the Slavic influences which are not likely to penetrate more than the surface of deep-rooted Germanic cultures. Today in many a German heart, whether in the Federal Republic of Germany, the German Democratic Republic, western Poland, or wherever, there lurks a thinly covered desire for not only a unified Germany, but a Germany that includes all of Deutschland.

EASTERN EUROPEAN REALM

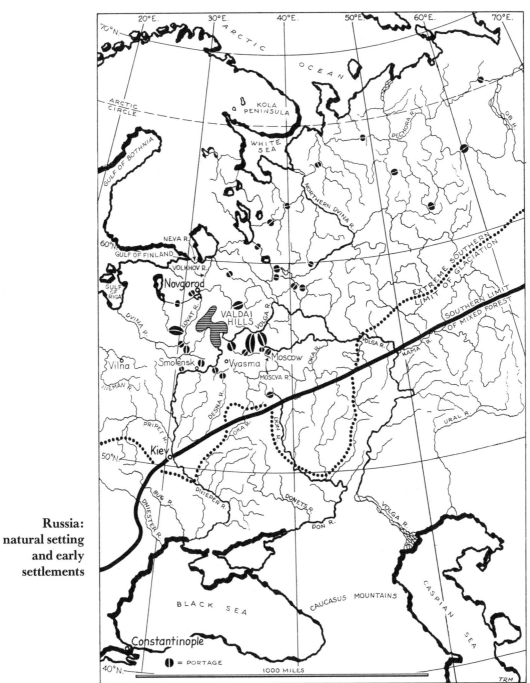

Russia:
natural setting
and early
settlements

8. Eastern Europe

115

The Eastern Realm of the European World is somewhat less clearly defined, both physically and culturally, than the other realms, and considerably less "European," if judged by standards of Northwestern Europe. Racially it is a mixture of Alpine and Nordic elements, plus some Mongoloids. Linguistically, although many different tongues are spoken, it is Slavic. Its culture traits, evolved on the broad eastern part of the European plain, are reasonably distinct from its neighboring realms and Worlds, and reflect the physical and cultural background in which they developed.

The Eastern Europe Realm spreads across the European plain from the Polar World on the north to the Dry World just north of the Caspian and Aral seas. Eastward it extends to the Pacific as a wedge between the sparsely settled taiga on the north and the Dry and Oriental worlds on the south. Westward it shades into the Shatter Belt, the zone of conflict and cultural mixture. In general, the boundaries of Eastern Europe are about those of the old Russian Empire, and the present Soviet Union, with the exception of the large portions of its 8.5 million square miles that lie in the Polar and Dry worlds.

PHYSICAL BACKGROUND

The cultural unity of Eastern Europe is in large measure a result of the flatness and extent of the eastern European plain. The vast plains of Russia, Siberia and Turkestan combine to form the largest flat-lying surface on the earth. Throughout the plains of Russia and those of Siberia, just across the low Urals, people faced the same problems of long, severe winters with their low temperatures, reduced hours of daylight, and frozen rivers and ground. When people in one area found solutions for the problems of living in such an environment, the same solutions were useful to people living miles away across the plains. Culture traits spread easily across these flat regions to produce widespread homogeneity in the Russian ways of life.

The flatness of the eastern European plain is such that over an area of about 2.32 million square miles the culminating elevation is only 1,062 feet, and over half the plain is below 600 feet. The northern two thirds of the plain were glaciated during the Ice Age, as shown by the presence of numerous lakes and wet marshy (grass) and swampy (trees) areas that lie between moraines. The highest point is in the Valdai Hills, northwest of Moscow. From these Hills radiate the rivers that form the major drainage systems of the southern and western plains. Over half the plain drains into the Volga system, which eventually reaches the landlocked Caspian. Plains to the south of the Valdai Hills are drained by the Dnieper system, and by the Dniester, Bug, and Don, all of which empty into the bottlenecked Black Sea. Comparatively little territory is drained by rivers into the Baltic. All of the vast northern area drains toward the inhospitable White Sea and Arctic. Although these river systems are enormous and include many hundreds of streams, they do little to interrupt the flatness of the plain. The valleys are typically broad and shallow, and the divides are wide and flat.

Rivers are, and have been, the traditional means of carrying goods in Slavic territory. The low divides made it easy to move goods from one river to another. Portages became strategic places, especially for the control of trade. In time, many of the portages were canalized, especially those around the Valdai Hills where goods converged from Arctic, Baltic, and Siberian points for movement on to the south and west. Today, river transportation is still of primary importance. Nearly one third of all freight in the Soviet Union travels by boat. Traffic over the 132,000 miles of navigable waterways is handicapped, however, by the long periods when ice closes the rivers.

With the rivers ice-blocked, much of the winter traffic moves by sled both on the rivers and across the frozen ground. This extensive use of winter sled transportation and summer river transport is necessary largely because the network of some 250,000 miles of improved roads is too limited to serve the area and unimproved roads become muddy quagmires in the summer rainfall. Roads are expensive to build, especially in the marshy area of northern Russia, and are costly to maintain because frost attack is so destructive to pavements. Railroads also are expensive to build, and although there are over 95,000 miles of track, they do not begin to serve the almost 9 million square miles of Soviet territory. It was not until 1900 that the first transcontinental line was completed, and although it has been augmented, most of the eastern Soviet Union is remote from a railroad. Some of this remoteness has been removed by the growing system of air lines.

With such poor communications, Russian resources long remained undeveloped, in sharp contrast with the rest of Europe. Industries, such as existed, were largely domestic. During the long winter nights while people were cooped up in their warm dwellings they made things that were needed by the family or that could be sold to others nearby. The Russian peasants were traditionally the most self-sufficient people in Europe and made trifling demands on commerce in comparison with Europeans to their west.

CLIMATE AND VEGETATION

Because so much of Eastern Europe lies at great distances from the sea, the climate is continental, with dry, cold winters and maximum rainfall in summer. Total precipitation is fairly low, about 20 inches in the westernmost part of the Russian plain, 15 inches in the central part, and only 10 inches or less in the eastern parts. Even less precipitation is received in the cold Arctic and dry Caspian margins. Most of the moisture that reaches the European part of the Soviet Union drifts in with summer air masses from the Atlantic, but in winter the cover of cold, dry Asian air prevents the arrival of warm, moist Atlantic air. Thus, snowfall is slight, although that which falls is dry and easily blown into high drifts. Blizzards, called *burans*, are uncomfortably frequent, and mark violent invasions of icy-cold Asian air from the north and east, which drop the temperature far below freezing.

The vegetation of Eastern Europe is varied, and that of the Soviet Union even more so because it includes the entire range from Arctic to desert types, in broad belts across the plains with gradual transitions between them.

Tundra vegetation covers about 27 per cent of the Soviet Union, mainly that part which lies in the Polar World, although arms of tundra swing south along the Urals and the mountains toward the Pacific. The taiga, which covers about 30 per cent of the Soviet Union, marks the transition zone between the Polar World and the wedge of the European World stretching east to the Pacific. This belt of taiga is the most valuable lumber resource on earth, containing extensive stands of pine, fir, and spruce.

South of the taiga are the mixed forests of coniferous softwoods and broad-leafed hardwoods, covering about 25 per cent of the Soviet Union. The original distribution of mixed forest was widest in European Russia and in the Far East toward Manchuria. Between these wider parts the belt is pinched by aridity, so the transition in central Asia is from coniferous forests directly to steppe, or dry-climate grassland. Most of the original mixed forest is gone and much of the area is used for crops. The cultural landscape is typically a combination of pasture lands, fields, and wood lots.

In a broad belt south of the mixed forest and taiga are various types of arid-climate vegetation, covering about 18 per cent of the Soviet Union. Much of this is steppe, or grassland, the native grass being tall near the northern margins and becoming shorter and less abundant toward the more arid areas. It is excellent for grazing and agriculture. In the desert, precipitation is insufficient to maintain widespread stands of even the shortest and scantiest grasses. The heart of the desert lies around the northern and eastern sides of the Caspian, and extends eastward to the margins of the highlands of central Asia. Up the sides of these mountains the vegetational transition is from desert or steppe through varieties of mountain steppe to alpine tundra, with a taiga-like belt below the tundra where precipitation is sufficient.

CULTURAL BACKGROUND

The patterns of eastern European culture arose and evolved during the gradual emergence of the Russian state. Many cultural facts and traditional attitudes in the Soviet Union today are understandable only when associated with their historical backgrounds. These go back to the very early Slavic settlers, the Scythians, whose cultural affinities were mainly Asian, and to the invasions of and contacts with other culture groups. At an early time racial mixtures became complex, though Alpine stocks were generally dominant and most people were speaking Slavic tongues by the time Russia began to emerge on the eastern plain.

The *Varangian period*, in the early centuries of the Christian Era, marks a time of Nordic invasions. Venturesome Varangians from Sweden came in the seventh century in search of trade possibilities. Before long they had developed routes down the Dnieper to the Greeks of Constantinople and down the Volga to markets as remote as Baghdad. Novgorod-the-Great arose near the Valdai Hills as a Varangian stronghold to control trade in the ninth century. A century later its inhabitants had become thoroughly Slavicized. A second center arose at Kiev, located on the active trade route along the Dnieper, between Novgorod and Constantinople. It enjoyed great prosperity while in Varangian hands, and like Novgorod, became Slavicized. Kiev became capital of Russia in A.D. 879, the country having acquired its name from Rus, a Varangian clan descended from the followers of Rurik. The Varangian-Slav state expanded by building blockhouses, *ostrogs*, at strategic sites. The purpose of these forts, placed at important portages, was to defend trading rights, but they became focal points for political control. Many of them grew to become the leading cities of Russia. By the end of the Varangian period, in the thirteenth century, a number of ostrogs, including Moscow, had developed into important settlements, and Christianity had begun to spread over Eastern Europe, as a consequence of contacts with the Greeks.

Mongoloid invasions from the east took on impressive proportions in the early thirteenth century when Genghis Khan appeared with his bands of highly organized horsemen bent on military conquest. There had been earlier arrivals of Mongols, but they were mainly peaceful settlers. Under Genghis the raids were forceful and widespread, the most spectacular conquests centering along the northern border of the steppes where his horsemen found the going easiest. When he died in 1227, his empire extended from the Pacific to the Dnieper, including Kiev. The Mongol empire was to continue to grow under the direction of his grandson who conquered most of Varangian Russia. The Mongols avoided forested lands where horses were not as well adapted to warfare as on the steppe, so Novgorod-the-Great escaped capture. It became a smoldering ember of Russian culture that later burst into flames that spread across eastern Europe to unify the land of the Slav. As for the rest of the area, it fared reasonably well under Mongol rule. Although the Khan was supreme and all property was owned solely by him, the lot of the common man was probably better than it had been. The captors were tolerant of established religions, and in many ways brought advances, such as setting up a uniform and rather liberal legal code, a fiscal system, and Russia's first postal system.

While the Mongols from the east were in control and freely roaming the land, from the west came a new threat, the growth of *Greater Lithuania*. The Slavic-speaking Polish state, established in the eighth and ninth centuries along the middle Vistula, developed religious and other ties with the Baltic-speaking Lithuanians to the northeast. Both groups adhered to Roman Catholicism, and had a common cause of opposition to the Greek Catholicism of the Russians. While Lithuanian raiders were harassing the borders, Germans, particularly interested in trade, were moving into various east Baltic ports, especially Riga, long one of Russia's main commercial outlets. By the thirteenth century they were in a position to demand and receive important trade privileges from a weak Russia surrounded by enemies. Novgorod and Smolensk eventually became members of the Hanseatic League. Also in the thirteenth century Lithuanian raiders reached the Valdai region, and during the next century extended their control eastward over much of Russia. Lithuania and Poland then united to form a large Roman Catholic nation intent on destroying the Orthodox (Eastern Church) Catholicism of the Russian Slavs, with whom they fought off and on until the middle of the seventeenth century. Russians were thankful for Mongol aid in warding off the thrusts of Roman priests and generals. It was viewed as a sad day when the Tatar-speaking Mongols were driven out of such centers as Smolensk and Kiev, even though many of the victors were Slavic speaking. Greater Lithuania grew to include all of Kievan Russia, and to extend to the Black Sea.

MUSCOVY

Waning of Mongol power permitted the rise of Moscow as the nucleus of a new Russian state. Founded as an ostrog between the Oka and upper Volga in the early twelfth century, it had prospered commercially, so that by the start of the fourteenth century it was the main commercial, military, and political center in the Moskva Valley. Under Mongol rule, Moscow

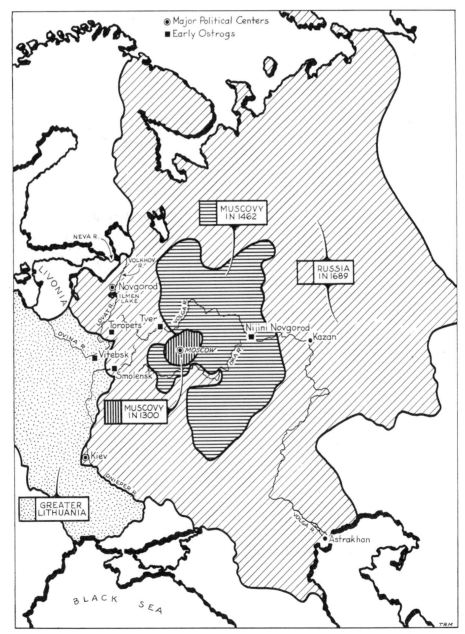

Growth of Muscovy

had fared well, in contrast to Novgorod-the-Great which declined when its food-producing regions to the south were cut off. Also, the Tatar khans of Muscovy, the territory dominated by Moscow, had given Russians important posts, enabling them to gain political experience which they immediately put to work in designing schemes to overthrow the Asians. Moscow became the rallying point for a liberation movement which finally succeeded in breaking the Mongol yoke in the fifteenth century. By this time Muscovy was the heart of Russia.

Muscovy expanded its area of control to the east, taking over a large part of the Volga trade, and to the north, opening new roads to the Arctic and the Siberian taiga. Furs, wax, walrus ivory, and other products poured into Moscow. Of special value was honey, the sweetener prized from before Biblical time until sugar making was established. Muscovy's trade expansion toward the Baltic was blocked by Novgorod-the-Great, and by the Germans, Swedes, and other hostile peoples that lined the shores. To the south it was cut off by Lithuanian control of a large segment of the Black Sea coast. The expansion of Muscovy into the Russian empire became mainly a struggle for seacoasts, the "urge to the sea."

Moscow gained new importance as the greatest center of Greek Orthodoxy when Constantinople fell to the Turks in the middle of the fifteenth century. All Eastern Christians looked to Moscow as the leading defender of their faith. It was with such backing that Ivan III, "the Great," ascended the throne in 1462. Muscovy was consolidated and ready to expand into the Russian Empire. Under Ivan III, the Russians moved west, capturing Novgorod and Kalinin, and posing a threat to Lithuania and Poland. Ivan IV, "the Terrible," or more exactly, the awe-inspiring, turned his attentions east and southeast, taking over the Volga all the way to its mouth at Astrakhan on the Caspian. During his long reign, from 1533 to 1584, Ivan IV enabled Russia to span Europe from north to south, but he failed in his westward ventures, and the country remained barred from western commerce.

ROMANOV INFLUENCES

The early Romanovs, starting in 1613, proved to be capable rulers and also had considerable success in expanding the Russian Empire. The Ivans had established Russia firmly as part of the European World; the Romanovs determined the extent of the Eastern European culture realm. They advanced the boundaries westward, mainly at the expense of the Poles, southward into the Ukraine, and eastward across Siberia. Although the eastward expansion to the Pacific brought under Russian control a huge territory, the westward expansion was of more significance. Peter the Great secured control in 1721 over Karelia, Estonia, Livonia, and part of Finland, giving Russia a firm foothold on the Baltic. Catherine the Great made further gains against Poland, and took part of the Black Sea coast from Turkey. Acquisition of Amur territories from China and the spread of Russian influences beyond the Caucasus completed the Romanov expansion of the Russian Empire.

Although the Romanovs' ability to expand Russian territory was impressive, of equal importance was their influence on Russian ways of life. Peter made significant strides in throwing off the Mongolian traditions, and in the adoption of European ways. He turned Russia's outlook to the west. Also, the early Romanovs adopted and encouraged the spread of the European lord-and-serf system where the land was in the hands of a few nobles and most of the population occupied a position little better than that of slaves. There was no middle class. Serfs might be attached to the land, or to individual households. If unruly, they could be banished to Siberia. Those fortunate enough to escape gladly fled to Cossack territory—to the "wild east," where they might become incorporated in the society of free men. The Cossacks formed a distinct cultural group, the name stemming from Kazak, a free man, a Russian beyond the borders of the state.

The later Romanovs, after Catherine, tried to remedy Russia's medieval social and economic conditions. Of course, the real purpose of their reforms was to destroy the power of the nobles who were a source of trouble to the Czars. Reforms, however, for whatever purpose, did come. The most sweeping reform was the Act of Emancipation of 1861, which freed the serfs and broke the large estates into smaller units by demanding that sections be sold to *mirs* (villages).

The introduction of the mir system changed landscapes enormously. Many of the nobles went to cities or off to live in luxury on the proceeds from the forced sales of their properties. Others turned to commerce or industry, bringing to Russia the first signs of the Industrial Revolution. Urban landscapes, as a consequence, began to change. So did rural landscapes. The mirs set aside certain tracts of land as *communes* under joint ownership for purposes such as common grazing ground. Strips of land were assigned to individuals to be worked, planted in rye and wheat as cash crops, but not owned. People continued to live under poor conditions, not even free to leave mirs. The mir system was gradually reformed, and in 1906 each peasant received his own share of communal land. European ideas of land ownership slowly became established, but few grasped the real significance of the change.

During the period of social reform from 1861 to the eve of the Revolution, a new class appeared, the *kulaks*. These were peasants who for one reason or another prospered and managed to acquire vast estates, thus approaching the position previously held by nobles. But they were a small minority among the ex-serf population which stayed in its traditional state of poverty. Between the two groups, the destitute peasants and the wealthy nobles and kulaks, there was a gap, for no true middle class developed. This was in sharp contrast to western Europe, as was the status of Russian agricultural development. In 1917, when western European farmers were reaping high yields as a result of using scientific knowledge to increase crop production, Russian farmers were still using medieval methods and per acre yields were extremely low.

Poor yields were even characteristic of the steppe, despite the fertility of the black soils, or *chernozem*. These grasslands, long used and fiercely protected by the Cossacks as grazing lands, were thrown open to plowing after the Ukraine had been subjected by Catherine. The land rush that ensued was comparable in many ways to that in the United States at about the same time, when grasslands west of the Appalachians were opened to farming. In both areas, people settled not only on the best sites but went beyond, into marginal lands where dry years meant loss of crops, disaster, or even starvation.

REVOLUTION

The Revolution of 1917, which ended the period of Romanov rule and substituted governments with extreme forms of socialism in their ideologies, upset agricultural productivity completely. The kulaks were promptly liquidated, and lower classes left the cities in droves to overpopulate rural lands. Farming conditions became chaotic. It was not until after five years of civil war, actually several revolutions, that a semblance of law and order appeared. In the end came the Soviet Union, but it took many years of hard work and careful planning before agricultural, commercial, or industrial output approached 1913 levels. Many of the changes had profound effects on the landscape.

The system of *kolkhozes*, or collective farms, was established in 1928, and within a decade over three quarters of all peasants had joined the plan. It achieved the goal of reasonable agricultural stability and productivity by applying industrial management techniques to farming. Land is pooled in large tracts and is operated by specialists. Each person is especially trained for his particular job, from the planners who decide what to plant, right through to the tractor drivers and harvesters, and each benefits financially in proportion to the services rendered. Farmers may augment this income by working, in their free time, little parcels of land assigned to them to grow vegetables or cash crops. The government aids the plan by providing extensive research and experiment activities.

There are also *sovkhozes*, or large farms operated by state governments. Here the workers are paid by the government, and are free of worries over bad years and crop failures. This system has considerable merit on marginal lands, as in the drier parts of the steppe where crop failure is a possibility any year, especially when rains do not come at the right season, or when new pests appear.

Another change, seen in recent years, is the combining of polkhozes into larger units, *polesok*. Since 1950 the number of collective farms has been reduced from one quarter million to about 90,000, each averaging about 4,000 acres. On these farms and the state farms are to be found about 90 per cent of the Soviet Union's 115 million rural population.

The Soviet Union nationalized not only agriculture but also industry, which, in the period following the revolution, was in complete collapse. Through a series of "five-year" plans which stressed industrial development, especially heavy industry, the country has managed not only to rehabilitate its industry, but also to increase its output of coal and steel to the point where the U.S.S.R. now ranks second only to the United States as a producer of steel and leads in coal output. Actual production of oil, steel, and electric energy in the Soviet Union, however, was far behind that in the United States in 1959. Crude steel production was two thirds that of the United States, and electric energy about one third. More than three times as much crude petroleum was produced in the United States as in the Soviet Union. The plans continue to emphasize heavy industry and, as in the past, this is largely at the expense of production of consumer goods, such as clothing and housing, which are insufficient to meet the needs even at quite low living standards.

Developments since 1917 brought many radical cultural changes and many that are rather natural in the light of Russian history. One of the changes was that of turning the face of Russia eastward again. The moves toward Europeanization made by Peter were largely reversed. The capital was removed from its Baltic outlook to the inner city of Moscow.

A wall was erected against European economic and cultural contact to make this "least European part of Europe" even less European.

At the same time, an active program was started to preserve the distinctions of languages, names, customs, and culture traits of minority groups. Within the Soviet Union there are some 185 different "nationalities," or linguistic and racial groups. Three quarters of the population are classed as Russians, mostly Great Russians, with some Little Russians and White Russians. The rest of the population includes Turks, Tatars, other Mongoloids, Jews, Finnic peoples, Germans, and some others. All together they use about 300 different languages. Books are printed in over 100 languages, newspapers in some 70. This linguistic variety is encouraged, showing a type of tolerance more Asian than European in tradition.

It is claimed that the entire Soviet Union population of over 200 million is literate, and that some 10 per cent have gone beyond the standard seven years of schooling. Schools have been provided for even the most remote sections, and education is carried on in the local tongue. It was necessary to create 50 new alphabets for minorities without a written language. These were mainly adaptations of the Latin alphabet rather than the Cyrillic alphabet used by the Russians.

POLITICAL ORGANIZATION

The Revolution of 1917 proclaimed Russia a republic. By 1921 the Red army had managed to conquer Ukrainia and Georgia, although Finland, Estonia, Latvia, Lithuania, and part of Poland were lost. However, the results of the Finnish War and World War II brought the Baltic States and parts of Finland, East Prussia, and eastern Poland again under Russian rule. These, plus other areas gained in the Far East and in the Shatter Belt, bring the area of the Soviet Union to more than 8.5 million square miles. This enormous territory, more than twice that of the United States, is divided into 15 separate republics which form the Union of Soviet Socialist Republics.

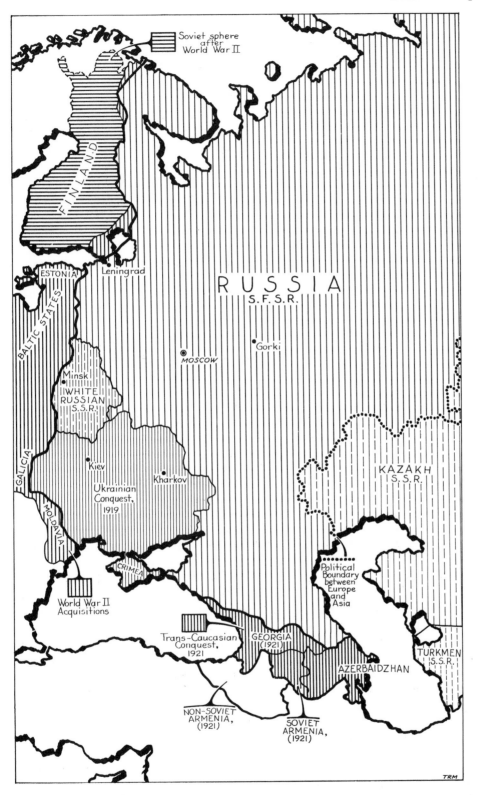

Soviet sphere after World War II

FINLAND

ESTONIA

Leningrad

BALTIC STATES

R U S S I A
S.F.S.R.

Gorki

MOSCOW

Minsk

WHITE RUSSIAN S.S.R.

GALICIA

MOLDAVIA

Kiev

Kharkov

Ukrainian Conquest, 1919

KAZAKH S.S.R.

CRIMEA

World War II Acquisitions

Trans-Caucasian Conquest, 1921

Political Boundary between Europe and Asia

GEORGIA (1921)

AZERBAIDZHAN

TURKMEN S.S.R.

NON-SOVIET ARMENIA, (1921)

SOVIET ARMENIA, (1921)

TRM

Growth of Soviet Union

TABLE 1

Approximate Areas and Populations (1959) of Republics in the Soviet Union

Predominantly European World

	Area, thousands of square miles	Population, millions
Russian S.F.S.R.	6,514	117.5
Ukrainian S.S.R.	225	41.9
Belorussian S.S.R.	81	8.0
Estonian S.S.R.	18	1.2
Latvian S.S.R.	25	2.1
Lithuanian S.S.R.	25.5	2.7
Moldavian S.S.R.	13	2.9
Georgian S.S.R.	38	4.0
	6,939.5	180.3

Predominantly Dry World

	Area, thousands of square miles	Population, millions
Armenian S.S.R.	12	1.8
Azerbaijan S.S.R.	33	3.7
Kazakh S.S.R.	1,073	9.3
Kirgiz S.S.R.	77	2.1
Uzbek S.S.R.	159	8.1
Turkman S.S.R.	189	1.6
Tadzhik S.S.R.	56	1.9
	1,599	28.5
Predominantly European	6,939.5	180.3
Total, Soviet Union	8,538.5	208.8

In theory any republic within the Soviet Union has a great deal of independence, even the right of secession and full power to enter into relations with foreign states. The three leading European soviet republics have been recognized by other nations to the extent of having been given individual representation in the United Nations. Though the republics are distinct, they are strongly bonded together, their unity having been tested by war and proved enduring.

The Russian Soviet Socialist Republic is by far the largest, including almost 80 per cent of the area of the Union and nearly 60 per cent of the population. It grew to its present size in 1956 when the Karelo-Finnish Republic was incorporated as an autonomous republic within the R.S.F.S.R. Most of the people are Great Russians, in contrast to the Ukrainian Soviet Socialist Republic where 80 per cent of the population is Little Russian. The Ukrainian S.S.R. is the most densely populated republic, with over 20 per cent of the Union's total. A large proportion of these people is in the mineral-rich Donets Basin.

Most of the White Russians are concentrated in the Belorussian S.S.R. Equally homogeneous from the linguistic standpoint are the small republics along the Baltic coast. The Moldavian Republic, by no means as uniform, emerged from a trying history with typical Shatter Belt minorities. At the top of the list for complicated linguistic and racial mixtures is the Georgian Republic. Thus, it is apparent that for the purposes of recognizing culture regions, the political divisions of the U.S.S.R. are not especially useful.

RUSSIAN CULTURAL LANDSCAPES

The part of the European World that has undergone most profound landscape changes in recent years is the Eastern Realm. At the time of the Revolution and for some time thereafter, Russian landscapes looked much like those of western Europe in medieval times. As conditions began to stabilize in the middle 1920's, there came changes akin to those of the combined Commercial, Industrial, and Agricultural revolutions of Northwestern Europe, and with them a great increase in urbanization. Landscapes were changed more in two decades than those of most Northwestern Europe during a century.

The most impressive change is the growth of cities in this land that remains largely agricultural. Almost half the people are now city-dwellers, and one sixth of these live in the great conurbations of Moscow and Leningrad. In general the population has shifted toward the east and southeast, away from the western borders of the Soviet Union and toward the thriving industrial centers, such as those in the Donets Basin, southern Urals, and Kuznetsk area. Many of these cities hardly existed in 1913 and some, like Magnitogorsk, were founded in the last 25 years.

(opposite)
USSR: index map

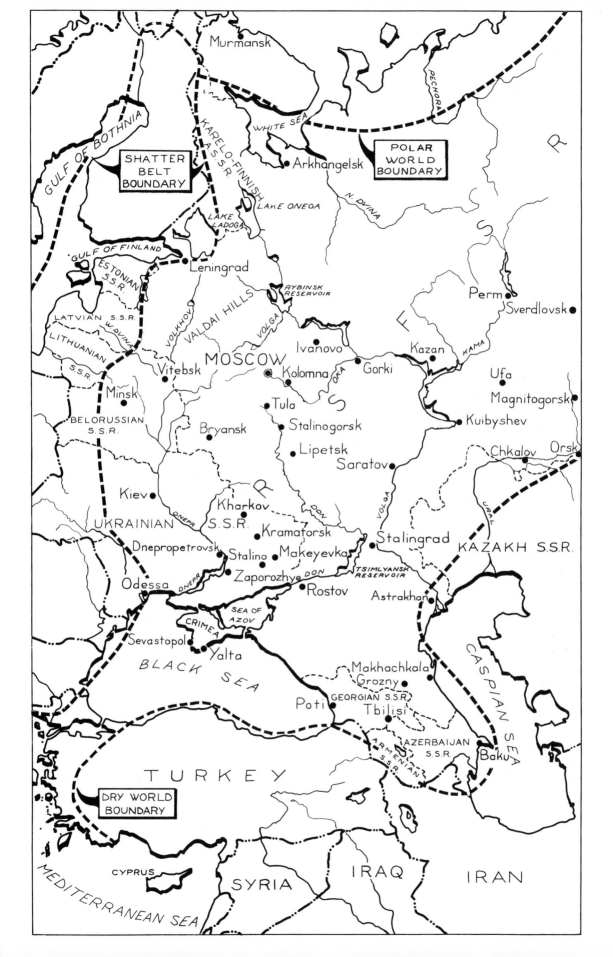

Another noteworthy change in the Eastern Realm is its expansion into other culture worlds, particularly the Polar World and Dry World areas that lie within the Soviet Union. In neither case, however, has the penetration gone far enough to allow incorporation of these areas in the European culture world. The arid Caspian areas have seen the growth of industrial cities that are truly European, and the erection of derricks and refineries in the midst of barren grazing lands. But the way of life is basically along Dry World lines. The Polar World, likewise, maintains its way of life, despite European penetration which consists mainly of Arctic outposts, such as ports, mining communities, and stations to aid navigation along the important Northern Sea Route. This Arctic route not only reduces the shipping distance from eastern Siberian ports, but it also provides an outlet for some 2,500 miles of coast with over 10,000 miles of navigable rivers that wind back through the world's largest reserve of useful timber, the taiga.

TAIGA

Until about a century ago the taiga served as a broad and almost complete barrier between culture worlds. Europeans rarely penetrated more than its southern fringe and Polar World tribes kept to the north, leaving the area almost uninhabited. It is still unattractive to Polar World peoples, but Europeans are making impressive inroads to exploit the resources of furs, minerals, hydroelectric power, and timber. Nevertheless, the population density remains very low.

Arkhangelsk (Archangel), on the White Sea, is the great city of the northern taiga. Its appearance suggests a latitude much farther south. Excellent buildings, paved streets, modern streetcars, an attractive opera house, and a large park "of culture and rest" are thoroughly European. Unlike more southerly cities, it gets its vegetables mainly from hothouses and most other food arrives by rail or steamer. Industry is concerned chiefly with forests, this being the

world's greatest concentration of sawmills. Logs are floated in during the summer, and lumber is sent out by ship during the six-months open season and by rail to Moscow throughout the year.

Murmansk, near the western end of the Kola Peninsula, is an ice-free port lying slightly beyond the northern limits of the taiga. Most of its people engage in commercial pursuits, woodworking, fish canning, and in metallurgical and chemical industries. Nearby sources of hydroelectric power and coal from Svalbard are used to treat ores of aluminum, iron, copper, and nickel. Phosphates are also mined in the area. Coasts are heavily fortified, for Murmansk ranks foremost among Soviet naval bases.

Leningrad is practically a taiga city. Though its site, picked by Peter the Great in the midst of the marshes near the bleak mouth of the Neva, was uninviting, it prospered as Russia's Baltic outlet. As the city grew, industries became established, despite the absence of coal, iron, and most other raw materials. Clothing, textiles, furniture, and other products supplemented the usual printing and related trades of a political center. But growth and prosperity ended abruptly with the Revolution and the removal of the capital to Moscow. Policy decreed that the border city was indefensible, so factories and people were shifted in large numbers to places farther east. Population sharply declined and much of the city fell into disrepair and decay.

As the Soviet Union grew more powerful, Leningrad received more attention and increased its industries. The development of hydroelectric power along the Volkhov and Svir rivers aided paper, cellulose, aluminum, and other industries. Shipyards were built as well as factories to turn out such things as electrical goods, typewriters, textiles, furniture, and railway equipment. About three quarters of all Soviet ships, and all the ice-breakers, come from Leningrad ways. From its factories come half of the electrical goods, one third of the paper, and one quarter of all machines and chemical products of the Union. This industrial recovery raised the population to over 3.3 million.

MIXED FOREST

South of the taiga population density increases and culture is more European, but the landscapes of the mixed-forest belt are not those of Northwestern Europe. Farmers live in log cabins, massively built to withstand the rigors of winter. On the relatively infertile soils, they raise rye predominantly north of the Volga, oats in the wet areas near the head of the Gulf of Finland, and potatoes toward the south, especially beyond Moscow. Very little wheat is grown north of the capital. Flax is the chief fiber crop in the west, and hemp in the east.

A large part of the mixed-forest belt lies within the Belorussian Republic (White Russia), a relatively backward area along the Polish border. The Pripet marshes were settled during the Mongol occupation by refugees who, under conditions of isolation, evolved their own tongue, White Russian, and became somewhat fairer in complexion than the Great Russians. Their wet and infertile lands produce rye, sugar beets, turnips, potatoes, and flax. New crops and increased yields will probably result from the current efforts to drain almost 700,000 acres, but at present the chief economic role of White Russia is to provide meat, leather, bristles, paper, and lumber. Lack of minerals and sources of power discourages industrial development, so the cities remain small. Of the three cities with over 100,000 population, only Minsk, the capital, has managed to grow to something over 500,000.

Moscow is in the heart of the mixed forest, about midway between White, Black, Baltic, and Caspian seas, on a minor tributary of the Volga, the Moskva. The city developed along Asiatic lines, with broad streets flanked by low, whitewalled buildings, including numerous churches. In its center is the oriental and ornamental Kremlin, a triangular walled city of palaces, churches, and gardens. Its gaudy magnificence makes even more dreary the drab concrete apartment houses and other ultra-functional buildings throughout the city. The Kremlin is the hub of the main avenues of the city, just as the city itself is the hub of the rail-road and the highway networks for the country.

Although Moscow had an initial commercial advantage of location near Valdai portages, industry developed rather slowly, and suffered setbacks, as a result of the Revolution, similar to those in Leningrad. Recovery, however, was more prompt because Soviet policies favored the capital. In addition to receiving many of Leningrad's functions, the city was modernized, streets were widened, tall buildings constructed, industry was enormously expanded, and even a magnificent subway system was created. Population increased to meet the needs both of government and of industries, such as the manufacture of agricultural machinery, machine tools, clothing, automobiles, and a variety of electrical and household goods. Well over 5 million people live in the city, and more than 2 million are in the surrounding suburbs.

Gorki, the second most populous city of the mixed-forest belt, lies some 260 miles east of Moscow at the junction of the Oka and Volga. A good share of its some 950,000 population works in its huge industrial district, sometimes called the Detroit of the Soviet Union. The specialty is automobiles, but many river boats are built and metal products of all kinds are manufactured.

About half of pre-Soviet Russia's manufacturing was concentrated in Leningrad, Moscow, Ivanovo, and Gorki, with Moscow foremost. Though there has been great decentralization in Soviet times, and in spite of the rapid strides made in the Urals and Ukraine, Moscow remains the center of the most active and diversified manufacturing district in the Union. Within a radius of 200 miles of Moscow are one quarter of all metalworking industries, turning out such products as airplanes, ball bearing, electrical equipment, railway engines, trucks, automobiles and machinery. In the southern part of the district are Kolomna and Bryansk, making locomotives and machinery; and Tula, Stalinogorsk, Lipetsk, and other centers of heavy industry. Textile industries center in the northern part. Moscow did almost all of Russia's cotton weaving, and with Ivanovo, it still accounts for 90 per cent of the output. The great strides of the

Moscow, mixed-forest, industrial district result from the fact that in about 10 years, the Soviet Union underwent as much industrial revolution as England did in 150 years.

STEPPE BORDERLANDS

The change from mixed forest to grassland is broadly transitional. South of a zone stretching northeast through Kiev and Kazan (see map Russia: natural setting) is the chernozem belt, about 200 miles wide and covered with black, fertile, lime-rich soils. Rural densities are as high as 250 per square mile in some places and average about 175. Precipitation of 15 to 20 inches a year is sufficient for crops but insufficient to leach plant nutrients out of chernozem soils. Grass crops of many thousands of years, each of which produced a greater volume of roots than blades, enriched the soil and gave it a dark color. Farther south, scant rainfall produces less grass and thus less humus, so soils are brown rather than black. Here agriculture is much more speculative than in the highly productive chernozem belt. The fertile "black-earth belt" of the northern borderlands of the steppe produces over half of the wheat, half of the barley, four fifths of the sugar beets, and two thirds of the tobacco grown in the Soviet Union.

Kiev, capital of the Ukrainian Republic, and third largest city in the U.S.S.R., with a population of over one million, has long been important as the great city in the heart of Russia's bread basket, the steppe borderlands. In recent years these borderlands have become the center of the collective farming movement. Guided by Russia's most skillful agriculturists, about two thirds of the Ukraine is intensively farmed. Half the land is in wheat, but rye, barley, oats, millet, and sugar beets are grown in large quantities. Livestock density, especially cattle, is greater than in other parts of the Soviet Union.

Rural landscapes in the Ukraine are more "European" than those elsewhere in the Union. Farms are neat and attractive, with well-kept, generally white-walled houses surrounded by beds of flowers. Villages usually have football fields, parks, libraries, and other evidences of Soviet culture. The people are often called "Little Russians," not in reference to their size, for they are generally taller than Great Russians, but to show that their language is really only a variant of the Russian spoken in Moscovy.

Kiev developed industrially as an agricultural center. Grassland heritage made it a leader in leather industries, especially boots and shoes, and in sugar refining. Agricultural implements and machinery are also among its leading products. Similar industrial development took place in the other main cities of the steppe borderlands to the northeast of Kiev. Many of these were first established as ostrogs to resist Mongol and Tatar invasions, but now are thriving industrial centers. Such places as Saratov, Kazan, and Kuibyshev have populations well in excess of one half million. Kuibyshev, which served as temporary capital of the Soviet Union during part of World War II, has benefited industrially by two new developments. The discovery of local oilfields, part of the "Second Baku" region between the Volga and the southern Urals, enabled Kuibyshev to become an important oil refining center. A new source of electric power for the city's industries comes from its huge 2 million-kilowatt capacity hydroelectric plant on the Volga, completed in 1956. This plant is part of the development plan for the "Greater Volga" and its tributary, the Kama, which provides for the construction of a series of dams along the river as sources of power and water for irrigating the dry areas of the lower Volga.

Odessa was long the main Ukrainian seaport and export center for wheat. It has one of the few good harbors along the north shore of the Black Sea, but poor rail connections have handicapped its growth. Its relative standing as a port is destined to further decline as a result of the opening in 1952 of the canal at Stalingrad connecting the Don and Volga which provides a Black Sea outlet through the Sea of Azov for the vast hinterland of the upper Volga.

THE STEPPE

The true steppe, south of the chernozem belt, is a short-grass region. State farms and collectives plant wheat, but at some risk. Soybeans and sunflowers have become important crops, the latter as a valuable source of vegetable oil. Barley is the most dependable cereal in this moisture-deficient area. The soils are fertile, and with irrigation they produce huge yields of wheat, rice, and cotton. New cotton-growing territories are being opened up in southern Ukraine along the Black Sea coast and eastward in the southernmost strip of the Russian S.F.S.R., just north of the Caucasus. Rice, a new crop for the Ukraine, is being sown from airplanes and harvested mechanically on some of the large state farms.

The real importance of the drier parts of the Ukraine is related to its coal deposits, the places of greatest population increase. Along the Donets, a tributary of the Don, are the Donbas coal fields covering an area of some 16,000 square miles. Every variety of coal is present. Krivoi Rog, 150 miles to the west, is an excellent source of iron, though its best ores are becoming depleted. Other iron of the phosphate variety lies in the nearby Kerch Peninsula of Crimea. For these reasons well over half of the pig iron produced in the Soviet Union comes from southeastern Ukraine. This proportion will drop because only about one sixth of the Union's coal supply is thought to lie west of the Urals, and in time sources far to the east at Karaganda and Kuznetsk will attract an increasingly large amount of heavy industry.

Kharkov, though not in the heart of the Donbas field, rose during the 1930's to become the industrial center of the Ukraine. Originally it was an agricultural market town, and at the time of the Revolution, it had acquired some industry, but its real growth came under Soviet auspices because its location away from the western borders made it relatively safe from invasion. A modern, attractive city was planned and built, including many factories. Electrochemical plants and other industries soon brought a huge increase in population and commercial importance. The safety of its location was disproved during the German invasion which left the city crippled, though recovery was rapid.

The Donbas area, with its great founderies at Makeyevka and Stalino, and its machinery and heavy-industry centers, such as Voroshilov-

grad and Kramatorsk, is the leading industrial region of the Ukraine. A second industrial concentration centers around the Dnieprostroy Dam at Zaporoshye on the Dnieper. Dnepropetrovsk has grown rapidly, primarily as a result of using local electric power to manufacture coke from Donbas coal, chemicals, aluminum, and steel from Krivoi Rog iron. Power is also wired to the Donbas basin and to the small industrial towns that have sprung up nearby.

Rostov, once a secondary trade center and seaport near the mouth of the Don, has risen rapidly both commercially and industrially. The Don-Volga canal at Stalingrad allows Rostov to be the outlet for the productive upper Volga and western Siberian wheat areas. It also manufactures vast amounts of railway equipment, machinery, and other items. It ranks as a leading city in the southern part of the Russian S.F.S.R.

Along the more arid southern borders of the Russian Republic, in the zone between the Sea of Azov and the Caspian, European World influences give way to the Dry World, although the area is becoming increasingly Europeanized. The greatest inroads into the Dry World have come as a result of the discovery and exploitation of the extensive reserves of petroleum along the north flank of the Caucasus, from Maikop in the west to Baku on the Caspian, and in the Emba area at the north end of the Caspian in Kazakhstan. From the fields and refineries of Baku, Makhachkala, and Grozny, oil moves north by pipe line, rail, and river barge to the industrial centers of Donbas, Moscow, and Leningrad. The Emba fields send their pipe lines to the cities of the southern Urals. The Soviet Union is the only European nation with huge reserves of petroleum within its home territory.

Stalingrad became a commercial center because of its location on a bend of the Volga where it comes close to the Don. Coal from nearby fields proved valuable when the city became industrialized. Its industrial area stretches along the Volga for some thirty miles, and specializes in tractors and other iron and steel products. It is an important transshipping point for oil from the south, and for waterborne cargoes coming from such distant places as the White and Baltic seas.

Astrakhan, the seaport near the mouth of the Volga, grew in a still more arid climate. An oasis strip along the Volga is its only agricultural hinterland, but the Caspian contains the greatest concentration of sturgeon in the Soviet Union and young sturgeon and sturgeon roe in the form of caviar are most highly prized foods among Russians. Like Stalingrad, it also serves as a transshipping point for Baku oil, much of which goes by barge up the Volga. Astrakhan is below sea level, but then so is the Caspian, whose very saline waters stand 92 feet below mean sea level and continue to drop as evaporation exceeds inflow.

The useful lands east of the Caspian, where half of Russia's cotton is grown, as well as Azerbaijan and Georgia, where 10 per cent of the cotton supply is produced, will be discussed in connection with the Dry World. In these territories Dry World cultures are still dominant among rural populations, though cultural changes are going on so rapidly that it may not be many decades before these Dry World Soviet republics are firmly incorporated in the Eastern Realm of the European culture world.

RUSSIAN RIVIERA

The Black Sea coast of southeastern Crimea and a narrow strip along the western end of the Caucasus Mountains have Mediterranean-like climate and vegetation. These attractive coasts became a playground for the nobility in the days of Imperial Russia. When the serfs were liberated, many nobles came to this riviera to retire in their beautiful homes. The area resembles the Mediterranean coast of France, hence the name.

Sevastopol became Russia's leading naval base on the Black Sea. Along the coast to the east is a string of attractive settlements, including Yalta. These health and recreation resorts continue along the Caucasian coast as far as Poti in Georgia. Here, members of the Red Army, labor unions, and other organizations come to relax in the numerous rest homes, some of which are luxurious.

URALS

Although the Urals form the divide between European and Asian watersheds, they are low, mainly under 3,000 feet, and crossed by several passes, such as that between Perm (Molotov) and Sverdlovsk which hardly rises above 1,000 feet. This area of gentle slopes has long been known for its great mineral wealth. Iron, copper, and coal are abundant. Platinum and several extremely rare associated metals occur in such quantities that the Urals have long led the world's production. Although some lead exists, the Urals are deficient in two basic industrial metals, lead and zinc. The richest mineral districts lie between 50° and 60° N., between the Ural Valley near Orsk and the region east of Perm.

Between Perm and Sverdlovsk is a string of industrial cities on the railroads and at places where coal is mined. A similar string of towns to the south connects Ufa and Chelyabinsk. Sverdlovsk is a great industrial center, manufacturing mining machinery, electrical goods, and many other things, as well as being the leading commercial center of the central Urals. To the west, Perm combines manufacturing activities with those concerned with its local gas and oil resources. The largest city in the southern Urals is Chelyabinsk, well supplied with coal for iron smelting and the manufacture of heavy machinery. Ufa, an oil refining center on the west side of the mountains, is thoroughly industrialized. Magnitogorsk uses its exceptionally pure magnetic iron ores in the production of pig iron and steel. Southward from Magnitogorsk in the Ural Valley, the nickel and copper smelters of Orsk are the basis of another industrial center, specializing in diesel engines, chromium plating, finished machinery, and other metal products. Chkalov, downstream, has not only become industrialized but is also important commercially as a center of food production, especially wheat.

ASIAN REPUBLICS

The trend of the Urals southward beyond the Ural River is continued in low, extremely arid

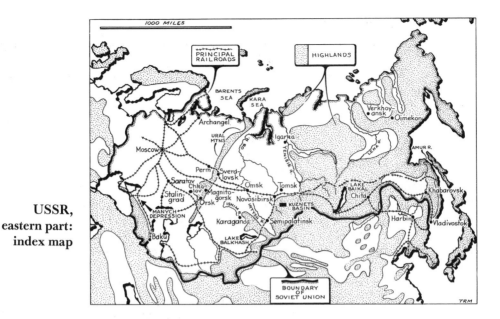

USSR, eastern part: index map

hills that point to the Aral Sea. The huge Kazakh Republic contains, in this arid region, the important Emba and other petroleum districts near the Caspian, and minerals at various places, most important of which are the coal deposits. In the midst of the vast coal area is Karaganda, a city flourishing industrially through the use of local coal and nearby sources of iron, copper, manganese, and bauxite.

Karaganda presents an excellent example of the kind of European World penetration into Dry World cultures that is taking place along the southeastern borders of the Soviet Union. The sparsely populated Kazakh S.S.R. is mainly desert or salt steppe where a grazing economy is typical of life in the Dry World. Discovery of iron and coal brought more than just industrialization; Europeans arrived to build European towns and live in European ways, ways that are being rapidly accepted in preference to native culture traits.

South of Kazakh toward the Caspian is the Turkmen S.S.R., four fifths desert. At its northwest corner is the strange Kara-Bogaz-Gol, a gulf whose salt-encrusted bottom and shores indicate the extreme aridity and high evaporation characteristic of the area. Along the borders of Iran, where more precipitation occurs and streams bring water for irrigation, great quantities of cotton, grain, and oil seeds are grown for export to the Russian republics to the west.

Urban centers are Europeanized, but the thinly spread native population is culturally part of the Dry World.

Along the northeast side of Turkmenistan is the Uzbek S.S.R., extending to the high foothills and valleys leading to the Pamirs. Here are the finest cotton lands in the Soviet Union, much mineral wealth, and the source of karakul fur. Highly developed and ancient Dry World cultures resist European inroads, although like Karaganda, the populous Uzbek capital Tashkent is becoming Europeanized as well as industrialized on the basis of abundant local resources of coal, lignite, petroleum, and hydroelectric power. Some of these resources come from the Tadzhik S.S.R., which lies upslope toward Afghanistan and Tibet, and which remains a stronghold of Asian nomadism. To the north and somewhat lower is Kirgiz S.S.R., where agriculture is better developed.

SIBERIAN WEDGE, WESTERN PART

Penetration of Great Russians beyond the Urals was slow until explorations by traders began in earnest toward the end of the sixteenth century. The Slavs thought the Mongoloid inhabitants of Siberia and central Asia were very strange and primitive. They lived in small, scattered tribal groups, and were highly diversified in language and other culture traits.

Slavs soon displaced the natives, taking over lands thought to be valuable, first for furs, and later for minerals, timber, agriculture, and industry.

The southern edge of the taiga was the main route of eastward penetration, and ostrogs established here and in the Ob-Irtysh drainage basin developed into rather significant towns at fairly early dates. But Siberia remained a remote territory, used for political banishment, until the end of the nineteenth century, when the railroads arrived. Siberian agricultural products became accessible, and colonization gained impetus. The trans-Siberian railroad followed the old traders' trail along the south border of the taiga. Settlement rapidly followed the railroad and towns arose at nodal points where the east-west rails crossed the north-south rivers. Migration into Siberia, especially by Ukrainians and Great Russians, has gone on at an increasing rate, especially in the last three or so decades, more than tripling the population.

Siberia is divided into its two distinct parts by the Yenisei River. To the west is lowland, and to the east is a plateau of ancient rocks, beyond which there is a complex territory of mountains, basins, and plains. The western lowland is the most important part of the Siberian Wedge, particularly the zone paralleling the trans-Siberian railroad and its auxiliary lines. In this narrow agricultural zone, spring wheat, oats, rye, and barley are grown. Flour milling and meat packing started the industrial development of such places as Kurgan, Petropavlovsk, Novosibirsk, Barnaul, and Semipalatinsk.

The agricultural zone is about 500 miles wide at a maximum and narrows toward Lake Baikal. The limitations are imposed by the Ice Age relic, permanently frozen ground that underlies three quarters of Siberia. Toward the northeast, frozen ground reaches to depths of over 1,000 feet, but thins to the south, where the surface thaws in summer to permit field agriculture. The flatness of the western Siberian lowland is also a gift of the Ice Age. A vast lake was formed here, surrounded by the Arctic ice barrier on the north and highlands on the other three sides. When the waters rose high enough to flood south, they used an outlet into the Caspian and then into the Black Sea along the Manych depression parallel to the north side of the Caucasus. Eventually the Arctic ice began to disappear in summer and the lake drained, leaving behind the sedimentary flats which account for much of the agricultural productivity of western Siberia.

Long, severe winters and inadequate transportation made the European population of Siberia extremely self-sufficient. This Slavic culture trait is nowhere else so strongly developed. Home industries reduced the need for industrial and commercial enterprises so severely that landscapes were affected. Siberian towns were always curiously deficient in stores, even by standards of eastern Europe.

The rapid rise of the industrial regions in the Urals upset many Siberian patterns of occupance and development. The planned economy of the government and especially the terrific influx of people during World War II brought revolutionary changes. Novosibirsk is part of an industrial conurbation of well over a million. Omsk, Krasnoyarsk, Barnaul, Tomsk, Semipalatinsk, and Petropavlovsk are now important towns.

The Kuznetsk Basin on the Tom, a branch of the Ob southeast of the western Siberian plain, now produces about one third of the coal in the Soviet Union. It also supplies large amounts of lead, zinc, silver, gold, copper, manganese, and some tin. Kuznetsk coal is used locally, and is sent west to the Urals in return for iron ore, which supplements nearby supplies. Stalinsk, Prokopyevsk, Leninsk-Kuznetski, and Kemerovo form an industrial conurbation of well over one million population engaged in steel production and diversified metal industries. To help meet food supply problems, collective farms around the Kuznetsk district raise wheat, potatoes, sunflowers, and cattle on lands not long ago ranged over by nomads of the Dry World.

In the two thirds of Siberia covered by taiga or tundra, European invasion is mainly limited to outposts, generally established along the north-flowing rivers. Logging is the main activity, and it centers in the Ob and Yenisei lowlands.

SIBERIAN WEDGE, EASTERN PART

Lake Baikal is the eastern extremity of western Siberia. This lake has the distinction of being the deepest in the world—over 5,700 feet. Northward and eastward from the lake the land is sparsely inhabited by Mongoloid tribes of Polar World peoples. Russian outposts in increasing numbers have been established along the rivers of northeastern Siberia, though the excessively cold climate makes settlement rather uninviting. Here is the northern hemisphere's "cold pole," with honors going originally to Verkhoyansk and now to Oimekon.

Russian explorers in the late seventeenth century followed western Siberian patterns of avoiding the taiga and so stayed south of the Lena Basin and penetrated along the Amur Valley east of Lake Baikal into mixed forest toward the Pacific. Here they met the Chinese, and went through the formalities of signing a treaty in 1689 which defined the boundaries of the two empires. But neither side took the treaty too seriously; the Russians continued down the Amur and into northern Manchuria without Chinese opposition. Later, the railroad followed this route to the north coast of Korea, with a second, shorter line, the Chinese Eastern Railway, branching at Chita and crossing Manchuria to Vladivostok. Defeat in a war with Japan, 1904–1905, excluded Russian control from southern Manchruia but not from Harbin and the route through northern Manchuria, which the Russians held until it was taken by the Japanese in 1931. It is now firmly back in Soviet hands.

Various connecting lines and alternate rail lines have been built or planned in the southern part of eastern Siberia, which in addition to opening new areas for the exploitation of timber, mineral, and animal resources, will also extend European World influences.

The Pacific maritime part of Siberia is an outlying fragment of the European World loosely tied to the Siberian Wedge by the trans-Siberian railroads. Such valleys as the lower Amur and the Ussuri are well-suited to European colonization and the growing of wheat, rye, oats, barley, and sugar beets. Coal exists in considerable quantity, both in the settled areas and in places farther north.

Khabarovsk is near the junction of the Amur and Ussuri, and is the commercial and political center of the Far Eastern Autonomous Soviet Socialist Republic, a division of the Russian Federated state. Birobidzhan, a short distance to the west, is an experimental Jewish colony. Komsomolsk, to the north down the Amur, is a rapidly growing steel center, founded in 1932. Vladivostok has coal nearby, so that it is an important industrial city as well as an ice-free port. Its significance may be reduced by the new port of Sovetskaya Gavan, southeast of Komsomolsk, but even more threatening is a trade agreement with China giving the Soviet Union free access to Yellow Sea ports.

A vigorous effort has recently been made to establish European World outposts on Kamchatka. Though Petropavlovsk was founded in 1741 on one of the finest harbors in eastern Asia, it remained only a small fishing center until the mid-nineteenth century when prosperity arrived with whaling. In recent years, canning factories have been built and crab meat has become a valuable export, along with plentiful fish, such as salmon, herring, and cod.

The recent acquisition of the southern half of petroleum-rich Sakhalin Island and the Kuril Islands from Japan, as a result of World War II, gives the Soviet Union complete control of the Sea of Okhotsk, and, for the first time, free access to its entire Pacific Coast.

SHATTER BELT

Southern Austria landscape
[O.V.W. Fettinger]

9. *Shatter Belt*

Between the Northwestern and Eastern culture realms of the European World is the Shatter Belt, a transitional area of political instability where contrasting cultures have met, clashed, and fragmented. It is also the transition zone between maritime and continental climates. It extends from the borders of the Mediterranean Realm in Greece to northern Finland, including Albania, Bulgaria, Rumania, Yugoslavia, Hungary, most of Austria, Czechoslovakia, Poland, Lithuania, Latvia, Estonia, and the western margins of the U.S.S.R.

Early Mediterraneans moving north into Europe before 2500 B.C. encountered Alpines with whom they blended to form the Dinaric stock, which now occupies a belt from Albania to the Po Valley and north into Hungary. Dinarics, Alpines, and traces of Mediterraneans

are the basic racial strains in the southern part of the Shatter Belt. In the central part the basic strain is Alpine, with Nordic and Baltic elements. Farther north, Nordic stock blends with Alpines and Mongoloids. With Mediterraneans and Alpines came Indo-European languages, while Mongoloids brought Ural-Altaic languages.

Most of the invaders of the Shatter Belt came from the east, and among them during the third to tenth centuries were the Asiatic Huns and Avars from the Ukrainian steppe, moving along the grassy plains north of the Black Sea and staying south of the Pripet Marshes. When they encountered the topographic barrier of the Carpathians, they went around its northern end to settle in the Hungarian Basin. Then Slavs arrived, going both north and south of the Carpathians. The ones going north and west

135

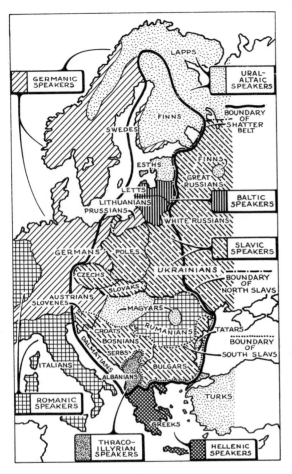

Shatter Belt: peoples

went to the grasslands of Hungary, the Upper Vistula, or on to Bohemia. Those going south reached the Wallachian Plain of the lower Danube, and the attractive valleys of the Balkan Mountains farther south. With the Slavs came Mongoloid Bolgars who settled in Macedonia and gave up nomadism for agriculture. Later came other Mongoloids, the Magyars, who took over the Hungarian Basin and formed a barrier between North and South Slav. By the end of the great migrations the Shatter Belt racial and linguistic patterns were fairly well established so that four main groups of peoples could be distinguished: (1) the northern non-Slavic Lapps, Finns, Esths, Letts, and Lithuanians; (2) the North Slavs, including Poles, Czechs, Slovaks, and Ukrainians; (3) the non-Slavic Magyars, who separated the main Slavic

elements and (4) the South Slavs, including Slovenes, Croats, Serbs, and Bulgars, and non-Slavic Albanians, Rumanians, and Greeks.

Migrations and invasions of less magnitude continued for several centuries, and with each, a struggle to possess the limited number of lowlands suitable for settlement. Mongols came from the east, Germans from the west during their eastward drive, Swedes into Finland and the Baltic States, Saxons and Thuringians into Bohemia, and finally Turks from the south who almost reached Vienna in the late seventeenth century. The results of all these invasions and dominations from first one side and then the other was some mixing of cultures, but mostly the Shatter Belt is characterized by little islands of various cultures, each marking some migration, and each stubbornly maintaining itself even though completely surrounded by subsequent migrations and invasions.

CULTURE REVOLUTIONS

The northern part of the Shatter Belt shared generally in the culture revolutions of northwestern Europe, with various periods of commercial prosperity and the appearance of the Industrial Revolution. In the southern part there were prosperous times during the thirteenth and fourteenth centuries, when Mongol-Tatar rule gave security to overland routes to Asia, and considerable transcontinental commerce was coming along the Danube. Peace reigned, for violent forms of nationalism had not yet risen. The southern cities that fell under Turkish domination, such as Lvov, Belgrade, and Budapest, prospered, but in general the people, especially the Christians who resisted Mohammedanism, were cruelly treated.

Prosperity in both parts of the Shatter Belt declined rapidly during the Commercial Revolution when ships replaced land transport in moving goods from the East. By the sixteenth century, most Shatter Belt peoples had been ground to serfdom, Germans and Jews had taken over internal trade, and nobles had taken the land. Nor did conditions improve in the next two centuries. When the Turks left, the Hapsburgs moved in, and by the eighteenth century the spoils had been divided, Poland partitioned among Prussia, Russia, and Austria, and the Baltic peoples parceled among Swedes, Germans, and Russians.

Neither an industrial nor agricultural revolution effectively touched the Balkans which were kept as suppliers of raw materials. Resentment naturally flared, and took the form of extreme nationalism. In the nineteenth and early twentieth centuries, each little group with reasonably distinct culture traits felt it deserved and must have national status. Nowhere else was the feeling of separatism so strong. But the sought-for independence did not everywhere bring the expected prosperity and economic stability. The Shatter Belt was and is predominantly rural, despite the industrial progress made locally in mineral-rich Bohemia, Silesia, and Bosnia. The new governments initiated agrarian reforms, breaking up the old estates. Improvements resulted in the Baltic States and Czechoslovakia, mainly due to support from

cooperative societies. Little impact was felt in Poland and Hungary where reforms were thwarted. In the rest of the Shatter Belt farm production declined because the ex-serfs and peasants lacked experience in managing the land. The situation became critical, and though European and American aid staved off many disasters, this help failed during the depression of the nineteen thirties causing widespread suffering.

The result of World War II has been to place the Shatter Belt rather securely in Soviet hands. Bessarabia, Carpatho-Ukraine, and a good share of Poland—all lands that were predominantly Russian anyway—have been incorporated directly. The Baltic States have become Soviet Republics. The rest of the Belt has been organized into a zone of friendly nations, a "security fringe" along the western boundary of the Union.

FINLAND

Extending roughly from 60° to 70° N., Finland (Suomen Tasavalta) is "the nation farthest north." It is about half the size of Texas, and one third of its 130,000 square miles lies north of the Arctic Circle. Its 4.4 million people are very thinly scattered north of the more populated coastal belt of southern Finland. It is a relatively flat land of very old rocks with few minerals aside from nickel. Finland is also a low country, only reaching some 2,000 feet on the undulating surface of the interior plateau near the Norwegian border. The break between the plateau and the broad coastal plain is abrupt, providing many sources of electric power.

All of Finland was intensely glaciated, as shown by the scoured plateau surface, the moraines on the coastal flats, and the thin soils. One eighth of the country is covered by its 60,000 lakes which are concentrated in the central and southern parts of the plateau. The Ice Age seems not far removed during Finnish winters, when temperatures of —45° F. and below are common in the northern half of the country. Snow persists for three or more months, and the growing season for plants is very limited.

Shatter Belt: index map

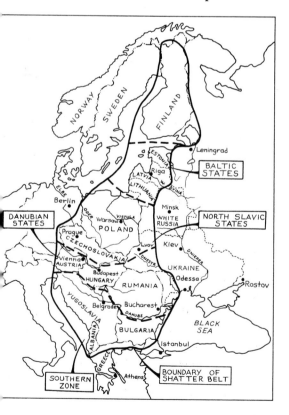

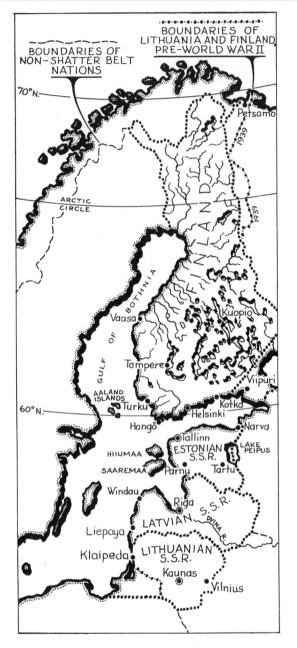

**Finland and the Baltic States:
index map**

Practically all of Finland lies in the taiga, some 60 per cent being forested. Forest is densest between the southern coast and the latitude of the head of the Gulf of Bothnia. North of the Arctic Circle trees exist only in favorable localities, and finally give way to tundra in the far north. About one third of Finland is tundra, bog, moor, or heath.

CULTURE BACKGROUND

Some 5,000 years ago Paleolithic people from the east appeared in northern Finland. These Mongoloids, speaking a primitive Ural-Altaic tongue, were the ancestors of the Lapps of northern Norway, Sweden, Finland, and the Kola Peninsula. There were several migrations of these peoples, and among them came the original Finnic stock, probably from northwest Russia. As they mixed with the Nordics coming in from the west, they became less and less Mongoloid, so that the Finns today are predominantly Nordic, especially in the west.

The Nordics were the earliest settlers in southwestern Finland, and these Swedish migrants occupied the coastal areas from Vaasa south, and along the shores of the Gulf of Finland. After the Finns arrived there was considerable racial mixing, but Swedes are still dominant along the coasts. Linguistically, the population is about 89 per cent Finnish, 10 per cent Swedish, 1 per cent Lappish, with a few Russians and Germans. The Swedes generally farm; the Finns live in the forested areas and prefer to engage in forest industries, though many farm; and the Lapps live north of the forests in Polar World fashion.

It was the Swedes who, in the twelfth and thirteenth centuries, introduced Christianity, law, order, and security in Finland. They took official possession from the sixteenth to the nineteenth centuries, and established new forms of government, schools, and Lutheranism, but their culture penetration was slight in the central plateau where most of the Finns lived.

The Russians took over Finland in 1809, making it an autonomous grand duchy, a status that was dissolved by the Finns during the Russian Revolution. Finland declared itself a republic in 1919, and negotiated boundary settlements that gave it the Petsamo area in the north, where a port could be developed, and a fair slice of Karelia. These gains were lost after Finland was twice defeated by the U.S.S.R. between 1939 and 1944. The boundary was

Medieval Church, Finland

[*Consulate General of Finland, N.Y.*]

moved west, especially in the southern part where it was too close to Leningrad for Russian comfort, and in the north where Petsamo became Russian Pechenga. The area lost was incorporated by the Finno-Karelian S.S.R. which in 1956 was absorbed by the Russian S.F.S.R. Despite this, or because of it, Finland has made a number of mutual assistance, friendship, and economic pacts with the Soviet Union in recent years.

LANDSCAPES

Most of Finland looks like a pioneer country, a natural consequence of its extensive forests, and of the emphasis on forest products. Lumber is the common building material, and logging operations and sawmills are seen everywhere. Industry is concerned mainly with making lumber, plywood, boxes, barrels, furniture, boats, matches, pulp, and paper. Nevertheless, more people are engaged in agriculture than in forest industries, but this is less apparent because farming is concentrated along the coasts. Only 5 per cent of the country is in crops and 5 per cent in pasture, yet half the population is rural. Hay, potatoes, rye, turnips, onions, and cauliflower are important crops; sugar beets are grown in the south, and some wheat in the extreme southwest. Hay occupies more than half the cultivated land and potatoes about one fifth. A surplus of dairy products is exported. In agriculture, particularly, the numerous Finnish cooperative societies play an important role. They handle about one fourth of the retail and half the wholesale trade. Not only do they serve as distributors of low-cost products to farmers, but they maintain stores, hotels, and other institutions, even in larger cities.

About half of the population of Finland lives in seven cities of over 10,000 people. Finns like the water, and population is densest on islands, lake shores, along rivers, and on the coastal plain. Helsinki is the largest city, with 10 per cent of the total population, and is the capital and cultural center of Finland. Its factories for printing, food processing, metal working, and machinery, make it the country's industrial center. Turku and Tampere are of equal size, each accounting for about 3 per cent of the total population. Turku is an important port, a producer of machinery and processed food, stronghold of Swedish cultural influences, and site of two of the three major Finnish universities. Finland boasts the world's highest literacy rate—99 per cent. The "Manchester" of Finland is Tampere, using its abundant hydroelectric power to make it a center for cloth, leather, and woodworking industries. Kuopio, still farther inland and at the head of the Saima lakes, engages in forest industries, match manufacturing, and flour grinding. From the south end of the lakes a canal leads to Vyborg (Viipuri), an old Finnish trading station which became an important commercial center, and is now in Soviet hands. It handled one quarter of all Finnish exports because of the canal to a chain of lakes extending well into the central

Log rafting, Vantaa River, Finland
[*Consulate General of Finland, N.Y.*]

**Southern Finland,
near Hämeenlinna**
[*Consulate General of Finland, N.Y.*]

plateau and forest area. Other important ports are Hankö (Hangö), the only ice-free port on the south coast, Kotka, and Porkkala, which was used as a Soviet military base until 1956.

BALTIC STATES

Estonia, Latvia, and Lithuania are now Soviet republics. Lithuania is the largest, 25.5 thousand square miles, and the most populated, nearly 3 million. Estonia is the smallest, only 18 thousand square miles and slightly over one million population. Though the Baltic States were organized and defined on substantial racial and cultural criteria, they became political entities only after World War I.

The Baltic States are low and flat, with numerous lakes, bogs, and swamps. Rivers are winding and sluggish, of little value for power or transportation. Coal is absent. Northern

Estonia has rich deposits of oil shale, a source of gasoline, phosphatic rock, used in making fertilizer, and limestone for cementmaking. Peat and wood are the chief fuels. Forests are fairly widespread, and soils are poor and thin, as in the mixed-forest belt of adjacent Russian S.F.S.R. The Baltic States are not particularly attractive lands nor has nature endowed them with many resources.

Estonia. The Esths are a Finnic people, and though they resemble Finns, they differ from them in that they are strongly mixed with Baltic and Alpine strains. Their two languages, Estonian and Livonian, are very close to Finnish. Like the Finns, they are mainly Lutheran, although one fifth are Greek Catholics. Of the million or so population, 88 per cent is Esth and 9 per cent Russian, the latter being mostly confined to the eastern section. The rest of the

Turku
[*Consulate General of Finland, N.Y.*]

population is made up of small numbers of Swedes, Jews, Finns, Letts, and Poles. A previously important group, the Germans, withdrew in 1939.

The Esths have managed to survive through a long series of invasions and foreign dominations. German traders practically enslaved them, then Teutonic Knights took their lands and firmly subjugated the people. Under Swedish rule during the sixteenth to eighteenth centuries, control was more liberal and the Esths made some advances, but the land was mainly retained by Germans and Balts. Following the Swedes, Imperial Russia took over, and developed Estonian ports as outlets for Russian goods. Throughout the nineteenth century, however, most of the Esths remained serfs. In 1918, Estonia, with a dominantly peasant population, declared its independence. There followed an agrarian revolt which gave the land

back to the peasants. Finally, in 1940, Estonia was taken over by the U.S.S.R.

Finnic people are endowed with a stubborn determination that is not readily overcome. In spite of the hardships and seemingly hopeless handicaps that faced Estonia, considerable progress was made during its brief independence. Two thirds of the land was put into crops, hay, rye, and hardy vegetables, and flax used for linen and for linseed oil and oil cake for livestock. Forests were exploited for lumber, pulp, and plywood, and mineral resources were developed. Trade and industry were encouraged. Education was fostered, and soon 80 per cent of the population was literate.

No great urbanization was possible but some towns became industrialized. Tallinn, long a Hanse port with picturesque medieval buildings, is by far the largest city, containing more than one quarter of the total population. It is an important port, ice free for about four months a year, and engages in sawing lumber, ship building and heavy industry. Narva and its textile mills benefit from the fact that Lake Peipus is 100 feet above sea level, and this drop is used to generate practically all the electric power in the country. Tartu is a university town and interior commercial center with forest and agricultural industries.

As a result of diligence and planning, Estonia produces a small surplus for export of timber, pulp, paper, raw flax, butter, eggs, potatoes, alcohol, cement, and cotton cloth.

Latvia. Letts are racially and linguistically similar to Lithuanians; both are Balts and both speak tongues of the eastern group of Indo-European languages. They have little in common with their northern neighbors except religion and history. Over half of the Letts are Lutheran, and the rest are about equally divided between Roman Catholic and Eastern Orthodox. The Letts went through about the same experience of foreign overlords as the Esths with an additional complication of being under Polish rule. A sizable number of Poles are still in Latvia, though its 2 million population is 75 per cent Letts, 12 per cent Russian, and includes many Jews. Most of the population is rural; less than 25 per cent engage in industry and commerce.

Riga, with more than one quarter of the total population, thoroughly dominates Latvia, whose fortunes rise and fall with those of its main city. As a Hanse port, founded in 1201, Riga became the world's leading lumber market. Prosperity was further increased while it served as Russia's main outlet to the west, but when this hinterland was cut off in 1917, Riga was plunged into depression, and so was the rest of the country. Commercial treaties with the Soviet Union, and then incorporation into the U.S.S.R., enabled both city and nation to recover. The port stays busy year-round, kept open in winter by ice-breakers.

About half of Latvia's 25 thousand square miles is under cultivation and one quarter is forest. It produces limited exports of butter, eggs, meat, and flax, and maintains some small industries based on imported cotton, coal, and iron.

Lithuania. Lithuanians have a strong nationalism and a proud past, dating from their Neolithic ancestors who practiced agriculture some 5,000 years ago. Their heyday came when Greater Lithuania controlled lands to the Black Sea. Lithuania's glory was surpassed by Poland after the countries were joined in the fourteenth century. The fifteenth century saw the countries parceled among Russia, Prussia, and Austria. Lithuania went to the Slavs, but its main port, Klaipeda (Memel), was retained by the Prussians. From Poland the Lithuanians received their Roman Catholic religion, and from Germany a feudal land-tenure system. Today's population of some 3 million is about 80 per cent Catholic. Four fifths of the people are Lithuanians, the rest being Poles, Russians, Jews, and Germans. These minorities, especially Germans and Poles, posed a problem when Lithuania became a nation in 1918, but more serious was the country's commercial collapse when in 1917 it ceased to be an outlet for Russian goods.

Prosperity was difficult to achieve because of the country's meager natural resources. Although about 80 per cent of the population is engaged in agriculture, less than half of the land is suitable for crops, and these are restricted to rye, wheat, barley, oats, potatoes, and flax. Flax is exported, along with dairy, livestock, and forest products. Little industrialization was possible because practically all basic materials were missing, and peat and wood were the only fuels.

When Lithuania became a nation, Klaipeda, then called Memel, was thoroughly German and so foreign to rural Lithuania that the League of Nations placed it under international supervision. The Lithuanians promptly seized it without objections from the League of Nations. Its improved port facilities and railroad ties with Russia make it the leading port of the Lithuanian S.S.R., although it is considerably smaller in population than the other two leading cities of the country. Vilnyus (Vilnius, Vilna), the capital, is about the same size as Kaunas, a commercial center. Although these three main cities are really rather small, they are distinctly larger than the little market towns scattered throughout rural Lithuania. An even greater difference exists between the rural, mainly Lithuanian peasant population, and the urban population, largely Germans and Jews.

NORTH SLAVIC STATES

Among the groups of peoples in ancient times who invaded the Shatter Belt from the east, were Alpines, many of whom went north along the Bug and Wista (Vistula) into what is now Poland where they found Balts. Both spoke Indo-European languages, though the Slavic tongues of the Alpines were quite different, as were their habits, for they established nucleated, agricultural settlements. By the start of the Christian Era, Polish Slavs were clearly differentiated in the Vistula Basin and had spread west into Pomerania on the Baltic and along the Oder.

Poland. For the past 10 centuries the only boundary of Poland that has remained fairly stationary is the southern one along the crest of the Carpathians, a distinct topographic divide. The other boundaries have shifted back and forth in response to pressures from Poland or its neighbors. Poland reached its greatest size after

the union with the Principality of Lithuania in 1386, and became a leading state of Europe. Major boundary shifts came with Poland's decline and the partitions of 1772, 1793, and 1795 when the country was divided completely among Prussia, Austria, and Russia. Years of resentment and frustration followed, but national aspirations were realized with the creation of the Republic of Poland after World War I, at the expense of Russia, Austria, Germany, and later Lithuania. In 1938, land was seized from Czechoslovakia, but the unsettled boundaries continued to shift, and in 1939 came the Fourth Partition. This time the country was divided between Germany and the Soviet Union, only to be reunited in 1947 as part of the Soviet bloc. But meanwhile, the boundaries had changed, shifting westward to give the U.S.S.R. some 70,000 square miles of land in the east, and moving Poland's west boundary to the Oder-Neisse as a 40,000 square mile gain from Germany. This shift brought much of East Prussia, Upper Silesia, Pomerania, and the city of Danzig into Poland, making its present size about 120,360 square miles, but its total population was reduced by about 7 million from the prewar level to a total of less than 30 million.

Poland's population has become slightly more homogeneous following these latest boundary changes. The people in the eastern area lost to

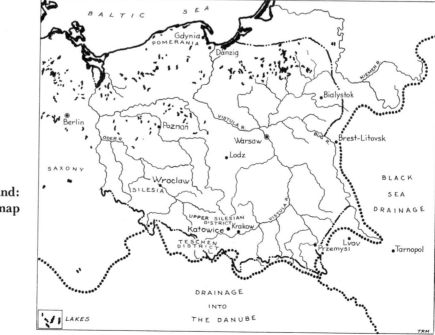

Poland:
index map

the U.S.S.R. were mainly non-Polish, and many of the Poles who lived there have been repatriated to fill the gaps left by the Germans who were expelled from land gained in the west and north. Nevertheless, there are still significant minority groups, such as the Germans and Jews who in the past had essentially controlled Poland's industry. About two thirds of the population is Roman Catholic.

Nearly half of Poland's population is agricultural. It is densest in the excellent farming lands that flank the Carpathians and Sudetes. Here are raised quantities of wheat, barley, potatoes, and other crops. The area is much like Saxony, both agriculturally and industrially, and is really an eastward extension of the southern foothill zone of Germany. The rural population of Silesia and the Carpathian Piedmont is more literate and progressive than that in areas to the north, which are also similar to those of Germany. Population density is low in the poor and infertile lands of the northern coastal plain, and in the boggy, marshy areas of the belt of morainal hills and the central depression to the south. The moraines tend to deflect the Bug, Wista (Vistula), and other rivers to the west, as is the case in Germany. The landscapes of northern Poland in many ways resemble those of northeast Germany and Lithuania. Oats and rye cover moraines, and sugar beets, flax, and cattle are widely produced. Few towns north of Warsaw are more than rural villages.

Population is very sparse in the extreme south, in the Carpathian belt. Peaks rise to 5,000 feet and more, but many low passes cut the area, much of which is below 2,000 feet. About half the area is forested, and the rest is devoted to oats, clover, root crops, dairying, and sheep and cattle raising.

Poland was slow in developing industrially despite a wealth of natural resources, such as wood, coal, iron, lignite, petroleum, natural gas, zinc, salt, and potash salts. Most of the minerals are found in abundance along the Carpathian front. Although the boundary changes of 1945 took from Poland the oil fields around Lvov and some of the potash resources, the acquisition of Upper Silesia with its enormous coal deposits and other metals, gave Poland a net gain industrially.

Two contrasting lines of industrial development are like those of Leeds and Sheffield. Warsaw, Lodz, and Poznam are textile centers with interests in agricultural industries. In contrast are the metal and heavy industry centers in the southwest between Krakow and Wroclaw (Breslau). Carpathian slopes with adequate water power, petroleum, and Upper Silesian coal favor manufacturing. In addition to metal products, there is a considerable output of cement, brick, tile and glass.

Warsaw, the largest city, having over a million population, lies in the heart of the agricultural plain of the Wista Basin. As a crossroads of Wista traffic and the Germany-Valdai route, it developed commercially and became the hub of the nineteenth-century rail net. It was also favored by being capital of the republic. Its industries include textiles, machinery, distilling, brewing, and milling.

The only other city with more than half million people is the textile center of Lodz. None of the southern industrial cities reach this size, although the closely spaced towns in the Katowice area of Upper Silesia have a combined population of well over one million.

Gdansk (Danzig) developed as a Hanse port and was thoroughly German. In 1920 Danzig and 754 square miles of surrounding land became a free city to provide a Baltic outlet for Poland. Dislike of the Danzig Germans prompted the Poles to build Gdynia a few miles away, a successful competitor for port trade. The free city area is now under Polish administration, having been captured by Germans and occupied by Russians during World War II.

Czechoslovakia. Little historic precedent existed for the creation of Czechoslovakia at the end of World War I. A Moravian Empire formed in the ninth century soon fell to the Magyars. Then the Czech state became the Kingdom of Bohemia, only to fall into Austrian Hapsburg hands. Czechs were long under Austrian rule, and Slovaks under Hungarian control. Though both speak similar Slavic tongues, Czechs and Slovaks are different in many culture traits.

Czechoslovakia is an inland country some 600 miles long and from 50 to 200 miles wide.

Topographically it may be divided into four main parts: Bohemia, Moravia, Slovakia, and the Hungarian Plain. Bohemia is a distinct basin which, with its rim of uplands, drains through the Elbe Gate to the North Sea. It has considerable mineral wealth, coal, vast forests, extensive lowlands that are mainly agricultural, and a reasonably mild climate, and it is the most densely populated part of Czechoslovakia. The Bohemian lowland extends into Moravia, but narrows northward to become the Moravian Gate, an easy pass between the Sudetes and Carpathians to Upper Silesia. Moravia is primarily agricultural, though the mineral resources of its part of Upper Silesia have given rise to considerable industrialization. Slovakia is a rough territory of hills and mountains given over to forest and grazing, with limited areas used for barley, flax, and vineyards. The Hungarian Plain extends northward into the southernmost part of Czechoslovakia and is used for raising barley, wheat, grapes, sugar beets, maize, and various deciduous fruits.

The Slavic-speaking peoples who invaded Bohemia and the mountains to the east had become differentiated by the sixth century from the Poles. Nordics and Alpines drifted in, and later, Saxons and Thuringians, but the Czechs clung to their Slavic culture traits, and were especially opposed to mixing with the Germans. Bohemia developed a rather pure Czech population centrally, surrounded by a population more than half German. The Slovaks had originally spread southward into the Hungarian Plain, but after the Magyars arrived they retired to the mountains to remain relatively pure culturally.

The population at the start of World War II was somewhat larger than the present total of around 13.5 millions, and about half were Czechs. They lived in a fairly distinct unit surrounded by Germans who outnumbered the Slovaks living to the east. Beyond the Slovaks were Ukrainians in Ruthenia, a territory ceded to the U.S.S.R. in 1945. An important minority group of Magyars lived south of the Slovaks. The Czechs ran the country and made Prague (Praha) the capital, instead of historic and more central Brno. They were urbane and assertive, while the Slovaks were backward and

Czechoslovakia: index map

rural. The total number of Germans in the country has been sharply reduced by their expulsion from Sudetenland after Czechoslovakia became part of the Soviet Bloc and the Communists took over the government.

Less than half of the population is engaged in agriculture, animal industry, and forestry. More and more of the people are going into trade, mainly with Soviet Russia, and industry, now nationalized and coordinated with the U.S.S.R. Industrialization has been favored by the presence of iron, copper, cobalt, nickel, sand, some uranium, and other minerals. Czechoslovakia also gains considerable income from tourists attracted to its spas, scenic areas northwest of Prague, hunting possibilities in the widespread forests, and the caverns and underground rivers and lakes in the limestone area near Brno.

Urbanization followed northwestern European patterns, though only one really large city developed. Prague, with almost a million population, is by far the largest city. It had a very early start because of its site at the head of navigation on a tributary of the Elbe. Its medieval prosperity is shown in the large number of buildings dating back to the Middle Ages, including the university. An industrial age brought factories making a wide variety of products, such as iron and steel wares, machinery, sugar, glass, soap, chemicals, fertilizers, paint, varnish, leather goods, textiles, railroad cars, and locomotives. Although only one third the size of the capital, Brno is the commerical center of Moravia. It is famous for marble, and manufactures woolens and other products, making use of local coal for its industries.

Austria: index map

Bratislava, to the south, is a commercial outlet for Moravia on the Danube. Near the Moravian Gate are several industrial cities clustered around Morovska-Ostrava. Pilsen, southwest of Prague, is not only a great brewing center depending on local supplies of barley and hops, but it also has coal, pure sand, and other resources that established glass and other industries culminating in the Skoda munitions factories, among the largest in the world.

DANUBIAN ZONE

The Slavic territory of the Shatter Belt is interrupted by a Danubian zone of linguistic intrusion. German is dominant in the upper Danube basins, Magyar in the middle basin, and Romanic Rumanian in the lower basin. The lower half of the Danube runs approximately along the northern boundary of the South Slavs, and between them and the North or West Slavs is the intrusive zone which politically includes Austria, Hungary and Rumania.

Austria. Before it was dismembered at the end of World War I, the Austro-Hungarian Empire contained a quarter million square miles and 51 million people. Out of this came Austria with its present 32,369 square miles and 7 million population. Most of it lies in the Eastern Alps and resembles Switzerland. The fourth of the country that is under cultivation produces grains, potatoes, and fruit. The densest rural population is in the productive lowland fringe in the extreme east. Cattle raising and dairying are widespread. The mountain streams provide abundant hydroelectric resources, now about half developed, but important for the growing industries. The excellent iron deposits and some coal in the southeast have fostered considerable heavy industry centering around Graz.

Vienna, once the thriving capital of an extensive empire, declined in wealth and population when its economic welfare became entirely dependent on only little Austria. Over one fourth of the country's population live in Vienna, a situation that places considerable strain on Austria's economy. Even the advantages of Vienna's site mean little, although it sits on the navigable Danube at the hub of

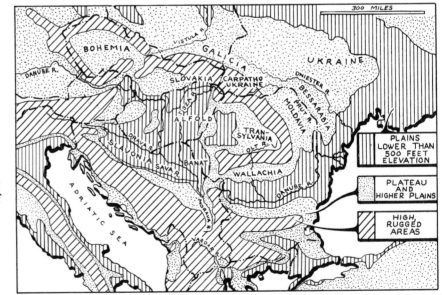

Danubian Basins: relief

Mountain landscape, Austria
[*Sketh*]

routes leading west and north to the Rhine Valley and northwestern Europe, southwest through Brenner Pass to the Po Valley, south to the Adriatic, east and south to Istanbul and Asian connections, and north through the Moravian Corridor to the Elbe Gate and beyond.

Hungary. The Alföld, the broad central Danubian basin, with its extensive grasslands, attracted many Asiatic invaders. Some remained and blended with the tenth-century arrivals, the Asiatic Magyars, who came in large numbers. The Alföld became the central European outpost of Asiatic language and culture. Racially, the Mongoloid stock of the Magyars has become so mixed with Alpine, Mediterranean, Nordic, and Dinaric, that Hungarians are much like their neighbors, except in culture. Their Ural-Altaic language bears little resemblance to the Indo-European tongues on all sides, and only with reluctance did they abandon their nomadic ways. Their contempt, tempered by fear, of the Slavs led them into several associations with the Germans, alliances that proved costly.

Defeat in World War I reduced the size of Hungary so that it no longer included the predominantly Magyar lands in Transylvania which went to Rumania, in Banat awarded to Yugoslavia, and in Slovakia and Carpatho-Ukraine given to Czechoslovakia. After an exchange with Czechoslovakia of Magyars for Slovaks, the Magyars now constitute 93 per cent of the total population of some 10 million. Two thirds of the population is Roman Catholic.

Most of Hungary's 35,902 square miles is a plain 300 to 600 feet above sea level, traversed by sluggish rivers. Precipitation is adequate, 15 to 20 inches a year, and soils are fertile. The plain is divided by the Bakony Forest highlands, a low spur of the Carpathians, used to produce wheat, swine, and wine grapes, such as the famous ones from near Tokay and the north shore of Balaton Lake. Southeast of the highlands is the Great Alföld, the attractive semi-steppe grassland east and north of the Danube

Hungary: index map

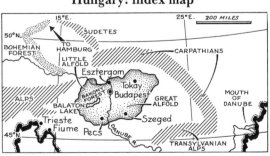

now used to raise grains, maize, sugar beets, flax, hemp, tobacco, hops, potatoes, melons, and paprika. The Little Alföld is along the valley of the Raab near the Austrian border, and is the most prosperous part of Hungary, having industry and commerce to supplement agriculture.

About two thirds of Hungary is under cultivation, about 16 per cent in pasture, 12 per cent in forest, and 6 per cent is barren sand or wet swamp. Extensive reclamation projects were needed, such as swamp drainage and flood control, to create this proportion of farm land. Much of the land has traditionally been in the hands of a few owners, as was common in other Shatter Belt countries. But the landlords, unlike those in the Baltic States and North Slavic territory, were not aliens. The land-owning Magyar aristocracy staved off an agrarian revolt until the last decade, when a movement started to break up the large estates.

In this dominantly agricultural country, industry remained unimportant except for processing farm products. Although some coal exists near Budapest and more near Pecs, and there is some petroleum, fuel supplies are insufficient for large-scale industrial development. A little iron and good quantities of bauxite allow some heavy industry. Urbanization has resulted in only one large city, Budapest, 1.9 million. No other city exceeds 200,000, for most of Hungary is a rural land with small villages. Asiatic influences are seen in the layout of the villages whose whitewalled houses of tamped earth face each other across a very wide road, a survival of the land provided for grazing livestock at night. Gardens surround the widely spaced houses. Lack of fuel and electricity make the villages lightless at night.

Budapest was originally two towns: Buda, a German fort, and the Magyar settlement of Pest on the opposite east bank of the Danube. Combined, they became the largest thoroughly Europeanized city east of Vienna. Its site on the river at the convergence of land routes from Slovakia and railroads from the south and east, favored commercial growth. Half of Hungary's industry is concentrated in the city. It is the leading European center of flour milling, and also contains sugar refineries, breweries, meat-

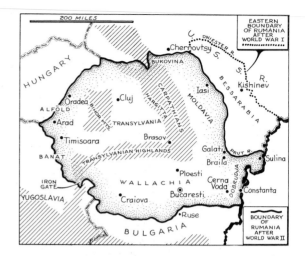

Rumania: index map

packing plants, leather tanneries, shoe factories, cotton-weaving mills, chemical plants, glass factories, and shipyards.

Szeged, in the south, and Debrecen, in the east, are also flour milling centers. Miskolc, in the northeast, has some heavy industry based on local iron. Györ, west of Budapest, is small but highly industrialized, with factories for machinery, railway equipment, matches, and other products. The loss to Italy after World War I of the Hungarian-built port of Fiume on the Adriatic, oriented the country's traffic toward Hamburg, an easier and cheaper outlet to reach.

Rumania. The earliest inhabitants of the lower Danube, the Thracians, were first taken over by the Romans, then, when the Romans left, they were forced to flee to the Transylvanian highlands to escape the invading barbarians, Slavs, Nordic Goths, Huns, Tatars, and, eventually, Turks. These Rumans clung to the language given them by the Romans. Later they crept down into the plains of Wallachia and Moldavia, only to receive another influx of Latin colonists in the twelfth century. The Romani lived in scattered tribes and were subjected to rule by Magyars, Poles, and Turks. It was not until the late eighteenth century that some self-government was granted, and in the last half of the nineteenth century Wallachia and Moldavia were united to form Rumania, which declared its independence from Turkey.

It was soon embroiled in a series of costly wars. Its losses during World War I were rewarded by considerable gains in territory, including Transylvania, Banat, Bukovina, Bessarabia, and rights to keep southern Dobrudja, a Bulgar area. These gains doubled the size of Rumania, but also brought in large minority groups. Both the size of the country and the number of minorities were sharply reduced after World War II when the Soviet Union took northern Bukovina and Bessarabia, and southern Dobrudja was returned to Bulgaria. Within its present boundaries are some 90,000 square miles and 18.1 million people.

Rumanians consider themselves racially close to Latins, though they are dominantly Alpine. Their language is closer to Latin than is Italian, but it includes many Slavic terms. Their religion comes from the Eastern Church rather than Rome, and today about 70 per cent belong to the Rumanian Orthodox Church which absorbed the Greek Catholic Church in Rumania. A great majority of their culture traits are of Slavic origin, and in many ways Rumania is the Shatter Belt nation least influenced by western European cultures.

About 80 per cent of the people are peasants engaged in agriculture and stock raising. Each year they worry about hail destroying their their crops, so they scatter their tiny fields in the hope that some of them will escape devastation. Most of the farms are small, and a limit of 200 acres was established by the agrarian reforms. These genial and inefficient peasants have managed to increase agricultural productivity, but when it comes to politics, they are hopelessly inept. They have no concept of government without rampant corruption.

Some 60 per cent of the land is agricultural, with maize and wheat the leading crops. Other grains, hemp, flax, sugar beets, tobacco, potatoes, and soybeans are other important crops. Many grapes are raised, but Rumanian wine is not highly rated. Sheep are numerous, as in Mediterranean countries, while larger livestock is less abundant. The Wallachian peasants use maize, or "Indian corn," as food, though in most of Europe it is considered fit only for animals. ("Corn" to anyone other than an American means grain, usually wheat.) Al-though forests cover 25 per cent of the country, and mineral resources are abundant, only 4 per cent of the people are engaged in forest industries and 8 per cent in industry. Rumania is mainly an exporter of raw materials, mostly cereals with some mineral and forest products.

Wallachia, old and nuclear Rumania, is the broad plain north of the Danube between the Iron Gate and the delta. Near the river the wide marshes attract many birds, and the river's abundant fish provide a living for a fair number of people. Lands near the marshes receive too little precipitation for agriculture, so sheep graze on the scant grass. Northward, precipitation increases and the soils are like the black earth belt of the Ukraine. Here quantities of maize and wheat are produced. Villages are located where water is available, at wells, springs, or valley mouths. Ferry towns exist along the Danube, which is bridged only at Severin near the Iron Gate, Ruse, and Cernavoda. Along the foothills of the Transylvanian Alps, north of Bucharest, are petroleum and gas fields, supplying the refineries at Ploesti. Although petroleum output has been large in the past, the fields have suffered from overdraining and unwise development, seriously reducing the reserves.

Bucharest is the largest city in Rumania, with one and a quarter million people. It is the political, commercial, and educational center of the country. Modernization is shown in new stores and offices, like those in Russia. Industry, partly based on nearby petroleum and salt, produces refined oil, chemicals, and bricks. Processing farm products, furniture manufacturing, and railway equipment repairing, are also important activities. Craiova is the leading grain market and commercial center of western Wallachia, and Galati and Braila at the eastern end of the plain are the main ports of grain export.

Moldavia, Bessarabia, and **Bukovina** are continuations of the Wallachian Plain around the eastern side of the Carpathians. Moldavia lies between the mountains and the Prut, Bessarabia between the Prut and the Dniester, with Bukovina to the north. Most of Bukovina and Bessarabia now form the Moldavian S.S.R. Its capital, Kishinev, is an agricultural manufacturing city surrounded by the Bessarabian continuation of the fertile black-earth belt. The rival center of Iasi lies just west of Kishinev, across the Prut, is about two thirds the size of its competitor, is chiefly commercial, and has a large Jewish population. Chernovtsy, in the part of Bukovina that went to the Ukraine, is the leading center of the upper Prut valley, and has developed a considerable industry in food-processing and glass-making.

Carpathians lie west of Bukovina and Moldavia, and are highly mineralized and forested. Some of the lower slopes have been cleared for vineyards and orchards. At the south is Orasul Stalin (Brasov), a rapidly growing commercial and industrial center. West of Orasul Stalin are the **Transylvanian Alps,** a beauty spot of Europe. This was the refuge of the Romani during invasions of Wallachia by the Magyars who joined them during Turkish rule. The valleys are densely inhabited by farming peasants, the slopes and high pastures are used for sheep, and above them tower summits rising to over 8,000 feet. Coal, iron, gold, silver, lead, and copper are mined in the west, and salt in the south. Lowland Transylvania, north of the mountains, is the most progressive part of the country, though it contains many strong minority groups. It is a picturesque area of scattered stone houses, which generally have long porches with doors leading to each room. In the west, the houses are often painted blue, a Serbian influence. The commercial and political center of the lowland is Cluj, but neither this city nor the other towns of Transylvania, including Oradea in the west, at the edge of the Hungarian Plain, are highly industrialized, although there is ample coal.

The Banat, a lowland continuation of the Alföld, is divided between Rumania and Yugoslavia. It has been handed around among several rulers, and contains a mixed population, dominantly Rumanian and Magyar. At the north end is the typical Magyar market city of Arad, and just south of it is Timisoara, a growing industrial center based on local fuel, iron, copper, and lead.

Dobrudja is a low, arid upland that deflects the Danube northward for about 80 miles before it makes the sharp bend at Galati to flow east to its delta and the Black Sea. Fishing is an important activity around the delta whose channels shift and shoal. The only improved channel is at Sulina. The arid grassland to the south first attracted Greek colonists, and then a variety of Asiatics. Gradually, a Rumanian majority accumulated to the north and a Bulgarian one to the south. Control passed back and forth, and finally the area was split, the north going to Rumania, the south to Bulgaria. The focus of the northern part is Constanta, an ice-free port that attracts some of the Danube trade and has a pipe line connection for petroleum export, but is mainly a wheat outlet.

SOUTHERN ZONE

South of the Danubian zone is an area of South Slavs covering Bulgaria and Yugoslavia, and beyond this belt, a marginal area of non-Slavic peoples in Albania and European Turkey. The South Slavs differ in written and spoken language from North Slavs who speak western Slavic languages and have adopted Latin alphabets. In the south the Slavs speak East Slavic languages and, like the Russians, use the Cyrillic alphabet.

Bulgaria. Slavicized Bulgars had ruled much of the Balkans for centuries before they were conquered by the Turks and suffered nearly five centuries of oppression. In 1878, Bulgaria attained the status of principality, and finally, became free from Turkey in 1908. Almost immediately it plunged into war, and within 30 years had engaged in four wars that left its manpower and resources exhausted. Political instability and frequent wars have made Bulgaria one of the most backward states of Europe, and only in recent years has it settled down enough to allow some development of its resources. Its "planned economy" is strongly tied to the U.S.S.R.

Within its 42,796 square miles is a population of nearly 8 million, predominantly Bulgars with a small Turkish minority. Most of the people belong to the Eastern Church. A considerable

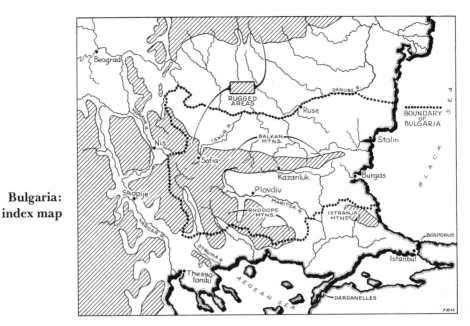

Bulgaria: index map

number of Bulgars live outside the nation in Greece, Yugoslavia, and Rumania. About 80 per cent of the Bulgarians are peasants, living in villages surrounded by their fields. A significant majority are members of cooperative farms which account for four fifths of the cultivable land. As in Russia, domestic industries are highly developed and commerce is negligible in rural areas. A large share of the peasant population lives in the lowlands, both north and south of the Balkan Mountains.

The northern third of Bulgaria, draining into the Danube, is similar to Wallachia, and produces wheat as its leading crop. The little Danubian port of Ruse (Ruschuk) is the chief wheat-shipping point and handles about one third of Bulgaria's imports. It also does some agricultural manufacturing. Another port, Stalin (Varna), on the Black Sea, serves as an ɔutlet for fruits and other Mediterranean products grown along the coast. It supports chemical industries and agricultural processing, and is about twice the size of Ruse.

Few people live in the upper parts of the Balkan Mountains, though they are less high and rugged than the Transylvanian Alps. Sheep graze on the rounded summits, and there is some industry based on the limited deciduous forests and local coal and copper. The basins and valleys, however, have a dense rural population engaged in raising wheat and maize in the west, and fruit, nuts, and tobacco in the

eastern section. Sunflowers, a source of vegetable oil, are raised in great quantities in drier places. The most populated basin is in the west, the site of Sofia, the capital, which contains almost 10 per cent of the country's population. Its eminence stems from its position at the hub of several important trade routes. Near Belgrade (Beograd) the valley of the Morava leads south from the Danube to Nis where the route branches to form one of the most important junctions in the Balkans. One line of passes and valleys leads to Thessaloniki (Salonika) on the Aegean, and the other, by way of Sofia and along the Maritsa, to Istanbul and Asia Minor, or to the Bulgarian port of Burgas. Sofia thus lies on the "Berlin to Baghdad" route. Northward the Iskur leads to the Danube plains, and southward, easy passes lead to the Struma and the Aegean. Sofia combines its commercial activities with marketing and processing the products of its surrounding orchards and fields, and with small industries, such as weaving and brick-making and tile-making. East of Sofia, especially in Kazanluk Basin, are many villages specializing in Damascus roses. The petals are used to make attar of roses, a base for perfume, previously exported to France and Turkey, and now to the U.S.S.R. and Shatter Belt countries. The surplus agricultural products of the basins along the southern Balkan Mountains are exported through Burgas on the Black Sea. Burgas also sends out copper, makes salt from sea brine, refines sugar and petroleum, makes soap, and weaves textiles.

South of the Balkan Mountains, lowlands extend along the Maritsa and eastward past its tributary, the Tundzha, to the Black Sea. Grains, vegetables, and cotton are grown, as well as rice, produced in impressive amounts both in southern Bulgaria and, more recently, on the Danube lowlands. The commercial center of the Maritsa Basin is Plovdiv, formerly called Philippopolis for Philip of Macedon, who founded the city in 350 B.C. It specializes in making silk, processing food, and exporting large quantities of "Turkish" tobacco grown in the vicinity. South of Plovdiv and the Maritsa rise the high and rugged Rhodope Mountains. The inhabitants are either mountain people or valley agriculturists without cities or towns. Sheep, lumber, porcelain clay, tobacco, and fruit are the chief products.

Yugoslavia. East Slavic-speaking peoples moved from southern Russia into the valleys and highlands north and east of the Adriatic as early as the sixth century. They enjoyed a fair amount of independence until the Turks arrived in 1389. Eventually, after a number of uprisings, Serbia won its freedom and became a nation in 1878. It doubled its size during the Balkan Wars, taking in considerable non-Serbian lands and peoples. After World War I a curious nation was created and named "The Kingdom of the Serbs, Croats, and Slovenes." Later the name was changed to Yugoslavia. Now it is technically a federation of the republics of Serbia, Croatia, Slovenia, Montenegro, Macedonia, Bosnia-Hercegovina, the autonomous region of Kosovo-Metohija, and the autonomous province of Vojvodina.

As would be expected, Yugoslavia's population of 18.4 million is composed of a variety of peoples. About half is Serbs, and the other half is mainly Croats and Slovenes, with minorities of German, Magyars, Albanians, and Rumanians. More than the other peoples, Serbs reflect the Eastern influence. They are mainly Greek Catholic and use the Cyrillic alphabet, although they speak practically the same language as the Croats. The Croats and Slovenes are generally Roman Catholic. Slovenian is a quite distinct language. More than 10 per cent of the people are Moslems. Each of the peoples tends to concentrate in its own area.

The Serbian nucleus is in the rugged eastern section, and dominates the strategic and long-used Morava-Vardar route from the central Danubian basin to the Aegean and to Istanbul. Other routes lead west past Sarajevo to the Dalmatian coast, and south past Skoplje to connections with Albania. Both Nis, on the Morava, and Skoplje, on the Vardar, are Serbian nodal points, and on the basis of local products, have grown into sizable market towns. From the surrounding fields, many of which have been irrigated for more than a thousand years, come rice, cotton, sesame, and a variety of vegetables. On the slopes are vineyards and orchards. In the highlands, sheep and cattle are pastured in summer, and are driven to the valleys for winter, a type of seasonal moving called *transhumance*. The area also produces lead, zinc, copper, and iron.

Serbs spread from their nucleus southward into Macedonia, and have long had an eye on, but could not acquire, Thessaloniki (Salonika) which is the best seaport for Belgrade and most of Yugoslavia. Spreading to the north, the Serbs went to the Central Danubian basin, to the area that today is the most densely populated part of Yugoslavia, between the Sava, Drava, and Danube. They produce wheat, tobacco, and wine, plus some maize, sugar beets, raisin grapes, and other crops. Pigs and beef cattle are the chief livestock. Subotica is a food-processing, peasant city on the Hungarian border, and to the south, Novi Sad and Osijek are market towns and railroad centers. But Belgrade (Beograd), with its half million people, is the great city of the Serbian plain, located at the junction of the Sava and Danube. It has suffered innumerable raids, occupations, and destructions, but has always risen again and today is the great Serb stronghold. For this reason, Croats, Slovenes, and others object to its choice as capital. To them it exhibits too much Eastern influence, with its extensive Turkish slums so near the modern buildings. Unlike the industrial centers in western Yugoslavia, Belgrade is primarily an agrarian trade and traffic center.

West of the Serbian strongholds is Bosnia-

Hercegovina, a complexity of peoples and religions. Serbs, Croats, and a number of others are included. They are mostly Christians, either Greek or Roman Catholic, but a large number are Moslems. The people are so mixed that it is impossible to draw boundaries around them. In the midst of this confusion is Sarajevo, the Bosnian commercial center. It exhibits strong Eastern influences, as a result of its 40 per cent Moslem population. Its workers manufacture cutlery, woolens, and leather goods, process tobacco, and engage in woodworking.

The mountains from Montenegro northwestward, fringing the Adriatic, reach heights of over 8,000 feet, and were used as refuges of freedom during Turkish conquests. The inhabitants, many in stages of primitive culture like those of Albania, fatten swine on mast in the oak and beech forests, engage in a little leather and wood working, mine a little copper and silver, and generally ignore the other resources of gold, iron, and zinc, as well as water power. They also raise geese and turkeys, and gather wild herbs, such as gentian, lavender, belladonna, and thyme. In the limestone areas topography is roughened by solution depressions, and landscapes appear barren despite the

rainfall. Fields occupy the thousands of little, saucerlike basins, *dolinas*, and where the basins link along old valleys, *poljes*, strips of soil permit the raising of tobacco and wine grapes as cash crops.

Along the Adriatic shore is a narrow and discontinuous lowland with hundreds of islands, known as Dalmatia, the Illyria of ancient times. Arriving Croats adopted the profession of piracy to become the only Slavs who attained a seafaring culture. The lowlands are quite barren, and the once forested slopes now support grass, vineyards, and orchards. Cattle, marble, and bauxite are among the exports, but the sea is an important resource. Strong Italian influence during Austro-Hungarian Empire days turned many a Dalmatian to the sea for sardines, tunny, or for commercial reasons. Even today Italian is generally spoken in the towns. Although harbors exist by the score, the lack of hinterland and access to the fertile interior has prevented the development of ports or sizable towns south of Rijeka (Fiume). This port was developed as the Hungarian rival of Austrian-built Trieste, located at the northern edge of the Istrian Peninsula. The whole peninsula including Fiume, as it was then called, went to Italy after

Yugoslavia and Albania: index map

World War I, but after World War II, all but the city of Trieste was transferred to Yugoslavia.

Interior Croats differ from Dalmatians in lacking seafaring tendencies and recent Italian contacts. Their lands have been overrun and ruled by a variety of invaders. The traditional capital and cultural center of the Croats is Zagreb, with over one third of a million people. This sesond largest city in Yugoslavia (no other city reaches even 200,000) is more central European than Balkan in atmosphere. It is a commercial, political, educational, and railroad center, with many financial interests. Its main industries are agricultural—milling, brewing, and food-processing.

Slovenia, unlike the rest of the country, has largely been spared conquest and costly wars. Culturally, the Slovenes resemble Tiroleans, and by their close association with Austria they have adopted Roman Catholicism and many Germanic culture traits, though they cling with pride to their Slavic heritage. Much of Slovenia is mountainous and forest-covered. Lumber and charcoal are produced in quantity and exported from Rijeka and Susak. Coal, iron, zinc, lead, and antimony have established local metal industries, many of which center in Ljubljana, the leading political and cultural center of Slovenia. Cotton weaving and glassmaking are important industries. Education in Slovenia is far above Balkan standards.

As a whole, Yugoslavia is 98,766 square miles of backward, agricultural, peasant country with 60 per cent of its population engaged in farming, cattle raising, and forestry, although the number of industrial workers is increasing. Only one quarter of the land is flat enough to produce field crops efficiently, but more than twice that amount is cropped or pastured. Forests cover one third of the land. The country produces and exports raw materials, and leads Europe in the production of copper. In recent years, emphasis on industry has increased the production of coal, iron, and crude steel, but it has reduced agricultural output, making necessary the importation of food. Still undeveloped are a number of mineral deposits, especially those in the mountains, which are difficult to reach on account of the inadequacy of the transport system. But Yugoslavia's most serious handicaps

are of human origin. Here have arisen religious hatreds, clan feuds, political misfortunes, and wars typical of the Shatter Belt at its worst. Cultures are so fragmented and contrasts between them so sharp that their adherents have given each other little opportunity to develop the country's resources.

Albania. Beyond the zone of South Slavs is the land occupied by non-Slavic peoples. Dinaric Albanians are in the west and Turks in the east, with mixtures of Alpines and Mediterraneans, generally known as Macedonians and Greeks, in the middle. To an even greater extent than in the zone to the north, the peoples here reflect the cultural influence of long Turkish domination.

The southern Balkans were originally inhabited by Illyrians, but as in other parts of the Shatter Belt, these lands were invaded over and over by groups coming from all directions. With each new arrival, more Illyrians packed up their belongings and headed for the mountains, where they remained as rather pure, but quarreling, clans. They clung to their ancient tongue, Thraco-Illyrian, a very early Indo-European language. It survives as Albanian today, with a few words borrowed from the Slavic, Hellenic, Latin, and Turkish languages of various invaders. Clans and tribes still form the main political units, and they are still quarreling.

After the Turks arrived in the fifteenth century, their missionaries converted many of the people to Mohammedanism. More than half of the present population of one and a half million are Moslems, living mainly in central Albania. To the north in the highlands are the Ghegs, almost wholly Roman Catholic, but constituting less than 10 per cent of the population. The rest of the people generally belong to the Orthodox Church of Albania. The Albanians are quite tolerant and happily celebrate all the holidays of the three main religions.

The most important racial and cultural boundary lies along the Skumbi (Shkumbi) River, dividing the country in about equal parts. The purely Dinaric stock of the Ghegs is exhibited in their extraordinary height, averaging six feet. They resist outside influence, still enforce ancient legal and moral codes, and live in fortlike houses with narrow slits for windows. In contrast, the Tosks on better southern lands have had more outside contacts and so have developed some commercial interests, although they are still feudalistic in many ways.

Poor little Albania remains the least developed of European countries, having made little progress from its independence in 1912 to its present Soviet satellite position. Only 8 per cent of Albania's 10,629 square miles is arable, but it supports an extremely dense agricultural population, up to 1,000 per square mile in some districts. In the fields, separated by brush fences, are wheat and corn. On the balmy but malarial coastal lowlands are grown tobacco, olives, lemons, wine grapes, and rice. Everybody has goats. Albanians take little interest in trade or development of resources, although they do export lumber from their heavily forested mountains, and a little copper, iron, and petroleum. They much prefer to plant, fish and hunt for home use rather than export. Also, commercial and industrial development is handicapped by lack of a road network. Durrës (Durazzo), the main port, has winding connections with Tiranë (Tirana), the capital, and with the little industrial city of Körce, but this hinterland is too small to allow the port to grow. The main routes in Albania are mule trails, about the only means of penetrating the Alpine landscapes of the interior where peaks rise to over 8,000 feet.

European Turkey. Although the Turks at the height of the Ottoman Empire controlled all of the Balkans, few settled in these conquered lands, and so there was no great population displacement when Slavs or Magyars returned to power as Turkey declined. But the activities of Moslem missionaries are still evident in the number of Mohammedans in these countries. By the end of World War I, Turkey had been forced out of all of Europe except a little corner bordering the gates of the Black Sea, a scheme of the European powers for keeping the Dardenelles, the Sea of Mamara, and the Bosporus out of Russian hands.

In this area of less than 10,000 square miles live some 2.7 million Turks, half of them in Istanbul. The scant rural population raises abundant sheep, goats, and cattle, and such crops as wheat, vegetables, and fruits. They live in thatched-roofed houses, distrust railroads, and enjoy the Mediterranean-type climate. Landscapes resemble those of other Mediterranean countries. The city people especially are becoming more and more Europeanized and abandoning Dry World ways. They have adopted the Latin alphabet to replace the Arabic, have Sunday as a day of rest instead of the Moslem Friday, and use Civil Law rather than the Holy Law of the Koran.

Istanbul traces its growth from its founding as a Greek trading post in 657 B.C., through its days as a bulwark against barbarian invasions, to its rise to become Europe's wealthiest and most powerful city before it began to fade in the thirteenth century and finally fell to the Turks in 1453. Most of this time it was called Constantinople, the Turks only recently having changed the name. Situated on its seven hills, protected by marshes and open water, it has long profited from its position on the crossroads of traffic between Europe and Asia. When Istanbul was displaced by Ankara as capital, the city lost many of its educational, political, and financial interests, and is more or less neglected by the Turkish government, which concentrates its developmental efforts in Anatolia.

Ottoman Empire, 1815

MEDITERRANEAN REALM

**Street scene,
northwestern
Spain**
[*Spanish National
Tourist Office*]

10. *Mediterranean Realm*

If the Mediterranean Sea were superimposed on the United States, it would stretch from San Francisco to Norfolk, and would lie in the latitudes between New Orleans and Ottawa. This sizeable sea is fenced on the north by the European east-west mountain barrier, and on the other sides by deserts and seas. Into this sea project three major peninsulas: Greek, Italian, and Iberian, and these constitute the Mediterranean Realm of the European World.

157

**Market,
northwestern Spain**
[*Spanish National
Tourist Office*]

There are several distinguishing characteristics of the Mediterranean Realm, some of which, such as the land use and agricultural practices, are strongly influenced by the climate, some reflect the importance and unifying effect of the Sea, and some are traceable to the ancient civilizations of the area.

Agriculture is considerably more important than industry in the Mediterranean Realm, and is characterized by terracing, irrigation, dry farming, and other special practices developed to fit the climate, distinctive for its hot, dry summers. Winter is the season of tillage, and crops are harvested in spring and early summer. Fruit from the abundant orchards is sun-dried during the dependable drought. Many of the fruits now grown are very ancient in the area or were introduced at a very early time, such as figs, pears, apples, olives, apricots, cherries, peaches, plums, pomegranates, lemons, and oranges. The productive grape has made wine the traditional drink of the Mediterranean. Cereals and grains, such as barley, millet, wheat, sesame, and rice, are also ancient Mediterranean crops. The general absence of wide agricultural plains precludes the use of field agriculture, the planting and cultivating of crops *en masse*, and places the emphasis on

horticulture, the care of individual plants. Small valley flats are used for grain and vegetables, orchards and vineyards cover the best hill lands, while the poorer hills support olives, and the mountains are sources of timber, or serve as summer pasture. To reach these pastures, sheep and goats are driven along broad, roadless highways leading from the lowlands used for winter grazing. A characteristic of Mediterranean landscapes is this provision for transhumance.

Summer drought and the need for water promoted to positions of supreme importance such weather gods as Zeus, Baal, Jehova, and Jupiter. Their temples were built on promontories and hills where precipitation was heaviest, but reliance on the gods for water was supplemented by the practice of irrigation, brought from Levantine lands to Greece prior to 1000 B.C. Aqueducts to bring water to the cities were built throughout Asia Minor and the Mediterranean during Roman times. Although streams are numerous, they are an untrustworthy source of water because of their sharp contrasts in flow between wet and dry seasons. In summer most of the beds are completely dry, and in winter they are flooding torrents. They are of little use for navigation or hydroelectric development but are so common to the area that every Mediterranean tongue has a term for them: *wadies* in north Africa, *ramblas* in Spain, and *fiumares* in Italy, and these are the equivalents of *arroyos* and *washes* in southwestern United States. These streams typically carry large loads of soil, gravel, and even boulders during their flood stages. This debris is deposited in *alluvial fans* where the streams reach the lowlands, or in deltas. Towns avoid sites threatened by floods or alluvial deposits, and even ports are not on streams, but are off to one side where they can serve the valley and still be free of the hazards of a delta location.

Rough topography, treacherous streams, and limited flatlands made overland communications difficult. People in neighboring valleys rarely trudged over the separating highlands to visit one another, so culture traits were spread via the water rather than the land route. Mediterraneans took to the sea at a very early date, and navigation dates back at least to 3000 B.C. These early navigators always tried to stay within sight of land, and guided themselves by landmarks, such as the temples helpfully built on promontories. They feared and avoided low coasts, especially near deltas, because of the hazards of shoal water and the lack of landmarks. The first lighthouse in the world was erected in Alexandria to overcome in part the disadvantage of a low coast location. Navigation skills were, of course, put to commercial uses, and some five centuries before the start of the Christian Era, the Phoenicians had established a sizeable maritime trade and had ventured well beyond the Mediterranean, having accomplished the circumnavigation of Africa. At the same time, their contemporaries from India and China were making regular runs to the head of the Persian Gulf, bringing textiles and ceramics. This trade was eventually taken over by Phoenicians and Greeks.

Maritime commerce always encourages piracy, and the Mediterranean soon had more than its share of raiders who were just as likely to attack a seaport or coastal town as a merchant ship. This danger forced many settlements to move a few miles inland. During the Middle Ages pirates were so numerous that many coastal lands were practically depopulated. It was difficult to tell a merchantman from a pirate, for even the Phoenicians, who usually found trade more profitable, turned to piracy and plunder when commerce was dull.

The rise of ancient city-states brought a new importance to maritime commerce for it was necessary to bring commodities to these places of dense urban population. Urbanization began in the Mediterranean centuries ahead of other parts of Europe. By 431 B.C. Athens had a population of some 230,000. Carthage was large and prosperous, with a population in 146 B.C. estimated between 700,000 and one million. Rome had grown to one million at the start of the Christian Era. The problems of supplying food, clothing, water, sanitation, other essentials, and luxuries to cities of that size are not simple. Without railroads, engines, steam or electric power, heavy iron and steel structures, and hundreds of items we consider commonplace, it is amazing that such metropolises could have existed at all. Goods were brought in from many distant places, grain from the northern shores of the Black Sea, lumber from the Caucasus, flax from Mesopotamia, silk from China, coarse cloth from France, fur from Russia, as well as luxury items, such as amber and ermine which were reaching the Mediterranean long before written history began. Aesthetic tastes sent ships to the African coast for saffron to make yellow dye, to India for indigo, to the Levantine and African coasts for the snail, *Murex*, source of red and purple dye, and to interior Spain for vegetable-dye materials. These trade contacts also brought cultural contributions which enriched the Mediterranean civilization.

One of the results of this urbanization was deforestation. The only forests that escaped were those in remote or inaccessible places. Otherwise, the land was stripped bare, the trees being used for masts, oars, structural timber, and for resin and tar. The Mediterraneans felt this to be no great loss for they traditionally feared the forest. Unlike the Balt or early Nordic, the Mediterranean felt insecure in an environment of closely spaced trees. Fear of forests kept the early Mediterraneans from migrating north of the forested east-west mountain barrier. As for the herdsman, he had his own reason for disliking forests. To him, they were unproductive lands of limited grazing possibilities. It was not with displeasure that he watched the frequent summer forest fires. Drought both favors the presence of oil and resins in the wood and increases the fire hazard. After a fire, grass and herbs spring up to offer fine grazing.

The Mediterranean may also be characterized as an area of present-day geologic activity. Mountain growth along the entire east-west Eurasian mountain barrier is evidenced in the frequency of volcanic eruptions and violent earthquakes. Movements along faults have destroyed cities and dropped populated islands below the waters of the Aegean. Not only the wall but most of Jericho has fallen when tremors accompanied a deepening of the Jordan Valley graben; in fact, they have fallen so many times that finally people gave up any attempt at restoration. To mention a few major Mediterranean earthquake disasters: 45,000 persons lost their lives in 856 at Corinth, Greece; in 1693, 60,000 at Catania, Italy; in 1755, 60,000 at Lisbon, Portugal; in 1783, 50,000 in Calabria, Italy; in 1822, 22,000 at Aleppo, Syria; in 1908, 75,000 at Messina, Italy; and in 1915, 39,000 at Avezzano, Italy. There is little wonder that cataclysmic cults have arisen among Mediterranean peoples and that their mythologies and religions include stories of destructions of large populations.

The heritage of ancient civilizations and traditions of classical culture are among the distinguishing features of the Mediterranean Realm. The origins of our civilization are traceable to the Mediterranean, and farther east to Mesopotamia and India. As early as 3000 B.C. Crete had become the center of the highly advanced Minoan civilization. Minoans from Cnossus had trade and culture contacts with Egypt and Greece, and eventually wended their way to the western Mediterranean in search of tin needed in the making of bronze. Bronze was to revolutionize cultures sufficiently to mark the beginning of a new Age in the history of man. As Minoan civilization began to wane, around 1000 B.C., the rapidly rising Greek civilization took over the lead. But the great spread of classical culture occurred during the Pax Romana, a period of peace enforced by the overwhelming power of Rome that lasted from 31 B.C. to A.D. 378.

Mediterranean culture was spread largely by way of the five main trade route connections with northern Europe: (1) Black Sea, via the Bosporus, (2) Vardar-Morava, (3) Eastern Alpine, across Slovenia and passes as far west as Brenner, (4) Rhone Corridor, and (5) Gate of Carcassonne. For many centuries raw materials moved south and finished products moved north along these routes between the advanced Mediterraneans and the backward inhabitants of other parts of Europe. The end of the classical period and advent of Europe's Dark Ages came

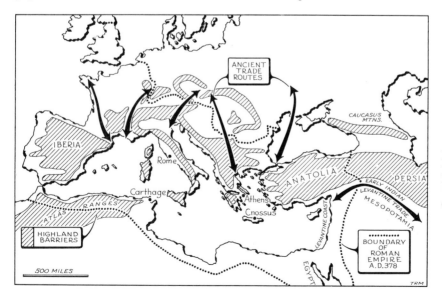

Mediterranean Realm: highland barriers and ancient trade routes

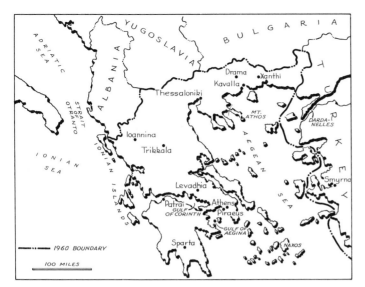

Greece: index map

when Romans were no longer able to enforce peace and control the trade routes, and had to give way to Germanic invaders. Nevertheless, basic elements of classical culture were preserved by peoples in the East, by Arabians, Levantines, and at Constantinople, and by monks and isolated groups in the Mediterranean region itself. A considerable amount of this culture was retained by northwestern Europeans who had come in contact with the Romans, and some of it was absorbed by the Germanic invaders.

GREECE

Hellenic-speaking people, who were probably Nordics, came south along the Morava-Vardar route in considerable numbers during the thirteenth to tenth centuries B.C. to settle in the Grecian peninsula, the Aegean Islands, and along the west coast of Anatolia. The fair-skinned invaders found the lands inhabited by dark Mediterraneans who were culturally their superiors because of their contacts with Minoan culture and with that of Mesopotamia, the Levant, and Egypt. The Hellenes and Mediterraneans blended, and developed the most brilliant scholarship and culture of the eastern Mediterranean by the fifth century B.C. Political development took the form of independent city-states, a form well suited to the ruggedly individualistic people and their land, with its many little valleys and islands. But it also led to disastrous internal competition and quarrel-

ing which so weakened Greek power that the Roman Empire was able to take over the country in 146 B.C. Toward the start of the Dark Ages, when the Roman Empire was split, Greece became part of the Byzantine Empire, so its Christianity developed along Eastern lines.

CULTURAL LANDSCAPES

The Grecian Peninsula, between the Ionian and Aegean seas, is the easternmost of the three great projections of European lands into the southern sea. Most of the land of Greece is rough and rugged, divided into isolated lowlands and valleys, and islands. Of its 51,246 square miles, which is less than the area of Alabama, islands account for almost 9,000 square miles, and more than half of the total is wasteland.

The highlands of Albania extend southward as the Pindus Mountains (Pindhos Oros). Here some Greeks live over 50 miles from salt water; no others are so far inland. This high, almost barren area is sparsely populated, as are the highlands of Epirus (Ipiros) and Thessaly (Thessalia), where population density is under 50 per square mile, as compared with over 150 for Greece as a whole. Life in the highlands is pastoral, and people share their little stone huts with their flocks. Culturally and physically, the people are rather Slavicized and Alpine, but like practically all other Greeks, are strongly Orthodox in religion.

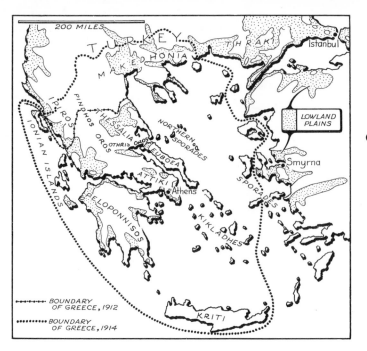

Greece: physical divisions

To the south is the Peloponnesos, a rough, partially drowned continuation of the highlands of Epirus that just barely escapes being an island. Its little land tie at Corinth (Korinthos) was severed by the construction of the Corinthian Canal. The people are Mediterranean in stock and culture, turning mainly to seafaring, trade, and market gardening. The limited amount of land which is available to agriculture is intensively cultivated. To the west are the Ionian Islands, stretching north toward southern Italy.

Thessaly, east of the Pindus Mountains, has important lowlands, but they are broken by ridges extending southeastward across Attica (Attiki) to the Cyclades (Kikladhes), and along the large island of Euboea (Evvoia) and other islands that mark the trend of a range of hills now mostly submerged. There are so many islands in the Aegean that no water lies over 40 miles from some coast. The fairly extensive Plains of Thessaly, north of the Othrys Mountains, are not as typically Mediterranean in culture as are the islands and lowlands to the south. The inhabitants are unable to make full use of the lowlands because cool winter temperatures prevent the growing of some Mediterranean crops, though wheat, olives, cotton, grapes, and currants are produced.

Macedonia (Makedhonia), a narrow strip between the Aegean and the southern boundaries of Yugoslavia and Bulgaria, is mainly a producer of wheat, tobacco, rice, and cattle. It remained under Turkish control until 1913, whereas land to the west was freed in 1832. It belongs culturally to the Shatter Belt, Bulgar and Serbian being its dominant languages with Greek having a minority status. The peoples are mainly Alpine and are generally Slavicized. Farther east, in western Thrace (Thraki), Bulgars and Turks are numerous, the Greek population being concentrated along the coast. Many of these Greeks were moved in from Izmir (Smyrna) which as late as 1900 had a larger Greek population than Athens. Large numbers of Greeks have historically inhabited the Dodecanese (Dhodhekanisos), islands that were taken by Italy in 1912 and returned to Greece in 1946. The people live by agriculture and sponge fishing, but the importance of this island group is its strategic control of the southeastern outlet of the Aegean between Anatolia and Crete, the heavily populated, fourth largest island in the Mediterranean.

Only about one fifth of Greece is normally under cultivation, and one sixth is in pasture, but little is flat enough to be plowed. The common crops are cereals, citrus fruits, olives, grapes and currants, and nuts. In Macedonia and Thrace the chief cash crops are cotton and tobacco. Farms are tiny, averaging less than 9 acres of cultivable land, and production levels are very low. Individual holdings are often broken into small scattered plots within walking distance of the village or house. The typical double-story stone farmhouses lie rather closely together along valleys or clustered around village squares. Small holdings and poor yields mean that of the 8 million total population, the 60 per cent dependent on agriculture live mainly on a subsistence basis.

Greece has little fuel other than lignite, and only very small deposits of iron, lead, zinc, and other metals, so industry is mainly concerned with agricultural processing. Wine, raisins, currants, olive oil, and tobacco are the main exports. This dependence on the production and export of these luxury commodities makes Greek economy very sensitive to conditions of world prosperity. Even in good times, imports exceed the value of exports by a wide margin. In times of war or depression, Greeks ordinarily starve or suffer extreme hardship because they have too little land in food production. To supplement income, Greeks, like Norwegians, engage in commerce and go to sea. The country gains some income from tourists who come in considerable numbers to view the many relics of the classical culture. Another important income is the money sent back to Greece by the many emigrants who have gone to other countries.

There is considerable question whether or not Greece is overpopulated, as many believe. For at least 25 centuries, Greeks have been leaving their country, as traders, fishermen, and colonists. It may be that the continued exodus of Greeks is simply an ancient culture trait, rather than a sign of population pressure brought on by an unbalanced economy and the threat of famine, as is often suggested. Opponents of the over-population theory also point out that much of the land that could be used remains idle, and that the population density is much less than that of Italy and a number of other places.

Greece is a land of villages and small towns. There are only three cities of any importance, Athens (Athinai), its port of Piraeus (Peiraieus),

and Salonika (Thessaloniki). Athens has essentially combined with its port, and together they are the most important knot of Greek population, totaling over 1.5 million. This modern city, watched over by the ancient Acropolis and other classical monuments, is mainly engaged in commerce, with some minor industries, such as textiles and leather goods. A little manufacturing is carried on in Thessaloniki but its main importance is as the outlet of the Vardar Valley. Manufacturing possibilities in these cities and the smaller towns, such as the cotton-spinning centers of Levadhia (Levadeia) and Trikkala, may be increased by recent hydroelectric power developments.

ITALY

Before the days of the Romans, Italy was occupied by small groups of typically Mediterranean peoples who were settled in villages located mainly on hill tops. The tradition of hill towns has lasted to the present. At a very early date these villagers, particularly in the south, had trade contacts with eastern Mediterraneans. From the twelfth to about the eighth century B.C. some colonization by Minoans and Levantines took place, and later the Greeks spread widely over the southern part of the peninsula, the lands of the Sicils and Illyrians. Rome was founded soon after the Greeks arrived, and its power grew rapidly. The Roman genius for military and governmental organization, exhibited in their ability to enforce Pax Romana, spread Mediterranean civilization throughout the lands between the east-west mountain barrier and the desert, and to the peoples as far north as the Danube and west beyond the Rhine. The decline of Roman power was followed by Germanic invasions and a dilution of Mediterranean racial stock, particularly by Nordic elements in the Po Valley, and by Alpine elements in the lands north of the Apennines. In general, the whole population became considerably mixed.

Although Italy is only 116.9 thousand square miles, slightly smaller than New Mexico, topographic barriers effectively partition it into segments which have been politically divided and reorganized many times. The present ar-

Italy: index map

rangement dates only from the eighteen-sixties when the various parts were gathered together into a nation. Political unity, however, has done little to reduce cultural contrasts among peoples in separated regions.

Mountains not only separate the parts of Italy, but tend to separate the whole of Italy from the rest of Europe. Around its northern border swings a series of ranges from the Maritime Alps along the Ligurian coast, northward through the Alps along the Swiss border, and eastward through the Rhaetian Alps, Dolomites, and Carnic and Julian Alps along the Austrian and Yugoslavian border. There are few ways of crossing this barrier and none is easy, although highways and railroads which make use of the high passes form effective links with the rest of

Europe. The Apennines, trending southeast from Liguria, form the southern boundary of the fertile Po Valley, wedged between them and the Alps to the west and north. From northern Marche the Apennines curve southward along the "leg" which averages about 100 miles in width. Well over half the peninsula is hilly or mountainous, and the mountains reach considerable heights. Peaks rise over 7,000 feet in the north, 9,500 feet in the central part, and over 6,000 feet in the south. Along both sides of this rugged range are narrow, segmented lowlands fringing the Tyrrhenian and Adriatic coasts.

Less than 10 per cent of Italy is actual wasteland, but a great deal of barren land with poor soils is present. About 75 per cent of the land is

**Italy:
physical and
cultural regions**

used for agriculture and grazing. Less than 16 per cent is in forest, mainly in the Alps. Use of the land is varied because of local differences in soils and available moisture. Only the Po Valley and the Alps receive summer rains, but the rest of Italy has a typical Mediterranean climate of hot, dry summers and cool, moderately rainy winters. Nearness to Africa, just a short step from Sicily to Cape Bon, is all too apparent when the *sirocco*, a hot south wind, blasts Saharan dust and heat over the southern part of the peninsula.

CULTURAL LANDSCAPES

Alpine Italy is an area of mixed cultures and languages, scenic grandeur, pastures, and power. Peoples speaking both common and uncommon Germanic and Romanic languages have spread over the borders into the Italian Tirol, bringing along their various culture traits and fitting them into the pastoral, agricultural or tourist activities. Large numbers of vacationers are attracted to the beautiful lakes, glaciers, waterfalls, and rugged peaks of this area, providing a substantial source of income for the inhabitants. Villas and resorts line the shores of the long lakes impounded by morainal dams. Sharing these valleys are vineyards which also cover the lower slopes of the mountains. Above a belt of forest is the pastoral zone. From the heights come the alpine streams, furnishing a large amount of Italy's hydroelectric power. The area also has some small but useful deposits of iron, copper, and lead. Idria, near the Slovenian border, furnishes Italy with a large surplus of mercury, the only mineral, other than sulphur from Sicily, that is really abundant. Lignite is the main mineral fuel of Italy, but some coal exists in the western Alps, Tuscany, Umbria, and Sardinia, and some petroleum and natural gas are produced in the Po Valley.

The Po Valley contains about 20 per cent of area and 40 per cent of Italy's 48.8 million population. The people are mainly Alpine, but Nordics and Mediterraneans are well represented. The area has long been politically important, and during Holy Roman Empire days its great city-states, such as Venezie (Venice), Padova (Padua), Verona, and Milano (Milan) became cultural and commercial leaders of all Europe. Here arose the unification movement that led to modern Italy. Here, also, is Italy's granary where large quantities of wheat, maize, and rice are grown. Hemp, sugar beets, fruit, and vegetable crops cover the lowlands. On the rocky, sandy areas at the foot of Alpine slopes, dairying is the main activity, producing, among other things, the famous Gorgonzola and Parmesan cheeses. On the wide, fertile valley floor, two distinct cultural landscapes are apparent. Downstream from Mantova (Mantua) there is a surplus of soil moisture, so it is necessary to ditch and drain lowland flats, thus dividing the land into little rectangles, often rimmed by trees used for windbreaks. Upstream from Mantova soil moisture deficiency makes irrigation necessary, so fields are outlined by ditches that wind with the contours of the land. Villages and towns cluster at high points.

Most of Italy's industrial development centers in the upper Po Valley, making use of abundant and cheap labor and electricity. Cotton, silk, and synthetic fiber textiles, automobiles, heavy and light metal goods, and iron and steel are the main industrial products. Milano, with about 1.4 million population, is the commercial and industrial leader not only of the Po Valley, but of all Italy. It is a silk center, as well as a producer of machinery, railroad equipment, electrical goods, expensive metal goods, and products of heavy industry, such as locomotives.

Italian-Swiss borderland
[*Swiss National Tourist Office*]

In the western end of the Valley is Torino, very much like Milano, but only slightly over half its size. These industrial centers are served by the busy port of Genova which does not lie in the valley itself, but handles most of the traffic for the western end of the valley, as well as being the main port for Switzerland and a supplementary port for southern Germany and western Austria. It ranks second only to Marseille in the Mediterranean. In addition to its activities connected with the steady flow of raw and finished goods through its modernized harbor, Genova has become one of Italy's largest steel-producing centers. Most of the local heavy industry products are used in its extensive shipyards and in machinery industries. In its earlier days, Genova indirectly mothered the Commercial Revolution. Genoese captains either discovered or trained others to discover practically all the lands and routes found during the Voyages of Discovery. It now shares the benefits of a Commercial Age to a far greater extent than Venezia, its old rival port at the head of the Adriatic. Once a thriving commercial capital, Venezia now relies heavily for income on the tourists who come for gondola rides along its canals. The city is built on, and surrounded by, marshes, and piles support its buildings, although there are a few streets and many walkways between its densely crowded houses and small factories. Some industry is being developed, and shipbuilding is to some extent reviving the port activities.

Tuscany, ancient Etruria, is more Mediterranean racially and culturally than the Po Valley. Much of the land is hilly or mountainous, and these sunny slopes are used to produce the grapes for making Chianti and other well known Italian export wines. Population densities are generally high, especially in the Arno Valley where they exceed 500 per square mile. This Valley is not only a rich food-producing area, but it is an important route to Bologna and the Po Valley, and to points in southern and central Italy. Toward the upper end of the Valley is Firenze (Florence), a leading cultural center and tourist attraction, which also produces some iron and steel goods, textiles, and macaroni. South of the Valley, near Siena in Central Tuscany, is Italy's best source of lignite. Pisa is an important cultural and tourist center on the Lower Arno, famous for its leaning tower which Galileo used to demonstrate a principle of gravity. Nearby, and south of the river mouth

is the port of Livorno (Leghorn), serving Tuscany and also producing glass, copperwares, and olive oil. The island of Elba, just off the coast of central Tuscany, is a source of iron and lignite for Tuscan industry.

Latium is a relatively poor territory with many large areas of infertile soil, and wide coastal marshes still malarial and only partly reclaimed. Rural population is sparse by Italian standards—only 50 per square mile. Much of the land is given to grazing, except in the Alban Hills, southeast of Rome, which are extremely productive of olives, figs, grapes, and fruits. In the general Latium landscape, the concentration of over 1.8 million people in Rome (Roma) is very striking, especially since the city is only very moderately industrialized. Rome's size is attributable to its ecclesiastical, political, and historical importance. Within Rome is the 109-acre Vatican City, an independent state ruled by the Pope. The City includes St. Peter's, the Vatican Palace and Museum, other buildings, and gardens.

Campania is generally a grazing area except in the Naples district where the rich volcanic

Urban square, Tuscany

[*Instituto Italiano di Cultura*]

Corsican town, Calis
[*French Embassy, Press and Information Division*]

soils produce an abundance of vegetables, grapes, and fruits as well as some rice and flax. Steaming Vesuvius, towering above the Bay of Naples, can be thanked for the soils, although in A.D. 79 it overdid its contribution by blowing large quantities of material and part of its summit into the air to settle on Pompeii and other villages, completely burying them. Napoli (Naples), with well over 1 million population, is the only good port on the west coast of southern Italy. Its industries are not very extensive, but include iron and steel, weaving, metal working, and shipbuilding.

The **Apennines** are most densely populated and most productive in the north, where terraced hillsides are planted with olives, grapes, and even citrus fruits. Some petroleum occurs on the northern slopes of Emelia. Another occurrence on the Apennine slopes is San Marino, the littlest republic, with a total of 38 square miles and some 150,000 population. Aside from its size, its claim to fame rests on a founding date in the fourth century, making it the oldest state in Europe. The central Apennines are fairly rugged and barren but their valleys produce cereals, flax, hemp, olives, and grapes, and their streams are sources of hydroelectric power. Southward, the land becomes more barren, more is used for pasturage, and agriculture is largely devoted to olive production.

The **Adriatic Coast** is served by rather good ports at Ancona, a center for wine and olive oil from Marche; Bari, a rapidly growing center of olive oil export and petroleum refining; Brindisi; and Taranto on the Gulf of Taranto. The hot, dry plain of Apulia produces a wheat that is especially good for macaroni and other paste products, as well as olives and grapes. Calabria, to the west, is grazing territory, partly forested, and with citrus and olive groves crowded into the limited lowlands.

Sicily is much older culturally than the rest of Italy, its prominence dating from the fifth century B.C. when, with Carthage, it controlled trade between the east and west Mediterranean. In ancient times, Sicily grew more wheat than Italy, its rich volcanic soils more than compensating for its rough terrain. Now Sicily presents the complete flavor of Mediterranean agriculture, with wheat, olives, citrus fruits, and grapes as the principal products. A reclamation program is increasing the amount and value of farm land, and is providing new roads and irrigation systems, as a means of furthering the productiveness of this island. Most of the surplus agricultural products are exported through Palermo, a city of over a half million, located on the north coast. On the east coast, Catania serves as a secondary shipping port for agricultural products, along with Messina, the commercial guardian of the two-mile-wide Strait of Messina. Sicily's industry is minor, but the island is an important source of sulphur and has some oil and natural gas. Sicily also has earthquakes and volcanic eruptions. Mt. Etna, 10,741 feet, is the main volcano and highest point in Sicily, and it last erupted in 1958. North of Sicily is the Lipari group of islands famous for Vulcano, which has given its name to all volcanoes, and Stromboli, one of the most destructive vents on earth. South of Sicily is the intensively cultivated, British island of Malta.

Sardinia, 9,283 square miles, is only slightly smaller than Sicily (9,927 square miles), but its total population of 1.3 million is less than one third that of Sicily. It is mountainous, endowed with deposits of lead, zinc, iron, and coal, and a producer of citrus fruits, olives and grapes. Corsica, a French island just to the north, is similar.

Population pressure has been a long-standing problem for Italy, which has a population increase of about 400,000 annually. To some extent growing industrialization can absorb these extra Italians. But many of the ingredients for large-scale industrialization are missing, so Italy is concentrating on mechanical products and textiles, and is successfully invading world markets with automobiles, fabrics and fashions, business machines, and sewing machines, cameras, chemicals, and cargo ships. Membership in the European Coal and Steel Community may bring these ingredients within financial reach of Italy. In addition to industry, the land is looked to as a means of supporting the population. Land reform laws enacted in 1950 are designed to increase productivity by the use of more scientific practices, reapportionment of the land (no holding can exceed 750 acres), and

reclamation of waste land. At present, however, neither industry nor land reform has solved the population problem, so hundreds of thousands of Italians each year leave the country, though most of them stay in Europe.

IBERIA

The Iberian Peninsula, 230,970 square miles, is not quite as big as Texas, but is well over five times as populous. Nearly 9 million people live in Portugal's 35,466 square miles, and about 29.7 million live on the 195,504 square miles of Spain. Nor is the population particularly homogeneous, for not only are the Portuguese distinct, but within Spain there are several different dialects spoken, and people tend to think of themselves as Castilians or Andalusians rather than as Spaniards. Topographic barriers have helped both to compart Spain and to separate it from the rest of Europe. The steep and rugged Pyrenees are crossed by only two railroads, and these, plus the railroads that skirt either end of the mountains, are the only rail ties with France. To the west, the Cantabrians tend to isolate coastal Asturias from the high central plateau, the Meseta, that covers two thirds of Iberia. The tableland is also cut up by deep valleys, with most drainage into the Atlantic, and by several ranges rising above the level of the plateau. A group of these ranges, Sierra de Gata, Sierra de Gredos, and Sierra de Guadarrama, between the drainage basins of the Duero (Douro) and the Tajo (Tagus, Tejo), form the most continuous and culturally most significant highland divide of the Meseta. Leon and Old Castile lie to the north, Extremadura and New Castile to the south. The valleys of the major rivers all house populations that tend to be culturally different from each other, and most of them have been political nuclei at one time or another. The great Andalusian valley of the Guadalquivir extends between the Sierra Morena and the Sierra Nevada. The Ebro, snug between the Pyrenees and the mountains that rise along the northeast edge of the tableland, ends its course in Catalonia, and is the only major Iberian river draining into the Mediterranean.

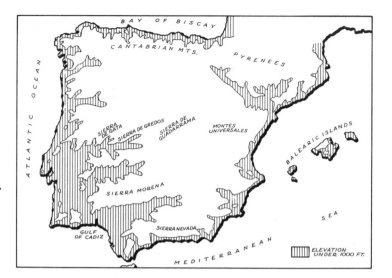

Iberian Peninsula: relief

Only the southern and eastern coasts have true Mediterranean climate, with cool winters, hot summers, and winter rainfall. Much of the interior verges on steppe climate. The northern and western coasts have a maritime climate like that of northwestern Europe, with abundant precipitation at all seasons, average January temperatures are somewhat below 50° F. and July below 70°. In Madrid, July is above 75° and in Andalusia, between 75° and 80°. Freezing temperatures are not uncommon in central Iberia but are rare along coasts.

Both Spain and Portugal are agricultural countries. About 35 per cent of Iberia is normally under cultivation, 25 per cent in pasture, 20 per cent in forest, and 20 per cent in waste. Although important deposits of iron, coal, copper, mercury, lead, zinc, silver, and other metals are being mined, production levels are low, and most of the ores are exported in crude state. Industry is not well developed, primarily because of a lack of power; both coal production and hydroelectric power are insufficient.

CULTURAL BACKGROUND

Settlement of Iberia dates back to the closing days of the Ice Age when primitive hunters sketched their drawings on cave walls and in other ways left evidence of their homes and culture, a culture very similar to that of their contemporaries in northern Africa. By the time prehistory had become history, and the Greeks were moving south of the Vardar into the Aegean, Iberia was inhabited by a Mediterranean people called the Iberians. They were essentially on their own until the fifteenth century B.C. when Levantine Phoenicians, ever on the search for business, arrived to establish a colony at Cartagena. These were joined several centuries later by Greeks and both left their imprints on the southern and southeastern coasts of the peninsula. Until Rome stepped in, in 201 B.C., Carthage used southern Spain as a source of tin, gold, copper, silver, lead, mica, and cinnabar (an ore of mercury).

The collapse of Rome provided the opportunity for Nordics to move south, and by A.D. 400, some had crossed the Pyrenees. Goths established an important kingdom in northwestern Spain, where today remnants of Nordic culture traits and racial heritage are still visible. Meanwhile, Vandals moved farther south, crossing into Tunisia. They were just getting really settled when the Moors arrived, dedicated to the spread of the religion of Islam. By 711 these followers of Mohammed had crossed Gibraltar, and soon spread across most of Iberia and into southern France. The northwest escaped the Moorish invasion mainly because these forested, fairly rainy lands, so attractive to Nordics, were repellent to Moors who, like Mongols, were used to open spaces and needed pastures for their animals. The Nordics formed the nucleus of the movement for expulsion of the Moors, a drive that slowly pushed the invaders south, and finally out of their last stronghold in Granada in 1492.

The 781 years of Moorish occupation left a significant mark of the culture, not so much along racial lines because both Spaniards and Moors are mainly of Mediterranean stock, but along many other lines. Spanish architecture is deeply indebted to these Africans for its most attractive elements. Spanish agriculture gained by the introduction of irrigation and other advanced practices. The religious purpose of the invasion eventually failed. All of Iberia is strongly Roman Catholic today.

Both Spain and Portugal took early leadership in explorations and land acquisitions during the Voyages of Discovery, and were the originators of the Commercial Revolution. Soon after Columbus returned, the Pope proclaimed that Portugal was to have all new lands in the Eastern Hemisphere and Spain was to have the Western Hemisphere. Portugal's enjoyment of this situation ended in 1580 when it came under Spanish rule, and all foreign trade was transferred to Spain. This enabled Spain to become the wealthiest and most powerful nation in Europe, financed by Latin American silver and other products. Soon this wealth was dissipated

TABLE 2

Remnants of Iberian Empires

Portugal	Area (thousands sq. mi.)	Population (millions)
Angola	481.4	4.4
Mozambique	297.7	6.2
Guinea	13.9	.600
Timor	7.3	.500
Cape Verde Is.	1.6	.166
In India (Goa, Damoa, Diu)	1.5	.649
São Tome and Principe Is.	.4	.061
Macao	.006	.200
	803.806	12.776
Spain		
Spanish Sahara (Southern Morocco Rio de Oro, Sekia el Hamra)	105.4	.045
Guinea & Fernando Po	10.8	.212
Ifni	.7	.038
	116.9	.295

in a series of wars, but the real blow to the crumbling empire occurred during the nineteenth century when almost all Latin American countries became independent. Portugal has had more success in holding its empire.

The Industrial Revolution was hardly felt in Iberia except in mining districts, such as Asturias, and more recently in Catalonia when

Iberian Peninsula: political divisions

Market, Portugal
[*Photo "Sni-Yan"*]

(*opposite*) **Mediterranean garden, Malaga**
[*Spanish National Tourist Office*]

Northern Portugal, landscape
[*Photo "Sni-Yan"*]

manufacturing activities began. An agrarian revolution started in 1931 but died in the extremely destructive Civil War of 1936–1939. This retarded development in a nation already backward by western European standards.

CULTURAL LANDSCAPES

The influence of the Moors in changing cultures and landscapes was greatest in the areas they occupied the longest. Their influence dwindles toward the north and essentially ends at the drainage basin of the Tagus. Galicia and Asturias are non-Moorish, while Andalusia is the epitome of Moorish Spain with its distinctive architecture, its Mediterranean farming,

terraces and irrigation, where horticulture prevails over field agriculture, and where life is adjusted to a slow, easy tempo.

Galicia and Asturias are non-Mediterranean provinces, without trace of Moorish influence. This is a Gothic area. Land is divided into small farms and people are very democratic. Their language, Gallegan, is foreign to the rest of Spain. The lower slopes of the pine-clad Cantabrians are used to produce wine of rather poor quality, and still lower are fields of flax, sugar beets, potatoes, and maize. Apple trees and cattle dot the landscape. One third of the nation's cattle graze in these fields. Along the coast, fishing and tourism are important. Asturias has considerable industry based on the large coal deposits near Oviedo and abundant iron, manganese, and hydroelectric power. Important steel mills and metal industries are located here, and at Santander and Bilbao to the east.

The **northern Meseta,** including Old Castile, Leon, and the Douro watershed, is also an area of Gothic heritage. Descendants of the old Gothic aristocracy gave birth to New Spain by forming the organizations that expelled the Moors. Here the land is mainly in large estates,

and wheat is the main crop, with oats and rye in higher areas. Villages are scattered and cities are few. Valladolid, the leading city, is a center for agricultural industries, such as flour milling, and it is on rail connections to all parts of Spain and Portugal.

The **southern Meseta,** in contrast, shows a fairly strong Moorish influence. It includes New Castile and Extremadura, which spread across the Meseta margins and take in some of the lower lands in the Tagus and Guadiana drainage basins. This territory is drier and less densely populated than the northern plateau, and has profited most by the Moorish introduction of Merino sheep, a fine wool-producing breed from the Atlas Mountains of northern Africa. Amid the extensive grazing lands, villages and towns indicate the presence of water, a semioasis condition. Olives thrive on the warmer dry slopes, but cold winters and high winds prevent raising many typical Mediterranean crops except in valleys and lowlands, particularly in Extremadura, where there are also groves of cork-oak trees. In this southern part of the region is one of the world's leading sources of mercury at Almaden, and deposits of coal and lead in the Sierra Morena. Jewelry and turbulent history are the claims to fame of Toledo, to the north, the picturesque Moorish city perched on the bluffs of the Tagus. Madrid, just north of Toledo, is a political and commercial center of 1.9 million population. This 300-year-old capital has the advantage of central location, not only in the country, but more significantly between New and Old Castile. The railroad network made Madrid its hub, so direct lines radiate toward all important centers in the centrifugal valley systems of the Peninsula. It has only such industries as a city its size demands, and has a fairly miserable climate of hot summers and cold winters.

Portugal was largely in Moorish Iberia. Its people are somewhat mixed racially, and, like their country, are backward; over 75 per cent are considered illiterate. Included as political provinces of the country are the Azores, 922 square miles, 0.319 million population, and Madeira Islands, 314 square miles, 0.280 population. Culturally, they are fairly typical Mediterranean islands. About half of Portugal is pasture or waste, one third is cultivated, and the rest is forested. In the hotter, drier southern part, wheat, citrus, cork, olives, and pigs are the main concerns; maize, vineyards, and cattle in the rainier, cooler north; and rye, sheep, and goats in the northeastern highlands. Alluvial lowlands are planted with rice. Wine making and cork manufacturing rank first and second among industries, and their products are important exports, as are canned sardines, tuna, and anchovies. Thus, agriculture and fishing form the basis of Portugal's industry, while mining and related manufacturing are of considerably less importance despite the abundance of a variety of metal and mineral resources, such as tungsten, tin, copper, sulphur, pyrite, lead, and uranium. General industrialization is handicapped by insufficient coal and hydroelectric power. Manufacturing largely centers around Lisbon (Lisboa) and Porto (Oporto). Lisbon, with less than a million population, is the capital, leading port, educational center, and main industrial city. It produces woolens, iron-wares, fertilizers, ships, and a host of minor items, imports coal, oil, iron and steel, and machinery, and exports wine, corks, copper,

resin, and rubber and cacao, products of the tropical colonies. Porto, considerably smaller, is the leading city and port of the north, and is a center for wine-making, textiles, and fish processing. Many buildings in both cities are Moorish in design.

Andalusia, Seville, and Granada remained longest under Moorish rule, and its influence is widely seen in the cities and in farming practices. The lowlands, especially the Guadalquivir Valley, the largest lowland in Spain, contain extensive irrigated tracts which produce sugar cane and sugar beets, and important quantities of tobacco, citrus fruits, olives, wheat, cotton, and grapes. Groves of cork oak are widespread, as are vineyards. The Jerez district, near Cadiz, is famous for its brandy. Fishing is important along the entire coast. The coastal cities have long served as outlets for the productive hinterland. Malaga, in the east, exports silver and lead, and is quick to point to its advantage of being able to trade with other Mediterranean cities without the necessity of going outside of the Strait of Gibraltar. Outside the Pillars of Hercules—the Capes of Gibraltar (Spain) and Sierra Bullones (Ceuta)— are the extremely old ports of Cadiz and Huelva. Both export the products of mines, Huelva being the main outlet for the Rio Tinto copper mines. Cadiz has been displaced, mainly by Seville, as the commercial outlet of the Guadalquivir Valley, but actively produces and exports salt, and carries on most of the banana trade with the Canary Islands. Far busier is the excellent harbor of British Gibraltar, 25,000 population in an area of 2 square miles. The elaborately tunneled fortress is a conspicuous landmark. Seville, approaching one half million population, is the leading city of Andalusia and the main port of southern Spain. The 70-mile Alphonse XIII Canal brings ocean-going steamers to the city, which exports silver, lead, and iron from mines in Sierra Morena and Sierra Nevada. Seville has become industrialized, with cork factories, iron foundries, and food-processing plants, but is still largely Moorish in appearance.

Murcia was the earliest territory to come into foreign hands and in many ways is the most affected by outsiders. Levantine Cartagena is still active as a port, exporting fruits and some iron, and refines much-needed oil. Inland Murcia, built by the Moors, is an active commercial center and railroad junction. The Segura furnishes water for irrigation, and from the intensive agriculture come typical Mediterranean products, wheat, olives, figs, citrus fruit, raisins, and grapes.

Valencia shows a mixture of mild Moorish influences and strong Catalonian influences, especially in its language. Introduced irrigation put the fertile lowland to work producing cereal crops, vegetables, and fruit. Ever-present grapes and olives come from the drier slopes above the irrigated lands. The exportable surplus of these products goes through the city of Valencia, whose more than half million population makes it Spain's third largest city. Available hydroelectric power allows a small development of steel and other industries.

Catalonia is industrialized, modern Spain though its culture, showing strong Frankish influences, is different from the rest of Spain and more closely akin, especially in language, to southern coastal France. The cleavage between Catalan and Spaniard is old and deep, and occasionally comes to the fore in demands for separation on the grounds that the rest of Spain is an economic and cultural drag on this densely populated, industrialized region. Actually, inner Catalonia, like Aragon, farther up the Ebro Valley, is a fairly backward agricultural region, but separatists ignore this and point to the highly industrialized Barcelona area as typical of Catalonian progress. Barcelona, with almost 2 million people, has a growing variety of industries, including textiles, metals, chemicals, paper, electrical goods, food and fruit processing, and, of course, wine making.

Basque territory is an enclave of French and Spanish Basques at the western end of the Pyrenees. This small group of people, isolated by slopes and forests, is racially Mediterranean, but speaks a language unrelated to any other, although it seems to be primitive in form and may be a relic of a tongue spoken before Alpines appeared in Europe.

The **Balearic Islands,** 1,935 square miles, with a population nearing one half million, are

Madrid
[*Spanish National Tourist Office*]

a Catalan-speaking Mediterranean outpost of Spain. Another outpost, **Ceuta,** on the African coast, is the equivalent of Gibraltar. The **Canary Islands,** 2,807 square miles and three fourths million population, lie off the coast of Spanish Sahara. The Balearic Islands, Ceuta, and the Canaries are all considered parts of Spain rather than colonies; their economic importance is limited to tourism in the Balearics and bananas in the Canaries.

Andorra, 191 square miles, lies on the Spanish side of the Pyrenees summits. Its Catalan-speaking population numbers less than 7,000, but staunchly maintains an independence that was achieved in 1278. Most of the people are Roman Catholics. Like San Marino, Liechtenstein, Luxembourg, and Monaco, Andorra is a curious relic of Middle Ages territorial mincing. Stamp collectors and tourists contribute in a major way to the support of these small countries.

WESTERN TRANSITION ZONE

Basel
[*Swiss National Tourist Office*]

11.   France, Switzerland

France is the largest country in Europe west of the Soviet Union, and is fourth in population.

Areas and Populations of Leading European Nations (1960)

	Area (thousands sq. mi.)
Soviet Union	8,538.5
France	212.7
Spain	195.5
Sweden	173.4
Germany	143.2
Italy	116.9

	Population (millions)
Soviet Union	208.8
Germany	72.2
United Kingdom	51.7
Italy	48.8
France	44.8
Spain	29.7

France is compact, being nearly a square with 600-mile sides, covering an area about 80 per cent that of Texas. The southernmost point in the eastern Pyrenees lies on about the same parallel as Detroit, Michigan, and its northernmost point on the North Sea is about equivalent to the southern tip of Hudson Bay. But the climate of France is in no way similar to that of these areas in North America. France has relatively mild climates. Brittany is cool, but never cold, and the southern coast is warm. Only the uplands and inland points enjoy a mild form of continental climate.

The landscapes of France are typically green, for most of the country receives more than 35 inches of rain a year, rather uniformly divided among the months. Only along the Mediterranean is there a summer drought, turning the landscapes yellowish-brown. In contrast, some of the higher mountains in southern and southeastern France have annual precipitation in excess of 60 inches, a fair share falling as snow. This is to be expected, for these mountains attain the highest elevations in western Europe. They reach well above the timber line, as does much of the plateau which covers about 25 per cent of France. More than half the country is lowland, mainly in the west where the European Plain extends to the Pyrenees.

The soils are as diversified as the topography. Barren rock and almost soil-free rock debris and glacial deposits are characteristic of the Alps and Pyrenees, and at lower elevations soil types range from gray, podsolic soils, typical of the mixed forest of the Soviet Union, to the deep brown soils of Mediterranean valleys which alternate with bright red soils where the bedrock is limestone. From highland peats, similar to those of the higher parts of Great Britain, there is a gradation leading to humus-deficient sands and gravels, similar to those in deserts.

NATURAL REGIONS OF FRANCE

Paris Basin resembles southeastern England, and Paris, like London, lies in the central part of a young-rock, rich-soil, agriculturally productive basin. Concentric escarpments surround Paris on all sides except the northwest. Their steep outward faces always handicapped invading enemies, whereas gentle slopes permitted defensive summits to be easily occupied from the Parisian side. The vales between the ridges provide rich strips of land for cereal crops, and, in fact, half of the wheat of France grows in and around Paris Basin. Toward the coast, where there is too much rainfall for the more valuable cereal, grows some 60 per cent of the French oats crop. To the northeast are the principal sugar beet fields, and near Paris and other cities market gardens produce a wide variety of vegetable crops. The drier uplands are used as sheep pastures, and the slopes are covered with vineyards. The chalks of the valleys of the Aisne and Marne produce a grape used in champagne, made by bottling the wine slightly before the fermentation process reaches conclusion. Within heavy bottles, stoutly corked, the final stages of fermentation yield carbon dioxide, so that the wine is naturally carbonated. Ordinary dry wine is produced in large quantity south of Paris along the middle Loire.

Textile production is widespread in the Paris Basin. Such towns as Lille, Amiens, St. Quentin, and Rouen are cotton centers, while Roubaix, Fourmies, and other towns along the Belgian

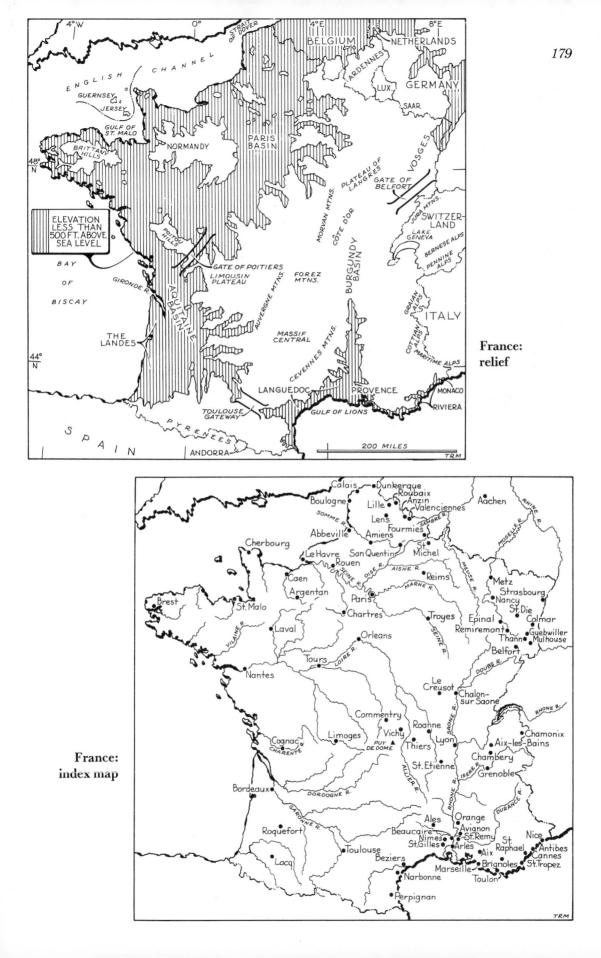

France:
relief

France:
index map

border, specialize in woolens, as do Reims and Orleans. Lille, Valenciennes, and other places in the extreme north of France are industrialized on the basis of coal deposits extending south from Belgium. But all towns are overshadowed by Paris, the gigantic conurbation of the basin.

Northeastern plateaus, extending from the Vosges to the Ardennes, are old-rock, poor-soil uplands with valleys of rich alluvium or terrace deposits that yield excellent crops. The sides of these valleys, such as the Moselle, produce wine grapes, and the fertile valley bottoms, as along the Rhine in Alsace, produce tobacco, sugar beets, wheat, fruits, and other crops. Vosges water is pure, and is so good for bleaching cotton that the largest centralized cotton industry in continental Europe is located in southern Alsace.

The extensive iron deposits in Lorraine account for 90 per cent of France's production. France ranks third among world producers of iron. A considerable iron and steel industry has developed in northern Lorraine, along the Moselle, at such centers as Metz and Nancy. Canals connect Nancy with Strasbourg, the main French port on the Rhine, and with the northern industrialized area around Lille, as well as Paris. Another important resource is the potash salt deposit north of Mulhouse, the basis for fertilizer and chemical industries.

Western plateau is an old-rock region extending west from Paris Basin through Normandy and Brittany. It is much like Cornwall, across the English Channel, in climate, soils, and resources. The country is barren, fairly rugged, and mainly used for cattle raising and dairying. Considerable cheese is produced, notably Camembert, and the abundant apples provide the famous ciders of Normandy. Fishing is important on all coasts. The main commercial ports are Brest, which is also a naval base, and Nantes, at the head of the Loire Estuary, which also builds ships.

Basin of Aquitaine lies in southwest France, west of the Central Plateau and north of the Pyrenees. The Gate of Poitiers, between the Poitou Hills and Limousin Plateau, leads to Paris Basin, while to the southeast, the Toulouse Gateway or Gate of Carcassonne leads to the Mediterranean. Most of the basin lies in the drainage of the Garonne, and is geologically similar to Paris Basin, with chalks and lime-

stones surrounding a plain flat area of younger rock. The lowlands produce abundant wheat, maize, plums, and walnuts, and vineyards cover the slopes. About one third of all the grapes grown in France come from the hinterland of Bordeaux. Medoc, Sauterne, Bordeaux and other wines originate in the eastern and southern parts of the basin. To the north, around Cognac, much of the wine is converted into brandy.

The coast south of the Gironde Estuary is straight, like that of Holland. It is very sandy, with broad beaches backed by dunes that are now planted with cork oak and pines, so that this area, called the Landes, is a producer of resin and turpentine. To the east is country useful for sheep. Roquefort, famous for its cheese, is south of Bordeaux in this barren territory.

Central Plateau (Massif Central) and marginal plateaus cover a large part of south-central France. The elevations of most of these uplands are from 2,000 to 3,000 feet, but several mountains and individual peaks rise above 6,000 feet. Much of the land is too high for other cereal crops, so it produces about half the rye grown in France. The plateaus are extensively used for grazing, and account for about 25 per cent of all sheep and 20 per cent of all cattle in France.

There is little mineral wealth, but about a quarter of the French supply of coal comes from the margins of the plateau. The best coal comes from St. Etienne, which is a steel and textile center. Farther north are many industrial towns such as Le Creusot, which make use of iron ores from the local Morvan region. To the west, clay deposits at Limoges are used for production of fine china.

Pyrenees slopes, separated from the central plateaus by the Toulouse Gateway, are wet toward the west and fairly dry and barren eastward. They descend from above the timber line through forest and into territory rather useless because of enormous deposits of coarse gravel and boulders. Grazing lands and vineyards cover the more useful parts of the slopes. The area is becoming an important source of fuels as the newly discovered huge natural gas deposits and oil fields near Lacq in the western foothills are being developed. The eastern sections are sources of bauxite which is smelted locally because of easily available hydroelectric power.

Rhone Corridor, the southern end of the Lotharingian route to the North Sea, was the main avenue along which Roman culture spread north. From its delta, the Rhone Valley leads north to Lyon; then the Corridor follows the Saone and Doubs valleys to the Gate of Belfort, an easy pass to the upper Rhine. Although the valley flats are narrow at places, in comparison with territory on either side, they provide the easiest route from the Mediterranean to northwestern and west-central Europe. Along the Rhone Corridor are many of the oldest, most historic towns in France, such as Arles, Beaucaire, Nimes, Avignon, Orange, and Lyon. Aside from Lyon, none are especially industrialized. A great variety of crops covers the small fields that crowd all flatland in the Corridor, and vineyards flank its sides. Northward the extent of flatland increases, so that Burgundy, in addition to producing famous wines, is a rich granary. The whole lower valley is subject to low temperatures brought by the *mistral,* a cold wind that blows each winter and spring.

Alpine slopes, east of the Rhone Corridor, are generally rugged and steep, and very attractive for Alpine sports and tourists. Although a pastoral atmosphere is created by sheep and goat grazing, grape raising, and wine and liqueur production, the area is becoming industrialized on the basis of abundant hydroelectric power from Alpine streams. Grenoble and other towns along the Isere are engaged in electrochemical and electrometallurgical industries, and aluminum smelters along the slopes south of Lake Geneva account for 50 per cent of France's aluminum smelting capacity. The bauxite mainly comes from Brignoles, to the south, and the Department of Herault, west of the Rhone delta.

Mediterranean coast includes Provence to the east and Languedoc to the west of the Rhone. Olive trees flourish on the poor soils, and the numerous vineyards produce about one third of French wines. The Riviera lies east of Marseille. It is an especially attractive coast with mild winters. Steep slopes lead from high alps to the deep blue sea. Close to the Italian border is the small country of Monaco, with an area of four square miles and a population of about 20,500. This independent principality is best known for Monte Carlo's gambling casinos which provide practically all the revenue for running the government and for maintaining one of the world's leading oceanographic research centers. Resort towns and villas dot the Riviera coast. Toulon is the main French naval base on the Mediterranean and a major port for export of Brignoles bauxite. Marseille, the leading port, will be discussed in connection with urbanization. Rhone delta ports were unable to compete with Marseille because they were handicapped by shifting, silting channels. The delta is rich in ancient artifacts, indicating continuous habitation since the sixth century B.C. West of the delta the coast is sandy, straight, and deficient in harbors and scenery.

NATURAL REGIONS OF SWITZERLAND

With an area of 15,944 square miles, Switzerland is slightly larger than Massachusetts, Connecticut, and Rhode Island combined. In this confederation of 22 cantons are more than 5 million people and seventy mountains of over 10,000 feet elevation. The highest, Monte Rosa, rises to 15,217 feet, 555 feet lower than France's Mont Blanc, and nearby are the Matterhorn and many other peaks, and icecaps and glaciers that make the Pennine Alps the main scenic attraction of all the Alpine ranges. Across the Rhone Valley to the north are the magnificent Bernese Alps. Toward the northeast, the Rhone and Rhine rise within a few miles of each other near St. Gotthard Pass. About three quarters of Switzerland drains into the Rhine. Other watersheds lead to the Rhone, Po, and Danube. There are more than 20 large lakes, and one of these, Lake Maggiore with an elevation of 650 feet, marks the lowest place in the country. It is extremely deep, its bottom lying 575 feet below sea level. The numerous large and small water bodies tend to regulate stream discharges, thus improving conditions for developing hydroelectric power.

There are three main natural regions:

Alps cover 61 per cent of the country. Fields

and vineyards extend upward to pastures and forest that ultimately give way to alpine meadows and barren heights. Deep valleys contain lines of concentrated population and serve as important routes, although railroads have to tunnel through the high mountains. In this high southern half of the country, summers are cool and winters cold, and the mountains are capped with permanent snow fields. Spring is hastened in valleys by *föhn* winds, local masses of air heated by increased pressures encountered during descent of slopes. There is considerable difference in temperature between south-facing slopes which receive more direct sunshine, and the cooler, shaded slopes facing north. Population distribution and the usefulness of land depend largely on these factors of local climate.

Central plateau, between Lake Geneva and Lake Constance (Boden See), covers 27 per cent of the country and contains 75 per cent of the population. Thus, most of the Swiss live below 2,500 feet. The Swiss Plateau is the main farming area, and although wheat, rye, and oats are planted extensively, cereal production is not sufficient to fill all needs, so wheat and potatoes are imported. Tobacco is a cash crop, and wine is a relatively important product. The leading agricultural industry, however, is dairying, and cheese, condensed milk, and chocolate

products are important exports. Cattle, pigs, and poultry are abundantly raised.

Although this is an area of tinkling bells on fat cows, it is also highly industrialized. About half the Swiss make their livings in industries, most of which are found on the central plateau. Here are numerous small plants producing engineering equipment, precision instruments, textile machinery, business machines, tools, electric equipment, and other items requiring highly skilled workmen. These products, together with silk, woolen, and cotton textiles widely manufactured throughout the eastern part of the plateau, are basic export items.

Jura Mountains lie along the northern border of Switzerland and cover 12 per cent of the country. Being mainly pastureland, the region is far less productive than the central plateau. Domestic industries long ago turned to specialization in watches and clocks, and now more than 400 watch factories dot the Jura region. La Chaux-de-Fonds on the French border is considered the world center of the industry. Other centers are Neuchatel and Geneva, which is also an important producer of electric goods. Basel, in the extreme north, is the center of the Swiss chemical, pharmaceutical, and dye industry, and as a Rhine port, is the home of the Swiss merchant marine, composed mainly of river barges.

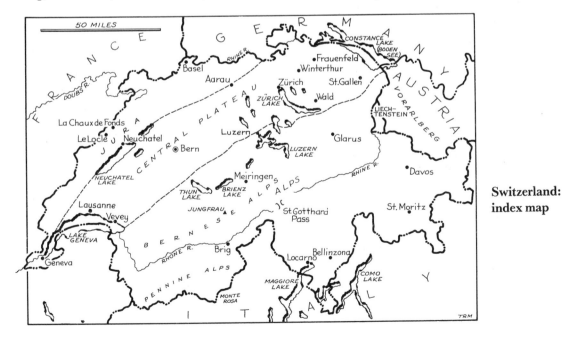

Switzerland: index map

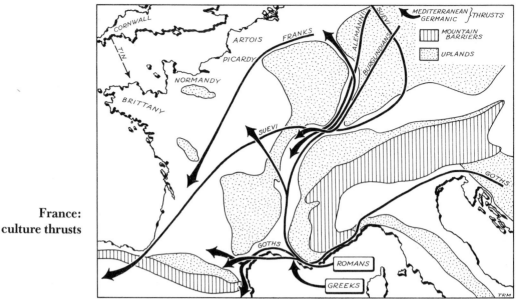

France:
culture thrusts

CULTURE TRANSITION ZONE

Unlike the Shatter Belt, between Eastern and Northwestern European cultures, which is characterized by sharp and irreconcilable conflicts, the corresponding transitional zone between culture realms of Northwestern Europe and Mediterranean is one of blending cultures and tolerant infusion. Switzerland and especially France witnessed invasion after invasion of both Mediterranean and Germanic cultures.

At a very early date Celtic-speaking Alpines overwhelmed the Mediterranean population of France. By 600 B.C. Greeks had arrived to establish colonies for trade and commerce along the coast of the Gulf of Lions, bringing with them Mediterranean culture traits. The relics of the Greek stay in the area are seen in the amount of Greek blood that remains in this territory, and in the artifacts and ruins of temples that have been uncovered. Less than 500 years later, Roman legions appeared on the scene, but by that time Germanic tribes were deeply invading France. The Romans managed to contain the Germanic tribes and control most of France and the Lotharingian Corridor until the fifth century A.D., and to implant a Roman variety of Mediterranean culture in the native population. Roads were built, temples erected, and law and order maintained.

As Roman control weakened, Germanic tribes, who had been constantly testing the strength of the Roman frontier, spread south. Switzerland was occupied by Burgundians in the west who became Latinized, and Alemanni in the east who kept to more Germanic ways. Nordic Franks occupied Paris Basin and Aquitaine; Alemanni, Suevi, and Burgundians came through the Gate of Belfort into eastern France; and Goths spread along the Mediterranean coast. Most of these were glad to accept many Roman ways of life, although by this time Rome and its civilization were becoming decadent and plunging into the Dark Ages. When the time for revival came, it was largely through Germanic auspices in northern Italy and France. During Holy Roman Empire days, these people maintained the tradition of Empire, crudely but tenaciously. Under Germanic influences arose such legal codes as the British Common Law, which had its basis in Roman justice. This period also saw the rise of feudal states in France, as in Germany. There was constant squabbling, largely over control of the three great granaries and storehouses—Paris Basin, Basin of Aquitaine, and Burgundy. The struggles of the noblemen against each other, and of the king against the noblemen in efforts to gain some power to go with the title, lasted until the middle of the seventeenth century, when the central power of King and Cardinal had won enough control over the petty states for France to emerge as a nation, though much of the old system hung on until the Revolution, 1789–1795. With Napoleon came something of a settlement of the brutal religious hostilities between Roman Catholics and Protestants, but other hostilities started as France spread its Empire and control across the Shatter Belt to Russia.

France's easter boundary has undergone many changes, in contrast to the more effective ones to the west and south. Although very few difficulties have arisen with Italy and Switzerland, serious questions are always coming up about the boundary with Germany. The French like to think of the Rhine as the boundary, although nowhere along the left bank do people use French as their native tongue. Alsace, Lorraine, Saar, and other states of the buffer region of Lotharingia have seen the French-German boundary move back and forth across them a number of times. Most Alsatians are German speaking, but many consider political affiliation with France a lesser evil than union with Germany. The peoples of the Palatinate (Pfalz) and Saar are predominantly German in every respect. Luxembourg is hostile to affiliation of any sort and has succeeded quite well in keeping its independence. Lorraine is about half German, half French.

The happiest solution to Lotharingian Corridor problems was found in Switzerland. In 1291 three German-speaking cantons around Lake Lucerne united to defend themselves against Austria. Other cantons joined the affiliation which was recognized as an independent state by the Treaty of Westphalia in 1648. Now there are 22 cantons, of which 16 are German speaking, 5 French speaking, and 1 Italian speaking. Some 72 per cent of the population regard German as their mother tongue, 21 per cent French, 6 per cent Italian, and 1 per cent Romansch (Rhaeto-Romanic). All four languages are official. About 57 per cent of the population is Protestant, mainly Calvinist, and 42 per cent Roman Catholic. Each canton has almost complete autonomy and centralized government is reduced to a minimum. Under such democratic conditions it is surprising that Switzerland is the only European country to bar women from voting.

Liechtenstein, between Switzerland and Austria, is a curious little country with an area of 62 square miles and a population approaching 15,000. It was part of the German confederation until 1866, then became a dependency of Austria, and in 1918 declared its independence. It soon arranged with Switzerland to have that country administer its postal service, customs, and foreign interests. It is headquarters for many large corporations which prefer to pay nominal local fees rather than taxes in nations where their business is actually conducted. The government rests with a reigning prince and an elected legislature. The only armed force is a

Lotharingian Corridor states

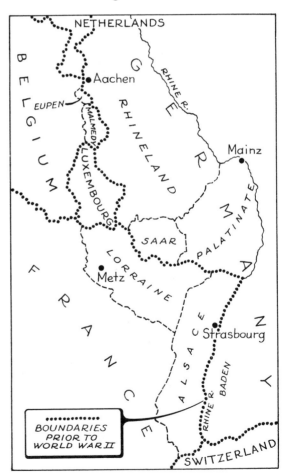

50-man police unit. The main industries are tourism and stamp-engraving.

The culture transition zone of western Europe emerged in modern times as mainly the two nations, France and Switzerland. Germany is predominantly a country in the culture realm of Northwestern Europe, while Austria laps over into the Shatter Belt. Italy and Iberia are Mediterranean. Belgium is mainly northwestern European, but to some degree shares transitional qualities with France. Its Roman Catholicism and bilinguality are evidence of Mediterranean influence. To France has gone much of the buffer territory between early Latin and Germanic cultures along the Lotharingian Corridor. Although diverse elements are grouped together in France and in Switzerland, each ranks as one of the most coherent nations in Europe. Racial and linguistic variety is accepted with extreme tolerance, and blending rather than fragmentation of groups is characteristic.

CULTURAL LANDSCAPES

In the nineteenth century France was described as a land of small peasant-shopkeepers. It has remained just that. Peasants still make up about half of the population and are the backbone of the nation. About 73 per cent of the land is used for crops or pasture, 18.5 per cent is in forest, and only 8.5 per cent waste, a poor term for magnificent scenery.

Rural population density is low compared with most western European countries, and farm sizes are fairly large, averaging 24 acres. Although villages are numerous, many property owners live on their farms, for cultivating the soil is a respected way of life, and the position of the peasant is one of dignity.

Wheat is the major cereal crop, and the total harvest accounts for about one quarter of all European wheat west of the Soviet Union. Paris Basin is the greatest single wheat-raising district. To the northwest are the wetter lands that raise oats. To the south are the rye-producing areas. Quantities of potatoes and sugar beets are also raised. The widespread vineyards of France each year produce about one billion gallons of wine. Some 50 million gallons are exported, and about three times that much is imported, chiefly from Algeria and Spain, for France leads the world both in the production and consumption of wine. France also leads Europe in fish consumption, and although its fisheries rank next to those of Great Britain, fish must be imported to meet the needs. Otherwise, France is fairly self-sufficient in food.

Although France has the greatest iron reserves in western Europe, it lags industrially because of a shortage of manpower and an insufficiency of coal to meet its needs. It takes a lot of coal to process a small amount of iron, so iron moves to the coal rather than the reverse, and heavy industry tends to develop near coal. Thus, Lorraine ore moves to Ruhr coal, but since there

Central Plateau, Puy de Dome

[*French Embassy, Press and Information Division*]

Alpine slope landscape, Savoie
[*French Embassy, Press and Information Division*]

is no point in returning barges and trains empty, they bring back some coal to iron centers to support the smelting and steel industry of the Moselle Valley. Lille, St. Etienne, Le Creusot, and other French sources of coal are industrialized. Lack of fuel is in part compensated for by development of the abundant hydroelectric resources in the south and southeast. Electricity is widely used by the railroads and the textile industry, and has helped the development of aluminum and other metal industries. Potash salts in Alsace and common salt and lime along the Mediterranean coast have promoted chemical industries. Since World War II, the main industrial output of France has shifted from its traditional exports of agricultural and luxury items to machinery and metalurgical products, textiles, chemicals, automobiles, and rolling stock. France now ranks fourth in the world in the automotive industry, in the textile industry, in the aeronautic industry, and in aluminum production.

In the past France has been handicapped commercially by being south of traffic routes used for goods exchanged between Northwestern European states, and by being avoided because of its troublesome customs regulations. More commerce may now flow through France as a result of French participation in the Organization for European Economic Cooperation and other cooperatives designed to facilitate trade and movement of goods by abolition of national barriers. France has excellent interior communications. The country is covered with an intricate network of railroads, totaling over 26,000 miles, with no place being over 25 miles from a railroad line. The highway network is even more dense. The 7,500 miles of navigable waterways, including more than 3,000 miles of canals, are vital connecting links and have made important ports of such places as Lille, Amiens, Strasbourg, Lyon, Bordeaux, Nantes, and Rouen. Paris has maritime interests, as well as being the hub of the rail and highway systems.

About 80 per cent of the imports of France are bulky commodities, such as cotton, iron and metals, petroleum, and food. Until recently, France's emphasis on luxury export items geared its prosperity directly to the purchasing power of its external markets. To lessen this reliance on the prosperity of other nations, France is now tending to stress the production of such necessities as automobiles, light and heavy metals, and chemicals. Another important item in balancing the economy is income from tourists. Yearly, France draws thousands of visitors to its marvelous chateaux, cathedrals, art collections, spas and bathing resorts, and alpine attractions. The lure of its cuisine brings eaters in droves.

Swiss Alps also attract numerous tourists, as Swiss traditional neutrality and stability attract international diplomatic organizations, and banking and insurance companies. The latter contribute a large share of the country's income, supplementing that from the export of high quality goods and specialties. Aside from some low quality iron ore, salt, and asphalt, all raw materials required by industry must be imported. An important export is dairy products, for almost half the milk produced goes into cheese and butter. Much of the arable land is devoted to pastures and hay rather than food crops, and so quantities of food must be imported. Almost one quarter of the people make their living from farming and livestock. Most farms are less than 25 acres, but some 10,000 cooperative societies give the farmers the advantages of large-scale purchasing and marketing. Most industrial workers are part farmers, or at least keep a cow, and prefer to live in rural villages. Factories are small and spread throughout the rural sections. A dense network of railroads is required to get raw materials out to the factories and gather the finished goods. Maintenance of railroads and the equally good road system is costly because of the many bridges, tunnels, heavy snowfalls, and avalanches.

URBANIZATION

Neither France nor Switzerland has experienced the phenomenal urbanization during the nineteenth and twentieth centuries that has been characteristic of England, Germany, the United States, and various other nations. In Switzerland, only one city has achieved a fair size, Zurich, with a population of less than a half million, and only one other, Basel, has over 200,000. Nearly two thirds of the population live in hamlets of less than 10,000. The situation is similar in France, where the majority of people live in rural areas, though they are not by any means all farmers. Only one French city exceeds 1 million, one other over 0.5 million, and, in all, only eight have populations above 200,000. Paris, with almost 3 million within its limits and a total of about 7 million in the conurbation of greater Paris, is the one giant. Like London, it occupies a central position in a rich agricultural area, is a bridge site, and traces its importance from Roman times. Though primarily important as a political, financial, and cultural center, Paris is the commercial nucleus of France and engages in a wide variety of industries. Calais, Boulogne, Le Havre, and Cherbourg are essentially its outports.

No other French city approaches Paris in size or importance. The nearest is Marseille, with well over 0.5 million, which carries on a large trade with Algeria and other Mediterranean places, and handles a considerable amount of Suez Canal traffic. In addition to its activities as the chief port of France, a diversity of industries is conducted, ranging from the making of

candles and soap to shipbuilding. Rouen and Le Havre also engage in shipbuilding. Lyon, with a population approaching 0.5 million, is a center of iron, steel and other metal industries, but the main activities are textiles and the making of textile machines. It also engages in the production of chemicals and synthetic fibers. Among the lesser cities are Bordeaux, an important wine-shipping and oil-refining port; Toulouse, a commercial and industrial center on the gateway between the Aquitaine Basin and the Mediterranean; and Lille, the heavy industries and textile center on the Sambre-Meuse coal field.

Zurich
[*Swiss National Tourist Office*]

POPULATION DEFICIENCY

In contrast with many other nations, the population of France has not grown fast enough to maintain the country as a great power. Although it was a cultural and military leader, and had amassed a colonial empire that included a large share of North America and other continents, it lost New France to the British in 1763, sold Louisiana to the United States in 1803, gave up its controls in India, and currently is seeing many of its overseas territories declare independence or autonomy with links to France similar to those of the Commonwealth nations with Britain. The revision of the constitution and the establishment of the Fifth Republic created the French Community, made up of 90 Departments of Metropolitan France, 15 Algerian Departments, 2 Saharan Departments, 4 Overseas Departments, 11 member states, and a number of overseas territories and trust areas, all of which are represented in parliament. Outside of France, the Community includes an area of 3.8 million square miles (British Commonwealth, 12.1), and a population of 39.4 million (British Commonwealth, 682.9). This colonial load is not particularly productive, and France is no longer able to finance or manage it.

To attribute the inability of France to keep abreast industrially with nations of northwestern Europe to lack of coal and fuel resources is hardly more reasonable than to attribute the backwardness of Poland to an insufficient sea coast. Switzerland has managed to do well without either coal or coast. The difficulty faced by France industrially has been primarily lack of manpower. Both World Wars took a terrific toll. Nor did the one-child peasant family provide a reserve. The land of small peasant-shopkeepers remained Mediterranean in its lag behind its northwestern European neighbors in the Industrial Revolution. A change has come since World War II: families of two and three children are common, and industry is being rapidly expanded, so it can be expected that the cultural landscape, long unchanged, will begin to undergo alterations.

FRENCH BARBARY

The most successful penetration of European World culture into the Dry World, save for that taking place in the Soviet Union, is occurring along the African Mediterranean shores, the western coast of Barbary, especially in Algeria. Algeria is divided into two parts: the northern territory with an area of about 80,000 square miles containing 15 departments and almost 9 million people, and a southern section of two Saharan Departments, comprising an area of 767.4 thousand square miles with some 820,000 population. Almost all of the 1.25 million Europeans are in the northern territory where in general the mixing of the French-Arab and French-Berber populations with their different racial, linguistic, and cultural backgrounds has proceeded peacefully. In recent years, however, there has been a growing strife between groups on both a political and religious basis.

The climate of coastal Algeria is similar to that of southern France. Leading agricultural products include wheat, barley, oats, maize, potatoes, artichokes, tobacco, flax, olives, and wine. Coastal lowlands and terraces are fertile and productive. A large export of agricultural products goes to Marseille. Considerable mineral wealth exists, including iron, zinc, lead, mercury, antimony, and copper. While commercial progress has been rapid in recent decades, there is little industrial development as yet. Algiers (Alger) is the capital and principal port.

Morocco to the west and Tunisia to the east were, until recently, French protectorates. Morocco came under French rule in 1912, was not completely pacified until 1933, but won its independence in 1956. Within two years it had incorporated Tangier and Spanish Morocco. It has not undergone notable Europeanization except in a few cities, especially Casablanca, its main Atlantic port of nearly 700,000, and Rabat, its capital, an excellent example of city planning. Tunisia became a French protectorate in 1881. Within the last decade more and more self rule was granted, and in 1957 it became an independent republic. Tunis, the capital, is the size of Casablanca, and is the main center of European influence. Europeans are a small minority of the over 10 million people in Morocco and 4 million in Tunisia, the bulk of the population being Arabs and Berbers. Products of the coastal areas of these countries are similar to those of Algeria, and the mineral resources include lead, iron, zinc, and phosphates, with some petroleum in Morocco.

DRY WORLD

Steppe landscape, North Africa
[*U.S. Army photograph*]

12. *Dry World*

South of the European World, climates are too dry for field agriculture, natural resources are too meager for widespread industrial and technological development, and food supply is too limited to support more than an extremely sparse population, except in a few favored places. To Europeans this is a strange territory, inhabited by utterly alien peoples. In the Dry World nature is niggardly in providing the essentials of life, physical environments test the powers of human endurance, and death may be the consequence of inexpert use of such resources as exist. If nature is harsh, man is even more tyrannical; lust, greed, and vengeance are commonly his compelling motives. Much of the Dry World is *balad-al-khuf*, the Saharan expression for a "country of fear," fear of the lurking robber band, fear of the fanatic of a different religious sect, fear that the distant waterhole has been poisoned, making death a certainty.

Many recognize such concepts as the "Moslem World," "Arab World," or "World of the Turk," but culturally there is unity that extends more widely, a Dry World, that embraces practically all of the arid territory of the Afro-Eurasian landmass in the northern hemisphere. Whether the religionist be a fanatical Mohammedan or an equally fanatical Buddhist makes

193

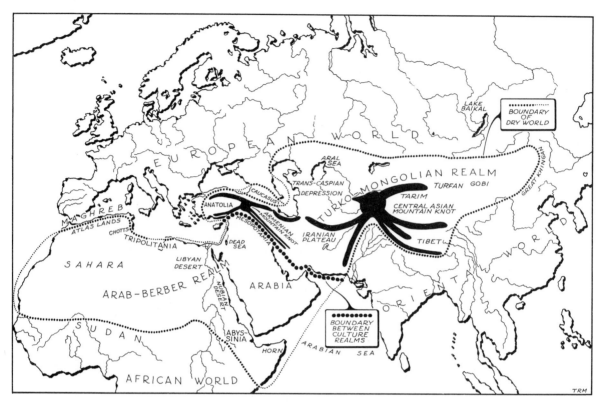

Dry World: index map

relatively little difference to the European. The things that separate the European World from the territories to its south are utterly different ways of life: pastoral nomadism, dependence of man on animal for sustenance, dependence of animal on the scantiest of vegetation, extreme contrast between areas supplied with small amounts of water and those that have none, fetters of taboos, contrasts in moral codes, tribal political organizations with little regard for political boundaries, and the low value placed on human life. It matters little whether the watchman is perched in a tower, as in ancient Tarim, or rides ahead of the caravan in the protection of sheltering dunes to climb stealthily up the lee of the crest to peer cautiously over the top to see whether an enemy is lurking along the trail, as in contemporary Arabia; each is an expression of Dry World culture. The Mongoloid Turki could adjust himself to the ways of the western Saharan Tuareg rather easily, as compared with the difficulty a European might

have in trying to become a member of either community.

Culturally the Dry World is bounded on the north by the European World and its Siberian Wedge. Its African part is bounded southward by the African World of the Negro. Its Asian part extends southward to the Oriental World. The boundaries shown on the index map are all more or less transitional, reflecting a blending of cultures, such as already has been described in the Barbary States of Morocco, Algeria, and Tunisia, and the area of the Soviet Union around the Caspian and Aral Seas. More significant than these boundaries are the core or nuclear areas. The real heart of the Dry World includes the Sahara, Libyan, and Nubian (Arabian) deserts of Africa, and in Asia, the Arabian, Anatolian, and Iranian plateaus, the low trans-Caspian depression, the extremely high Plateau of Tibet, the basin of Tarim, and the basins of Mongolia with the Gobi Desert (Shamo).

CLIMATES

Aridity is the main unifying characteristic of the Dry World. The heart areas ordinarily receive less than four inches of precipitation annually. The air is dry. Relative humidity, that is, the relation of the capacity of the air to hold water to the moisture present, is commonly below 3 per cent, and evaporation rates are high. The dry air desiccates everything in contact with it. During the heat of summer, when evaporation is most intense, the lakes of interior Asia lower at rates of up to three feet per month.

For most of the Dry World, an average rainfall figure is rather meaningless: an area may experience many years of complete drought but no area is absolutely rainless, though precipitation may be very infrequent. For example, at Cairo, fewer than half of all years have even a trace of precipitation, and the entire interval from 1909 to 1916 was rainless, yet the *average* annual precipitation is 1.27 inches.

Contrary to ordinary belief, it practically never rains long and violently in deserts. The air is simply too dry to create a cloudburst or anything approaching it. But, paradoxically, severe floods and widespread effects of water erosion are characteristic of even the driest deserts. No sandstorm has ever killed a person, but death by drowning is fairly common in the Sahara and other deserts. Only the ignorant would camp in a stream bed, however dry it may be, because whenever there is even a small shower, run-off is rapid and water is soon concentrated in these channels. There is no vegetation or soil to hold surface water. A stream bed dry for many years may suddenly accommodate a flow several feet deep, which arrives with an almost perpendicular front, even though less than half an inch of rain has fallen.

Deserts are windy places. Small dust devils or little whirlwinds are almost daily occurrences, and larger windstorms are common, such as the *sirocco* of Algeria which carries dust as far as Europe, and the *burans* of Asia, which may be icy cold in winter. These parching, sand- or dust-sand-filled winds are extremely unpleasant, but they are not fatal, nor do they bury caravans. Near dry and unpacked sand they produce *sand-blast*, which burns the skin, wears away fixed objects, and is most severe within a yard of the ground. The major dust storms occur in the steppes and more humid sides of the dry regions, where fields are plowed. Most desert surfaces were long ago swept clean of dust or sand.

Temperature is a matter of secondary importance in the Dry World. Arid regions are subject to extreme daily ranges, the clear skies permitting both the effective transmission of insolation and rapid radiation. Ground surfaces become very hot in the daytime, and cool rapidly after sunset. Seasonal temperature ranges depend on latitude and continentality, and vary from a January-July range of 85° or more, as in the northeasternmost part of the Dry World, to less than 10°, as in the southern Sahara.

From a cultural view the most significant temperature boundary in the Dry World is the isotherm of January 32° F. On the warm side of the line, winters are mild, the date palm is the common food provider and tree of the oasis, and Arabic is the almost universal tongue. On the cold side, life is adjusted to the recurring season of cold, the fruitless willow and poplar are the oasis trees, and languages are almost entirely non-Semitic. This isotherm roughly approximates the boundary between the Semites on the warm side of the line and the Turkish and Mongoloid peoples on the cold side.

VEGETATION

In general, deserts are places of impoverished, but highly specialized, vegetation, without grass, so grazing is extremely poor. Steppes have somewhat more abundant vegetation, and grazing is relatively good. Grass is taller and plant life more and more diversified toward the humid borders of the dry climates. The real key to Dry World vegetation is moisture, for even desert soils are generally fertile. The contrasts between oasis and unproductive desert are sharp, depending on the outer limit of water supply. The peculiar modifications in desert plants are concerned with conservation of moisture rather than adaptation to temperature. In the driest areas are *xerophytes*, deep-rooted, ground-hugging, small-leafed or thorny, grey plants. When there is even the slightest shower, seeds of numerous annual plants spring to life. The life cycle is short, a matter of only a few days. Seeds are protected by drought-resistant cases, so they remain viable until the next wetting. In the slightly more moist areas, uplands and steppes, shrubs grow taller and more closely spaced. The Dry World is by no means barren of *hydrophytes*, or water-loving plants. In marshy places there are sedges, cat-tails, reeds, and other grasses, as in the locally-wet spots in Tarim where reeds grow 25 feet in height and two inches in diameter. Along the sides of streams are *gallery forests* extending for hundreds of miles beyond the normal forest limits toward the dry hearts of Asia and Africa. In the most elevated parts of the Dry World, as Tibet, alpine tundra is widespread.

ANIMAL LIFE

Among the larger animals of the desert the antelope is most abundant. Fleet of foot, he ranges widely, and some types, such as the adax of the Sahara, are able to store large amounts of water. The antelope is present throughout the Dry World, and in considerable variety. The one-humped dromedary of southwestern Asia and the two-humped camel of inner Asia occur both in wild and domestic forms. Mountain sheep, yak, wild ass, and other herbivores become abundant toward the steppes of Asia. The steppes of Africa are ranged over by giraffe, elephant, rhinoceros, buffalo, and other big game. The jackal, wolf, fox, and other carnivores accompany the larger grazing and browsing animals. The hare is widespread, as are reptiles, especially lizards. Many varieties of fish inhabit streams, some being able to survive in moist mud. Beetles, mosquitoes, and other insects are everywhere, the fly being the worst animal and human tormentor of all.

Oxen, horses, and camels are the typical pack and burden animals of the desert. The yak is the mainstay of Tibet and other high parts of Asia. The camel, sheep, and goat provide meat and milk. Dogs are as numerous as local economic conditions permit.

LANDFORMS

Deserts and arid steppes have no water surplus to feed the ocean systems. The only through-streams rise in places of abundant precipitation, so they maintain a flow despite diminishing discharge while crossing arid places. The Nile, middle Niger, and middle Hwang Ho are examples, as is the Colorado in southwestern United States. The typical arid-climate stream flows into an enclosed basin, coming from the uplands and spreading its *distributaries* out over a depositional cone of its own making. Any water that succeeds in reaching the bottom of the cone ends in a saline lake. The cone-building distributaries shift from channel to channel as their work of filling enclosed basins, *bolsons*, progresses.

Extensive or deeply depressed sub-sea-level lands are peculiarities of arid climates. In more humid areas such basins would become lakes. In Africa, large below-sea-level lands occur in the Chott (Shott) region, west of the Gulf of Gabes, which approximates —100 feet, and in the Qattara Depression in the northern Libyan Desert, —440 feet. The Jordan Valley *graben*, or down-dropped block, culminates in the Dead Sea, whose shores are the lowest lands on earth, 1,292 feet below sea level. The extensive Caspian Depression reaches more than —90 feet. The most spectacular depression in inner Asia is Turfan, a deep graben east of the Tien Shan that has a depth possibly exceeding 400 feet below sea level.

The deserts are also the scene of powerful agents of debris transportation. Winds whisk off dust and shift sands. Rain, falling on heated rocks, can cause the surfaces to crack. During rains, loosened materials are quickly swept into channels and moved downslope. Desert mountains are stripped of debris about as rapidly as it accumulates on their surface, so they present barren, hard-rock exposures and tend to retain steep slopes. Jagged peaks, steep escarpments and abrupt rims of resistant rock characterize desert landscapes. The boundary between the solid rock of the mountain or upland, and the sand or gravel deposit of the adjacent basin is sharply defined. The slope of the deposits is rather steep near the mountain and gentler toward the basin. Basin deposits cover considerably more of the desert surfaces than do mountains. They are differentiated according to their surfaces, each of which has a distinct name in the vocabularies of desert peoples.

Reg (Western Sahara), *serir* (Eastern Sahara), or *gobi* (Asia) is the most common type of desert surface—a gravel surface. It covers at least half of the Sahara and more than three quarters of Arabia and other deserts. The reg is cut by *wadies*, *arroyos*, or *washes*; typical desert stream channels, which, when in flood, bring debris toward the basin floor. The materials brought by the wadies are soon winnowed by winds, leaving the reg covered with a layer of larger stones too heavy to be windblown. The stones soon gain a shiny, dark brown surface called *desert varnish*. Together the stones form a *desert pavement*, usually a good surface for automobile travel, but coarser types of reg are almost impassable to automobiles, camels, or men on foot. Reg materials become finer toward basin flats, which may consist mainly of clay. Many basins contain salt flats (sabkha, playas), white and glistening in the sun. Salts in solution are brought down by surface or subsurface drainage, and collect as the water is evaporated. Of the little water that reaches the low basins, much is useless to man because it is saline or alkaline.

Extensive sand fields, *erg*, form wherever the sand supply is abundant, as in basins near the winnowed reg, near vigorous wadies bringing sufficient fine materials, or near beaches of Ice Age lakes. Few places have sufficient sand for erg development, so not more than one quarter of any desert is covered by erg. These are true sand-seas, the erg surface being covered with wave crests in a more or less fixed position. The waves are complex in plan and shape and only superficially resemble the sand dunes of places where sand supply is scant. Ergs are quite stable features, their margins remaining unchanged over centuries. The surface of the larger waves, wherever the sand is firm, is covered with ripples, an inch or so high. Soft sand is unrippled and practically impassable.

Where the supply is rather limited, sand travels as waves downwind. In some cases *dunes*, or processions of dunes are formed. Most spectacular is the *barkhan*, with a steep face of soft sand between its forward-projecting horns and a gentle slope of harder sand facing the wind. Barkhans are practically unknown in the Sahara, but occur in Turkish and Mongolian

Sahara: ergs and wadies

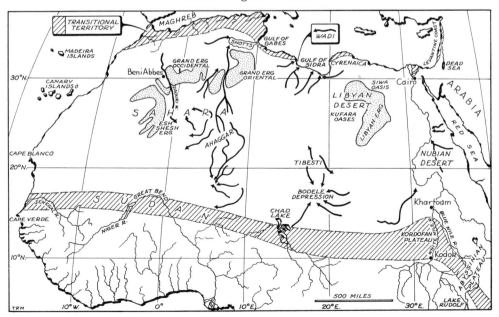
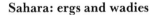

deserts, in the southwestern United States, and elsewhere. They are commonly over a thousand feet from horn to horn, and rise fifty feet or more above the surface they are traveling on.

True rocky desert occurs mainly in mountains, but some plateaus and lower territory form rocky desert, or *hammada*. These bare surfaces, shining with desert varnish, are difficult to cross if rough and elevated, but if they are formed on flat-lying rocks, they may be used as roadways.

The prevailing color of the desert is gray— vegetation, animals, and rock debris are all about the same color. Mountains may exhibit hues of red or purple, but across most of the desert surface, the reg, no color appears to enliven the drab monotony of gray landscapes except during the infrequent periods when annual plants bloom.

PEOPLES

Although people are scarce in arid regions, the Dry World has been inhabited by man for a very long time, probably since the late Ice Age when northern regions were inhospitably cold and the deserts were considerably wetter than they are today. Ancient artifacts indicating Negroid origin are relatively abundant, and early Negroid peoples are evidenced in the racial characteristics of today's population in the belt between the more purely Negroid parts of Africa and southeastern Asia. Caucasoid stock, however, is now dominant everywhere in the Dry World west of India and south of the trans-Caspian Depression. Practically all races of Caucasoids are represented, Mediterranean stock being the most common and most diversified. Most of the eastern part of the Dry World is inhabited by Mongoloids, the Neoasiatic stock being dominant.

From the standpoint of prehistory it is reasonable to suppose that the Dry World east of the great central-Asiatic mountain knot, the Pamirs, was originally inhabited by Mongoloid peoples. Paleoasiatics, Mongoloids resembling Caucasoids, were gradually invaded and admixed with Neoasiatics. To the west were other roundheaded peoples, proto-Caucasoids, who migrated southward from the trans-Caspian Depression and across the Anatolian and Arabian plateaus. Here they encountered Mediterraneans, with longer heads. Other Mediterraneans were living in southern Europe. Negroid peoples, once widespread from western Africa to the Pacific, were displaced by both round-headed and long-headed Caucasoid stocks everywhere in the Dry World west of India. It is a long and complicated history that has left a racial medley in its evolution. Practically all ancient peoples of the western Dry World were long-headed and those of the east, round-headed. The invasion of round-heads into the central part of the Dry World probably occurred at the end of the Ice Age, and certainly was prehistoric. The Hittites of Asia Minor and the Sumerians of Mesopotamia, the earliest western Asiatics known to history in even a fragmentary way, were round-headed. The small-headed, round-headed peoples of southeastern Arabia probably remain as evidence of these early appearances of round-heads in the Dry World.

Aside from such shiftings of Dry World peoples as the spread of Arabs northward and westward after the death of Mohammed, or the arrival of Turks in territory south of the trans-Caspian Depression, there have been several notable invasions by outsiders during historic times. Nordic Vandals and Goths went into Africa, and along the coast east of Gibraltar as far as Tunis. Chinese have penetrated dry lands as far west as Sinkiang, in Tarim Basin. Russians of various racial stocks are making inroads today along lands beyond the Soviet frontier. The western part of the Dry World has a considerable Negroid population resulting from slavery. The natives, *haratin*, of Saharan oases are very largely Negroids of recent introduction. Remnants of the original Negroid inhabitants of the Sahara are seen in the "Bantu-speaking" Negroes along the borders of the Sudan, in the Tibbus of the remote highlands of central Sahara, and the Borkus, south of the Tibbus to Lake Chad.

The list of languages spoken in the Dry World would be many times longer than a list of European World tongues, but most of them are spoken by only a limited number of people and few have a written form. To the south and west of Mesopotamia, Semitic tongues prevail, with Arabic the one great language with a literature. To the north and east, the language situation is more complicated, but the main languages are Ural-Altaic. Western European languages, such as English, French, Italian, and Spanish are spoken in cities and in some rural territory along the northern coast of Africa and in the Levant. Greek is spoken around all the fringes of Anatolia, while in the plateaus to the east are Armenian, Persian, and Afghan, as well as several minor Indo-European languages. Great Russian has made important invasions around the Caspian Basin and to the east. Indo-Chinese is present as Tibetan, in the high plateaus south of the central Asiatic basins, and Chinese dialects have widely invaded Mongolia and Tarim.

Hamitic languages were once almost universal and exclusive in northern Africa. Survivals of these languages exist as Coptic, the ritualistic language of Egypt; Berber, the widespread speech of mountain peoples of north Africa; Ethiopian (Cushite), the common tongue of the Abyssinian highlands; and other languages spoken around the Horn of Africa and along the Indian Ocean coast. A tremendous variety of Negro languages, generally called Sudanic, are spoken by peoples along the entire southern fringe of the Dry World in Africa.

Peoples of the Dry World have tended to put their gods in the sky, toward which they look for rain and from whence comes their heat. Worship of the sun, or of sun deities, has been almost universal in their primitive forms of religion. From these developed Zoroastrianism, Jehovah worship, Judaism, Christianity, and Mohammedanism. Today the Dry World is mainly non-Christian. Its western part is solidly Mohammedan, and its eastern part is divided between Mohammedanism and Buddhism. Buddhists extend north from Malaysia to southern Siberia and eastward to the Pacific. In the Dry World they occupy Tibet, part of Tarim Basin, and most of Mongolia. Christianity in an old form survives in Ethiopia, and modern Christianity has accompanied Euro-

peanization of lands in north Africa where the Roman Catholic Church has made important gains, while the Greek Catholic Church has influence around the borders of Anatolia, and in some Dry World parts of the Soviet Union.

The rise of Mohammedanism after the death of its Prophet in A.D. 632 was almost meteoric. The sword of Islam marched rapidly north into Mesopotamia and west across northern Africa, reaching Spain by 711. Prior to the year 1000, the religion had a firm foothold in lands as distant as China, the East Indies, and the east coast of Africa. The Moslem World today covers northern Africa extending south to the delta of the Niger and down the east coast to Mozambique, across the Indian Ocean to Indonesia, and across Arabia, Anatolia, and the Iranian Plateau to western India. It fringes the Caspian, extends northeastward into parts of Siberia and across Tarim to parts of northwestern China. In the world today there are some 425 million Moslems, 325 million of whom are in Asia and 87 million in Africa as a compact, mainly Dry World bloc. This may be compared with 849 million Christians of whom 510 million are Roman Catholic, 129 million Orthodox Catholics, or with a total of 12 million Jews, and a world population of 2.9 billion.

ECONOMY

The typical Dry World inhabitant is a pastoral nomad, for agriculture is possible only in a few favored areas. The desert nomad has his herd of camels, oxen, asses, horses, sheep, or goats, but little else. His life follows routines dictated by the needs of his animals, which provide his clothing, shelter, and food. Trade is by barter and is a strictly local affair, certainly never reaching international proportions. The Industrial Revolution has affected him but slightly, yet some of its products have become necessities, such as guns, ammunition, cloth, and various metal wares. He lives in a passive poverty, cherishing his few possessions, a small tent and crude, home-made implements. In general he suffers from malnutrition and deficiency diseases.

The pastoral nomad has little means of supplementing his income, though pillage and robbery have risen almost to the level of professions in remote areas. If death be the penalty for failure, it is accepted with complete indifference. The Mohammedan is a stoic and a believer in predestination. Conscience or religious scruple rarely stands in the way of the pillager; on the contrary, they often spur him on because his victims are commonly people of a slightly different sect, or members of tribes with whom feuds have long been in progress. With amazing skill he can track enemies or friends, and read the subtle signs of the desert.

Caravan owners are the true nobility of the Dry World. They not only are transporters but also merchants and traders, conveyors of news, and frequently owners of oases, flocks, or natural resources such as salt deposits. They match wits with pillagers, provide protection for goods and charges, bargain successfully with producer and consumer, and plan journeys with utmost skill and precision. Their pack animals, camels, can travel a week without water, but eat almost daily. Caravan leaders plan their routes according to the availability of pasturage,

and secondarily on the location of water holes. Though the ridiculous camel shuffles along in an awkward, slow, loose-jointed way, a caravan normally moves about three miles per hour while on the trail, or twice the speed of fastest oxen transportation.

The agriculturist occupies a lowly place in Dry World society. As often as not he is a Negroid Haratin, sharecropping the property of the landed nobility who prefer a nomad life. The caravan owner pays him the lowest possible price for his surplus and exacts highest prices for the wares he brings. The oasis is ordinarily rife with filth and disease, especially malaria, but it is a place of dependable water supply, so it supports a small resident population. Although many oases are fairly small, the grandest ones are entire river valleys, such as the Nile Valley, Mesopotamia, and Syr Darya and Amu Darya leading to Aral Sea.

During the last decade or so, important changes in local economy have accompanied the development of the vast petroleum resources in Arabia and the Middle East and in Egypt and other places in north Africa. Some of the

Dry World: population density

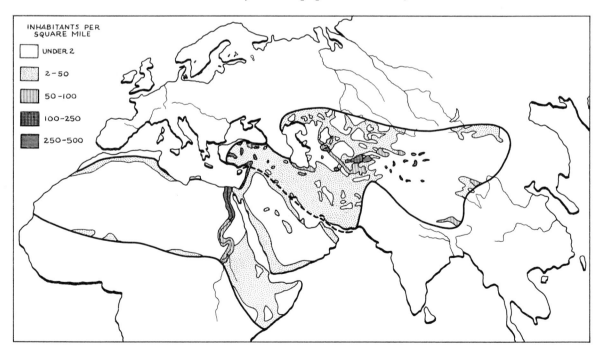

INHABITANTS PER SQUARE MILE

UNDER 2

2 - 50

50 - 100

100 - 250

250 - 500

revenue from the exploitation and export of oil trickles into internal improvements, such as irrigation projects, and mass welfare activities, such as free medical care, but for the most part, these changes have little effect on the general way of life in the Dry World.

CONTRIBUTIONS TO CIVILIZATION

The orign of Europe's Neolithic culture was in the Dry World. Use of copper began prior to 5500ᐟB.C. in the Dry World, but did not reach Europe for well over 2,000 years. Dry World peoples began using bronze before 3000 B.C., but Europeans were slow to accept technological achievements. The Bronze Age was well established by 2500 B.C., but took 500 years to reach Europe, as did the Iron Age, which started in the Dry World prior to 1000 B.C. Western civilization springs mainly from the great centers of Nineveh, Babylon, Assyria, and Egypt. Governmental organization was so fully developed that royal dynasties arose in Egypt by 3200 B.C. and the erection of pyramids was begun in 3000 B.C. Before 2200 B.C. astronomical observations were being taken in Babylon where the circle was divided into 360 degrees. Most of our basic mathematics comes from Dry World peoples.

During Europe's Dark Ages the Arabs and other Dry World peoples were caretakers of much of the civilization of the Ancients. They escaped the ravages of the Germanic tribes and the smothering effect of European theological disputes on learning. While Europe reverted to barbarism, the Arabs were busy conducting trade with the Far East and bringing back the luxury items that in time made the European Voyages of Discovery a necessity. They were also advancing as the greatest explorers and scientists of the western world.

To Dry World peoples we owe the domestication of most animals that are amenable to the will of man: horse, camel, sheep, goat, pig, yak, ox, and possibly the dog. To them we owe most of our cereal plants. Only the American Indian vies with the Dry World inhabitant in the matter of adapting and improving wild plants for man's use.

CULTURE REALMS

The Dry World is relatively homogeneous and need be divided into only two culture realms.

The Arab-Berber Realm is mainly Caucasoid, Semitic-speaking, and Mohammedan. Arabic is its main language. It is a closely knit realm covering the warm-winter part of the Dry World. Rainfall is mainly in the winter season. The date palm is the mainstay of oases. Foreign culture ties are principally with the European and African worlds.

To the north of the isotherm of January 32° F. lies the Turko-Mongolian Realm where people must provide against the cold of winter. Though languages are mainly Ural-Altaic, they exist in great number, and many important intrusions of other tongues exist. Mohammedanism gives way eastward to Buddhism and other religions. Agriculture is difficult, and the date palm is replaced by the useless poplar or willow. Such rain as comes falls in summer, winters being clear and bleak. Outside contacts are with the Eastern Culture Realm of the European World, or with the Oriental World.

The boundary between culture realms is fairly sharp with almost no "shatter belt." Linguistically it is the northern limit of Semitic-speaking peoples, and politically, it extends along the southern boundary of Turkey and the western boundary of Iran, the Persian Gulf and Gulf of Oman continuing eastward.

ARAB-BERBER REALM

Steppe-Mediterranean landscape, Tunisia
[*U.S. Army photograph*]

13. Arab-Berber Realm

The Arab-Berber Realm of the Dry World is remarkably homogeneous. It is dry, hot-summered, mild-wintered, Arabic in tongue, Moslem in religion, and Mediterranean racially. Its eastern part is historically old, the home of the ancient patriarchal empires of Egypt and Babylon. The transition between Dry World and European World cultures is broadest in the western Mediterranean where southern Iberia shows the Moslem-Moorish influence and much of coastal North Africa has been Europeanized.

The southern border of the Dry World across Africa lies along a broad belt of transition into the Sudan, where humid-savanna climate occurs, rainfall is ample and grass grows tall, and where Negroids are the dominant race. The

real distinction between the Arab-Berber Dry World and the Sudan in the African World is cultural. To the north is a region of nomadism and oasis agriculture. Home is a tent, society has a tribal basis, and animals are used as carriers and for drawing loads. To the south is a land of hoe agriculture, with some grazing. Home is fixed in position and usually of wood, society is related to towns and property lines, and no draft animals are used in the primitive agriculture. This transition zone extends from Senegal eastward to the vicinity of Lake Chad, then to the south of the Kordofan Plateau of the Sudan, past Lake Rudolf, and on through southern Somalia.

The Arab-Berber Realm of the Dry World

203

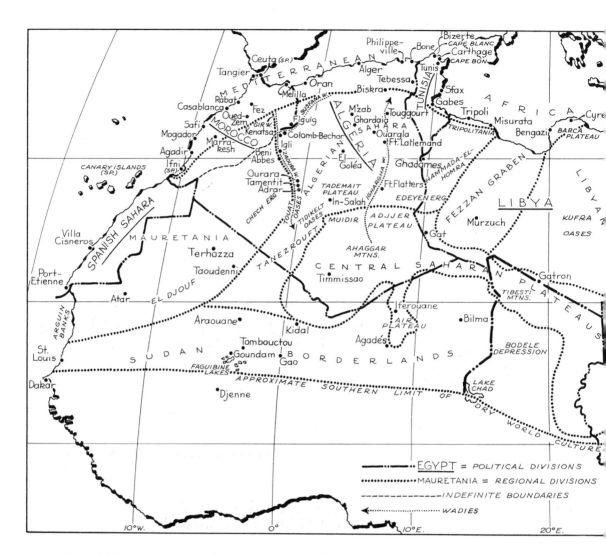

may be divided into an Asiatic, or Arabian, section, and an African section which consists of the Sahara, and Egypt, and Hamitic lands of East Africa.

SAHARA

Most of the Sahara is a vast "wilderness" estimated to be some 3 million square miles, but along the north is a narrow strip, Mediterranean Africa, which in climate and culture resembles southern Europe rather than other parts of the Dry World. Mediterranean Africa includes the Atlas Lands, or northern parts of Morocco, Algeria, and Tunisia, a small coastal strip of Tripolitania, and the Barca Plateau of

Cyrenaica, or roughly 500,000 square miles. About 10 per cent of the population of 21 million is of European descent. The landscapes of this transition zone are similar to those of the Mediterranean Realm. Deciduous and coniferous forests clothe the high, rugged Atlas Mountains that parallel the coast of Morocco and western Algeria, summits in the High Atlas of Morocco rising above 10,000 feet. At lower elevations are cedars, cork oak, maquis, and typical Mediterranean plants. Mediterranean agriculture flourishes along the coastal lowlands, and produces large crops of wheat and other cereals, vegetables, citrus fruit, almonds, olives, and grapes. These landscapes are really fairly new, having come about through the

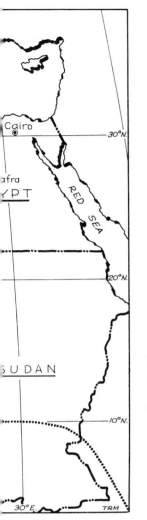

Mediterranean and Saharan Africa: index map

small minority among a population made up mainly of Berbers, Arabs, Jews, and other Mediterraneans. Because of their strong affinity to Europe, especially France, these lands were briefly discussed with that country.

South of Mediterranean Africa is a desert region roughly equivalent to the area of Australia. In the main the Sahara is a region of unfolded rocks, a continental shield where faulting has elevated some blocks and depressed others. Volcanic activity accounts for some high plateaus and mountains. The proportion of exposed bedrock, however, is minor in comparison with extensive surfaces of desert deposits.

CULTURAL BACKGROUND

Although the Sahara is and has been a barrier between Mediterranean and African Worlds, desires for trade prompted the use of routes across it at a very early time. Sudan trade, from the vicinity of Lake Chad, across the Air Plateau, along the Fezzan graben, to the west coast of the Syrte Depression, is extremely old. This shortest and least-desert route was known to Herodotus and used, in turn, by Greeks, Carthaginians, and Romans. Pliny knew at least two routes to the Sudan. Along them gold, ivory, ostrich feathers, animal pelts, and slaves came to the north, and textiles, metal wares, salt, and dates went to the Sudan. The Ghadames Oasis, with its excellent springs and artesian water supply, was known by Greeks, Egyptians, and Romans, but none of them ventured across the Grand Erg Oriental to the Algerian oases, nor far to the south.

These contacts, including the unsuccessful attempt of the Carthaginians to colonize the coast of Morocco in 520 B.C., brought very little change to the Sahara. The first really great culture revolution came with the introduction of the camel. This awkward creature, more adapted than any other animal to the desert, was brought to Egypt in 525 B.C., from Persia, for caravan use between Red Sea ports and the Nile. Horses and oxen had been the traditional beasts of burden throughout North Africa and remained so in the Sahara until 47 B.C., when the Romans brought camels to Ghadames. The

Europeanization of this territory during the last century. European expansion into Mediterranean Africa was prompted by attempts to stamp out piracy. Rome had established military forces in Tangier to keep the sea-robbers in check, but by the eighth century their activities were greatly accelerated by the Mohammedan conquests in which booty was taken from enemy infidels. Turkish control of Algeria, Tunisia, and Tripolitania also encouraged the corsairs, Barbary piracy reaching its zenith in the seventeenth century. The French conquest of Algeria in 1830 marked the end of Saracen marine activities in the western Mediterranean. It also marked the beginning of the Europeanization of these coastal lands where Europeans are a new animal was readily adopted, and wobbling along on its back, the Berber was able to shove the Caucasoid-Negroid frontier southward from the foot of the Atlas to the Sudan, where it is today. The original Negroid population of Edeyan Erg, south of Ghadames, was quickly diluted with Mediterranean Berbers, and today, because of the many sources of water, the region supports some 50,000 people and is one of the main commercial districts of the Sahara. Remnants of some groups of early Saharan Negroes are found in the Air Plateau, where many retain Neolithic culture traits, and to the east, in the Tibesti Massif, where the Tibbu, some 10,000 homogeneous people, still speak a central African language.

The Tuareg Berbers, irrepressible nomads who wrested the western Sahara from its original Negroid inhabitants, dress like Tibbus in that they wear a face veil which they never remove. The purpose is not to shield the face against the relentless sun or blasts of sand, but to keep evil spirits out of the body. They sport arm bands of polished stone, use a Neolithic manner of attaching ax heads to handles, and refuse to eat a large lizard, the uran, which they consider as embodying the spirit of their maternal uncles. Other Saharan peoples relish the animal as food. The place of women in society is far better than among Arabs for vestiges of matriarchal rule remain strong in their social organization. Though Moslem, they speak Berber and are unable to read the Koran, so they feel the influence of Islam less strongly than most Arabs. The traditional enemy of the Tuaregs, the Arabs, invaded the Sahara by moving west along the foot of the Atlas ranges. Some settled along the Mediterranean coast, but most remained nomadic in steppe lands near oases, or continued as caravan traders. Many of the best oases are owned by Arabs, who introduced the irrigation of date palms in the nineteenth century. Work in oases is done mainly by Berbers and Negroes, who receive a small share of the return.

REGIONS

Mauretania, the Sahara southwest of Wadi Zaoura and including Spanish Sahara, is the least explored part of the desert. There are some oases inhabited by Negroid and Berber peoples, but they have no contacts with the European World. The few villages, such as Villa Cisneros, are refuges for bandits and centers for smuggling, and French attempts to police the area are unsuccessful.

Algerian Sahara, extending east from Mauretania to the central plateaus of Ahaggar (Hoggar) and Air and the Fezzan Depression, is the best-known part of the Sahara other than the strip from Fezzan to the Syrte coast or the im-

European modification of steppe, Tunisia
[*U.S. Army photograph*]

mediate borders of Egypt. During the Ice Age precipitation was sufficiently heavy along the southern Atlas and in central Saharan plateaus for long wadies to be extended into what is now severe desert. Reg and erg materials were brought down by streams. For thousands of years the surface has lain barren and been worked over by winds. Most of it has become relatively smooth reg, but some huge sand fields have formed. Old valleys are now much drier but there is considerable subsurface seepage, so that strings of oases follow the Ice Age stream courses, such as the Zaoura wadi system. Here, in the tenth century, *foggaras* or extensive underground water systems were constructed as far south as lower Touat. An astonishing amount of labor went into the construction of foggaras, for many are deep and extend for miles. Tunnels lead out in various directions for trapping water and large underground reservoirs were constructed to retain it. Vertical shafts for removal of rock and for ventilation dot the surface above the underground workings. West and south of the foggaras of lower Touat is **tanezrouft,** a lifeless area without oases.

East of the Zaoura is the Grand Erg Occidental, a tremendous sand field about 300 miles long and 100 miles wide. Farther east, beyond the 620-mile long Wadi Ighargha, is the Grand Erg Oriental, somewhat larger than the erg to the west. Most oases north of Grant Erg Oriental are owned by Arabs who pasture their camels on the Tademait Plateau and various other open ranges, including the better territories within the ergs. Oasis settlements are urban in aspect, fortified trading posts with markets, cafes, dens of iniquity, accommodations for reprovisioning caravans, roofed streets, and mud-brick buildings several stories high. These *ksars* are populated mainly by Negroes, *haratin* (cultivators), a residue of slave population.

Central Saharan Plateaus include the Ahaggar and the Tibesti. Mt. Tahat, culminating peak of the Ahaggar, rises to 9,842 feet, and experiences an occasional blizzard that sweeps across the uplands. Channels of Ice Age wadies lead radially in various directions: to the Chotts (Shotts), toward the western tanezrouft, and toward the Niger. Tuareg tribes range the highlands, and although Negroid population increases southward, in Air, Tuaregs are their masters. The healthiest and most scenic caravan trails to the Sudan follow the southward continuation of the Fezzan Depression that separates Tuareg Ahaggar from Negroid Tibesti where one of the volcanic peaks rises to 11,209 feet.

Fezzan Depression, from the Gulf of Sidra to the gap between the highest volcanic regions of the central plateaus, retains its old racial mixtures and commercialism. Many of its people are trilingual, speaking Berber, Arabic, and Tibbu.

Libyan Desert, between Fezzan Depression and the vicinity of the Nile, contains the largest erg and most inaccessible wastes in Africa. It lacks an Ice Age wadi system, and its oases, such as those at Kufra, are remote and isolated.

Sudan Borderlands are the transition zone to humid, tropical savanna climates, and have mainly Negroid populations. The chief stronghold of Caucasoids is in the vicinity of the Dry Bend of the Niger, where it swings from a northeast to a southeast course. Tuaregs wrested this area from Negroids, and under Tuareg control Tombouctou (Timbuktu), once a city of 12,000 and center for the salt works in El Bjouf, has dropped to about half that size and retains little importance. To the east, Lake Chad has remained in Negroid territory. The lake changes size from year to year depending on the amount of water it gets from several large streams from the south. Much of the lake is bordered by marshes, and seepages lead northeast to the Bodele Depression.

MODERN CULTURAL IMPACTS

The Sahara means very little to the rest of the world except as a minor source of metals, coal, and petroleum. But on the Sahara the impact of European culture has been revolutionary, especially in Algeria where it came earliest and has been most effective. Over many important routes the old caravan speed of three miles per hour has given way to modern motor transport. European cloth and other supplies find their way even to the most primitive peoples. Date growing has been stimulated both by modern wells and higher prices. Tourists are finding novelty and attraction in desert landscapes. Hotels and warehouses line even remote routes, such as the difficult one between Atlas Lands and Tombouctou. Least affected is the almost ungoverned Spanish Sahara. Near its southern border, the French established Fort Etienne to exploit the Arguin fishing banks because of the tremendous demand for fish in the nearby African World which faces grave food-supply problems, especially since the tsetse flies have killed so many cattle.

Railroads have made minor penetrations into the fringes of the Sahara, but two motor routes have been established across it. One follows the Zaoura and lower Touat, crosses the tanezrouft, and connects at Gao with roads both up and down the Niger. The other, more attractive motor road leads from Touggourt across the Ahaggar and Sudan Borderlands, to a railhead at Kano, Nigeria. Along both the northern and southern sections of the Sahara numerous other connecting roads have been constructed. Several air routes traverse the Sahara, and many a remote oasis has its own airfield. With such transportation improvements it is to be expected that European culture will spread more widely south of Mediterranean Africa, which may also witness further Europeanization through the expanded development of mineral resources, such as the manganese, lead, coal, copper, and other deposits in Morocco, the phosphate, iron, and lead ores of Tunisia, and numerous occurrences of petroleum and natural gas. Colomb-Bechar, with manganese, copper, and lead in its neighborhood, may well develop into an industrial center of the Sahara.

EGYPT AND HAMITIC EAST AFRICA

Egypt, now joined with Syria in the United Arab Republic formed in 1958, has an area of 386,200 square miles and population of 25.6 million. Of this area, about equal to that of Texas and New Mexico combined, only about 18,000 square miles are actually useful. Some 13,800 square miles are under intensive cul-

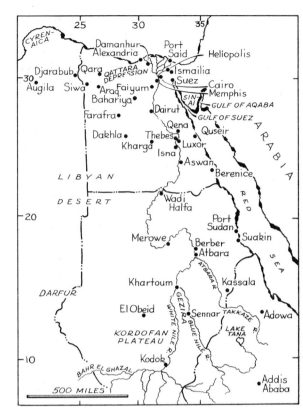

Egypt and Sudan: index map

tivation; almost 2,000 are used by date plantations, canals, and roads; and some 2,850 are occupied by the Nile waters and marshes. The Nile extends through Egypt for 960 miles, about 700 of which lie below its first cataract at Aswan, the head of navigation on the lower course. Egypt has always had but two essential parts: the Nile flood plain which is not much over 10 miles in width at any point, and the delta, a triangular tract with a Mediterranean base of about 150 miles and inland depth of 100, extending south to Cairo. Practically the entire population is crowded into this kite-and-tail-shaped area.

The physical geography of Egypt, in simplest terms, consists of the Nile Valley and flanking deserts and barren highlands. East of the Nile, the Nubian, or Arabian, Desert slopes upward to a string of highlands along the Red Sea. Separated from the northern, lower end of these highlands by the Gulf of Suez, is the rugged desert territory of Sinai Peninsula bordered on the east by the Gulf of Aqaba, which is a continuation of the Jordan Valley graben. West of the Nile is the Libyan Desert, sloping northward to the Qattara Depression where there are several small oases, such as Qara, Araq, and the famous Siwa with its ancient temple of Jupiter Ammon. Southward in a string of depressions in the Libyan Desert are isolated groups of oases, such as Kharga and Dakhla, populous centers of date production. But although these oases are important locally in the midst of their drab, dusty surroundings, they are minor compared with the Nile Valley.

For its last 1,700 miles the Nile receives no perennial tributary. The Atbara, which rises as the Takkaze in Ethiopia, is the last stream to contribute water at all seasons. Farther south is the junction of the major Nile tributaries, the Blue Nile and the White Nile. The White Nile, with its dependable, uniform flow, rises south of the equator and passes through an extensive flat area south of Kodok where it spreads sluggishly into broad marshes with many vegetation-clogged channels before it joins the Blue Nile. Both the Atbara and Blue Nile depend on monsoonal summer rains which furnish huge volumes of water for relatively short periods. These reddish, silt-laden waters have made life possible in Egypt, bringing water and new soil during the annual flood which starts in late June, reaches maximum stage in October, and ends in November. The Nile dwindles in volume as it crosses Egypt where the annual inch of rain cannot begin to make up for evaporation and irrigation losses. Today the Nile is a highly artificial river, and very little water ever reaches the Mediterranean through the channels of its delta.

CULTURE BACKGROUND

Second only in size to Mesopotamia as an oasis in the Arab-Berber Realm, Egypt is an isolated land that has been spared conquest, invasion, and unpleasant contacts to a remarkable degree. To the east and west are deserts. To the north is a desolate and harborless coast and the inhospitable, marshy delta. Above Aswan the Nile is studded with a series of rapids, or

cataracts, and farther south are broad savanna marshes. These barriers were so formidable that the ancient Egyptians did not trace the sources of the great river upon which their culture and lives depended. Thus enclosed, Egyptians remained aloof. Although trade brought Phoenicians, Greeks, and Romans, Egyptians stayed at home, living according to their own cultural traditions. Even today, few Egyptians migrate to other lands, and about 80 per cent of the present population is descended from the peoples who built the pyramids and developed the earliest irrigation systems. Most Egyptians have remained downstream from Aswan where in the twenty-sixth century B.C. a fort was erected, "Door of the South," through which products were exchanged with Ethiopians. These and other trade contacts did nothing to change the culture of the Egyptians who held tenaciously to their ancient Berber tongue.

The stay-at-home Egyptians were nevertheless greatly interested in foreign lands and their products. By 2000 B.C. Quseir had become an important port, and commerce so flourished that Thebes, 100 miles to the west, became the capital of Egypt. From India came ivory, gold, perfume, cinnamon, sandlewood, myrrh, muslin, peacocks, and apes. From the Himyarites (Arabs from the Red Sea) came tall tales of hardships at sea and difficulties of Far Eastern trade that awed the Egyptians and encouraged them to pay fancy prices for imports, such as tin and indigo. To find out about Africa, King Necho, 600 B.C., chartered a Phoenician fleet to circumnavigate the continent, which was done in three years. In general, Egyptians left the business of exploration to others even though they were long-time users and builders of boats, which first appeared on the Nile about 6000 B.C. In this almost treeless land, boat-building was a tedious job of fitting together short planks from the little acacia trees. Smaller skiffs were nothing more than bundles of papyrus, the sedge whose pulp was made into a kind of paper.

Protected from the ravages of barbarians, and isolated from its impoverished neighbors, Egypt developed a high degree of civilization which was maintained for a tremendous interval of time. Quite in contrast was the other center of ancient civilization, Mesopotamia, where the sedentary population was constantly being over-run by nomadic raiders from one side or another.

AGRICULTURAL HISTORY

Irrigation began in about 5000 B.C., and in time developed into a system whereby tracts of 5,000 to 50,000 acres were surrounded by low dikes, and were flooded for a month or so in summer. Millet, wheat, barley, and other crops were planted in the fall and harvested in the spring. Then the land stood fallow, dry and cracked until the next flooding, which would bring fertile silt as well as moisture. Originally the system was applied only along the left bank, where even today most of the villages and transportation lines are located. The higher right bank was harder to bring into production for water had to be lifted by such primitive methods as screws turned by the Nile current, water wheels that lifted small buckets to be emptied into flumes, or dipping buckets attached to balancing poles, operated by hand. Some of these devices are still in use. A change from basin irrigation came in A.D. 1820 when weirs, and later, dams, were used to divert water into ditches that led downstream to fields. The advantage of the new system is that water is applied only when plants need it, and two or three crops can be raised each year. Cotton, rice, sugar cane, and maize became summer crops, and date groves came under irrigation. The major disadvantage is that beneficial silt is no longer evenly distributed over the land, and constant cropping reduces soil productivity. Crop rotation and fertilization are necessary. There was considerable difficulty in educating the Egyptian peasant, *fellah*, in the proper use of perennial irrigation, for he was inclined to use too much water, drowning his crops and washing away soluble nutrients from the soil.

Some 6 million acres are now under irrigation, thanks to a number of dams built across the Nile. Navigation is not impeded because canals and locks lead around the dams. The irrigated lands produce relatively good yields despite the fairly primitive methods of farming.

Water buffalo and oxen are widely used as draft animals, and a hoe, wooden plow, and hand sickle are the common tools of a fellah. His tools, animals, chickens, and his numerous children are all sheltered together in his other possession, a mud hut.

Although cotton, the long-staple Egyptian kind, occupies only 20 per cent of the cultivated land, it is the main export and cash crop. Other important crops are wheat, maize, barley, rice, beans, and sugar cane, but the population is so dense that Egypt is unable to feed itself, and must import large quantities of food, as well as wood, textiles, chemicals, and manufactured goods.

POPULATION

Egypt has been a land of extreme luxury for a few and dire poverty for most of its people. Little in the way of a middle class developed except at foreign Alexandria, one of the brightest spots of the Ancient World educationally and socially. It is about the same today. The great mass of the population, the fellahs, are poor tenant farmers to whom luxury is unknown. In spite of current government efforts to educate and medicate the illiterate, diseased peasant, improvements in his lot are slow in coming.

The population, 25.6 million, is 91 per cent Moslem, 8 per cent Christian, and about 0.3 per cent Jewish. Rural densities range to 1,500 per square mile. Villages are numerous; cities are few, only two being of any real size.

Cairo, 2.8 million, is the largest city in Africa. Its site is the most advantageous in Egypt, at the head of the delta, within easy reach of Suez, Ismailia, and other places at the head of the Red Sea, and at the start of the main route west through Siwa to Cyrenaica and to the commercial routes through the Fezzan Graben. The present city, much of it above the flood plain, was founded in A.D. 968 near the original Memphis and the Pyramids, associated with with some 70 centuries of history. As capital of both Egypt and the United Arab Republic, and as the largest city in the Mohammedan World, it is an important political, commercial, and financial center, but has little industry.

Alexandria, 1.4 million, second city of Africa, is the main port and commercial outlet of Egypt. Its protected harbor at the extreme western edge of the delta escapes channel silting. Although it survived Roman and Arab destruction, the Voyages of Discovery and the appearance of the Turk dealt severe blows. When trade turned to the Atlantic, commerce along the Red Sea and across Egypt through Alexandria to Mediterranean ports ended and Alexandria became a remote port on a commercially stagnant inland sea. The opening of the Suez Canal, in 1869, led to commercial revival. At the northern end of the Suez Canal is Port Said, a naval base, port of call, and railroad terminus. The canal—104.5 miles long, 196 feet wide, and 35 feet deep—is used by about 5,000 steamers a year. In 1956 the Egyptians took over the Canal and ended the 74-year British occupation.

Lack of urban centers reflects the limited industrial development. Although there are oil deposits around the Gulf of Suez, production does not meet the needs. Iron ore deposits near Aswan, coupled with available hydroelectric power from the Nile, may in time promote local steel and metal industries. Other mineral resources, such as phosphate, manganese, sodium salts, gypsum, gold, and building stones, although of commercial importance, have not produced much industrialization.

SUDAN

Beyond the "Door to the South" lies a country of almost 970,000 square miles consisting mainly of uninhabited desert, barren steppe, or savanna-climate marshes. Its 10 million people and its economic life largely center along the White and Blue Niles. Above the junction of the rivers at Khartoum, the capital, the White Nile is navigable for a thousand miles, well into the Bahr El Ghazal, a sparsely inhabited marshy region. This is a traditional communication line between the Berber Dry World and Negroid African tropics. People in the northern two thirds of the Sudan are Arabs and Nubians, mainly Moslems, while in the south are Half-Hamites and Negroid tribes. The bushy hair

Sudan, agricultural landscape
[*U.S.D.A.*]

of these southern tribes gained for them the name Fuzzy-Wuzzy during the British intervention which ended the Dervish tyranny in 1898, and which brought about the joint Anglo-Egyptian rule of Sudan. The Republic of Sudan became independent in 1956.

The desert and steppe regions of northern Sudan support a nomadic population, with camels, sheep, goats, and cattle. Hides are a fairly important export item. To the south, gum arabic plantations in Darfur and on Kordofan Plateau supply practically all the world's needs. Vegetable ivory and various groundnuts are produced in the more tropical, southern part of the country, which also supplies true ivory, skins, mahogany, and other tropical woods. But the heart of the Sudan's agricultural productivity is in and around the Gezira Plain, between the White and Blue Niles. Here several million acres are under irrigation, producing quantities of long staple cotton, Sudan's principal export.

Nearly all the exports, as well as the large amounts of imports of manufactured goods, fuel and timber, go through Port Sudan on the Red Sea. From this well-equipped harbor, a rail line leads west to Atbara where it connects with the railway that extends from Wadi Halfa almost

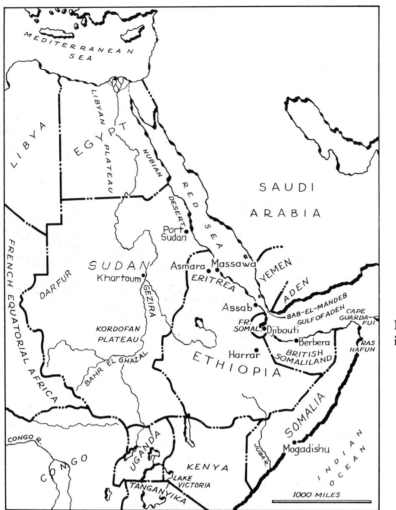

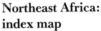

Northeast Africa: index map

to the Ethiopian border, with a branch to the west beyond El Obeid, a center for the collection of gum arabic. A branch of the railroad from Port Sudan goes through Kassala, another important cotton-producing center. Neither these railroads nor the river transports along the Nile and its tributaries are able to handle the rapidly developing commerce.

ETHIOPIA

Ethiopia, 350,000 square miles and 18.5 million population, is a plateau, most of which is over a mile high. Considerable area is above 10,000 feet, and peaks reach over 14,000 feet. This vast highland is the most extensive well-watered region in the Dry World. Rainfall is sharply monsoonal, with July and August as

wettest months, and January ordinarily dry. In spite of fertile, volcanic soils and ample rain, Ethiopia is culturally part of the Arab-Berber Realm. Its people generally prefer raising live-stock to agriculture. More than half the population are Hamitic Gallas who are largely Christian, but with many Mohammedans and pagans. The ruling class, however, is some 2 million Amharas, Coptic Christians, Semitic in speech and culture.

As in other tropical territories, elevation is a dominant factor in determining landscapes. Land below 5,000 feet yields ebony, bananas, rubber, tobacco, coffee (the main export), dates, cotton, and sugar cane, except in the desert and savanna areas in the east and northeast. In the next zone are cereals and other Mediterranean crops, with vast stretches of rough land covered with bamboo and other tall grasses. Above 8,000 feet it is quite cool, and much of the area is pasture lands, producing hides of cattle, sheep, and goats, as well as sturdy little polo ponies, donkeys, and mules. Some cereals, beans, and flax are grown.

Although some mineral resources, such as iron, coal, gold, and copper, are known to exist, most are undeveloped. There is an active and hopeful search for petroleum. Industry is still in its infancy. Such commerce as there is moves mainly on the backs of animals along pack trails, for the road system, although being expanded, is fairly limited and there is only one railroad, from the French port of Djibouti to Addis Ababa, the capital and home of some half million people.

As ancient Axum, Ethiopia was a protectorate of Rome. This accounts for much of its cultural affiliation with northern lands, as well as the tenacity with which many of its people cling to Christianity, though surrounded by Mohammedans. Italy decided to reestablish its control, and invaded the country in 1935. Ethiopia was freed by British forces in 1941. The Italian bid for control of Ethiopia started in Eritrea, which was taken over by Italy in 1890. After World War II this Italian colony came under British administration, and in 1952 was federated with Ethiopia.

Eritrea, 48,350 square miles and 1 million population, has a coastal zone that is extremely hot, dry, almost uninhabited, and malarial where water is present, and an interior that is only slightly better. As in Ethiopia, gold and other metals exist. Petroleum has been discovered near the Red Sea. The cooler, rainier upland supports some agriculture and livestock raising. The upland city, and political center, Asmara, is on the railroad that leads from Massawa, the main port, westward almost to Kassala.

ETHIOPIAN BORDERLANDS

Lowlands and low plateaus, like those of Eritrea, extend across the Horn of Africa and along the Indian Ocean coast to the Juba River, and are the easternmost African parts of the Arab-Berber Realm. Politically, France has a small Somaliland colony of 9 thousand square miles and 67 thousand people located at a very strategic place, on the African side of the Red Sea opening, Bab-el-Mandeb. Djibouti, its main city and port, handles most of Ethiopia's trade. Former British Somaliland, 68,000 square miles, runs a considerable distance along the Gulf of Aden, and its 650,000 people mainly occupy themselves producing hides, resins, gums, sheep, and goats for export through Berbera. The tip of the horn and a rather broad belt along the coast to Kenya is in Somalia which used to be an Italian colony, but achieved independence in 1960 and incorporated British Somaliland. Most of Somalia's 1.3 million people in its 194,000 square miles of barren, dry land are busy just surviving, but they do produce exportable amounts of vegetable oils, gums, hides, kapok, resin, ivory, and half the world's supply of incense. Its chief port is Mogadishu.

The Ethiopian borderlands are unattractive areas of steppe climate, comparatively poor soils, and scrub forest. Their mixed Negroid and Mediterranean populations are mainly Hamites culturally and Mohammedans, though some are pagans. Although dark of skin and often strongly Negroid, the people do not take kindly to agriculture, preferring to live according to the manner of Dry World nomads and to gather such vegetable products as grow without cultivation.

ASIAN ARAB-BERBER REALM TERRITORIES

Four fifths of the vast Arabian Peninsula is occupied by *Saudi Arabia*, 870,000 square miles, 8.5 million population, and much of the rest is in various sheikdoms and the British colony and protectorate of Aden. Traditionally Arabia has three parts: Arabia Petraea, the highlands at the head of the Red Sea, now lost to Egypt and Jordan; Arabia Deserta, the northern desert; and Arabia Felix, happy or blessed Arabia, which originally designated most of the southwest area but now applies to the Red Sea coast. Most of Arabia is geologically part of Africa, the Nubian ranges and plateaus continuing eastward past the graben of the Red Sea. The highest parts lie close to the Red Sea, and much of the area between the Gulf of Aqaba and Bab-el-Mandeb is over 5,000 feet, and well over 8,000 feet in Yemen. These rocky uplands were deeply carved during the more pluvial climate of the Ice Age when water courses plunged down the steep western slopes, cutting channels and depositing their loads across the lower territory. Somewhat less rugged surfaces were cut toward the east where slopes were gentler, although a few wadies managed to flow the entire distance to the Persian Gulf. Reg and erg surfaces have since developed on the wadi deposits. The proportion of reg to erg may be similar to that of the Sahara, and although Rub al Khali is thought to be mainly a sandy desert, there is much still to be learned about interior Arabia. In general it can be said that about half of Arabia has a desert climate and extremely sparse vegetation. The rest is mainly steppe, most useful toward the western highlands. Only Yemen and Oman highlands have precipitation ample for field agriculture. Their rains are quite reliable because they come with the summer monsoon.

The population is predominantly Basic Mediterranean. Bedouin Arabs of most of the peninsula are purely Caucasoid. In the south, however, are conspicuous evidences of the old Negroid peoples who probably once covered the peninsula. Negro slavery has been a common institution for many centuries. With few exceptions speech is Semitic, mainly Arabic and closely related languages. In the south Hamitic and other languages are found.

Unlike Egypt, Arabia has been dominated by its nomads, as is the case in the Sahara. Traditional social and political organization has been on a patriarchal and tribal basis. The most powerful tribal head today maintains his chief capital at Riyadh. Although nomads still range over most of Arabia, the majority of the population is settled in cities or engaged in sedentary pursuits.

Hejaz, along the Red Sea coast, is the cultural hearth of modern Arabia, centering in Mecca, the largest city in Arabia, and birthplace of Mohammed. In its sacred Ka'ba is the black stone supposedly given by Gabriel to Abraham, toward which all Moslems turn and prostrate themselves five times daily. Some half

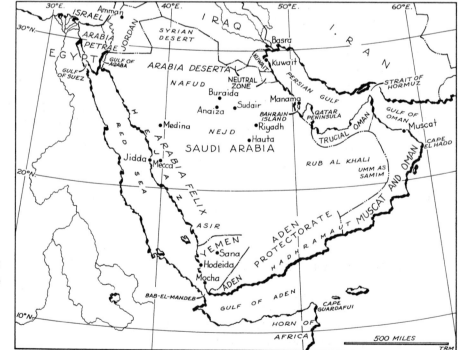

Arabia: index map

million Moslems each year make the pilgrimage to Mecca. Medina is somewhat less sacred but contains the tomb of Mohammed. Medina is the terminal of the now abandoned railroad from Esh Sham (Damascus). Jidda, chief port on the Red Sea, lies 55 miles from Mecca, and is the seat of foreign diplomats who are accredited to Mecca, but who, as infidels, are not permitted to enter the sacred city. Its imports are heavy, serving much of Arabia plus the needs of the pilgrims. Chief exports are hides, wool, and gums. The agricultural population

Oasis architecture, El Harj, Saudi Arabia
[*U.S. Army photograph*]

of Hejaz raises wheat and barley on the uplands, dates and fruits below, while many non-nomadic herders tend flocks of sheep and herds of horses, donkeys, and camels. Industry is chiefly agricultural and fairly primitive.

Nejd is the central part of the peninsula, a limestone plateau cut by wadies along which grazing is good and water holes are numerous. Between these old stream courses is extensive steppe. Practically uninhabited deserts lie at lower elevations to the north, east, and south. Most of the Nejd population is more or less sedentary, living in such settlements as Anaiza, Buraida, and Riyadh, the rapidly growing capital that is being modernized in the European sense by the current tribal ruler of Saudi Arabia, King Saud. Though in the minority, nomad tribes are the rulers and dominant people. Government appears to be fairly well

organized over the 350,000 square miles of Hejaz, Asir, and Nejd, but amounts to little more than an attempt to collect a small annual tax on each camel from nomads of the more distant and inaccessible parts of Arabia. Not included in the lands of the King of Saudi Arabia are Yemen, Muscat and Oman, Bahrein, Qatar, Trucial Oman, Kuwait, and Aden and its protectorate. Within his own territory the King has managed to curb the pillaging and raiding activities of the nomads because they realize that the government has modern tanks and guns to enforce order. His strength lies both in his leading position in the Moslem World and in the income he receives for petroleum concessions. Saudi Arabia ranks fifth among world petroleum producers. Modern, air-conditioned oil towns near the Persian Gulf are European World outposts in an extreme desert.

Yemen, a 75,000 square-mile kingdom with 5.0 million population, is the part of Arabia that deserves the name "felix," for garden agriculture begins at an elevation of about 4,000 feet. Here grew the famous coffee, "Mocha," that became "Java" when the Dutch took it to the East Indies. Hodeida, the Red Sea port, suffers from having dangerous routes to the interior where coffee, grain, and hides are in surplus, so much of the trade goes to British Aden. Sana, the capital, is an ancient walled city.

Aden is a small British colony at the strategic "south tip" of Arabia, backed by the 112,000 square-mile Protectorate. Aden is a fort and coaling station, and the main commercial distribution center for the whole peninsula. This city of nearly 150,000, with its excellent port, has one of the world's largest petroleum refineries, and also produces salt and cigarettes. Practically all food and fuel must be imported, and water is obtained by distilling sea water. The Aden Protectorate includes much of Hadhramaut, the once-commercial southern coast of Arabia, now dotted with decadent ports, and cities of many storied buildings hidden in interior valleys. Farther inland are broad expanses of steppe and erg, ranged over by nomads. East of the sand fields of Rub al Khali, toward the highlands of Oman, is Umm

(*opposite*) **Europeanized oasis, Tunisia**
[*U.S. Army photograph*]

Agricultural landscape, Judean Hills, Israel
[*Israel Office of Information*]

Traditional urban landscape, Israel
[*Israel Office of Information*]

as Samim, vast salt plains with treacherous desert quicksands.

Muscat and Oman and **Trucial Oman** occupy the coasts of southeastern Arabia, which are far more diversified in landscape than other parts of the peninsula. Peaks approaching 10,000 feet commonly have winter snow caps. Along the shore are coconut palms, and dates grow farther inland. Summer rainfall allows some agriculture, and exportable amounts of dates and other fruits are produced. In this area of 112,000 square miles are some 700,000 people who are quite unlike those of the rest of Arabia. They are mixed, but commonly have small bodies, very small, round heads with fuzzy hair, little facial hair, almost black skins, large, dark eyes, but noses and lips that are typically Caucasoid. A considerable part of the population stems from the slaves brought in from the African coast. For centuries the inhabitants of this area have taken to the sea. Occupying a particularly central and strategic position in the days when maritime activities were restricted to voyages along coasts, this area was an important link between the peoples of the Mediterranean and those of India and the Far East. Commercial ties today are mainly with India, and trade for the whole area funnels through Muscat.

Qatar is a little Arab sheikdom occupying a peninsula just east of Trucial Oman along the Persian Gulf. It enjoys the benefits from large oil deposits similar to those found nearby in Saudi Arabia and the island of Bahrein. Oil from this area is mainly piped to Saida, Lebanon, for export. In terms of oil production and reserves, the 5,800 square miles of *Kuwait* are especially valuable for it leads Middle East production. Although most of the benefits go directly to the British-controlled Sheikh, the population of over 200,000 is gaining a little from the various economic and other programs financed by these profits. Kuwait, the capital, is an important Persian Gulf port. There is considerable British and American influence both in oil exploitation and in the governments of the little sheikdoms and sultanates that border Saudi Arabia.

Jordan includes part of old Arabia Petraea, a small, fertile section west of the Jordan River, and an extensive tract of steppe and desert between the Jordan Valley and the Syrian Desert.

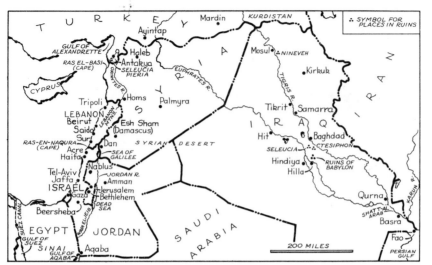

Near East: index map

Within its 37,500 square miles, the 1.5 million population consists mostly of Mohammedan Arabs, who greeted with great enthusiasm independence from the Palestine Mandate, gained in 1946. Most of the people live in the western part where irrigation makes it possible to raise crops. In this section is the old city of Bethlehem, and Jordan's control includes part of Jerusalem, a center for Arab refugees from Israel. Border clashes between the two countries are routine. The part of the Dead Sea within Jordan is a source of potash which, along with other exports, goes down the railroad to Aqaba, Jordan's only port.

MESOPOTAMIA

The northeastern frontier of the Arab-Berber Realm lies along the foothills of Kurdistan and the ranges of southwestern Iran. The great focal area of the northeast and largest oasis in the entire realm is Mesopotamia, a lowland about as extensive as the Mississippi Valley below Cairo, Illinois, and with about the same number of people. This lowland is a continuation of the depression of the Persian Gulf, which has been filled southward from Hit and Samarra with deposits from the Euphrates, Tigris, Karum, and other rivers. Most of Mesopotamia has steppe climate, but desert occurs to the south and east. Maximum rainfall comes in winter, as might be expected in territory so near

the Mediterranean. Summers are both dry and hot, temperatures of 120 being common. Winter is cool on the lowlands and cold in the uplands. The melting of winter snow on mountain ranges to the north, and the winter rains, bring floods which reach Mesopotamia in May and last until June, "too late for winter crops and too early for summer crops."

CULTURAL BACKGROUND

Legend and some Biblical scholars would place the Garden of Eden in Mesopotamia. Be that as it may, there is mounting evidence that in or near this area man made the important change from being a hunter to being an agriculturist. Plants, especially grains, were domesticated, and so were cattle, sheep, goats, and pigs. This beginning of the cultivation of plants and the herding of animals made it possible for people to have permanent settlements, rather than just roaming the countryside in search of game. Settled village farming communities began to appear in this area some 10,000 years ago. It took a while, a thousand or more years, for man to develop the art of irrigation, thus increasing his ability to produce food, and making the supply more dependable. The methods of irrigation worked out in Mesopotamia were different from those in Egypt. They were designed to cope with the roaring, destructive floods that receded just when water was needed, at the start of the hot, rainless summer. The timing of the Nile floods was much more convenient. The dam was developed, starting probably as a few bundles of reeds and some stones dumped into small channels on alluvial fans, and in time becoming a very elaborate structure, but with the same purpose of holding back flood waters so they could later be spread by ditches to the crops. The impact of agriculture and of the domestication of animals cannot be over-estimated—they brought a major change in man's way of life. Food became more certain than it had been for the primitive hunters, value was placed on land and its ownership, permanent settlements became possible, and with them, contacts, growth of trade, development of rules for the use of water and maintenance of dikes and canals, which led to further social and political organization, and finally, the advent of cities in which craftsmen could trade their skills for the surplus food produced by farmers. Well before 3000 B.C. Mesopotamia had towns with monumental temples and public buildings, carefully laid out streets, and two- or three-storied houses. These were mainly in southern Mesopotamia where by 4000 B.C. the Sumerian civilization had developed a very sophisticated social system, had invented writing, and was busily engaged in a lively export trade of rugs, textiles, jewelry, and weapons.

Around 3000 B.C. the center of power shifted north from such places on the lower Euphrates as Ur, birthplace of Abraham and site of the Tower of Babel, to Babylon. One of several reasons for the decline of Sumer was over-irrigation which raised the water table to the point where mineral salts deposited on the land reduced the yield, first of wheat, and later of barley. By this time, farming had become much more advanced, plows and rakes were in common use, and fields were manured. The control of the Babylonians then spread north along the Euphrates, through the Syrian Saddle to the Levantine coast where port cities were built to handle trade with Egypt. But life was far from peaceful during the next several centuries; chariot-riding barbarians appeared on the scene, there was widespread destruction of cities,

Kassites and Hittites invaded Babylon, all topped off with a series of earthquakes in the fourteenth century B.C. Nevertheless, a new empire arose, Assyria, north of Babylonia, with its capital at Nineveh, near modern Mosul. Nineveh finally fell to the Medes in 612 B.C. Greeks, Romans, Saracens, and then Turks were the more recent invaders. The Ottoman Turks almost wiped out the old culture. Most of the invaders came from the north, for the Syrian Desert and lowland wastes along the Persian Gulf furnished some protection from the south. Along the entire northern frontier were open valleys from the plateaus of Asia Minor and Persia, and the Tigris and Euphrates offered easy routes, much used in ancient times.

The Turks held the area until the end of World War I, putting the final touches on general decline and decay. Misery and poverty were widespread where once there had been prosperity. The population decreased by more than half, and Baghdad housed only 40,000 people where once 2 million had lived. It was considered the poorest, most remote provincial capital of Turkey. But the potentials of Mesopotamia were not overlooked by European powers. Italians were covetous, knowing that the area had possibilities of supporting a population of 30 million according to European standards. Germans were interested in its commercial potentialities, as gateway to the East, over the Berlin to Baghdad Railroad, completed in 1940. The French wanted to add it to their possessions on the northern Levantine Coast. After World War I, however, it was the British who obtained political control and petroleum concessions in what turned out to be one of the richest oil reserves on earth. The Soviet Union is deeply interested in this petroleum at present.

IRAQ

Iraq achieved independence in 1932, ending the British control under the League of Nations mandate. Within its 175,000 square miles are some 6.5 million people. Aside from about 90,000 Christians, the population is solidly Arab and Mohammedan, the Jews having migrated to Israel. Despite recent educational programs, financed by oil profits, the population is largely illiterate and disease-ridden. Population density is greatest along the tidally irrigated banks of Shatt al Arab, which is essentially a 100-mile-long date grove from Qurna to Fao, producing about 80 per cent of the world's export of dates. Dates rank second to petroleum production which comes from extensive oil fields at Basra, Kirkuk, and around Mosul. Oil royalties are paying for such improvements as irrigation and flood control programs, drainage of swamps in the lower valley, advancement of farming practices, and school construction. The raising of sugar cane and opium poppies in the south, rice and fruit along the rivers, cotton, wheat, barley, sesame, millet, and maize farther upstream, and sheep and wool in the north, occupies most of the population. Tobacco is grown along the Kurdish hills. Industry is almost non-existent, although Baghdad now has a few factories making soap, yarn, bricks, and cement. Baghdad, the capital, has grown to 1.3 million, a thriving commercial center on the navigable Tigris, served by steamer, air, and rail connections with Basra. Most trade is with Iran. Basra, Iraq's second city, is the seaport, served by ocean vessels able to use Shatt al Arab, and it has rail connections with Tehran. Mosul is a trade center on the Tigris where it emerges from the Kurdish hills, mainly a pastoral region. Oil production in Kirkuk and other places has brought new commercial activities since 1927.

SYRIA

The old Turkish province of Syria was about equivalent to the Levantine part of the Arab-Berber Realm. Today this territory includes Israel, Lebanon, and modern Syria. The former extends north from Egypt along the coast to Ras en Naqura, not far south of Sur (Tyre). To the north is coastal Lebanon, to beyond Tripoli. Modern Syria includes the northernmost coast of the Levant and a broad interior region containing the Syrian Saddle, some of upper Mesopotamia, and the hinterland of Esh Sham (Damascus). Syria, now a part of the United Arab Republic with Egypt, has an area of 72,234 square miles and a population of 4.0 million. Israel has 8,048 square miles with 2.0 million people. Lebanon's 4,000 square miles contain 1.5 million population.

Mountains and plateaus lie close to the Levantine coast. The plain along the Mediterranean is broken and narrow toward the north, but widens in Israel. Rainfall decreases southward, so where the plain is widest, it is also most arid. East of the coastal mountains, and parallel to them, is the deep graben, the Jordan Valley, most pronounced from Lebanon southward. The graben isolates the coastal mountains which are highest in Lebanon, where the peaks, reaching 11,000 feet, accumulate snow in winter. The mountains are broken in places where rivers running along the graben cut through to the coast. The Orontes River forms such a gap near Antakya (Antioch) just north

Mediterranean agriculture, Israel
[*Israel Office of Information*]

of the Syrian border. This gap was one of the important ancient routes across the Syrian Saddle to Mesopotamia. To the south, the El Kebir River cuts through the mountains just north of Tripoli, providing an easy route to Homs. The Litani forms a similar gap where it turns westward around the southern end of the Lebanon Mountains. The Esdraelon Plain, a fertile, wheat-raising region extending inland from Haifa, provides an easy route to the graben, Damascus, and other interior points, but there is little traffic these days between Arab and Jewish places. Southward from the Sea of Galilee, much of the graben is below sea level, including the lowest lands on earth, 1,292 feet below sea level, along the shores of the Dead Sea. The extreme arid southern part of the graben extending to the Gulf of Aqaba, with unbearably hot summers, is an excellent boundary between Israel and Jordan.

Neither graben nor highlands to its east are very distinctive in northern Syria. Southward the western margin of the plateau leading to the Syrian Desert is more abrupt. Most of the upper part of the plateau is steppe, but this grassland belt merges into desert eastward, at lower elevations, toward the Syrian Desert.

CULTURAL BACKGROUND

The coastal lowland corridor, attractive agriculturally, strategic commercially, and the connecting link between Egypt and Mesopotamia, has been used by various peoples since prehistoric time. Great ports were built here during early Babylonian times, and from here the Phoenicians carried on their maritime activities in the Mediterranean. During the second millennium B.C., Egyptians, Assyrians, Hittites, and Phoenicians struggled for control of the northern part of the area, while the southern part was being settled by a very advanced people, the Philistines. Jaffa became their commercial center. The interior was a land of tribal nomads.

The ancient Levantine trade involved such articles as pearls, spices, and jewels from India; gems and embroideries from Babylon; sheep, goats, and wine from northern Mesopotamia;

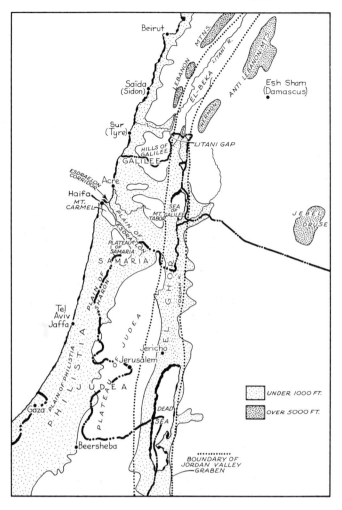

Levant: relief

horses, cattle, and metals from Armenia; and gums, perfumes, ivory, and cloth from Egypt. From the Mediterranean shores traders brought olive oil, wine, copper, and purple dye. In Lebanon and on Cyprus were sources of timber. Trade continued to flourish through Roman times, which also brought other gains, such as peace, aqueducts, better buildings, and roads. With decline of Roman power, the Syrian Saddle came under the depressing rule of Antioch. The coming of the Saracens in 638 saw a revival of trade, Far Eastern goods moving in quantity from the Persian Gulf, through Mesopotamia, to the Mediterranean. The Crusaders, who reached the Levantine Coast at various times after 1098, were just as interested in this

Modern urban landscape, Tel Aviv
[*Israel Office of Information*]

thriving trade as in suppressing Mohammed-anism. In 1268 Egyptians gained control of the Saddle and held it for two centuries until the Ottoman Turks overpowered them and brought a period of blight to all of Syria, Mesopotamia, and most Saracen lands. The usefulness of the Syrian Saddle declined when Far Eastern trade began to move via the Red Sea, and the final blow came with the Voyages of Discovery when trade turned toward the Atlantic.

The differences among invaders of old Syria have been cultural and political, rather than racial. Most invaders were peoples of Mediterranean stock, the main exception being the appearance of considerable numbers of Armenians. Since the creation in 1948 of the State of Israel, almost a million Jews have migrated to that country, and about an equal number of Arabs have departed. The Jews came mainly from Europe and are a composite racial mixture, with Alpine and Nordic, as well as Mediterranean strains. Their cultural backgrounds are extremely varied. The uniting bonds are

religion, and the fact of having escaped from persecution.

CULTURAL LANDSCAPES

Relics from Antiquity occur in the form of ruins of cities, fragments of Roman aqueducts, erosional consequences of deforestation, and the like. Syria is a typical Moslem land in which slender minarets dominate the skylines of cities and towns. The dry interior is a region of nomads, water-holes, and trails; typically Dry World. Population is concentrated in oases, in Dry World fashion, but along the Mediterranean coast, life becomes more European. The coastal cities are white masses of angular buildings, commonly surrounded by bright green citrus trees, framed by rather barren highlands above the deep blue of the sea, with much the same appearance as cities of Greece, Sicily, or Barbary. The coastal population and landscapes are culturally Mediterranean. Syria is a transitional zone between culture worlds.

Most of the population is agricultural, raising wheat, barley, maize, millet, cotton, sesame, melons, figs, citrus fruits, tobacco, olives, and grapes. The areas of Jewish immigration are particularly productive. The plains of Sharon and Esdraelon, and the Negev, the semi-desert region in the south, have witnessed the development of important collective farms of modern design. Citrus fruits are the main cash crops, and quantities of wheat, barley, millet, olives, grapes, and vegetables are grown. Nevertheless, Israel has to import food, together with machinery and raw materials needed by growing industries which are producing exportable quantities of automobiles, textiles, pharmaceuticals, wine, and polished diamonds. Except for oil refining, the industries of Syria and Lebanon are mainly those associated with agriculture.

Seaports north of Tripoli are comparatively unimportant, but serve local hinterlands. Tripoli, connected by railroad with Homs and by pipeline with oil fields east of Mosul, is an important export center for petroleum, and manufactures olive oil and soap. Some of the Iraqi oil goes north by a branch pipeline from Homs for export through Baniyas, Syria. Beirut, with rail connection to Esh Sham (Damascus), is capital of Lebanon, chief port of Syria, and an important outlet for citrus fruits, olive oil, soap, tobacco, hides and other products. Saida exports lemons and is terminus of a petroleum pipeline from Saudi Arabia. The fine harbor of Acre was the main port for the Crusades, the place where Medieval Europeans came into contact with arts and sciences their ancestors had forgotten, and developed tastes for foods and luxuries that stimulated trade which finally resulted in the Voyages of Discovery and the Commercial Revolution. Haifa, on the plain of Acre, is the main outlet for products of the plain of Esdraelon, and, until the Arab-Israeli difficulties, was an important exporter and refiner of petroleum. Tel-Aviv-Jaffa is the main outlet for the oranges, olive products, wine, and other items from the plain of Sharon, and is the largest and most modern city in Israel.

An inner belt of cities extends south from Baleb (Aleppo), largest city in Syria, and crossroads of rail lines leading through Turkey to Europe, through the Syrian Saddle to Baghdad and Basra, and south through Esh Sham to southern Jordan. It has considerable textile industry, as has Homs. Esh Sham, capital of Syria, is an oasis site with textile mills, tanneries, cigarette factories, flour mills, and other industries. Jerusalem is a Holy City to believers of three flourishing and large religions: Jews, Christians, and Mohammedans. The city has been in the hands of a number of conquerors, and at present has an uncomfortable status of being part under Jordan, part under Israel, and claimed by both. A tremendous number of pilgrims and tourists visits Jerusalem, and Bethlehem, not far to the south, where the Church of the Nativity is said to be the oldest Christian church in the world.

The creation and growth of Israel brings European World culture into an area long in the Arab-Berber Realm. Conflicts between arriving Jews who consider this their historic homeland, and Arabs whose ancestors have held the territory since the thirteenth century, are deep and continuing.

TURKO-MONGOLIAN REALM

Khyber Pass landscape
[*Embassy of Pakistan, Washington*]

14. *Turko-Mongolian Realm*

North of Syria and Mesopotamia ways of life change, the date-palm oases disappear from the landscape, and it is necessary to find protection from the winter cold. These changes were unattractive to the Arabs, who contented themselves with the conversion of peoples in Anatolia and the Iranian Plateau to Mohammedanism, but did not remain as settlers. Later, the Turks conquered lands as far south as southern Arabia, but they preferred to stay in the north and govern from afar. Therefore, political and religious history has not greatly modified the culture break which occurs at about the isotherm of January 32° F. This culture break, however, is based on more than environmental changes. In large measure it stems from contrasts in the cultural heritages of Turks and Mongoloids to the north and Arabs and Berbers to the south which produced somewhat different culture traits. Nevertheless, the major patterns of Dry World life, such as pastoral nomadism and sedentary agricultural populations around oases, extend from the Atlantic Ocean to Mongolia.

The Turko-Mongolian lands cover much of the heart of central Asia (see Dry World: index map), and are bordered by two realms of the European World to the west and north, the other realm of the Dry World to the southwest, and the Oriental World to the southeast. Politically they are fringed by the Soviet Union along their entire north border.

225

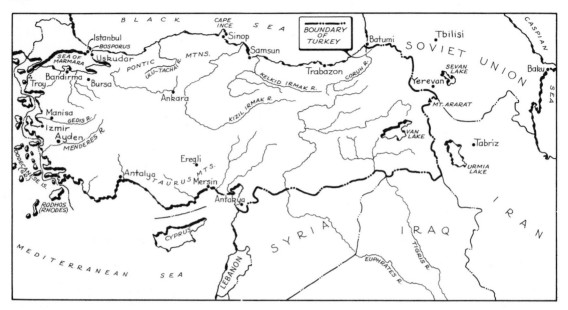

Anatolia: index map

ANATOLIA

Most of Anatolia is a plateau some 3,000 feet high in the peninsula, rising eastward to over 5,000 feet. Around the edges of the plateau, and rising above it, are mountain ranges which, along the north and south coasts, slope steeply down to narrow coastal lowlands. The whole peninsula is part of the east-west Eurasian mountain barrier, and the frequency of earthquakes shows that many Anatolian mountains are still growing. The most useful lowlands lie in the west where the highlands are like a hand with slightly-spreading fingers pointing toward the Aegean. The lowlands, between the fingers, are readily accessible from the Aegean and European Turkey.

Anatolia receives more precipitation than is typical of the Dry World; over 20 inches annually being common along the coasts and seaward slopes, and even more than that on parts of the eastern Black Sea coast. Many short streams lead to the Mediterranean and Aegean, about half the peninsula drains into the Black Sea, and the southeastern part drains into the Persian Gulf through the Euphrates and Tigris. The only interior basins, typical Dry World drainage patterns, lie north of the Taurus

ranges. In these and other interior parts, winters are rather severe, and summers are hot and dry. Most of interior Anatolia is cold-winter steppe, with appropriate Dry World landscapes, quite in contrast to the coastal belts which enjoy Mediterranean climate, with mild winters and cool-season precipitation. Winter rains are effective for growing cereal crops, and summer drought provides a dependable harvest season and an opportunity for drying fruit. Landscapes of the lowlands, especially around Izmir (Smyrna) and Ayden, are essentially Mediterranean in character. Transition to the Dry World lies behind and above, beyond a zone of maquis.

CULTURAL BACKGROUND

Anatolia has always served as a connecting link between most of Asia and southeastern Europe. Peoples moving west commonly came along the steppe route across southern Russia, and their paths converged with others from the southeast at the Sea of Marmara. The traditional westward route for both invaders and commerce crossed Asia Minor close to the parallel of 40° N. through Ankara. This traffic, plus invasions from the west, resulted in considerable mixing of racial stocks. When Ankara was capital of the Hittite Empire, in about 2200 B.C., the people were Armenoid, the racial stock still dominant. Dinarics and Mediterraneans often invaded from the west, especially during the spread of Greek power. Greeks occupied the coastal lands, and at times their ambitions extended farther inland. Population stocks were mixed accordingly.

In the third century B.C. Anatolia was one of the most advanced participants in western civilization, with numerous industrial settlements noisily making cloth, carpets, pottery, wines, and wares of bronze, gold, silver, and iron. Coastal districts prospered during Roman times, but generally declined when Roman control weakened. The Turks began to arrive in the eleventh century A.D. These Dry World inhabitants from east of the Caspian were Mongoloid, and used Ural-Altaic languages quite unlike the basic Indo-European tongues of the peninsula. Waves of horse-riding Ottoman Turks later swept across the country, bent on plunder and conquest and on conversion of peoples to Mohammedanism, the religion the Turks had adopted while conquering Saracen lands. In 1683 they were at the outskirts of Vienna, where they were repulsed in a battle that was quite largely responsible for most

Europeans being Christian today, rather than Mohammedan. With the zeal of new converts, the Turks spread their religion and persecuted infidels with greater thoroughness than the Saracens in their crossing from Africa to Iberia.

During the last two and one half centuries the Turkish Empire has declined and shrunk, especially with the loss of Armenia, Syria, Mesopotamia, part of Arabia, and Palestine during World War I. At the end of that war Turkey became a republic, and placed its capital in Asian Ankara, away from European Istanbul. Paradoxically, retreat to Asia was soon followed by considerable Europeanization. The severe restrictions of Mohammedan faith were abolished, rights of non-Turkish people recognized, slavery and polygamy went overboard, the Gregorian calendar and 24-hour clock were adopted, as was the metric system, and schools were established. Compulsory, free education is now provided for all children.

Turks have intermixed with the Armenoid and Dinaric stocks to such an extent that Mongoloid traits have practically disappeared, as they have in Hungary. Turkey is almost purely a Caucasoid land today, although the Ural-Altaic Turkish language, Osmanli, is widespread. Helenic Greek survives on some coastal plains as a relic of expelled Greeks. In the east the language is Indo-European Armenian.

Islamic and Turkish advances

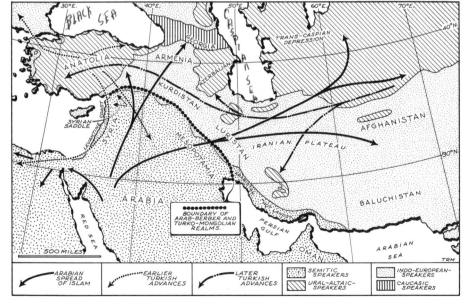

MODERN TURKEY

The Republic of Turkey has an area of 296,500 square miles and almost 27 million population, mainly distributed in the northwestern half of the country in patterns that lack concentration in oases and other Dry World characteristics. Most of the people are farmers, operating in fairly antiquated ways, and living in small, mainly isolated villages. Programs for mechanization and modernization of farms are only beginning to make themselves felt. Although only about 10 per cent of the land is in crops, they account for the bulk of the national income, the leading exports being wheat, barley, tobacco, and cotton. Dried fruits, nuts, and grapes are products of the Mediterranean lowlands. These and other exports, such as silk, sesame, olives, and opium, are largely shipped through Izmir, the principal port, which also serves as an outlet for the more typical Dry World products of the interior, such as grains, hides, and livestock.

Much of the interior plateau is called home by nomads, with herds of sheep and goats. The main item of diet is yoghurt, made from soured milk. The summer abode is a tent, but in winter both nomads and sedentary folk retire to squalid villages of mud huts where they carry on such home industries as weaving and rug making. The sharply seasonal climate favors transhumance, which is far more characteristic of the Turko-Mongolian than of the Arab-Berber Realm.

Somewhat out of character with its surroundings is the modern city of Ankara, main city of the interior and capital of the country. Its half million population, however, is overshadowed by the more than a million in Istanbul, which serves as Europe's gate to Asia Minor, has an excellent natural harbor, and conducts a variety of industries, such as shipbuilding, munitions manufacturing, and fishing.

Turkey's progress toward industrialization has been slow, largely because of inadequate transportation facilities, rather than lack of raw materials, for the country is well endowed with mineral resources. Lignite is widespread in the peninsula, and coal deposits are being exploited to develop a steel industry. Turkey leads in the world production of chrome, and mines considerable amounts of copper and lead, but has not fully developed its deposits of manganese, zinc, antimony, silver, and other minerals. Increasing production of salts and sulphur forms the basis of a growing chemical industry. Textiles, long a basic industry, are essentially self-sufficient, using home-produced cotton and wool.

The continuation of recent trends will remove most of Turkey from being transitional territory between culture worlds. Like coastal Barbary, it is rapidly becoming part of the European World, although the interior lands are likely to remain part of the Dry World.

ARMENIA

Most of the region between Syria and the Black and Caspian seas is politically within Turkey, but actually is dominated by peoples who speak Armenian, Iranic, and Tataric languages. It is chiefly high, rugged territory, where life is tribal and nomadic. Government control by Turkey, Iran, and the Soviet republics of Georgia, Armenia, and Azerbaijan is not very strong. But the boundary between Turkey and the Soviet Union is very real, Turkey having determined to be a bulwark against communism.

Along the Black Sea coast, east of Cape Ince, are Greek- and Armenian-speaking peoples, while eastward, across Georgia, is Caucasic- and Tataric-speaking territory in part dominated by European World influences. Batumi, main seaport of western Georgia, is also the end of a pipeline from oilfields at Baku, the capital of Azerbaijan, which is predominantly part of the Dry World. In the lowlands of Azerbaijan and Armenia people engage in agriculture wherever sufficient water exists, raising cereals, cotton, grapes, and various fruits. Life in the volcanic, barren uplands is nomadic except near mining and industrial centers, such as Yerevan, on the rail line from Tbilisi to Tabriz. Plants for making synthetic rubber, cement, and other products rise here and there amid rather barren surroundings. Settlements vary from mud hovels, partially underground on account of the winter cold, to attractive settlements of German Mennonites, or Persian-type oasis towns. Above the timber line in the highlands are rather poor pastures, while in the deep valleys are rice fields and irrigated plots of cotton and tobacco. Here and there a camel caravan lends contrast to horse-drawn carts or automobiles along occasional roads.

Tabriz, a city of some 300,000 in northwestern Iran, is the leading political and commercial center of one of the most densely populated parts of Persia, the fertile lands east of Lake Urmia. Here the people speak Tataric-Turkish, read and write in Persian, and pray in Arabic. The city has a long and stormy history, including periods of power and prosperity, misfortune and decline, invasions, sackings, and earthquakes. The new rail connection with Tehran may perk up its commerce, and if the link with the Turkish railroads is completed, trade may again flow along the ancient caravan route to the west, providing a non-Russian outlet for its world-famous wines and rugs.

IRANIAN PLATEAU

Southeast of the high mountains of Armenia and Kurdistan is the extensive Iranian Plateau, extending to the highlands of Afghanistan and the borders of India. Politically this area lies in Iran (Persia), Afghanistan, and Baluchistan. Most of the people of the sparsely-inhabited Iranian Plateau and its immediate highlands are Caucasoids, mainly Irano-Afghan Mediterraneans who are tall, long-faced, high-headed, and hooked-nosed. Indo-European languages of the Iranic family are dominant. Mohammedanism, the leading religion, is mostly of the Shiite branch which rejects many of the orthodox beliefs and practices of Islam.

Population density reaches a maximum across a belt from the Caspian to the head of the Persian Gulf. The old Elamite civilization

Iranian Plateau: index map

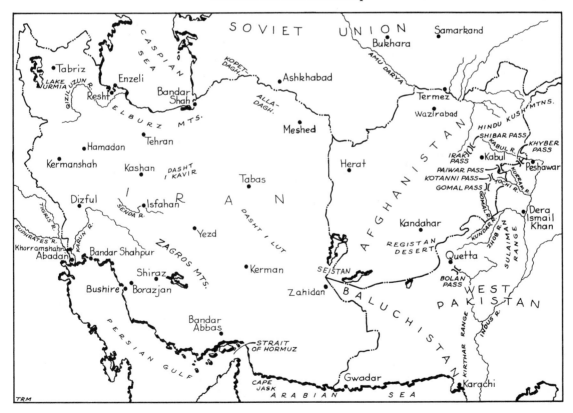

centered in this area, just north of the Persian Gulf. Sometime prior to the seventh century B.C. trade routes led north and east across the northern part of the plateau to Bactra (later Balkh, now Wazirebad) in northern Afghanistan, then along the Amu Darya and across Pamir to Tarim. Silk and gold came west from China to Persia. By the sixth century B.C. goods were coming by boat from India. Susa, near existing Dizful, was the center and most important capital of ancient Persia, but it and the country began to decline toward the end of the fifth century B.C., and the following centuries witnessed invasions by Saracens, Armenians, and various Mongoloid peoples from the northeast.

IRAN

Iran (Persia), 628,000 square miles and 20 million population, has somewhat the shape of a sugar scoop tilted eastward. Rather continuous highland rims flank either side, with the main plateau sloping and widening eastward toward the desert of Lut and the large enclosed basin of Seistan. Amid the highlands of western Iran, from the Tabriz region through the Zagros Mountains, where most of the land is above 8,000 feet and some peaks rise above 14,000 feet, are many fertile valleys producing wheat and barley. These highlands are also the home of Turks, Kurds, and Arabs, nomads who wander up and down the slopes in search of grass for their herds of sheep and goats. Although they are the producers of most of the wool used in the famous Persian shawls, rugs, and other textiles, they are also noted pillagers and robbers, resisting governmental control, and maintaining tribal and patriarchal organization in the Dry World manner. From the herds come quantities of butter and cheese, as well as hides which are mainly tanned at Hamadan.

South of Dizful the mountains give way to the Mesopotamian plain where dates and various Mediterranean crops are grown. A refinery and shipping port for Iranian oil, which is produced near the head of the Persian Gulf, has been built on the delta island of Adaban. Just upstream is Khorramshahr, a major trading port and, like Bandar Shahpur, a terminus of the railroad from Bandar Shah on the Caspian.

Mountains parallel the Persian Gulf, as do "hot lands." Along the eastern Gulf coast, summer temperatures commonly rise above 100° and annual rainfall rarely amounts to 10 inches. The port of Bushire is the main trade center for this hot desert region, and the outlet for interior Shiraz, a commercial center and one of several important oases on the inner side of the rather inhospitable ranges. Although this interior region receives little rainfall, considerable agriculture is made possible by irrigation, using the ample water supply of the Senda River, and by water supply systems resembling the foggaras of the Libyan and western Algerian oases. Kanats, or networks of small tunnels, carry the water from the sources to the oasis ditches. Wheat, fruits, rice, millet, maize, cotton, opium poppies, and tobacco are typical oasis crops. The leading metropolis of the oasis belt is Isfahan, a center for making brass and other wares, rug industries, and opium processing. It is a distinctly oriental city. Other important oases are Kashan, a textile and food-processing center, and Yezd and Kerman, centers of agriculture and carpet making.

In contrast to these interior dry regions, are the well-watered coastal lowlands along the Caspian Sea, where rice, cotton, olives, lemons, citrons, deciduous fruits, and sugar cane are grown. Most towns avoid the lowest, malarial flats, and lie on the more healthful slopes leading up to the Elburz and other ranges that rim northern Iran and extend eastward to the high Hindu Kush of northeastern Afghanistan. Snow-capped peaks of these ranges rise high above extensive alpine pastures and forests. On the south slope of the Elburz Range lies Tehran, the capital and leading city of Iran, with nearly 2 million population. Nearby Mt. Demavend looms well over 18,000 feet. Tehran occupies an important crossroads site, at the hub of highway and railroad lines: east-west routes connecting Meshed with Tabriz and points in and across Anatolia, north-south routes between the Caspian Sea and Persian Gulf, and branching lines to other centers in western Iran. Most of the growth of Tehran has occurred since 1920. The older parts of town contrast sharply with the newer, modernistic buildings. There has been some industrial development, but the main interests are political and commercial.

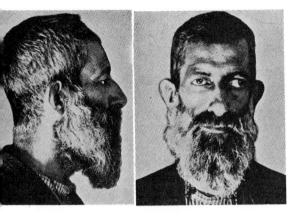

Irano-Afghan Mediterranean

[*from E. A. Hooton,* Up from the Ape, © *1946, The Macmillan Company*]

About one third of Iran's population are pastoral nomads, living mainly in the arid interior, especially the western parts where extensive areas are covered by steppe vegetation. Toward the east and southeast there are fewer and fewer inhabitants because of the aridity coupled with extremely hot summers and bitterly cold winters. Unattractive to nomads and everyone else is Dasht-i-Kavir, an extensive salt desert, and the even more arid Dasht-i-Lut. Almost no one lives in these places of broad reg and scattered high dune fields or in their continuations into southeastern Iran.

To the rest of the world Iran is important because of its petroleum. Of less importance are its exports of carpets, cotton, fruits, wool, hides, rice, gums, and various drugs, including opium. Petroleum exports are worth more than all of these, and are the major source of Iran's income. Until nationalization of the oil industry in 1951, most of the petroleum was produced by the British-controlled Anglo-Iranian Oil Company, although American and Soviet Union interests had some concessions. After three years of internal strife and widespread unemployment because of the closing of the Adaban refinery, an agreement was signed in 1954 between Iran and oil companies in Britain, America, Nether-

lands, and France to operate the refinery and thus assure a much-needed supply of petroleum for Great Britain and Western Europe as well as income for Iran.

Other mineral resources are only partially known or developed. Coal exists on both slopes of the Elburz and is mined near Tehran. Turquoise mines have long operated near Meshed. Iron, copper, lead, manganese, nickel, and cobalt are produced in small amounts, as are salt, borax, and marble.

BALUCHISTAN

Southeast of Iran and extending along the southern border of Afghanistan, is Baluchistan, a sparsely-inhabited, typical Dry World territory with extensive deserts, unimportant oases, and an extremely barren coast. It was along this coast that Arab navigators experienced greatest hardships in carrying on trade with India. Long under British control, the area is now part of Pakistan, but is cut off from the heart of West Pakistan, the Indus Valley, by the Kirthar and Sulaiman ranges. A lowland between the ranges leads to 6,000-foot Bolan Pass crossed by road and rail to Quetta, from which roads lead westward to Zahidan in Iran, and northward to Kandahar in Afghanistan. Quetta was practically demolished by an earthquake in 1935, but has been rebuilt. Here, rainfall is sufficient for raising sorghum, the main cereal food, wheat, barley, and fruits.

AFGHANISTAN

The dominant state of the eastern part of the Iranian Plateau is Afghanistan, 250,000 square miles and 12 million population. Its importance lies in passes across the Hindu Kush leading from the Indus to the Amu Darya, and its command of routes to Tehran. Historically, the high Afghan passes have been gateways for peoples and culture traits invading the lowlands of India, so British India supported Afghan independence as a means of creating a buffer against Russia. As a route state, Afghanistan is an anomaly, for it lacks adequate roads. The

people are fairly primitive and backward, mainly of Irano-Afghan Mediterranean stock, speaking Indo-European languages. In the east and south, Pashto is the common tongue, as it is in the adjacent part of Baluchistan. In the west, Persian and Iranic dialects are spoken. The religion is almost solidly Mohammedan.

The most famous pass of Afghanistan is Khyber, between Kabul and Peshawar, crossed by a road that winds through the mountains slightly south of the Kabul River gorge. To the south are other passes, such as Paiwar, Kotanni, and Gomal, and in the narrow easternmost extension of Afghanistan are several passes between the upper Indus Valley and the upper Amu in Tadzhik S.S.R. Most of the trade, however, goes through Khyber Pass.

Large areas are suitable for agriculture, and winter wheat and barley, and summer millet, maize, rice, and tobacco are grown, in addition to a variety of fruits. Mountain snows supply water for irrigation. Mineral resources include little-worked deposits of copper, lead, iron, silver, and some coal. Petroleum occurs in the north and west. But these resources are of little interest to the Afghans who prefer nomadic to sedentary pursuits. In a land averaging over 4,000 feet in elevation, between the high Hindu Kush territory rising to over 25,000 feet, and the low, extremely hot and barren Registan Desert, are rough grazing lands much to their liking. Here they raise sturdy ponies, camels, cattle, goats, and the native fat-tailed sheep. The tail fat is important in Afghan and many

**Turan:
index map**

during their two-year army service. Kabul, the capital, is the leading political and educational center. Herat, in addition to being a route center, has considerable textile and rug industry.

TURAN

North and northeast of the Iranian Plateau is the trans-Caspian or Turanian depression, a typical Turko-Mongolian territory. Ural-Altaic Turkic languages are spoken by most of the peoples from the Caspian across this arid belt to Mongolia. The dominant religion of these Mongoloid peoples is Mohammedanism. Topographically, the culture region of Turan is a southern extension of the Siberian lowland, but the contrast between the northern and southern parts is a matter of climate and vegetation. Turan is essentially a region of pastoral nomadism, desert, and oasis agriculture, whereas the Siberian lands are useful for field agriculture and forests. Politically, the Turan region includes most of the area within the Soviet Republics south of the Russian Soviet Federal Socialistic Republic and east of the Caspian. The areas and populations of these five republics are somewhat greater than those of Turan because they include lands that are culturally Siberian along the northern parts of Kazakh S.S.R. and considerable areas of highlands of the great central Asian ranges in the east that are not typically Turanian. Also, Turan has been invaded by European ways, especially in urban centers and in areas possessing mineral wealth. Nuclear Turan covers an area of about 1 million square miles and has a population of about 15 million.

TABLE 4

Approximate areas and populations of Turanian Soviet Republics (1959)

	Area, thousands of square miles	Population, millions
Turkman S.S.R.	189	1.6
Uzbek S.S.R.	159	8.1
Tadzhik S.S.R.	56	1.9
Kirgiz S.S.R.	77	2.1
Kazakh S.S.R.	1,073	9.3
	1,554	23.0

other Turko-Mongolian diets as a substitute for butter. In the northern part of the country an important source of revenue is the karakul lamb. Commerce and industry thus specialize in animal products. The main exports are hides, wool, textiles, sheepskin coats, and ghee, a clarified semifluid butter made by melting butter from various animal milks, cooling, and pouring off the liquid part, ghee.

Though remote and primitive, Afghanistan is making considerable progress toward modern ways of living and improved agriculture and industry, largely with the help of financial and technical aid from the United States and the U.S.S.R. In 1932 slavery was abolished, and the University of Kabul was established. All education is free, and is compulsory for men

Since earliest times Turan has experienced upsetting invasions. The many fine oases and broad zones of good grazing land along the flanks of the central Asian mountains in southeastern Turan attracted nomadic invaders. They came mainly from the east, moving across the steppe-lands of Mongolia, through Dzungaria, to Lake Balkhash. Some peoples continued across the grazing lands of northern Turan to the steppes of southern Russia. Others went into southeastern Turan, the traditional home of Turkic peoples since prehistoric times. Chinese came, and at the start of the Christian Era they held lands as far west as Aral Sea. Arabs from the southwest arrived in the eighth century A.D., planting Mohammedanism throughout Turan. Then Genghiz Khan and his Mongols appeared. During the latter days of the Khan empires Turan rose to its political highpoint. Timur (Tamerlane) made Samarkand his capital in 1370. It was one of the most lavish, enlightened, and powerful cities the world has known, but it and the empire crumbled after Timur's death. Ottoman Turks, replacing the tolerant and learned Mongols, hated all foreigners, had no respect for cultural refinements, and were ruthless conquerors. After a long period of decline, Tashkent and Bukhara fell into Russian hands. It remained for Soviet control, however, to advance the lot of Turanian peoples or to bring about anything more than minor development of their resources.

CULTURAL LANDSCAPES

Most of Turan receives less than 10 inches of precipitation annually, and at least half the area is desert. Summers are hot and winters are cold, the below freezing temperatures making it necessary to protect animals. The main desert belt extends from Lake Balkhash to the Caspian, and includes the Muyun Kum, a reg and salt-flat desert, the Kyzyl Kum with extensive reg, Kara Kum, a black sand desert, and Ust Urt Plateau, mainly reg and hammada. Aside from oases and centers established along routes, these deserts are practically uninhabited.

The steppes are of more value, although the summer drought, experienced especially in the east, forces the nomads to take long journeys in search of pastures for their horses and fat-tailed sheep. Late summer finds the grass withered and the many playas in the Kirgiz Steppe have become saline flats. Lake Balkhash, the largest Kirgiz lake, is saline except near the mouths of streams that feed it, such as the Ili. The steppes are the home of the Kirgiz, living in collapsible, felt-lined yurts (a type of tent in use as far east as Mongolia), ranging widely, and depending almost wholly on animals for food, shelter, and livelihood. They are considered the most purely pastoral nomads on earth. Their domain shades off northward into areas of marginal dry farming. The vast Kirgiz Steppe is in the giant Kazakh S.S.R. Its capital, Alma Ata, lies in the east, in territory that raises livestock, wheat and other grains, and that commands the Ili Valley route to central Asia. To the north, across deserts and Lake Balkhash, is the great Karaganda industrial region. Far to the west is the Ural-Emba petroleum region. Both of these European World outposts in the Dry World have introduced ways of life very foreign to the Kirgiz-speaking nomads who range over the intervening lands.

Streams fed by some of the highest mountains on earth enter Turan from the east. The Ili and the Chu are not very useful, but the Syr Darya and the Amu Darya are the "Niles" of Turan. Syr Darya rises in western Tien Shan and flows into the important valley of Fergana. This densely populated region produces a large share of the Soviet Union's cotton. In addition,

Kara Kum landscape
[U.S.D.A.]

this intensively cultivated, irrigated valley also grows such typical Turanian crops as wheat, barley, vegetables, flax, sesame, sugar beets, melons, and fruits. Andizhan, Fergana, Leninabad, Namangen, and Kokand are thriving agricultural centers. Osh is a route center, lying on the ancient commercial connection between the Far East and western lands that crossed Terek Pass between Fergana and Kashgar in the Tarim Basin, and on routes southward, across high passes, to the upper Amu Darya. Tashkent, on a tributary of the Syr, not far below Fergana Valley, is capital of the Uzbek S.S.R. and the leading industrial city of Turan. It manufactures textiles, steel, and agricultural products. Mineral resources in the Republic include coal, petroleum, sulphur, and copper. Karakul fur, ordinary wool, and hides are among its surplus commodities.

The Kirgiz S.S.R. is comparatively small and restricted to mountainous territory north of Fergana and east along the Tien Shan to Tengri Khan, a peak rising to 23,622 feet. It is rich in minerals, including lead, zinc, copper, tin, gold, silver, and petroleum. Wheat, rice, sugar beets, tobacco, vegetables, and fruits are grown by its once purely nomadic inhabitants, who still produce a valuable surplus of karakul, wool, and hides. Their domestic crafts are mainly rug weaving, preparing hides, and making leather articles. In Tadzhikstan, the mountainous republic to the south, these handicrafts have largely been replaced by heavy industry based on abundant hydroelectric power and local mineral deposits. The chief occupation, however, is agriculture. Irrigated crops of cotton, cereals, rice, and sugar cane are grown in the valleys, with fruits and grapes along the slopes. From high Tadzhik, the Zeravshan flows westward toward, but dries up before it reaches, the Amu. Along the Zeravshan is a string of oases, such as Samarkand, in the Uzbek S.S.R., now an agricultural center, but with turquoise-tiled buildings, arcaded passages, elaborate tombs, and Eastern atmosphere that are relics of its fifteenth-century glory when it was one of the jewels of the Mongol-Mohammedan world. Bukhara, the last Zeravshan oasis, is an important route center, on the main railroad from

Fergana and Tashkent to the Caspian and on a branch line connecting points along the Amu.

The Amu Darya, second of the Turan "Niles," leads from the Pamirs to Aral Sea. The upper valley, divided between Afghanistan and the Tadzhik S.S.R., produces cotton and other crops, while the lower valley leads through deserts with large ergs, and contains a string of agricultural oases from Kerki to Kungrad and Chimbai on the delta. Aral Sea, like other terminal desert lakes, is saline, and variable in size. West of Amu Darya is the sandy Kara Kum, with very few oases except along the Murghab south from Mary where typical oasis crops of cotton, grain, and oil seeds are grown. The Kara Kum occupies most of the Turkmen S.S.R. Coal, petroleum, sulphur, barite, lime, and gypsum are the main mineral resources. Ashkhabad, the capital, is a center of trade with Meshed, and is on the rail line to Krasnovodsk, the Caspian port for steamers to Baku.

It is estimated that about 15 per cent of lowland and foothill Turan is under cultivation. Cotton is the main cash crop. Rice is raised wherever enough water is available. Most crops are irrigated, but some cereals are raised by dry farming. The nomads are mainly Kirgiz speaking, while the urban population and the agriculturists are mainly Turkic speaking. The most advanced of the Turkic peoples are the Uzbeks, who are dominant in the good lands and oases from Fergana to Bukhara. European World impacts, all of fairly recent date, are seen in improved agricultural methods, the rise of industry, the development of resources, and improved transportation, the effective railroad net now being supplemented by airlines.

CENTRAL ASIAN MOUNTAIN KNOT

The Pamir Plateau is a nodal point in the east-west Eurasian mountain barrier, and is studded with peaks reaching 25,000 feet in height. Toward it converge the Iranian highlands, the Hindu Kush of Afghanistan, and the Sulaiman Range of West Pakistan. Northeast from Mt. Stalin, 24,589 feet, highest peak in the Soviet Union, run the "Heavenly Mountains," the Tien Shan toward the Gobi. North of

Dzungaria the Great Altai, Tannu Ola, Sayan, and other highlands follow a trend that extends northeastward to Bering Sea. East from Pamir is the Karakorum, highest range on earth, although its highest point, K2 (Godwin Austen), 28,251 feet, is exceeded by Everest, 29,028 feet, in the Himaiaya. East of the Karakorum, the Kunlun and its branches lead east and north across Tibet and along the Mongolian border. South of the Karakorum is the great arc of the Himalaya, turning southward at its eastern end as do other ranges to extend into Malaya and the East Indies.

There are numerous glaciers and many beautiful lakes in the high valleys. Surrounding landscapes are typical of the alpine tundra. The high pastures are used for grazing throughout the year, their Turkic inhabitants moving to sheltered places on south slopes during the cold season. Below a taiga-like timber belt, limited on the high side by cold and on the low side by dryness, are grazing lands used by flocks that winter at lower elevations. Oases fed by glacial streams are especially favored, because the flow of water is thoroughly dependable.

CENTRAL ASIAN SOVIET FRONTIER

Along the Soviet Union borders of southern and eastern Turan (once called Russian Turkestan) rail connections are well developed, with branches into China and Siberia. This transportation system is useful both for military purposes and for directing commercial relations toward the Soviet Union. The frontier zone is populated mainly with Mongoloid peoples who are strongly communistic. The individuality of the various tribes and groups has been maintained largely through the Soviet policy of promoting the retention of language and other culture traits by so-called "nationalities" within the Soviet Union. The Iranic-speaking Tadzhiks and various Mongol- and Turkic-speaking peoples along the frontier, extending along Siberia, have been given more or less autonomy. The Turki-speaking peoples of *Tannu Tuva* are an example. The upper Yenesei basin between the Tannu Ola and Sayan mountains was formerly part of Outer Mongolia and loosely under

Chinese control, but from financial and military standpoints, it was a protectorate of the Soviet Union long before it was absorbed in 1946. The inhabitants of this sheep- and cattle-raising frontier area essentially rule themselves, and retain their religion, Buddhist Lamaism.

OUTER CHINA

Outer China includes Chinese Turkestan (Sinkiang), Tibet, and Mongolia, territories that were and still are controlled by China to some extent. The areas and populations of these lands of the eastern arm of the Turko-Mongolian Realm of the Dry World are not exactly known, but approximately they are:

TABLE 5

Areas and populations of Outer China

	Area, thousands of square miles	Population, millions
Sinkiang	634	6.00
Mongolian Republic	587	1.74
Tibet	469	2.78
Inner Mongolia	348	6.10
	2.04	16.62

To these rough estimates should be added the area and population of old Inner Tibet, now parts of Chinghai and Kansu provinces of China, which lie within Outer China. Whether the totals are exact or not, it is quite clear that this whole area has only about six to eight persons per square mile, a low density even for the Dry World.

CHINESE TURKESTAN

Sinkiang includes within its borders the almost uninhabited Tibetan-type lands of the mountains of Kunlun and Altyn Tagh in the south, and the high Tien Shan farther north, beyond which lie the low plains of Dzungaria and Chuguchak. But the heart of Chinese, or Eastern, Turkestan is the Tarim Basin, enclosed on all but the eastern side by mountains that rise more than 15,000 to 20,000 feet above the Basin floor which lies between 2,500 and 5,000 feet above sea level. The Basin has no outlet, and for hundreds of thousands of years it has been the dumping ground for debris

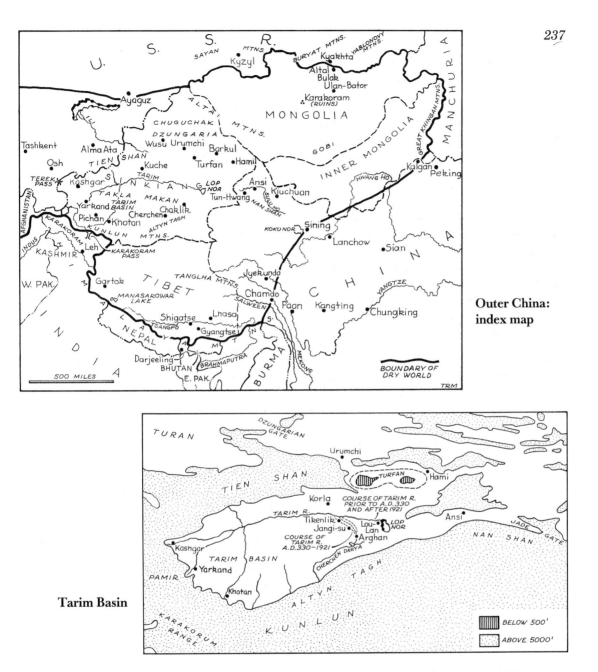

Outer China: index map

Tarim Basin

brought down from the surrounding uplands. These mountains, like all central Asian mountains, are geologically young, and the numerous earthquakes experienced in the area are evidence that they are still growing.

The Takla Makan, desert heart of Tarim, is among the drier areas of the entire world. The average annual precipitation is less than one inch. The dryness combined with the extremely high summer temperatures, frequent sand-storms, desiccating winds, and cold winters that cover lakes and streams with layers of ice, makes most of Sinkiang a difficult place in which to live. The broad erg that covers much of the desert is without rural population and almost routeless. Between the erg and the mountain flanks a belt of reg offers some grazing possibilities, and here are concentrated the caravan routes, marked by cairns and ancient watch towers, that have been used since the beginnings of written history. The caravans are in constant danger from the pillaging and robbing nomads of Tarim who prefer this trade to the pastoral activities pursued by the nomads in Dzungaria and some of the mountains. Many of the nomads are Tungusic-speaking Mongoloids. The merchants, traders, and oases inhabitants are Turkic-speaking. To the east, Chinese are agriculturists and merchants. The population of Chinese Turkestan is concentrated in places with water, where streams leave the mountains, and along their banks as they flow in dwindling volume into the Basin.

The Tarim River, the dominant stream of the Basin, flows eastward from the western mountains, across the northern side of Takla Makan to Lop Nor. Most of the oases and cities of Tarim Basin lie on tributaries, actual or potential, of the Tarim. There are a considerable number of people who make their livings fishing, a Dry World anomaly. The settlement patterns, tied to the river, have been forced to change as the river changed. Until A.D. 330 the river followed about the same course as today. At that date it suffered a major *diversion*, or change of route, abandoning its old course to Lop Nor, in favor of a southeastward course through Tikenlik, Jangi-su, and Arghan to the terminal basin of the Cherchen Darya. Below the diversion point the river became dry, so the Old Silk Road from China to the west, which followed the Tarim, was abandoned, watch towers fell into decay, and the important city of Lou-Lan was deserted. Then, in 1921, another diversion sent the Tarim back into its old channel. Half the population immediately left the oasis of Tikenlik and people along the newly abandoned channel were forced to move to find water. The impressive ruins of Lou-Lan again look down on the waters of Lop Nor, for the dry, salt-encrusted lake bed was soon covered by a sheet of water—a lake 60 miles long and half as wide.

The change in settlement patterns in Tarim Basin, with the people chasing after the river, is an example of one of many causes that force steppe and desert populations to shift about. In marginal areas, where grazing is good at times and fails at others, or where crops grow in years of unusually heavy precipitation, there is an endless record of alternating use and disuse by man. This is amply illustrated along the dry margins of the Great Plains of the United States. Sometimes a favorable period will last a decade or more, and people become numerous, building houses and roads only to abandon them when drought returns. But the buildings remain, and in areas such as in Tarim, that have experienced settlement and abandonment over tens of centuries, the ruins of numerous waves of occupance are left on the landscape. These confuse some people into believing that all the occupants of these relics were living in the area at the same time, and this results in a gross overestimation of previous populations, and in unjustified assumptions of climatic changes.

The appearance of central Asian languages in Europe, the migrations that brought roundheads westward, and the arrivals of Tatars and other Mongoloids are events that seem to correlate with such things as the ruins of Lou-Lan, or the abandoned watch towers along old caravan trails. To connect the two and then assume a climatic change as the cause of westward migration is a popular but hazardous idea. The more we learn about such events the greater the importance of strictly psychological choices appears as a motive for migrations. People inspired by the Great Prophet passed their inspiration on to others, and soon the Arabs had crossed the Pyrenees. Population pressure may result from adoption of some new moral code. Physical events, such as the diversion of Tarim River, bring abrupt changes locally, but displaced people seek new homes nearby, rather than rush thousands of miles to find a place to live. It seems to take climatic changes on the order of a major advance or retreat of continental ice caps to displace many people for considerable distances, and it has been more than ten thousand years since such an event occurred. No historic migration has the slightest relation to these major climatic changes.

Tarim Basin is provided with several important roads and routes. Most of the old caravan trails across the reg on either side of Takla Makan are suitable for trucks and automobiles. Ansi is an important junction point of Tarim routes and the main road and railroad from Lanchow that leads north through Hami, Turfan, Urumchi (Tihwa) to Wusu where the road takes a northerly route to Ayaguz while the railroad goes through the Dzungarian Gate to connect with the road system of eastern Kazakhstan. This was "China's Back Door," the supply route during World War II after the Burma Road was closed. Westward from Ansi routes skirt the northern and southern borders of Takla Makan to join at Kashgar (Shufu), from which numerous trails lead west, the main road passing over 12,700-foot Terek Pass to Osh in Fergana. All the routes have a long history of use. Mongolians moving west favored the good grazing lands of Dzungaria, making that the important migration gate, while trade generally followed the Old Silk Road until the diversion of the Tarim River made it useless. The trade route west of the Jade Gate then shifted to the southern edge of the Tarim Basin, going through Khotan to Kashgar. This was the route Marco Polo followed on his eastward trek. It was most prosperous during the days of the Khans, but trade ended in about 1400 when Ottoman Turks to the west cut it off.

The political hold of the Chinese on Eastern Turkestan has never been strong, and has alternated with that of various Turki peoples, notably the Uigurs, and Mongols. Today Turkic-speaking peoples predominate, and Chinese constitute less than 10 per cent of the population. The main religion is Mohammedanism, although there are many Buddhists and Taoists in the east. In recent years, Soviet influence has been strong. Sinkiang came under Soviet control in 1949, then was returned to China, and was declared autonomous in 1953. During the short period of Soviet control, a number of transportational, educational, industrial, and commercial advancements were begun. Landing fields were constructed, and roads and towns were modernized. Europeanization is similar to that going on in Turan. The discovery of petroleum along the sides of Tien Shan and Altyn Tagh has not yet produced any great changes, but these will come as this resource and others, such as tungsten, molybdenum, copper, zinc, and uranium, are de-

veloped. Industry remains rather primitive, in spite of resources sufficient to support a number of manufacturing centers.

The population of Tarim Basin is almost wholly confined to a few major oases. These centers of irrigation produce crops of wheat, millet, sorghum, rice, beans, cotton, tobacco, and a variety of fruits and vegetables. Kashgar is the nodal route town of the west and a commercial center, with oriental bazaars displaying many imports from the Soviet Union, wares from China and India, and goods of local origin, mostly textiles of cotton, silk, and wool. Yarkand is commercially important for trade with India. Khotan, the largest city in Tarim, is the probable source of much Chinese jade— no European has ever found a place where it is mined. To the east, the well-watered farm lands around the oasis of Ansi are mainly in Chinese hands, while the town merchants are Turki peoples. The surrounding steppe, fairly good grazing land for camels, supports Mongoloid nomads, who are also concerned with plunder and a lively smuggling trade, including opium. Other oases, such as Hami, and those in the below-sea-level depression of Turfan and along the south side of Tien Shan, support little groups of farmers and traders. In the mountains and across the steppe of Dzungaria, nomads graze their horses, camels, and sheep. Population is far less concentrated in Dzungaria than in Tarim because more adequate pasturage permits extensive pastoral nomadism.

MONGOLIA

Mongolia's political boundaries coincide roughly with its natural boundaries. The Great Khingan is a satisfactory eastern limit for Mongolia and the Dry World. The Sayan, Buryat, and Yablonovy mark the transition between Mongolian and Siberian tribes. The Nan Shan is a rather definite boundary toward Tibet. The Gobi or Shamo separates the two traditional parts of Mongolia. Inner Mongolia, the more habitable and more Chinese part, lies just outside the Great Wall, built to keep back invasions of "foreign devils." Outer Mongolia, much larger, more barren, more nomadic, and mainly non-Chinese is now an independent republic within the Soviet sphere of influence. Its 587,000 square miles support a population density of under 4 per square mile, while the 348,000 square miles of Inner Mongolia support a density of 17 per square mile, which is about the average in better Dry World territories.

Aside from the Altai and mountains in the northwest, most of Mongolia is plateau between 3,000 and 4,000 feet in elevation. Most of it is reg (Mongolian term is *gobi*). The Gobi covers two thirds of Mongolia, and is useful grazing territory by Dry World standards. Precipitation is under 10 inches, but soil moisture is preserved by long periods of winter freeze and low evaporation rates. Summers are warm, with many days of over 90° temperature, and January temperatures drop well below freezing. Grasses and shrubs cover all but the driest places, and coniferous trees appear in the uplands. Agriculture is possible in the extreme south and north, but most of Mongolia is characterized as a "land of yurt, yak, and yoghurt." It is a region of pastoral nomadism with millions of sheep, goats, horses, cattle, camels, and of course, yaks, the agile relatives of the bison, whose strength and ability to withstand cold make them popular draft animals throughout the highlands of Mongolia and Tibet. Animals provide food, clothing, felt for the yurts, and transportation for milk, cheese, butter, and other animal products. As in most Dry World lands, the dung of animals is carefully collected and dried for fuel and building material.

The principal routes across Mongolia lead from Kalgan, the important pass from Peking, to Ulan-Bator, the capital, then on to connect with the Siberian railroad just west of Lake Baikal. From Ulan-Bator a route leads west, keeping north of the Altai, while farther south, a road and railroad lead west from Kalgan, skirting the great northern loop of the Hwang Ho, to connect at Lanchow with the main routes west through Sinkiang. Ulan-Bator, at the junction of the important east-west and north-south routes, is an export center for pastoral goods to China and the Soviet Union, as well as being the capital and religious center for the People's Republic of Mongolia.

To the west of Ulan-Bator are the ruins of Karakorum, which under the Mongolians Khans served as one of the most powerful capitals the world has known. Mongolia had been a remote land of obscure tribes until the early twelfth century, when Genghiz Khan started his vast empire that eventually spread from the Pacific across Eurasia to the Black Sea. For some two centuries and under five rulers Mongolia was the center of the most advanced, tolerant, and learned realm of its time. Scholars, missionaries, scientists, artists, and leaders of all kinds came to Karakorum. Visitors from Europe brought back reports of the pageantry of the court, and tales of yurts, dung gathering, rainless winters, high winds, and dust storms, but it took Marco Polo to awaken western interest in the Far East. His experiences, gained during long residences and wide travel, were fortunately preserved in written form, so they could be read by many people. European contacts were broken off, however, when the Khan Empire collapsed, and especially when the western domain fell into the hands of the destructive Ottoman Turks shortly after 1400.

Most of the population of Mongolia is Neoasiatic, closely related to such peoples as the Chinese, Koreans, and Manchurians. About half the population is strictly Chinese, mainly as a result of heavy Chinese migration in recent years to lands along the Great Wall. Most of the people are Buddhist Lamaists. Each family is supposed to contribute one son to the priesthood, so the priest-monk population is extremely large. Monks are concentrated in large monasteries, which formerly were the only schools. Taboos against disturbing the soil kept Mongolians from agriculture, even in the few places where it might have been carried on, prevented development of mines, and prohibited the burial of the dead. These taboos have been modified, and Mongolia now mines some gold, coal, and marble, and looks forward to the development of oil deposits discovered in 1950. There is considerable contrast between the populations of the two Mongolias. It is estimated that not over 10 per cent of the people of the Mongolian Republic are either Chinese or Russian. Inner Mongolia is predominantly Chinese. The milk, butter, cheese, and mutton diet of the Mongolian nomad contrasts with the more largely vegetable diet of Inner Mongolia where barley, millet, and various vegetables are grown and life becomes a blend of Oriental World and Dry World ways.

TIBET

Modern political lines reduce the size of Tibet, which traditionally is the great highland region between the Himalaya and the Altyn Tagh and Nan Shan. A broad, high, and extremely rough belt to the east is transitional into typical China. About three quarters of Tibet is above 10,000 feet in elevation, while peaks in the surrounding mountains tower to heights of more than 25,000 feet in the Himalaya and over 20,000 feet in Kunlun. A large part of Tibet is too high for nomads, with ground frozen for two thirds of the year and boggy in the thaw season, or else stony and barren, where little or no vegetation exists for grazing. Both daily and seasonal temperature ranges are extreme. At mid-day it can be 90° F., and down to 10° early the next morning. Frost may be experienced almost any day during the year. Strong winds that blow throughout the year may in winter bring blasts as cold as —40°. The steady monsoon winds that in summer dump quantities of Indian Ocean moisture on the south side of the Himalaya, fail to bring much precipitation across the barrier, so most of the plateau is dry, with interior drainage ending in saline lakes. Only in the east where the mountain trend bends toward the south, do the moisture-laden monsoon winds penetrate Tibet, bringing precipitation in amounts sufficient for a surplus run-off. Here rise the main rivers of southeast Asia: Brahmaputra, Salween, Mekong, Yangtze Kiang, and Hwang Ho.

Though Lhasa, the capital, is closer to the equator than Cairo or New Orleans, which means that the hours of possible sunshine are about the same summer and winter, the climate is too severe and the growing season too short for agriculture in most parts of Tibet. Most agriculture is carried on in the valleys to the south, along the Tsangpo (Upper Brahmaputra) and its tributaries. Barley and peas are the main food crops. From barley is made chang, the national drink, and tsamba, the national dish. Some wheat, fruit, and vegetables are also raised. But the chief wealth of Tibet lies in animals, goats, sheep, horses, asses, and yaks. Yak milk is particularly rich and yields a butter which is a staple of Tibetan diet, among other things being an essential ingredient of tea.

Tibet was conquered by the Chinese in A.D. 650. Genghiz Khan brought it into the Mongolian Empire in 1209. After Kublai Khan became converted to Lamaism, a form of Buddhism, he established that as the basis for governing Tibet, setting up a rule by Lamas, or priest-kings. Although the Chinese have long claimed Tibet, it has in reality been governed by its Lamas, and as a result has been almost completely secluded, with very few foreign contacts. In recent years, the British and the Soviet Union have taken an interest in Tibet, mainly because it wields an important religious influence over many millions of Asians through its dual and rival leaders, the Dalai and Panchan Lamas. In 1928, Tibet was politically divided, Farther Tibet being recognized as independent from China, and Nearer Tibet being incorporated into provinces of China. Farther Tibet lost its independence in 1951, and became an autonomous state in the People's Republic of China. More and more Chinese are coming into Tibet, especially in the southeast where they are in the majority. In the rest of Tibet are Paleoasiatic and Neoasiatic peoples whose prevailing language is Indo-Chinese. Chinese dialects are widespread in the east.

The main social distinction is between Lamas and lay people. The Lamas are priests, monks, educators, and in general the political class. At the bottom of the social scale is the Porus class—people who till the soil, butcher cattle, and take care of the dead by cutting them in pieces small enough to be carried off by vultures, after being taken to hill tops or mountain peaks. There are many tribal distinctions among the nomads, such as the numerous Mongoloid Pachens and the fierce Ngoloks.

Lhasa, with 50,000 population, is the one city

of Tibet. It is a sacred-political center and contains the Potala, an impressive hilltop building that in the past has served as capitol, home of the Dalai Lama, and resting place of his predecessors. To it come pilgrims, many of whom lie prostrate, mark the position of finger tips, rise, lie prostrate again, one body length closer to their goal, traveling long distances like so many inch-worms. As a commercial site, Lhasa commands the principal routes of Tibet, although these are mainly trails, difficult to travel and harassed by bandits. Near Lhasa is the one modern, steel bridge in the country. Elsewhere the trails cross rivers on precarious swinging bridges, on little ferries, or by fording. The main route to India leads westward from Lhasa, follows the Tsangpo, used by river craft for some 400 miles, then leads past Manasarowar Lake, a holy place to millions of people in India and Tibet, and on to Gartok on the upper Indus. Branching routes to the south lead across high, difficult, and often snowbound passes through the Himalaya. Important routes from Lhasa to China lead east through Paan and northeast through Sining and Lanchow. Tea and cotton goods come to Tibet in exchange for gold, wool, hides, yak tails, and rhubarb.

Tibet is an outstanding example of the negative character of mountainous and high plateau territory from the cultural standpoint. It belongs mainly in the Dry World, but has some Oriental World characteristics. The dominance of nomadism is a result not only of extensive areas with little precipitation but also of extreme height, which restricts vegetation to the limited growth of the tundra. Inhabitants of Tibet have much in common with Polar World peoples. Both face the problems of protection against extreme cold and of using animals to graze lands with scanty vegetation. A wholly cultural matter, relative security of individual life and property, is the basis of a tremendous contrast between Polar and Dry World peoples. In the former culture, peoples are extremely cooperative. In the Dry World, from the smugglers and thieves of Villa Cisneros, in Spanish Sahara, to the opium smugglers of Mongolia, the culture is one in which he who possesses the best arms and most alert sentries is most likely to be wealthiest and most powerful. It is false to attribute these characteristics to limited resources. Polar World peoples cheerfully make the best of what little they have. The contrast is not racial, since both Polar World and Turko-Mongolian Realm peoples are Mongoloid. Culture traits are acquired through association with one's fellow men. Tibet has contributed almost nothing to the world, but has taken certain traits, such as language and religion, from the Oriental World and many of its ways of life from neighbors who inhabit the arid lands to the north.

AFRICAN WORLD

Gallery forest, Tanganyika
[*British Information Service*]

15. Natural Setting and Peoples

The African World is the world of the Negro. It includes the two thirds of Africa south of the Dry World. Here the distinctive cultures of the African World developed, but not in isolation. Old Stone Age cultures diffused freely through the continent. Ancient Egypt exerted influences on cultures to the south. Food crops, domesticated animals, and house types reveal many traits identical with those of southeastern Asia. Dry World contributions in the form of a grazing economy spread deeply into the continent. Arab influences were great enough to cause the

245

Eastern Sudan to shift from the African World to the Dry World. And, in return, the African World has sent traits of its own invention to other culture worlds.

African cultures are primitive by European standards. Dominant are simple gathering and hunting peoples, pastoral nomads, and hoe agriculturists. Written languages failed to develop. Nevertheless, the cultures serve well the needs of their practitioners. Problems of subsistence find satisfactory solution, and such matters as social, political, and military organization, and economic and artistic development have reached levels higher than primitive. Most certainly cultural attainment is such as to demonstrate that the Negro is not handicapped by mental deficiency in the struggle for human accomplishment.

The New World Revolution reached Negro Africa when contacts were established with modern Europeans. Native cultures have crumbled before the technically superior equipment of the invaders. But this does not mean that African peoples are to be replaced by other racial groups. Quite the contrary, for some of Africa is densely populated, and whatever the future effects of the New World Revolution may be, the resulting cultures will be those of Negroid peoples.

PHYSICAL BACKGROUND

Africa's area of 11.5 million square miles gives it continental rank second to Asia's 16.5 million and ahead of North America's 9.4 million. In form Africa resembles a giant figure-9. There is a great indentation of the west coast, the Gulf of Guinea, and directly opposite on the east coast is a projection, the Horn of Africa. The coastline is very regular, without long estuaries and bays to carry either ships or climatic modifications inland. There are few harbors, few fishing banks, and few islands. Of the last, Madagascar stands alone in size and importance. Africa is the only continent squarely astride the equator, its 5,000-mile length stretching both north and south of the equator about 35 degrees. But the areal bulk and greatest breadth (about 4,000 miles) are north of the equator.

The surface configuration and geologic history of Africa are both fairly simple. There are only four major relief elements: old plateaus, younger plains, volcanic peaks and flows, and the Great Rift Valley. The oldest and most widespread relief features are the plateaus, their old eroded rock indicating a long period of stability. The plateaus rise sharply above the lowland plains at an average distance of 20 miles from the coast. They are higher in the southern part of the continent and along an eastern prong extending to Ethiopia. The surface of the high plateau, generally in excess of 3,000 feet elevation, is hollowed by the basins of several rivers, the Zambezi, Orange, Congo, and Nile. Around the continent is a very narrow, discontinuous coastal plain of sedimentary rocks deposited during a geologic period when the margins of the land were temporarily under the sea. At a rather late geologic time there were volcanic eruptions that capped the high plateau of eastern Africa with great thickness of volcanic materials, and gave rise to the continent's highest peaks, the double peaks of Kilimanjaro, 19,340 and 17,564 feet, and Kenya, 17,058 feet. Volcanic activity near the apex of the Gulf of

Africa: relief

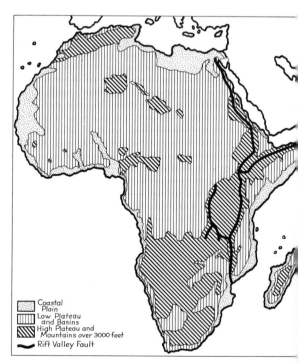

Coastal Plain
Low Plateau and Basins
High Plateau and Mountains over 3000 feet
Rift Valley Fault

Guinea resulted in 13,350-foot Cameroon Peak. During this volcanic activity there was also faulting on a very grand scale, resulting in a most remarkable and prominent feature known as the Great Rift Valley. It is really a graben, a depressed block of the earth's crust bounded by faults, and looks much like an enormous ditch. Its straight-sided walls are from 15 to 100 miles apart, and its bottom is a few hundred feet to nearly a mile deep. The Great Rift Valley begins its course across the plateau near Beira, Mozambique, and goes northward to include fiord-like Nyasa. A western branch is outlined by Lakes Tanganyika, Edward, and Albert. The less-continuous eastern branch includes the basin of Lake Rudolph, then joins the complicated pattern of fault features occupied by the Red Sea, Gulf of Aden, Dead Sea, and River Jordan.

Africa's drainage patterns are as complex as its form and structure are simple. There are seven major river systems: the Nile, discharging into the Mediterranean; the Senegal, Niger, Congo, and Orange, flowing into the Atlantic; and the Limpopo and Zambezi, entering the Indian Ocean. About a third of the continent has interior drainage. Each major stream and many minor ones tumble off the edge of the plateau in rapids or waterfalls, the most notable scenically being Victoria Falls on the Zambezi. Although beautiful, these falls and rapids prevent through navigation, and all the major rivers except the Congo have deltas and bars at their mouths, a further deterrent to navigation. Only the Congo has a broad, open estuary, and it is navigable 95 miles above its mouth. After an interruption of rapids and falls it is navigable for hundreds of miles. Shallow-draft river craft ply the upper courses of the major rivers and most of the minor ones.

The very rapids and falls that have delayed the commercial penetration of Africa by obstructing navigation, are of greatest possible benefit to man. Combined with other favorable factors they give Africa the greatest hydroelectric potential of any continent. Particularly in the Congo system there is a desirable combination of heavy, regular volume of water, uninterrupted by cold winters.

On a small-scale map the few little islands along the African coast disappear. Not so Madagascar, for this 228,642-square-mile island is the world's fourth largest, coming after Greenland, New Guinea, and Borneo. It has a fault-block structure, that is, the island is a crustal block that has been uplifted and tilted. Above its straight eastern coast the island surface

Falls, St. Paul River, Liberia
[*Consul General of Liberia, N.Y.*]

abruptly rises to the crest of a 9,500-foot range of mountains. The land slopes gently to the west to the irregular coast bordering the 320-mile-wide Mozambique Channel, which isolates the island from the non-seafaring peoples of Africa. Culturally, Madagascar is closer to the Malayan Realm of the Oriental World than to the world of Negro Africa. The tiny island of Zanzibar, within sight of the Tanganyika coast, has played a far greater part in things African than has large Madagascar.

One other matter of great importance to man that is related to Africa's geologic history, is minerals. Neither continental nor marine sedimentary rocks are abundant in the African World, and their associated minerals, coal and petroleum, are likewise scarce. On the other hand, the old rocks making up the plateaus that constitute most of the continent are outstanding in the world production of several minerals. Africa leads in gold and diamond production.

The Katanga copper deposits are among the world's best, and other copper deposits are widespread. There is important production of uranium, radium, chromium, tin, manganese, lead, zinc, and tin. Iron ores have been mined and used by Negroes for centuries, and commercial deposits seem to be extensive. Most of the known mineral deposits are in the southern part of the continent.

CLIMATE AND VEGETATION

The distribution of climates and vegetation zones of Africa is symmetrical on either side of the equator, as a result of its being bisected by the equator, and of its lack of a high, continuous mountain barrier that could prevent free circulation of air across the continent. Except for a few minor variations, the pattern of climates and vegetation is simple. Tropical rain forest follows the equator from the Guinea coast to the plateaus of East Africa. On either side is tropical savanna, with areas of modified savanna west of Lake Victoria and in the Ethiopian highlands. In these highlands and those in the south in east Africa there is considerable cooling because of elevation. Beyond the belts of tropical savanna are steppes and deserts. Bordering the arid areas both north and south are Mediterranean regions. The narrowing of South Africa crowds a subtropical climate against the Mediterranean belt of the south coast. Coastal currents tend to modify this general pattern locally. Warm waters along the Indian Ocean and Mediterranean coasts encourage precipitation, and may be seasonally responsible for warming the adjacent lands. Along the Atlantic coast the Canaries current flows southward and cools the coast from Gibraltar to Cape Verde. The cold Benguela current flows northward and is effective from Cape Town to the mouth of the Congo. Both currents cool the adjacent coastal strips but restrict precipitation, and thus create severe desert conditions.

The pattern of continental winds and precipitation changes with the season. In the northern-hemisphere winter a vast low-pressure area covers most of southern Africa, and air tends to circulate toward it, bringing northerly winds to North Africa, northeasterly winds to the Horn and East Africa, and westerly and southern winds to western South Africa. The winds bring maximum precipitation to southern Africa, the heaviest rainfalls occurring in the southern-Congo and Zambezi basins. Madagascar is drenched, particularly in its eastern section, and the Mediterranean coast receives its only precipitation.

In the northern-hemisphere summer, the wind system shifts. Most of Africa south of the equator experiences southeasterly winds, while north of the equator the winds are southwesterly as far north as the middle Sahara. The belt of rainfall thus moves north of the equator, and brings heavy precipitation to the Guinea coast and moderate to heavy rains all across the continent to the Ethiopian highlands. Madagascar is again drenched. This seasonality of precipitation is exhibited in most of Africa. Only the central Congo basin which receives from 60 to 80 inches a year, the Guinea coast of Nigeria and the Cameroons which receives over 100 inches, and eastern Madagascar, with over 120 inches, have rainfall well distributed throughout the year. The Liberia-Sierra Leone coast is one of the rainiest regions in Africa, but most of its rain comes in summer. Exclusively winter rainfall is characteristic of only the Mediterranean coast and a thin coastal strip of southernmost Africa. Rainfall-deficient at all seasons are the Sahara, the Horn, and a large section of southwestern Africa.

Tropical rain forest is both a climatic and a vegetational term, and is characterized by persistent and abundant heat, rainfall, and humidity. Temperatures are rarely excessively high, but monotonously hover at about 80° F. with little daily or seasonal change. The high humidity makes this a real "hothouse" climate in which plants flourish. Tropical rain forest is best developed in the Congo basin, but also exists along coastal areas to the west and east, and in Madagascar, as shown on the map. A characteristic feature is the intricate pattern of channel-full streams, often obscured by vegetation. The tropical rain forest is broad leaved and evergreen. Growth is continuous, with no

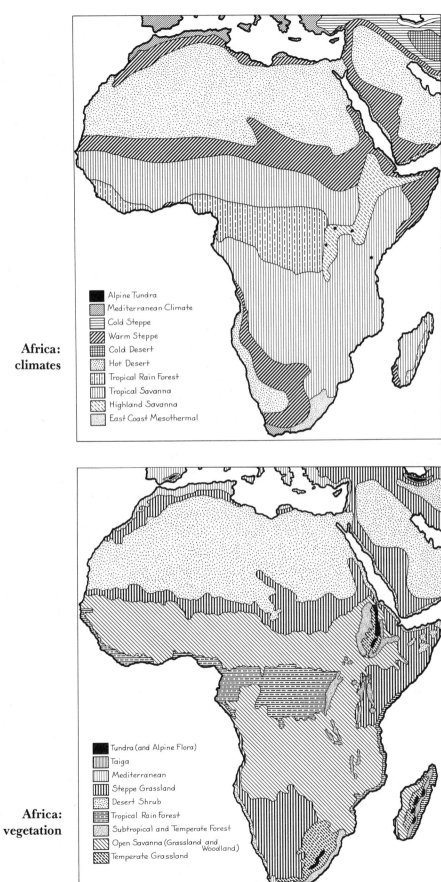

Africa: climates

Alpine Tundra
Mediterranean Climate
Cold Steppe
Warm Steppe
Cold Desert
Hot Desert
Tropical Rain Forest
Tropical Savanna
Highland Savanna
East Coast Mesothermal

Africa: vegetation

Tundra (and Alpine Flora)
Taiga
Mediterranean
Steppe Grassland
Desert Shrub
Tropical Rain Forest
Subtropical and Temperate Forest
Open Savanna (Grassland and Woodland)
Temperate Grassland

High plateau landscape, Natal
[*South African Information Service*]

(*opposite*) **Tropical rain forest, Kenya**
[*British Information Service*]

Thorn bush landscape, near Mount Nyiro, Kenya
[*British Information Service*]

dormant period. The forest is a stratification of many lesser and a few greater trees whose foliage make a green, wavy canopy through which little sunlight penetrates. In the gloom of the forest floor there is little undergrowth, but innumerable vines wrap around the trunks and hang from the branches of trees. Mahogany, tulip, ebony, and walnut are common rain-forest trees, together with various rubber-bearing plants. Along the rainy coasts is mangrove, a tree with many prop roots that grows at the water's edge.

The gloomy, grassless rain forest is not the home of "big game," but teems with birds, reptiles, fish, and animals such as monkeys and apes. The python, cobra, and other poisonous and non-poisonous snakes abound. Pools and streams are occupied by the dreaded crocodile, the amphibious hippopotamus, and a variety of fish. There are, of course, innumerable insects, the beautiful and harmless as well as the malarial mosquito and the carrier of sleeping sickness, the tsetse fly.

Savanna is climatically and vegetationally a transition region between the rain forest and the arid climates. It has hot, humid summers and dry, warm winters. North of the equator the climatic savanna is the 400-mile wide Sudan belt stretching from the Atlantic to the borders of highland Ethiopia, and to its north is a belt of steppe. South of the rain forest is another region of savanna much like the Sudan belt. In both

regions there is an annual range of about 20° in temperature, but the southern or Veld (Afrikaans term for field) savanna is colder because of its higher elevation. Summer is the rainy season, and winters are dry, windy, and dusty. Maximum temperatures come in spring, just before the summer rains. Total annual precipitation varies from 40 to 50 inches near the rain-forest border to 8 to 10 inches along the arid margins. In East Africa, the high plateaus of Tanganyika, Kenya, Uganda, and Ethiopia have cooler temperatures than those of the Sudan or Veld, resulting in a modified savanna climate.

The natural vegetation of the savanna varies with the transitional climatic conditions. From unbroken tropical forest there is gradual change to open savanna woodland in areas with 40 to 50 inches of rain. Evergreen trees are replaced by those that are deciduous during the dry season. Grass grows 5 to 20 feet tall during the rainy season and withers in the winter drought. Beyond the woodland where there is less preci-

pitation, 30 to 40 inches, trees are more widely spaced in a park landscape. Grass between the flat-topped mimosas is less tall because the wet growing season is shorter. The smaller the annual rainfall, the shorter the grass and the more it tends to grow in clumps, while trees are more and more separated, and commonly thorny. True forests are restricted to galleries that flank perennial streams. Finally, on the arid borders of the savannas are broad expanses of almost treeless, low grasslands that are wonderful grazing grounds. The African savannas are the homes of many millions of antelopes, zebras, giraffes, elephants, and buffaloes, and, of course, their predators, the lion, leopard, and hyena. The flightless ostrich and the baboon also live here, as do the tsetse fly and mosquito.

Arid climates, outside of the Sahara which is culturally part of the Dry World, occur in an area that covers about a third of the continent south of 10° S., and includes the Kalahari, a climatic steppe centering in southwestern Bechuanaland, and Namib Desert along the coast of South West Africa. Because of the cold Benguela current, the coastal border of the Namib Desert is cold, foggy, and damp, with almost no rainfall. Farther inland annual precipitation amounts to 2 or 3 inches. Along the whole coast of southwestern Africa there is a wide belt of shifting, vegetationless sand dunes through which no perennial stream passes. Back of the coast there is an isolated fragment of high plateau with adequate water. Most of the interior desert and steppe has scant vegetation; here and there are salt-encrusted pans, lakes, or swamps into which intermittent streams bring the interior drainage. The steppe is drab during the dry winter, but it bursts into bloom in the rains of summer and is visited by herds of grazing mammals from the savanna.

Mediterranean climates occur in Negro Africa only at the very southern tip of the continent, around Cape Town. Mild winters, cool to warm summers and winter rainfall are characteristic here as in all other Mediterranean-climate areas. Typical also is the vegetation, with evergreen, broad-leaved trees, shrubs, and grasses in the limited flat lands, and maquis (chaparral) on the drier slopes. Without question, of all

TABLE 6

Racial Classification of the African World

Primary Race: Negroid

Primary Subraces	*Characteristics*	*Distribution*	*Remarks*
1. African Negro	Woolly hair; dark pigmentation; broad, flat nose; variable stature; long-headed.	Dominant in western Sudan, Congo basin, and South Africa except arid region.	"Purest" Negroes; major source of American Negroes
2. Nilotic Negro	Slender; tall; very dark; long-headed; nose occasionally narrow; lips less thick than in African Negro.	Eastern Sudan and Nile headwaters; occasionally elsewhere	Probably mixture of Negroid and Mediterranean
3. Negrito (Pygmy)	Very short; wooly hair sometimes in peppercorns or spiral clumps; skin yellowish to chocolate brown.	Equatorial Africa	Widespread outside of Africa

Composite Race: Bushman-Hottentot

Secondary Subraces			
1. Bushman	Short; slight; peppercorn hair; mesocephalic; prominent cheek bones; Mongoloid eye; yellow to yellow-brown skin; steatopygia.	Kalahari, South Africa	Probably Pygmy-Mongoloid–Primitive mixture
2. Hottentot	Taller than Bushman; skin yellower and head longer.	Southwestern Africa	Bushman-African Negro-Mediterranean mixture

Negro Africa, the Mediterranean section is climatically best suited to Europeans.

Humid subtropical climate (east coast mesothermal) covers an area eastward from the Mediterranean section to the Limpopo River. Characteristics of this climate, found also in the southeastern parts of the United States, China, Australia, and South America, are mild winters, hot summers, and abundant rainfall distributed throughout the year. The South African humid subtropical area extends from coastal lowlands to interior plateaus, so change of elevation and exposure are reflected in the climate. The coastal sections and steep east-facing slopes have rather low annual temperature ranges, few or no frosts, and high annual rainfall (40 inches and over) distributed evenly or with a short winter dry season. Inland, at elevations of 6,000 feet or so, the annual temperature range is greater though the temperatures are slightly lower, precipitation is less, winter frosts are frequent, and so are dry dust-laden winter winds blowing from the desert. The vegetation is also varied, with dense forests of palms, bananas, and other tropical plants along the coast, a belt of grass and thorn bush above the forest to about 4,000 feet, and above that a temperate grassland.

NATIVE PEOPLES

Africa and the Negroids play very respectable parts in the racial history of man. Possibly one of the significant steps in the origin of modern man was taken in Africa, for ancient remains with manlike traits have been found, such as *Homo rhodesiensis* or Rhodesian man dating from perhaps 125,000 years ago, and other skeletons in East Africa resembling Neanderthal man. These very probably are ancestral to modern Negroid types found in South and East Africa that are considered to belong to the early-middle Ice Age. But fragmentary as this information is, there seems little doubt that Africa was an important site in the biological development of man, and that modern types of Negroids appeared at a very early date.

Whatever may be the relative timing of the emergence of Negroids and Caucasoids as distinct racial divisions, whether contemporaneous or one ahead of the other, the Negroes are certainly not simply primitive survivors from an earlier age. The broad, flat nose and the projection of the lower face, characteristic of the Negro, are probably very ancient. But the distinctive Negro hair texture, scarcity of body hair, small ears, full everted lips, and possibly the black skin are wide departures from the characteristics of primitive man. Nor is there eivdence that the Negroes are mentally backward. There is no reason to believe that the lag in cultural attainment of the African World is to be attributed to lack of intellectual capacity on the part of Negroid peoples.

Even prior to the modern spread of Negroid peoples to the Americas and other parts of the

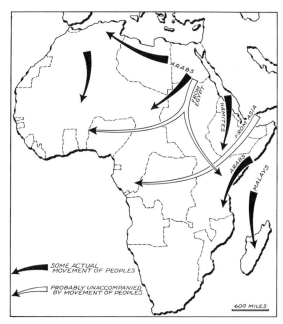

Africa: culture thrusts

Zulu dancers, Durban

[*South African Information Service*]

world, they were by no means confined to Africa. Negroid or part-Negroid peoples are found in all the peninsular projections of southern Asia, and the islands of Indonesia, Melanesia, and the Philippines. The proportion of Negroid blood among some Polynesians is very high, and Negroid traces are found among American Indians and native Australians. Throughout the African World all native peoples, with the exception of some Madagascar tribes, are basically of Negroid stock. Within this primary division of mankind there are a number of types or subraces based on physical characteristics. Table 6 is an adaptation of the classificatory scheme and terminology of Hooton.

Despite finding the remains of pre-modern man in Africa, the continent is not generally regarded as the birthplace of all mankind. Man is believed to have entered Africa from the northeast. Probably the first to come were a short Negroid people, ancestral to the Pygmies and Hottentot-Bushmen, who eventually landed in the Congo basin. Accompanying them or following closely were the African Negroes who went to eastern and southern Africa. Very early there pushed into northeastern Africa the first of a long series of Caucasoid Hamite invasions, and by the New Stone Age the African Mediterraneans had moved south into Ethiopia, the Horn, and well into the East African Plateau. These and other movements pushed the preceding peoples farther toward the continental margins, and created mixtures of various racial elements. The Bushmen were pushed southward and eventually restricted to the inhospitable, arid Kalahari. Some lagged behind, mixed with Hamitic Mediterraneans and African Negroes, then as Hottentots moved south to adjoin the Bushmen in extreme South Africa. Essentially pure African Negroes were secluded in the remote Guinea Coast region. Pygmies and African Negroes went into the equatorial forests. Mixtures of Hamites with African Negroes gave rise to the Nilotic Negroes, still living along the invasion route.

House moving, Kenya
[*British Information Services*]

The last great movement was that of the Bantu-speaking Negroes at about the time of the Hamitic invasions. These racially African Negro peoples seemingly originated as a linguistic stock in central eastern Africa, and became warlike carriers of the Bantu language to nearly all of Africa south of the equator, except the Hottentot-Bushmen area. The Bantu came in contact with many peoples and mixed with them to become highly diverse racially. Considerable mixing resulted also from the Hamitic and Semitic invasions along the north and east borders of Negro Africa. Arab traders and slavers went into the Sahara, the Sudan, and south along the coast to Mozambique and Madagascar. Everywhere the invaders left their blood and cultural influences.

Madagascar has an even more complicated racial history. The original inhabitants were Negroid, possibly from Melanesia. Very early, settlers arrived from the East Indies, and migrations continued into the sixteenth century. Even assuming that the Malayans followed the coast, the trip was a masterly accomplishment for people using only outrigger boats. Arabs brought in Bantu-speaking slaves. The modern inhabitants of Madagascar exhibit a heterogeneity matching their history, but Negroid blood is dominant.

NATIVE LANGUAGES

The *language families* (groups of related languages) in Negro Africa are Sudanese, Hamitic, Bushman-Hottentot, Bantu, and Malayo-Polynesian. Sudanese includes a number of what may be independent language families, and the diversity of speech found in the Sudan makes it a real language shatter belt. Sudanese languages dominate the Sudan from the Atlantic to the edge of the East African Highlands. Hamitic tongues are spoken in both East Africa and western Sudan. Bantu is the most widespread of native tongues, occupying the vast area lying south of the Sudan, with the exception of most of Hamitic highland East Africa, and the Bushman-Hottentot area of arid southwestern Africa. Malayo-Polynesian is the exclusive native language family of Madagascar.

Language diversity in Negroid Africa has made inter-tribal communication difficult, so trade languages have been adopted in many places. In West Africa the common trade tongue is the Hamitic speech of the aggressive Hausa tribe. Even more important is Swahili in East Africa, a Bantu tongue enriched by additions from many languages. It should be noted that none of the languages of Negro Africa is simple. They are complex, expressive, and useful, and have been no handicap to the cultural development of the Negroid peoples.

NATIVE CULTURE AREAS

The native cultures of Negro Africa began feeling the influences of Western civilization when Europeans rounded the continent on their way to the Indies during the fifteenth century. A century later, when Europeans still knew only the coastal sections, depopulation of the native peoples was well started by the introduction of strange diseases, and new crops from America were already established. The native cultures of the African World that preceded European inroads can be divided, according to Herskovits' classification, into six culture areas: Bushman, Hottentot, East African Cattle Area, Guinea Coast-Congo, Western Sudan, and Madagascar. Almost everywhere these pre-European primitive cultures have been modified to some degree, but following customary practice, they are described in the present tense.

Africa: native culture areas
[*Modified from Herskovits*]

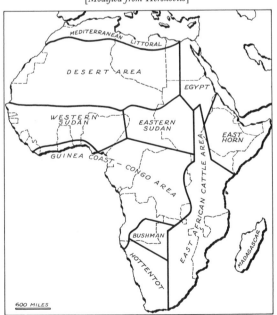

East African cattle herders
[*British Information Services*]

The Bushman area, centering in the northern Kalahari, is a land of scant grass and shrub, little available water, desolate salt pans, and dry stream channels, but it has a fair amount of animal life. The Bushmen are nomadic hunters who live where they make a kill. They are also gatherers. From the acacias they get gum; from ant hills, eggs. They eat with gusto not only honey, ostrich eggs, and roots, but even locusts and lizards. There is no agriculture and no herding. Animals are trapped, caught in pitfalls, and taken in community drives. Bushmen are excellent stalkers and trackers of game, and equally good at finding water, both in water holes and in plants. The bow is the chief weapon, and an effective one, especially when used with poisoned arrows. Their tools and utensils are limited, but include a light hunting spear, stone scraper, and digging stick. Axes, pottery, and throwing clubs come from other tribes. Crude leather sandals and leather cloaks constitute the Bushman's wardrobe. They have made very clever adaptations in learning to live in a rather difficult area, but they make few lasting changes in the landscape. They live in caves or brush and bark wind breaks that are readily abandoned. A few simple belongings are tucked in a carrying net when a little band of Bushmen moves certainly to its destination without benefit of path or trail. Little is left to mark the old site.

The Hottentot area is mostly arid, especially in the Namib Desert, but it also reaches into the humid high plateaus of South Africa. Virtually all the area is open, grazing land. The Hottentots are cattlemen and most of their material needs, such as clothing and food, are supplied by herds. Gathering of wild produce and hunting supplement herding in a minor way, but there is no agriculture. The Hottentots are necessarily nomadic, changing pastures frequently. Villages are well adapted to caring for cattle and frequent moving. Surrounding the village is an effective fence of piles of thorn brush. Inside is an irregular cluster of beehive-shaped dwellings and an enclosure for holding the cattle at night. During the day the herds are carefully tended as they graze outside the fence. When it is time to move to new pasture, the house coverings of grass mats or hides are taken off the domed framework of poles, the poles are taken down, and everything but the thorn fence is dragged to the new location. Personal possessions are meager. The bow, throwing club, and spear are the principal weapons. Knives and spear blades are made of iron that is smelted and worked by the Hottentots. They also make pottery and weave mats and baskets.

The East African cattle area, occupying all the high plateaus of eastern Africa, is mostly open or park land landscape, with ample grass for cattle and few tsetse flies. Herding is important, but equally important is agriculture, which dates from the original Negro inhabitants. Herding was brought in by Hamites. Farmers are more Negroid in blood, and are more or less sedentary, while the herding tribes are more Caucasoid and are fierce warrior nomads. These two different systems exist side by side in places, and in the south women do the agricultural work and men herd the cattle. The herds supply many needs, especially food, such as sour milk, meat, and blood, for in some areas cattle are regularly bled. Butter is used principally to anoint the bodies of the upper classes.

Leather is made into clothing and war shields. Spears, swords, and clubs are used in fighting, but they are generally made by the artisan agricultursits. The farming tribes grow millet, plantains, bananas, sugar cane, peas, and beans, to which they have added maize, cassava, tobacco, and sweet potatoes from America. They have dogs, goats, poultry, and cows if they can get them. They are also craftsmen, making hoes from home-smelted iron, working wood, moulding pottery, weaving baskets, and pounding out bark cloth. They build villages for the herdsmen. The two cultures have two types of settlements. Around the herdsmen's village is a thorn-brush *kraal*, and inside are round thatched houses or rectangular ones of mud. Herds graze outside during the day, guarded by young men, and are brought in and milked at night. The village is abandoned when it is necessary to move to fresh pasture. The agricultural villages are usually not surrounded by a thorn fence, but are often located so as to be protected from marauding herdsmen. The village is a cluster of thatched, round houses, with a small raised house used to store the harvest. Close at hand are the fields, tilled with the iron hoe.

The Guinea Coast-Congo area includes nearly all of Africa's rain forest. It is a region of constantly high temperatures, heavy precipitation, low elevations, heavy forest cover, dense network of perennial streams, and an enormous population of malarial mosquitoes and tsetse flies. Racially the Congo basin is the most Negroid of all areas, and includes all the Negritos or Pygmies. Culturally there have been almost no Hamitic, Arabic, and Mohammedan influences. The scarcity of grasslands and the prevalence of the cattle-prohibiting tsetse fly have kept out the herdsmen Arabs and Hamites. Shifting agriculture is the main activity in the Congo area. Fields are cleared of trees and brush, the refuse is burned, and then the top few inches of the ground are broken up with iron hoes. After two or three crops the ground is exhausted and is host to many plant-destroying insects, so the field is abandoned and quickly overgrown. The permanent agriculture developed along the Guinea coast is exceptional.

Bananas and plantains are staple crops, but

millet, so important and so old in East Africa, is missing. Other food plants include yams, beans, sugar cane, oil palm, and a number of American importations: maize, sweet potatoes, peanuts, tobacco, and cassava or manioc. Domestic animals are all considered edible: pigs, fowls, goats, and dogs, and these are supplemented with fish and other wild animal foods ranging from elephants and pythons to caterpillars, bats, and maggots.

The Guinea Coast-Congo peoples are workers in iron, and occasionally in bronze and brass. Woodworking reaches a degree of excellence in no way primitive, although tools are limited to axes and knives. The men make many elaborate and beautiful articles, such as decorated door posts, boxes, large and small dugout and large plank boats, stools, dishes, chains, spoons, masks, drums, and beds. Human and animal forms are carved in ivory. Pottery and baskets are good and abundant, and cloth for the little clothing needed is made by weaving young palm fibers, or pounding the bark of the wild fig tree.

The people live in villages ranging in size from a few families to an exceptional hundred-thousand inhabitants. Dwellings are arranged irregularly around a guest house and the religious shrines. The houses are rectangular and gabled, with walls of wattle or thatch, and the roof, invariably thatched, projects beyond the house to provide an open, cool space, protected from sun and rain. Many of the household tasks, such as weaving, winnowing, and grinding, take place in the yard behind the house. Some villages are protected by ditches or fences, or they are hidden back from the rivers which are the main routes of travel. The cycle of activities calls for little traveling away from home except to the markets that are such striking features of the Congo culture pattern. Scattered through the Congo are Pygmy settlements, villages of small dome-shaped houses hidden in the forests, not for protection but to be near the game that is the chief source of Pygmy livelihood. They are protected by their normal-sized neighbors and highly respected for their

Nigerian landscape
[*British Information Services*]

prowess as hunters. Aside from hunting, they show little skill, and have to obtain their pots, baskets, tools, and crop foods from the Negroes, from whom they even borrowed their languages.

There are striking cultural similarities between the Congo area and the Oceanic Negroids of Melanesia, such as the rectangular thatched house, banana as a staple food, clothing of palm fiber or bark cloth, a straight bow strung with rattan cord, wood carvings of the human figure, and the pig and fowl as important domestic animals. A culture combining the same elements is found nowhere else in Africa, and does not occur between the Congo and the Melanesian Realm of the Pacific World. If there was a cultural connection, as this suggests, it was very ancient.

The Western Sudan area, extending eastward to Lake Chad, is mainly savanna and the humid margin of the steppe, open grassland useful for grazing because of the general absence of the tsetse fly. Culturally, this is the most advanced area of Negro Africa, and has long been subject to the influences of strong non-Negroid peoples. In spite of these outside influences, the Negroes retain their own Sudanese languages and cling to their native faiths. The main activities are agriculture, herding, and trading. Clothing is made of leather and of excellent cotton cloth long woven in the area. Basketry is good, but ceramic art and pottery making are of very high quality, as are tools and weapons of stone. Iron work is the best in all Negro Africa, and the Western Sudan is frequently regarded as the area from which iron spread to the rest of the African World. These skilled craftsmen ply their trades in the large native cities that have been characteristics of the area as far back as records go. Kano is a modern example.

Madagascar is only geographically part of the African World. Racially it is probably more Negroid than Mongoloid, but linguistically it is Malayo-Polynesian and culturally it is an isolated outpost of the Malayan Culture Realm of the Oriental World. Many culture traits of Madagascar are distinct from mainland ways, for example, the use of a digging stick and iron spade instead of a hoe, the use of Malayan-type outrigger canoes, and the cultivation of rice on irrigated terraces as in the East Indies.

EXPLORATION

The Sahara was a considerable barrier, yet there were contacts between Negro Africa and the outside world dating from before recorded history, as indicated by the ancient diffusion of many culture traits. The first creditable accounts of Negro Africa come from Herodotus, the Greek historian-geographer, who described a circumnavigation of Africa by Phoenicians around 600 B.C. Later Phoenician traders and explorers from Carthage went down the west coast, reaching the Gambia River about 500 B.C. By the first century A.D. Greek traders had gotten as far south on the east coast as Zanzibar. But it was left to the practical and adventurous Arabs to complete the major accomplishments of exploration prior to the Age of Discoveries. With camels they established trade routes across the desert, and down the east coast beyond Zanzibar. By the twelfth century Arabian and Persian slavers had established several substantial colonies, as at Mombasa on the Kenya coast. The next centuries were prosperous ones, but the fifteenth century brought European competitors, and the rivalry for political, cultural, and economic domination was intense. The Arabs produced profound changes in the areas along the northern and eastern margins of Negro Africa, introducing the Arabic tongue, the Islamic faith, and such material innovations as rice and sugar cane from India, but Dry World influences did not reach the forested interior, the damp west coast, nor the plateau savannas.

To the Portuguese belongs the credit for opening Negro Africa to Europeans. Following the expulsion of the Moors from the Iberian Peninsula in the fifteenth century, the Portuguese invaded Africa, and sent expeditions down the west coast in search of tropical riches. At the mouth of the Gambia and on the Gold Coast they established trading posts to draw gold from the interior. On south they went: Diaz first rounded the Cape of Good Hope in 1487 and explored part-way up the east coast; da Gama went further and visited the Arab trade settlements; then the Portuguese seized political control of these settlements; and everywhere they went they attached Portuguese names to every prominent coastal feature. But by this time the thrill of Africa was gone and the Portuguese were looking toward Indian trade. Following the advice of Arabs of East Africa, the Portuguese began making use of the seasonal monsoons to speed their ships to India and bring back to eager home markets rich cargoes of spices, gems, and textiles. Their African ventures, with the exception of the slave trade, dwindled in competition with those involving the Indies and Brazil. On the Guinea Coast the Portuguese were the first Europeans to engage in the lucrative slave trade between Africa and the Americas and they continued until the abolition of the practice.

As Portuguese influence in Africa declined, Mohammedan strength revived along the East African coast. As late as 1832 the sultan of Oman transferred the seat of government from Arabia to Zanzibar. Nevertheless, it was the Portuguese who pioneered in bringing a part of Negro Africa into the New World by originating the slave trade, outlined the coast of Africa south of the Sahara that was hitherto unknown to Europeans, dealt in gold and ivory, and aroused the envy of other European maritime powers. The Portuguese delivered the first blow of the European impact and fired the first shot in the New World Revolution that initiated for Africa a still-uncompleted commercial, political, and cultural transformation.

The effects of the impact of Europeans upon aboriginal New World peoples, including those of South Africa, are revolutionary. Common is a depopulation, through the introduction of new diseases fatal to primitive peoples, and through warfare with superior weapons. The idea gained by the primitive peoples that European material ways are superior may be carried over to social, moral, and spiritual values, but the native cannot immediately select the best aspects of his older ways and those of European ways best fitted to his needs.

The result is a demoralization of the natives for a period during which they flounder about, robbed of their own adjustments for living and unable to make a quick and complete transition to European ways. In time a new system may evolve, a mixture of old and new ways, but invariably with concessions to a commercial rather than a purely subsistence existence. And while all this is happening, the Europeans tend to make short work of the natural resources of these "pioneer" lands, for their very vastness inspires a feeling of inexhaustibility of resources and the urge for profits promotes both lavish use and waste. Even when resources are frighteningly diminished or gone, it is difficult to change attitude and manner of utilization. Whether it be aborigine or European working blindly toward a stable and satisfying way of life, the profound changes involved are well named New World Revolution.

NEW WORLD REVOLUTION IN AFRICA

In broad plan the pattern of the New World Revolution has been the same the world over, but the timing and details vary. First come the explorers, amazing and impressing the primitive aborigines. Hard on their heels come the traders, paying the aboriginal gatherers or producers for such things as furs, slaves, metals, gems, and forest products, with European-made goods: trinkets, tools, textiles, tobacco, foods, and whiskey. The natives soon become dependent on these goods, and hopelessly enmeshed in the net of the European commercial system. In the midst of this the missionaries arrive, to save the souls of the pagan natives, incidentally spreading the European economic system by inducing the natives to wear clothing and adopt civilized customs like those of the missionary. The only way the native can supply the newly created need for European goods is to deal with the trader. Often on the pretense of protecting trader or missionary, the soldiers arrive, and with them the political administrator and the protectorate, a system that starts by allowing the native rulers a measure of control and ends by absorbing them into an empire. The status

European cultural landscape, Lourenço Marques
[*Casa de Portugal*]

of empire possession encourages the investment of capital by reducing risk, and exploitation of natural resources is then conducted on a grander scale than could be managed by the trader. Frequently this takes the form of large mining enterprises or extensive and intensive production of agricultural crops. Typical expressions of colonial economy are plantation agriculture, large mining operations, and the exploitation of forests, all supplying raw materials needed by the home countries. Native populations provide the labor, and a closed market for European goods. It is a system devised for the economic benefit of the colonial powers and not for the aborigine. Colonization by Europeans is a possible but not a necessary step in the completion of the New World Revolution. Where it occurs, it is accompanied by urbanization, industrialization, and the establishment of other European culture patterns. The New World Revolution is completed in an area when it has attained a large

measure of economic and political independence and stability within the system of world relationships. That is, when a country is politically sovereign and occupies a position of economic independence similar to that of the more advanced European nations, the New World Revolution has run its course.

In Negro Africa, European exploration started with the Portuguese in the fifteenth and sixteenth centuries, but later in the sixteenth century they were expelled from much of the east coast by their rivals, the Arabs, and in the next century were superseded on the west coast from the Senegal River to the equator by the Dutch, British, and French, who conducted very little additional exploration. Traders frequented the coast from Gambia to the Cameroons, but did not venture inland, conducting their dealings through native middlemen. The only new region that was opened was that around Table Bay, just north of the Cape of

Good Hope, where the Dutch established a settlement to provide water, provisions, and repair facilities for ships making the long trip to or from the Indies. Agriculture was fostered to meet food requirements of vessels calling at Table Bay. The Dutch farmers or Boers expanded slowly to the northeast, but detailed exploration of South Africa had to await the nineteenth century.

The scientific attack by Europeans upon the unknown interior of Negro Africa was formally inaugurated with the organization of the African Association of London in 1788. Attention was first turned to the Sudan and central-western tropical Africa, then later to south and central Africa. The list of African explorers embraces many famous names, among them Park, Barth, Livingstone, and Stanley. Exploration was accomplished at the cost of many lives, for tropical Africa held many dangers for Europeans in the form of diseases and warlike natives. By 1875 the basic exploration of the continent was completed.

Commercial exploitation had begun during exploration. White traders began operating coastal posts where they obtained slaves, ivory, gold, and pepper in exchange for European goods. Trade rivalry was keen among Europeans during the seventeenth and eighteenth centuries all along the coasts of Guinea. The Grain or Pepper Coast, Ivory Coast, Gold

African World: European exploration

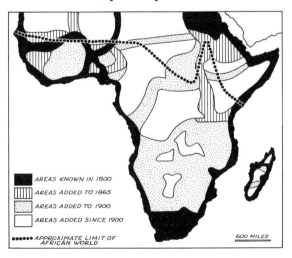

AREAS KNOWN IN 1800
AREAS ADDED TO 1865
AREAS ADDED TO 1900
AREAS ADDED SINCE 1900
•••••• APPROXIMATE LIMIT OF AFRICAN WORLD
600 MILES

Coast, and Slave Coast are names indicative of the commercial interests in the area. By the end of the eighteenth century the slave trade had reached large proportions. Portuguese, British, Dutch, French, and American vessels were transporting some hundred-thousand slaves a year to the plantations of America, in the famous triangle trade: slaves from Africa to America; sugar and other plantation products from America to the home port; then rum, cloth, and other manufactured articles back to Africa in exchange for slaves. On the east coast, Arabs were busily transporting slaves to Arabia, Persia, and other Asian lands.

Gradually the exploitation of Africa and the European attitude toward it changed in response to economic developments at home. With the growth of the industrial age, Africa became looked upon as a source of raw materials and foodstuffs for Europe and a market for cheap manufactured products. Oil from oil palms, timbers, and eventually rubber and other products became of value. To secure stability of production and marketing opportunities, a measure of political control was deemed necessary, so toward the end of the nineteenth century semiofficial companies were set up by the British, French, and Belgians, and given vast grants of land to control. Plantations were established, and soon Uganda, Tanganyika, the Cameroons, the Belgian Congo, Nigeria, the Guinea Coast, and other areas were involved in the production of a growing list of plantation crops: cacao, hemp, cotton, coffee, sugar, bananas, palm oil, tobacco, rubber, pyrethrum, and many others. By this time, slavery had been abolished, but the lot of the natives was not improved, for slavery was replaced by a system of forced labor, in which natives were recruited where they were numerous and transported to other areas to work. The shift of 2 or 3 million people accompanied the concession system as practiced in French and Belgian equatorial Africa. Fewer were involved elsewhere, but the practice was widespread. These important population shifts caused cultural and racial changes. Material changes in the landscape were also taking place. The clearing of forests and the establishment of plantations, mines, and communities of Europeans were radical innovations in the older cultural scene, as were the new ports, steamers on the rivers, and railroads into the interior.

Accompanying the cultural and material changes were political changes. Negro Africa was partitioned by European imperial powers: Great Britain, France, Germany, Belgium, and Portugal. France started it with a planned program of colonial acquisition in the middle of the nineteenth century, and began expanding into the Sudan from bases on the Ivory Coast, Dahomey, and at the mouth of the Senegal. These lands later became French Equatorial Africa. The British, alarmed at French progress, and fearful of being restricted to isolated coastal territories, began a belated expansion inland in the Gold Coast, Nigeria, and the Crown Colony of Sierra Leone that had earlier been established as a home for liberated slaves. The Germans entered the arena late, but with startling abruptness. In 1884 they made their first African territorial claim, and within the year they held Togoland, the Cameroons, and South West Africa. Belgium jumped into the colonial grab under the guise of fostering scien-

tific exploration, and soon had political control of the large section of equatorial Africa that became the Belgian Congo. Portugal's claims to Angola and Mozambique rested firmly on discovery and trade utilization, but recognition of the claims was the result of French and German attempts to thwart Britain's expansion in southern Africa. Britain, nevertheless, acquired the lands that became Northern and Southern Rhodesia, and soon added Kenya and Uganda to the list of British possessions. Germany came away from the struggle with East Africa, now Tanganyika.

In South Africa the Dutch-founded Cape settlements have been British since 1814. Resentful Dutch farmers pushed northward to found the independent Orange Free State and Transvaal. After the discovery of diamonds and gold in the Dutch territories, the British found reasons and excuses for absorbing the areas into the empire, but it took the Boer War to do it. Cecil Rhodes' dream of a continuous British sphere "from the Cape to Cairo" was realized with the division of German possessions at the end of World War I, when Britain acquired most of German East Africa, and South West

Europeanized family, Nigeria
[*British Information Services*]

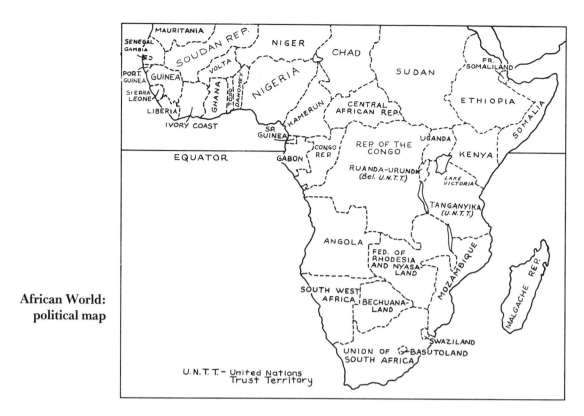

African World: political map

Legend: U.N.T.T. – United Nations Trust Territory

Africa became part of the Union of South Africa. A slice of highland East Africa was added to the Belgian Congo, and to France went the larger parts of German West Africa.

For three decades following World War I, most of the African World was politically affiliated with European powers, although the degree of control varied. Only Liberia was completely independent. The approach of the middle of the twentieth century was marked by more and more outcries expressing the deep yearnings of the peoples for independence and sovereignty that indicates the final phase of the New World Revolution. As a result, important political changes were made. The British Commonwealth of Nations, which includes autonomous members as well as colonies, revised its composition by recognizing the independence of a number of colonies. Ghana, the former Gold Coast Colony, led the parade toward self-government, taking with it British Togoland, to become in 1957 an independent state associated with the Commonwealth on the same status as the Union of South Africa. Nigeria soon followed. Virtual self-government was granted to the new Central African Federation of Rhodesia and Nyasaland, with each of the three

territories handling its own local matters. The French colonies achieved independence in 1958 when, having voted in favor of the Constitution of the Fifth Republic, they were granted autonomy within the French Community, each with the same rights as the Republic of France. French Guinea rejected the Constitution and became completely independent. From French Equatorial Africa emerged four new republics: Chad, Gabon, Central African (Oubangi-Chari territory), and Congo (Moyen Congo). Former French West Africa became six republics: Islamic Republic of Mauretania, Republic of Senegal, Ivory Coast Republic, Voltaic Republic, Soudanese Republic, and Niger Republic. The growing list of independent countries includes Togo, Kamerun, and Somalia.

The attainment of self-government brings with it many problems for peoples who until a hundred years ago were entirely primitive, and who still are 90 per cent illiterate. In many places tribal organization is the dominant control, and the willingness of tribal chiefs to relinquish powers to a central government is problematic. The enormous leap to Space Age problems will seriously test the abilities of peoples of the African World.

Cape Town
[*South African Information Service*]

16. *Modern Cultural Landscapes*

The African World embraces a total area of about 7.7 million square miles, with a population of roughly 150 million, of whom all but 3 million are Negroids. The average density of population is close to 20 per square mile, lowest of all the inhabited continents except Australia. Variation from this average is great, as in arid Bechuanaland and South West Africa where the density is about 1 per square mile, in contrast to Ruanda-Urundi where the density is well over 200 per square mile. The principal region of European settlement, South Africa, has an average density of 30.5 per square mile. In general the Guinea coast, from Nigeria to Gambia, and the highland territories of Uganda and Ruanda-Urundi are among the most densely populated portions of Negro Africa.

In addition to the distribution of population, another striking imprint on the landscape is the transportation system, notably the railways.

265

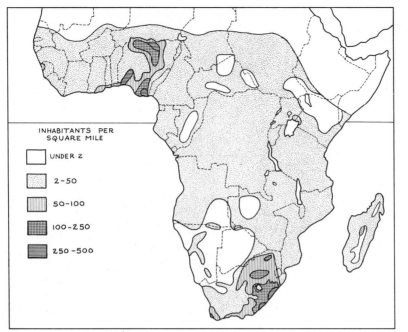

**African World:
population density**

INHABITANTS PER
SQUARE MILE

UNDER 2

2 - 50

50 - 100

100 - 250

250 - 500

Most of the lines are unconnected, extending inland from a coastal port, or joining navigable sections of interior rivers. Only in southern Africa are there connections from coast to coast, and here also the network is densest, that of British southern Africa being comparable with other advanced world regions. Increasingly, of course, air and automobile transport are being used, and the road network is being expanded.

A third significant landscape form, the city, has strong implications regarding the cultural status of its builder. In the Africa of the Negro there are large cities only in the Sudan and Nigeria: Kano and Ibadan, for example, the latter with 500,000 inhabitants. The largest cities of the African World and the custom of living in cities are expressions of European culture, and are largely related to commercial or industrial development along European lines. Thus South Africa, where European ways and peoples are thoroughly established, has almost a monopoly on the cities. Johannesburg, with over one million, is the largest city in the African World. Cape Town and Durban have over 600,000 each. With the upswing in industrialization, urbanization is increasing, and more and more cities are reaching the 100,000 and over class.

It is hardly possible to divide the African World into satisfactory culture realms because, not only are detailed studies lacking on which to base such a division, but European influences and new-found independence are too recent to have allowed the development of criteria for delimiting culture regions. As an expedient, then, the political and geographical basis of division is used in discussing the present landscape. The divisions are shown in Table 7.

GUINEA LANDS

The Guinea lands are all tropical and in general attain only moderate elevations. The coastal margins are, typically, mangrove-fringed and swampy, with a heavy cover of tropical forest. The exceedingly smooth coast line is flanked by offshore sandy beaches beyond shallow lagoons. There are few good harbors: Dakar, the Gambia River, Freetown, and Takoradi. Not far inland from the coast there is normally an abrupt rise to a low plateau, and the tropical forest gives way to more-open savanna country where wild and domestic herds can safely graze, away from the tsetse fly-infested forest. The forested coastal lands receive abundant rainfall, but with a marked summer maximum. In winter, the dry, dusty

TABLE 7

Divisions and Regions of the African World

Divisions and Regions	*Area in thous. sq. miles*	*Population in thousands*	*Political status and remarks*
The Guinea Lands			
Senegal	76.10	2,280	Republic in French Community
Gambia	4.00	291	British
Port. Guinea	13.94	554	Portuguese
Guinea	94.90	2,498	Independent
Sierra Leone	27.92	2,500	Independent state in British Commonwealth
Liberia	43.00	2,750	Independent
Ivory Coast	124.47	3,100	Independent
Ghana	91.84	4,763	Independent state in British Commonwealth
Togo	22.00	1,093	Independent
Dahomey	44.68	1,715	Republic in French Community
Nigeria	373.15	35,300	Independent
Kamerun	166.75	3,223	Independent
Spanish Guinea	10.83	212	Spanish; Rio Muni, Fernando Po, Corisco, & Annobon
Western Sudan			
Soudanese Rep.	464.75	3,730	Republic in French Community; largely outside African World
Voltaic Republic	105.81	3,380	Republic in French Community
Niger	458.87	2,450	Republic in French Community; largely outside African World
Central West Africa			
Gabon	102.29	408	Republic in French Community
Congo Republic	134.71	762	Republic in French Community
Central African Republic	241.64	1,140	Republic in French Community
Republic of the Congo	895.17	13,124	Independent
Ruanda-Urundi	20.91	4,568	Trust Terr. administered by Belgium
Angola	481.23	4,355	Portuguese Overseas Province, including Cabinda
East Africa			
Kenya	224.90	6,450	British
Uganda	93.96	5,680	British
Tanganyika	361.71	8,760	British trust territory
Zanzibar & Pemba	1.02	300	British
Southern Africa			
Federation of Rhodesia & Nyasaland	483.70	8,350	British self-governing federation
Northern Rhodesia	288.06	2,240	
Southern Rhodesia	150.29	2,860	
Nyasaland	45.35	3,250	
Bechuanaland	274.16	331	British
Union of South Africa	790.57	14,942	Independent, associated with British Commonwealth; including South West Africa
Basutoland	11.71	651	British; native reservation
Swaziland	6.70	260	British; native reservation
Mozambique	302.25	6,170	Portuguese Overseas Province
Malagache Republic	227.74	4,930	Republic in French Community

Urban landscape, Johannesburg
[*South African Information Service*]

Harmattan wind blows out of the desert to the north and affects weather nearly to the coast.

The Guinea coast has a bad reputation regarding health conditions for it is the home of many diseases: malaria, blackwater fever, sleeping sickness, yellow fever, dysentery, typhoid, smallpox, meningitis, pulmonary disorders, tuberculosis, and a host of others. Many of these are a reflection of lack of sanitary measures.

The density of native populations in the Guinea lands is well above the average for the continent. There are innumerable tribes, and a great diversity of native languages and cultures. Along the coasts are tribes particularly proficient as canoemen. In the forest belt, shifting agriculture is the basic native economy, while pastoralism becomes important in the open, grassy interior. All native groups still show competence as metallurgists and woodcarvers. Despite long contact with Hamitic and Semitic peoples at the north and with Christian missionaries along the coast, the Guinea natives remain dominantly Negroid racially and pagan in religion. There are very few white people in

these lands, and they are not colonists or settlers, but associated with the government or with commercial enterprises. For one thing, the climate is not congenial to Europeans, and for another, the lands are already occupied, in spots to saturation, by a virile people, the Negroes. In south-central Nigeria the population density in places is as high as 1,000 per square mile. Headed by mud-walled Ibadan with its half-million inhabitants, there are at least nine native cities in Nigeria with populations in excess of 30,000, and several of over 100,000.

Following the early period of European exploitation when pepper, rubber, timber, gold, slaves, and ivory were exported in quantity, the plantation system was introduced, and the export of products that were gathered, and of minerals, declined. Later, the opening of the country to prospecting, aided by modern transportation, ushered in a new period of mineral production. To gold have been added diamonds, platinum, bauxite, columbite, chromite, manganese, molybdenum, iron, and tin. The future of mining as an important industry is assured. But agriculture is and will doubtless remain the primary source of wealth. Native food crops are still what they have been for some time: yams, sweet potatoes, sugar cane, cassava, bananas, with millet and rice in favorable locations. Plantation and commercial-farm crops supply a wide range of exports to temperate lands: peanuts, rubber, palm oil and nuts, kapok, bananas, pineapples, coffee, cacao, ginger, tobacco, kola nuts, and timber, with pastoral products from the grasslands. Production of these crops, of course, varies in significance from country to country. In Liberia, for example, rubber from the vast Firestone plantation exceeds all other crops, while in Ghana the leading export crop is cacao, and in Senegal it is peanuts.

The Guinea lands have been perfect examples of colonial economy. They produced to satisfy European needs, and provided markets for European manufactures. Although European powers agreed on the economic position of Guinea lands, they differed in their attitude toward the native residents. France attempted to break down all native governments and customs, to make Frenchmen of the Negroid inhabitants. Britain attempted to preserve native institutions as working devices in administration.

The advancement of the various countries in terms of sanitation, education, miles of railroads, and other symbols of European culture is a measure of the progress of the New World Revolution. Progress is largely related to the European governing power. In the van are British Sierra Leone, Ghana, Nigeria, and French Ivory Coast. Here railroad and highway building are far advanced, diseases are controlled, and the natives are schooled and their rights respected. Most backward are Spanish and Portuguese Guinea and independent Liberia. The backwardness of the Spanish and Portuguese colonies is typical of all their possessions. The situation in Liberia, a country dedicated as a haven for liberated slaves, is ironical. A minority of Christian, English-speaking Americo-Liberians holds in virtual slavery the pagan native majority.

Guinea cities, products of the New World Revolution as opposed to native cities, are ports and trade centers. They are hardly European in appearance, and certainly not in population, but they perform the functions of commercial cities. Examples are: Dakar, an administrative center with an excellent harbor; Freetown, chief city of productive Sierra Leone and main port for a large hinterland; and Lagos, the main port of Nigeria and coastal terminus of a railroad that reaches inland to the old native town of Kano, the trade center for northern Nigeria.

WESTERN SUDAN

Most of the area of the Soudanese and Niger republics lies in the Dry World, but most of their population is in the African World rather than in the northern desert areas. The Voltaic Republic is entirely within the African World. These Western Sudan areas are mainly in the savanna-steppe transition zone; a region of grasslands and park landscape, of summer rain-

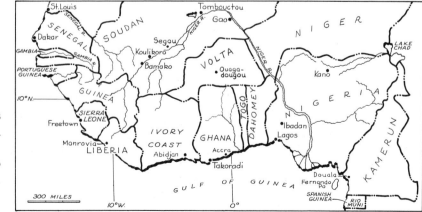

Guinea Lands and Western Sudan: index map

fall totaling 10 to 20 inches, and of warm, dry climate more acceptable to Europeans than the coastal rain forests. Two major rivers, the Niger and the Senegal, are of great importance because they bring precious water to a semiarid land and provide transportation during part of the year.

Negro blood is dominant right up to the desert margins which mark the border and battleground between two culture worlds; Arab vs. Negro, Mohammedan vs. pagan, pastoralism vs. agriculture. Farming and irrigation are old in this area, and were basic to the economy of the vast Negro empires that flourished from the seventh to the sixteenth centuries. These empires demonstrated that the Negroes were capable of organizing and maintaining efficient governments for long periods, but not entirely in peace. Bloody wars were the frequent result of trade rivalry, and strife between racial groups, religions, and cultures. Thriving settlements, such as Gao and Tombouctou, changed hands many times, and other cities, such as the capitals of Ghana and Mali Empires, were completely destroyed.

Not until the twentieth century did France begin to realize the potentialities of the Sudan. Sections remote from the coast have been slow to develop because of lack of transportation. This handicap is being overcome by the gradual extension of roads into the interior. The main outlet for the upper Niger agricultural region is the railroad connecting Bamako, the capital, and Koulikoro with coastal Dakar and St. Louis. The Volta's connection with the coast is the railroad from Ouagadougou, the capital, to Abidjan and its new harbor. Considerable effort is being made to increase the agricultural productivity of the region, especially along the Niger above the bend where there are excellent alluvial soils. Irrigation works make available some 2 million acres and can be readily extended to 5 million more. The densest native populations are in the agricultural regions along the Senegal, the Niger, and in central Volta. Peanuts have long been a leading crop, but both cotton and rice production are increasing. Raising of cattle and sheep in the grasslands is also expanding.

CENTRAL WEST AFRICA

The countries that compose Central West Africa have a combined area of about 1.9 million square miles and 24.4 million total population, of which about 150,000 are Europeans, mainly in Angola. The low average population density of roughly 12 per square mile falls to 4 or 5 over large areas and rises to well over 200 in Ruanda-Urundi, a region of rich volcanic soils and healthy highland climate. The Europeans are concentrated in these highlands and in the healthier, higher and drier parts of Angola and the Katanga district of the Congo. The whole

Jebba, Nigeria
[*British Information Services*]

Home in northern Nigeria
[*British Information Services*]

region is centered in the equatorial rain forest, and its drainage is dominated by the vast Congo system. Despite numerous falls and rapids, the system provides some 6,000 miles of navigable waterways, a decided advantage in a region of extensive, almost impenetrable forests. North of the rain forest the Central African Republic reaches through savanna and steppe toward the limits of the African World. To the south, interior Angola is largely savanna and steppe while the coast is part of arid southwestern Africa.

The native Africans are not only fewer in number, but they are much more primitive culturally than are the aborigines of the Guinea Coast and Western Sudan. Economically they are primitive agriculturists, hunters, and fishermen, and have produced no great native cities like those in Nigeria. Nor has the New World Revolution been of much help. The stage of exploitation, with its goals in ready riches from slaves, gold, ivory, and forest products, was everywhere in Africa an infamous chapter in European-primitive relations, but was particularly black in Central West Africa. The system of large private concessions and forced labor practiced in French and Belgian colonies was little better than the actual slavery existing in Angola until recent times. Only in the last two or three decades have there been substantial

development programs in this region, rich in minerals and agricultural potential. The first step was the improvement of transportation, providing routes from the low, malarial coasts to interior places where the major mineral deposits are located and where natural conditions are most suitable for Europeans.

The French, Belgian, and Portuguese territories, which have somewhat different natural endowments and recent courses of cultural development, are sketched separately.

French Equatorial Republics are poorly developed. The only railroad in the three republics is in Congo (formerly Middle Congo), from Pointe Noire on the coast to Brazzaville on the Congo, 300 miles away. Improved roads are equally scarce. Air transport, as in the other French African areas, is good, and handles considerable freight. Despite efforts and plans to improve and extend roads, transportation is poor over most of the region, and cultural landscapes thus remain primitive.

From the coastal regions come timber, palm oil, and cacao. In the higher interior are plantations producing coffee, peanuts, and cotton. Gold, diamonds, and lead are exported, together with petroleum from the newly discovered field at Port Gentil, Gabon. Mineral exploration has located manganese and iron deposits in interior Gabon, and there are known,

Iron ore, Liberia
[*Consulate General of Liberia, N.Y.*]

but unexplored, deposits of copper, zinc, and tin. Hydroelectric power development, such as the Kuilu River project in Congo, should provide the basis for metallurgical, chemical, and other industries. There is little industry at present, aside from a large plywood factory in Port Gentil, and such activities as iron foundries and ship building at Brazzaville, the region's largest city, over 200,000 population.

Republic of the Congo is the most equatorial of African countries. From its forests come timber, rubber, and a tremendous production of palm oil from large plantations. From plantations in the eastern highlands and around Ruanda-Urundi come valuable harvests of coffee, cacao, and other crops. Here also are found most of the cattle herds and their owners, the tall, regal men of the Watusi tribe. In the lower areas, cotton and rice are widely grown. But economically most profitable are the mines of Katanga and the highlands in the east which produce quantities of copper, gold, radium, uranium, cobalt, diamonds, tin, and other minerals. The Katanga district is more accessible from Angola ports than from those in Congo, which has only 27 miles of coast. The leading city is Leopoldville, with over 350,000 population and considerable industry: textiles, iron and steel products, chemicals, and food processing. It is 225 rail miles from Matadi, a deep-water port 80 miles up the Congo from the sea. A thousand miles up the Congo from Leopoldville is Stanleyville, a center for cotton milling and sawmilling, named for the Anglo-American explorer. Center of the Katanga mining district and second only to Kenya as a focus of white settlement in tropical Africa is Elizabethville, more closely connected with Rhodesia and Angola than with the rest of the Republic.

Angola is a country whose potential productivity is only now being realized. Four rail lines

European urban landscape, Luanda, Angola
[*Casa de Portugal*]

Central West Africa: index map

EAST AFRICA

East Africa, as considered here, includes four countries under British control. As is apparent from Table 7, Uganda is the most densely populated and Tanganyika the largest. As in the rest of the African World, behind a narrow coastal plain rises a plateau to about 3,000 feet. Here it is called the Great Lakes Plateau. Above it loom Africa's highest mountains, volcanic peaks dominated by Kilimanjaro in the east, and in the west, the Mountains of the Moon. The lakes along the eastern Uganda and Tanganyika borders mark the Great Rift. The uplands are mainly grasslands and park landscapes, with some semiarid scrub areas, while the higher mountain flanks and the lowlands are forested. In all natural respects, the plateau of Kenya and the high parts of northern Tanganyika are very attractive to Europeans, and although malaria, blackwater fever, and sleeping sickness occur, in general, East Africa is more healthful than areas so far discussed.

East Africa is racially Negroid, with some Hamitic admixtures, especially along the coast

East Africa: index map

have been built across the narrow coastal plain to the plateau which rises above 3,000 feet and has a favorable climate for Europeans. The Benguela Railway, which actually terminates at the excellent harbor of Lobito, is a direct connection to Katanga and handles a huge volume of its ores. Connections from Elizabethville lead through the Rhodesias to Beira on the Indian Ocean.

Angola has a variety of resources. The cold Benguela current provides excellent fishing. In the coastal plain are asphalt lakes, and near Luanda, the biggest city and capital, is an oil field feeding a large new refinery. From lowland to plateau there are many crops: oil palm, coconuts, cotton, maize, sugar cane, and sisal, but most important is coffee. Cattle are grazed in the drier southern part of the country. Diamonds are an important export, but little has been done with deposits of manganese, copper, iron, tin, phosphates, and sulphur ores.

Plateau Angola is "white man's country," and Portugal is assisting land-hungry people from the mother country to form colonies. To date, the 100,000 Europeans live in peace with their Negro neighbors, a unique situation in Africa today.

where there have been long foreign contacts. It was also a meeting ground of old basic agriculture and pastoralism brought by Hamites, and an arena of conflict between Mohammedanism and Christianity in efforts to convert native pagans. Islam succeeded along the coast and was more successful inland. Although in the minority, the modern ruling and commercial groups are non-Negroid. In East Africa this means Indians, for they are the most numerous non-Africans except in Zanzibar and adjacent coastal areas where Arabs are the dominant outsiders. Indians came early to East Africa as traders under Arabic auspices, and later as indentured laborers for Europeans. Now, with the exception of Kenya where their activities are legally restricted, Indians largely monopolize trade, urban rental property, and industry, and are important plantation owners. Between them and competing Europeans there is no love lost. European permanent settlers are ordinarily plantation owners, and are most numerous in Kenya where some 30,000 live mainly in the 8,000 square miles of highlands reserved for them.

Each of the four political divisions represents something of a different approach in political administration, so each is individually discussed.

Kenya is climatically and governmentally the chief country for Europeans in East Africa. The plateau produces nearly every variety of fruit, vegetable, and domestic animal familiar to temperate Europe. Europeans have created, in their 5 per cent of the area, a landscape reminiscent of the homeland. On large plantations maize, coffee, tea, wheat, sugar cane, and sisal are grown. In the midst of a highly productive section of the plateau is thoroughly modern Nairobi, capital and chief city. It is on the railroad to the densely populated native areas around Lake Victoria. Natives have been rapidly increasing in number, mainly as a result of British efforts to improve health and living standards, and to stamp out tribal warfare. Pressures on the land are thus steadily mounting, as are the feelings of the agricultural tribes against the Europeans. Various measures for solving the problem are being taken: instructing the natives in improved agricultural practices to

increase the yield and variety of cash crops, rehabilitating land destroyed by over-cultivation, expanding cattle production, absorbing natives in industry and commerce, and searching for other sources of wealth, such as mineral deposits.

Aside from Nairobi, the principal city is Mombasa, the seaport and eastern terminus of the Uganda railroad. Preferential rates have allowed it to become chief entrepot for the region, and to assume the position once held by Zanzibar.

Uganda, smaller but more densely populated than Kenya, has been recently administered with the interests of the native African population held paramount. Political administration is in native hands, European settlement is restricted, and native economy is fostered. The country has both low, hot, forested sections and high, dry grasslands, and includes a big segment of Lake Victoria, the world's second largest fresh-water lake. On its shore is charming Entebbe, seat of British administration, and nearby is Kampala, chief city and native capital. Agriculture is the main activity, with plantain and millet as the chief subsistence crops, and coffee, cotton, cereals, fruits, tea, and rubber as the commercial and plantation crops. Cattle, sheep, and goats provide important exports of hides. Mineral exploitation has not reached great proportions. Still the area is a major source of tantalum, and produces copper and tin as well.

Tanganyika as a trust territory of the United Kingdom is administered with equal representation of British, native, and Indian populations. In general, the natives are the farmers and workers, the Europeans are administrators and owners, and Indians control the business life and service activities, as well as many plantations. Like other East African countries, Tanganyika has a narrow coastal plain succeeded by a tableland 3,500 to 8,000 feet high. Forest is limited and most of the plateau is open grassland and park landscape, but these grazing lands are cursed by the presence of the tsetse fly. Agricultural products from plantations and native farms are the principal source of wealth and exports. Cash crops are sisal, cotton, coffee, tea, maize, sesame, and hides. The list of exported minerals includes diamonds, gold, silver, tungsten, and tin. The country is fairly well off in terms of transportation, with thousands of miles of dry-weather roads. A German-built railroad connects the seaport of Tanga with the chief areas of European settlement at the base of Kilimanjaro. Another line goes from the port of Dar-es-Salaam, capital and largest city of Tanganyika, to Kigoma, center of heavy native population on Lake Tanganyika. A branch line leads to the cotton, gold, and diamond-producing Shinyanga area at the south end of Lake Victoria.

Zanzibar and the island to the north, Pemba, are semi-autonomous remnants of the Arabic Empire in Africa. The heterogeneous mixture of peoples in these islands reflects a varied history. About 80 per cent of the population is Bantu Negroes, and the rest are Arabs, with a few Indians and other Asians. Not more than 300 Europeans brave the low, damp, tropical conditions marking the coastal location. Under sultanic rule, Zanzibar was the center of a lucrative slave trade, but its fortunes declined as the slave trade dwindled early in the nineteenth century. Its position as the great east coast entrepot was later assumed by Mombasa, leaving the city of Zanzibar an interesting but unhealthy spot of slowly declining commercial importance. The chief activity of the islands is clove production,

and they supply 80 per cent of the world's needs. The only other significant agricultural product is the coconut. Both cloves and coconuts come from plantations owned by Arabs and Indians.

SOUTHERN AFRICA

Southern Africa is a very general term for the nine southernmost territories of the continent. Natural unity is lacking, since the latitudinal range is from 8° to 35° S., and elevations vary from sea level to over 10,000 feet. Much of the area is sub-humid to arid, tropical rain forest is small in extent, and the only non-tropical portions of the African World are within southern Africa. Culturally the area also lacks unity. Among the aboriginal inhabitants are the Malagasy of Madagascar, the Bantu, Hottentot, and Bushmen, each with a distinctive cultural orientation. Yet in southern Africa the New World Revolution has gone farther than anywhere else in the African World, and only here do Europeans constitute a vigorous and substantial part of the population. Politically the region is British, except for Madagascar and Mozambique.

The Federation of Rhodesia and Nyasaland, established in 1953, is virtually self-governing, with each of the three territories running its own affairs. In area the Federation is about

Somali and camels, northern Kenya
[*British Information Services*]

the size of Angola, but with almost twice the population. Less than 5 per cent of the population is European, mainly concentrated in Southern Rhodesia. Nyasaland is the most densely populated, even more so than the figures in Table 7 would indicate because almost one quarter of its area is water.

Nyasaland, tucked along the western and southern shore of Lake Nyasa, has both lowlands and plateau, the latter being divided into a number of sections by streams flowing into the lake. The lowlands surrounding the lake are hot, damp, and unhealthy, in contrast to the pleasant Shire Uplands, the portion of the plateau paralleling the Shire River, where most of the Europeans live. The economic backbone of the country is agriculture, despite known mineral resources, notably bauxite. The variety of natural conditions permits a range of crops: tobacco, maize, cotton, rice, some coffee and rubber, and quantities of tea. Commercial progress is limited by transportation facilities which consist of about 1,000 miles of automobile roads and a rail line from Lake Nyasa to the port of Beira in Mozambique. Towns are few and small, including Zomba, the capital.

The Rhodesias, named for Cecil Rhodes, are separated by the Zambezi River. Most of Northern Rhodesia is a plateau, 2,000 to 5,000

feet high. Its tropical temperatures and numerous diseases make it unattractive to white settlement in general, except where the lure of mineral wealth overcomes marked disadvantages. Along the railroad from Livingstone, through Lukasa and Broken Hill to Elizabethville in the Republic of the Congo, are the bulk of the European population and most of the mines that are the basis of the country's economy. Copper, cobalt, vanadium, and zinc are the principal minerals produced. Although much of the area is open country suitable for grazing and farming, cattle raising is limited by the tsetse fly. Among the agricultural products are tobacco, sugar cane, maize, cotton, vegetables, and cereals.

Southern Rhodesia has the advantage of being farther from the equator, more accessible, and higher, averaging 4,000 to 5,000 feet, with a moderate climate favorable to the good health and energy of Europeans. The excellent soils of the rolling plateau surface support a savannasteppe vegetation, now largely given over to farms and grazing. Minerals are abundant. Most striking of the natural features are Victoria Falls of the Zambezi River. Some of the vast power potential of the Zambezi has been developed by the construction of a dam and hydroelectric plant in the Kariba Gorge, 300 miles

Coastal Plain landscape, Kenya
[*British Information Service*]

Masai herdsman
[*British Information Services*]

below Victoria Falls. Electricity is a vital need of the industries which extract and process minerals. Mining has been important in the economy since before the coming of Europeans with the British South African Company of Cecil Rhodes, but the Company did most to develop mining, as well as to build roads and railroads, and encourage agriculture and stock raising. Today Southern Rhodesia is one of the highland tropical areas successfully settled by Europeans, the colony numbering about 200,000, largely English. Typical of the European-built cities are Bulawayo, a commercial and industrial city, and Salisbury, Federation and territorial capital, and trade center for products from the mines, farms, and herds. In Southern Rhodesia maize is the leading crop, followed by wheat, tobacco, citrus fruit, and dairy and pastoral products. Chrome ore is the most significant mineral product; gold, asbestos, and platinum ore are also mined. The region contains one of the best African coal deposits.

Bechuanaland, a British Protectorate, is a large, sparsely populated country, a last refuge of the Bushmen. Although it receives 15 to 25 inches of precipitation annually, the value of the rainfall is reduced by the sandy, absorbing soil. The northern section of the country has interior drainage, wet-season streams flowing into Ikavango Swamp, Lake Ngami, and Makarikari Salt Pan. Although most of the country has vegetation suitable for grazing, the absence of water prevents the use of much of it. The lack of marked agricultural and mineral resources has meant that few Europeans have come in, and the area remains a sanctuary for its scant population of Bantu and Bushmen. British interest stemmed from a need for a passage between Cape Colony and Rhodesia that avoided the independent and often hostile Transvaal and Orange Free State. The resulting railroad is still the only one in the country. There is no truly European city, but there are a number of rather large native settlements, such as Serowe. Some pastoral production, a little gold and silver, and the native preparation of wild-animal pelts and skins comprise the commercial economy.

Basutoland and Swaziland are native reservations within, but not politically part of, the Union of South Africa. Both countries are British protectorates. Only a few licensed whites are permitted to live in Basutoland, and none can own property. In Swaziland there are 2,000 European concessionaires who control about two thirds of the land. Both these plateau countries have an invigorating "white man's" climate and open grasslands extensively used for grazing. Swaziland has a wide range of crops, and excellent deposits of tin, gold, and asbestos that are mined by Europeans. In Basutoland the prevalence of frost and seasonal aridity restrict the cultivable area. Small farms on the communally held land produce mainly subsistence crops, wheat and maize. Wool is the principal commercial asset, since there is no mining. Roads are few and towns are small.

Mozambique is a very large country to which the Portuguese have had claim since the fifteenth century, and they have fought Arab and Zulu to hold it. Their first interest was gold, their second, slaves. In the seventeenth century the Portuguese brought Indians to the east coast, thus introducing what is now an important racial and cultural group that controls trade. Although the country has rich agricultural resources and some mineral wealth, its prosperity derives mainly from its use as a transportation corridor to the mining and industrial areas of southern Africa, and even Republic of the Congo. It has two major cities.

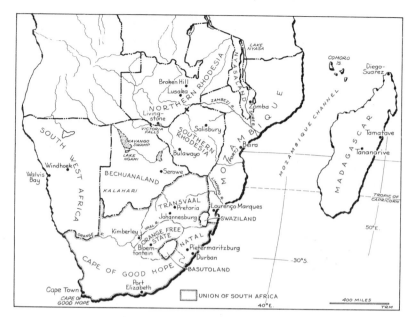

Southern Africa: index

Each is a busy port, a terminus of a railroad to the southern interior, and a center of European population. Beira is the port for Rhodesia, Nyasaland, and Katanga. Modern, spacious Lourenço Marques is a major outlet for the Rand district of Transvaal, and a second port for Rhodesia. Without the income from this corridor activity the country would be economically hard pressed, for its own resources are far from fully developed. The very wide coastal plain offers agricultural and grazing possibilities, but in the southern and central portions there are serious handicaps: seasonal aridity, labor shortage, and floods, on both the great Zambezi delta and the plains of the Limpopo. Maize is the main crop and cattle raising is widespread. The northern plain is the leading agricultural region, producing cotton, rice, cashew nuts, peanuts, sugar cane, coconuts, tea, and a variety of other crops. The mineral resources, such as gold, coal, and copper, are mainly in the plateau, and are largely undeveloped. As in Angola, the Portuguese government is spending large sums of money to develop the resources of the Province, extend transportation facilities, increase industry, improve agriculture, and provide a home for surplus people from Portugal.

Madagascar, one of the world's largest islands, has a trade-wind climate; its exposed, steep eastern side is rain forest, while its sloping-plateau, western surface is savanna. Both flora and fauna are quite un-African, showing many resemblances to South America. Culturally Madagascar is also non-African, exhibiting basic similarities to Malaya. Even in modern commerical relations, Madagascar is largely outside the African orbit. It shares, however, with other tropical African countries the condition of being under-developed. Industry is only in a beginning stage, roads and railroads are inadequate, leaving large sections essentially isolated except for airline service. Although towns are numerous, there is only one real city on the island, Tananarive, a trade and manufacturing center as well as capital. All in all, the island still has a long way to go in the New World Revolution, although in 1958 it became an independent republic in the French Community. About 98 per cent of the total population is native Malagasy, and most of them engage in agriculture in the densely settled coastal plain along the east and in the highlands around Tananarive, or are cattle raisers in the drier, sparsely settled western sections. Less than 3 per cent of the island is cultivated, but a variety of crops is produced for subsistence and export: rice, cassava, sugar cane, beans, sweet potatoes, vanilla, maize, cloves, bananas, coffee, coconuts, and cacao. To these are added pastoral and forest products. Mining has not been pushed, but it yields graphite, mica, quartz, uranium, radium, and phosphate, and coal and other mineral resources are known to exist. Most of the export and import trade is with France, and comes through the island's leading port, Tamatave, which has rail and road connections to the central highlands where two fifths of the total population live.

The Union of South Africa is an independent state associated with the British Commonwealth of Nations, and is made up of four semi-autonomous provinces: Cape of Good Hope, Natal, Orange Free State, and Transvaal; and a mandated territory, South West Africa. This is predominantly plateau country, highest in the east where it reaches elevations over 10,000 feet in the Drakensberg Mountains, and sloping toward the interior. The outward, seaward-facing edge is an escarpment at distances from the coast that vary from 250 miles on the eastern side to 50 miles in South West Africa. Over this surface, the population is unevenly distributed; even the average densities of 76 per square mile in Natal, 50 per square mile in Transvaal, 24 per square mile in the Orange Free State, and 18 per square mile in Cape Province, give only an approximation of the concentration of population, while that in the highlands and along the eastern coast reaches local densities of well over 100 per square mile. Of the almost 15 million total population, about 65 per cent are Negroes, 20 per cent are Europeans, and the remainder is divided between Indians and "colored" or mixed bloods. Considerable racial strife exists today, which has its roots in the history of settlement.

Expansion of the Cape Town base was slow; after almost 150 years Europeans totaled only 20,000, but the general advance was toward the east and northeast, toward the areas of greater rainfall and higher elevation. Here the pioneering Dutch Boers met the advancing Bantu, who were not only fighting among themselves but also were pushing the Hottentot and Bushmen into the least desirable sections of southwestern Africa. The great movement of Europeans inland to the High Veld, the higher plateau region of the Orange Free State, was brought about by the sale of the Dutch Cape Colony to the British in 1814. The Boers broke with the British over abolition of slavery, and left the Colony, moving eastward to found Natal and its port, Durban, which the British promptly occupied. The Boers gave up, and 10,000 of them started the famed Great Trek in 1836, packing their possessions on ox wagons and heading north across the Orange River onto the High Veld. There they defeated the Zulu Bantu and pushed on across the Vaal to establish the Dutch South African Republic, composed of the Orange Free State and Transvaal. On the high windswept plains the Boers became a thoroughgoing pastoral people. But pastoralism was threatened, first by the discovery of diamonds in 1867 on the Orange River, and later by the discovery of gold in Transvaal, which brought thousands of eager British and other miners and prospectors into the area. Friction with the Boers was inevitable, and the Boer War, 1899–1902, was followed by the absorption of the Dutch republic into the British Empire, but the submergence of the Boers was temporary, for in time they gained political dominance in the whole Union.

Although the Boers are in control, the Bantu Negroes are now and are likely to remain the most numerous, constituting 9.6 millions out of the total population. The bulk of them live in the eastern part of the nation, and for the most part are thoroughly detribalized. They occupy an economic and social position resembling that of the Negroes of the United States 50 years ago, with very restricted economic and educational opportunities. Yet they are vital in this country where custom is against a white man's engaging in manual labor. The gravity of the problem of White-Negro relations outweighs all others in South Africa. Greater economic and political opportunities for the majority group seem absolutely necessary to a permanent solution. In recent years the Europeans have granted limited voting rights to the coloureds, but they and the Indians share with the Negroes many of the severely limiting rules imposed by the Europeans in their support of *apartheid*, a system of complete separation of European and non-European peoples. The Indians, most numerous in Natal, the Rand, and northern Transvaal, are regarded by Europeans as a menace because they are worthy economic competitors. They

Plateau landscape, Natal
[South African Information Service]

are traders and land owners, where not prevented by restrictions. Of less concern to Europeans are the Cape Coloureds, mixtures of European and Negro, found mainly in Cape Town and western Cape Province, where they are valued as agricultural laborers and house servants. A small but distinct group of Cape Malays in Cape Town, descendants of Malay slaves brought in during colonial days, are also no economic threat to Europeans.

Among the 3 million Europeans there are some internal problems between Boer and Englishman, stemming from differences of language, traditional rivalry, and the common feeling of antagonism between city and country dwellers. About 60 per cent of all Europeans are Boers, and their high birth rate assures an increasing majority. Europeans of British stock are most numerous in the Rand, the port cities, and generally in Natal. The distribution and use of Afrikaans (Dutch) and English, the two official languages, are indicative of the rural-urban relationship between Boers and British. Afrikaans is the native tongue of 41 per cent of the city dwellers, while 84 per cent of rural whites use the language, and the percentage in the cities is increasing as country-bred Dutch invade the English strongholds. Movement to the city has created another European headache, a growing group of poor whites, a low-order social and economic class, who compete with the native in the unskilled labor market.

In addition to this heterogeneous population, there are two other striking and significant characteristics of South Africa today: the nature of its economy; and the progress of the New World Revolution, as expressed in urbanization, industrialization, and their associated phenomena.

National economy is unhealthily dependent on minerals. South Africa supplies almost half of the world's gold, mainly from the Rand, a great lode of gold 70 miles long lying on either side of Johannesburg, the "Golden City." Increasing amounts of gold are being mined in the Orange Free State, so even if Transvaal fields peter out, South Africa will probably remain first among world producers. From gold ore tailings, uranium is being extracted, not an inconsequential by-product, for it now outranks diamonds in South African exports. The deep diamond mines at Kimberley and Pretoria are closed, and the center of diamond production is shifting to the Republic of the Congo and Tanganyika. Of other mineral production, coal is the most important, for in a continent poor in mineral fuels, South Africa is favored by an abundant supply of good coal. It is extensive in the Transvaal, Natal, and eastern Cape Province, and around it and nearby iron deposits has grown up a thriving iron and steel industry. Added to this list of minerals are copper, tin, platinum, and manganese. South Africa's industrial future will not fail because of lack of minerals. Dependence on mining, especially of gold, however, lays the country open to disaster when mines decline or the world changes its monetary standard. Further, mining tends to discourage the development of agriculture and the arts upon which a nation's health and well-being must be based.

Most extensive of agricultural pursuits is pastoralism, for the western half of the country is too dry for crops, being cut off from rain-producing winds from the Indian Ocean by the high Drakensberg. Vast cattle and sheep ranges provide exportable quantities of meat, dairy products, wool, and hides. In the production of merino wool, South Africa is second only to Australia. Cultivation utilizes hardly more than 5 per cent of the total area, partly because of the dryness and lack of irrigation, and partly due to the traditional Boer liking for stock and reluctance to farm. Three areas, coastal Cape Province, Natal, and the High Veld, illustrate three distinct types of agricultural production, to some extent climatically determined. Coastal Cape Province, particularly the Mediterranean section, concentrates on grapes and wine, citrus fruits, wheat, and tobacco. On the warm, humid coast of Natal, sugar cane, tea, citrus fruits, wattle bark, and other tropical and semi-tropical crops are the rule, but at higher elevations and especially in the High Veld of the Orange Free State and Transvaal, maize or "mealies" is the principal crop. Maize is food for animals and Negroes, but for Europeans has never replaced wheat as a bread-stuff. From the fine farming lands of the High Veld come other grains, dairy products, meat, and wool. It is notable that methods of agriculture and over-crowding, especially in areas of native farming, have led to widespread erosion and soil depletion, results so often associated with commercial agriculture in other parts of the New World.

Farm products not only provide food, but are the basis of rapidly growing industries concerned with processing foods, sugar, tobacco, leather, and wool, the last going into an expanding textile and clothing industry. These industries, plus those based on mineral production, give South Africa a wide lead over all other regions in the African World in terms of industrialization and urbanization. There are six towns of over 100,000 each, and three of these have more than a half million each. Leading the list is Johannesburg with over one million population. The gold mines of the Rand are the reason for the city's existence, but it has also become an industrial center and a primary transportation point in the midst of a rich agricultural district. A number of lesser cities adjoin Johannesburg along the belt of Rand gold fields, and to the north lies Pretoria, capital of Transvaal and the Union, and like Johannesburg, a center of metal, food, and other processing industries. Second in size to Johannesburg is Cape Town, site of the oldest European settlement and seat of the legislature of the Union. Although it has an excellent harbor, it is somewhat off center with respect to the productive Transvaal, and even the rest of Cape Province, which is also served by Port Elizabeth, a growing center for machinery, chemical, and processing industries as well as for assembling automobiles imported from overseas. Like Cape Town, Port Elizabeth is a thoroughly British city, as is Durban, the chief city of Natal, third largest in the Union, and principal port for the Rand and South African coal. Other important cities include Bloemfontein, capital of the Orange Free State and an industrial and agricultural center; Pietermaritzburg, capital of Natal, and an iron and metal center; and Kimberley, once the world center of diamond mining and finishing. Windhoek, capital of South West Africa, is located on a plateau in the midst of grazing lands for goats, sheep, cattle and horses. It is typically German in appearance, and is on the rail line to Walvis Bay, the principal harbor of South West Africa and a main fishing and whaling port.

South Africa, unlike most parts of the African World, is a modern country well along on the course of the New World Revolution, with cities like those of Europe, extensive roads and railroads, nine universities, and numerous artists, statesmen and scientists. But it has its difficult problems, both economic and political. Its rapidly expanding industries may help solve the economic problems, but only wisdom, tolerance, and an understanding of personal dignity can solve the other issues.

ORIENTAL WORLD

Jute fields, East Pakistan
[Embassy of Pakistan, Washington]

17. Asia

The land area of the earth totals about 57.5 million square miles, of which 56.6 lie on the seven conventional continents: Asia, 16.494; Africa, 11.529; North America, 9.364; South America, 7.097; Antarctica, 5.363; Europe, 3.781; and Australia, 2.975. The Afro-Eurasian landmass contains about 55 per cent of all the land. Asia itself accounts for about 29 per cent of all the earth's land, an area equal to all the land in the western hemisphere. The Asian mainland is somewhat rectangular in shape, extending 5,300 miles north-south and 6,000 east-west. It is about three times as wide as the distance between the coasts of South Carolina and southern California, and spans the latitudes

between 77° and 1°, equivalent to that between Cape York, in northwestern Greenland, and the mouth of the Amazon, in Brazil. The East Indies are bisected by the equator and extend to 10° 45′ S.

The coast line of Asia is intermediate between the simplicity of Africa and the complexity of Europe. Over half of it is unused and of little value. The main maritime coasts are in the south and east. These trend at approximate right angles, and as can be clearly seen on a globe, the east coast of Asia is practically a straight-line continuation of the west coast of the Americas. The east coast is also notable for its island arcs, several great festoons that more or

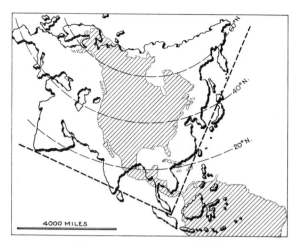

**Eurasia and America:
comparative latitudes and areas**

less enclose a series of seas: Bering Sea, Sea of Okhotsk, Sea of Japan, East China Sea, and Yellow Sea, and South China Sea. The map of Asia: *geologic structures and volcanoes*, shows these seas and their enclosing islands, as well as the East Indian system of festoon islands lying in an arc from Arakan Yoma to Ceram. Many of these islands are associated with volcanic activity, for the Pacific Ocean has a girdle of fire, a volcanic belt that runs from South America through the island arcs of Asia's east coast and on to New Zealand. A second great volcanic belt extends from the East Indies arc along southern Asian mountains into the ranges of the east-west Eurasian mountain barrier. Asia thus shares in both of the main zones of today's major volcanic activity. This means it also has many high mountains along both these zones, and the mountains are still growing rapidly. Associated with geologic growth are many major catastrophies for man, volcanic explosions and earthquakes, many so violent that hundreds of thousands of people are killed. Most of the world's great earthquakes occur either around the borders of the Pacific or along the belt from the East Indies to Iberia, along the two main volcanic zones.

The average elevation of Asia exceeds that of the other inhabited continents: Asia averages about 3,000 feet above sea level; North America, 2,000; Africa, 1,900; South America, 1,800;

Australia, 1,000; and Europe, 980. Asia's great elevation is due to the extremely high plateaus and mountains along the east-west barrier and northeastward across eastern Siberia. As a rule, high elevations are hostile to dense population and use by man. Roughly half of Asia consists of mountain or high plateau country and about 8 per cent is over 10,000 feet above sea level. The mountain chains along the east-west barrier and the Pacific coast reflect a geologic history full of activity, with much folding, faulting, and crumpling of the bedrock topped by volcanic peaks which are geologically very young. In sharp contrast to the mountain barriers are three Asian regions of very old rocks which have had an uneventful geologic history: (1) eastern Siberia, (2) the Deccan Peninsula of India, and (3) Arabia. Part of eastern Siberia is a shield, or region of ancient rock that has remained unfolded for an extremely long time. The Arabian shield is part of the African shield, separated by the Red Sea graben. It is possible that the Deccan is a fragment of the same shield, but in any event, it and the African shield are similar to each other, and very different from the mountain belts of badly dislocated and deformed rock.

Asia is relatively deficient in lowland, although it has vast low areas. Much of the northwestern section is an eastward continuation of the European Plain. Along the two maritime coasts interrupted lowlands of various sizes extend from the Amur River to the delta of the Yangtze Kiang, and across southern Indo-China and Thailand (Siam) to the valleys of Burma and the great Indo-Gangetic plain. The total area of these extensive lowlands exceeds that of any other continent, but it is only a small proportion of the vast continental area of Asia. What is even more important is the fact that relatively few of the lowlands are useful. They extend into tundra and taiga areas where cereals cannot grow, and into desert and steppe regions where there is water enough to irrigate only very limited areas. In the southeast, some are in territory so hot and wet that it is extremely hard to raise crops in competition with rank and luxuriant natural vegetation. Less than 10 per cent of Asia is actually under cultivation.

CLIMATE AND VEGETATION

Most of Asia has extremely cold weather, 70 per cent of it averaging below 25° F. during the month of January. In the cold part of Asia there are only two seasons, summer and winter. Ground stays frozen from November until May or June when the thaw and rather high air temperatures allow plants to start a vigorous but short season of growth. There is no truly warm season in the Arctic belt, in many of the high mountains, and across the most-elevated plateaus. About 12 per cent of Asia has no month with an average above 50° F. and is therefore in the Arctic or Alpine Tundra type of climate, with either no, or only stunted, vegetation.

Nearly half of Asia has deficient precipitation, and about 30 per cent has interior drainage.

Northwest of a line from the mouth of the Indus to the mouth of the Amur there is little territory that receives as much as 20 inches of precipitation, and comparatively little on the southeast that does not. In the dry, cold-winter, interior Asia, such precipitation as falls comes mainly from Atlantic Ocean moisture. In the summer this moist air can invade parts of Siberia, and with it come frontal storms and precipitation, gradually diminishing as the air dries out in its travels toward the east. But in winter the cold Polar Siberian air mass builds up over the northern interior, and both blocks the invasion of Atlantic air and sends its own icy blasts to chill the plains of European Russia or bring cool weather even to Arabia and western Europe.

In great contrast with conditions of the interior are those along the southern coast, east of the Indus. The relatively warm Indian Ocean

Asia: geologic structures and volcanoes

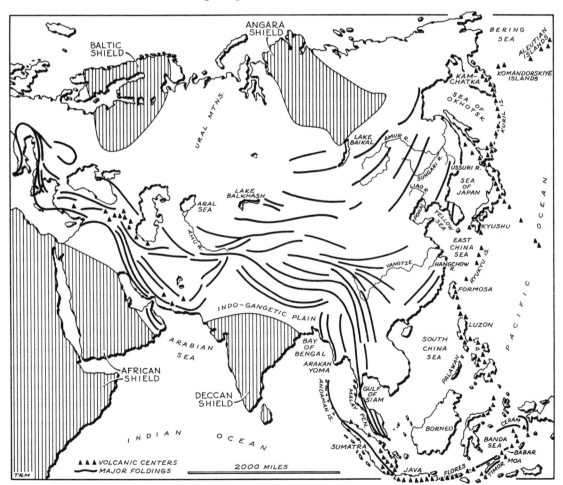

sends enormous quantities of water vapor into the overlying air. During summers, when temperatures rise high along the belt just south of the Himalaya, the barometric gradient is toward the land and the oceanic air mass sends rather steady winds from the southwest. This wind is the *summer monsoon*. With even slight rises, condensation forms heavy layers of cloud and precipitation occurs. The rainiest places are westward and southward slopes of hills and mountains. Prolonged, heavy rains are common, with record falls of 30 to 40 inches in a single day. The wettest place on earth in terms of actual precipitation may lie in the Khasi Hills, just northeast of the Ganges-Brahmaputra Delta. Here Cherripunji averages 452 inches a year in spite of dry winters, and nearby stations are even wetter. (Mt. Waialeale, in the Hawaiian group, averages 460 inches, which is claimed as a world record.)

Before the arrival of the summer monsoon, the weather is hot and variable. Often the warmest month of the year occurs in late spring, before the heavy monsoon clouds lower temperatures a little, but then the humidity becomes so high that the summer weather is regarded as unpleasant. By winter the wind has reversed, the *winter monsoon* blowing from the northeast toward the lower pressures of the Indian Ocean. This continental air is dry at the start, but it picks up enough moisture as it sweeps across the Bay of Bengal to bring winter precipitation to southeast and southern Deccan and Ceylon. Along the eastern coast of Asia there is also a seaward drift of air in winter, bringing rains to the west coast of Japan as a result of moisture collected over the Sea of Japan. In summer the air drift is landward.

Tropical storms, known in the western Pacific as *typhoons* and in the Caribbean and Gulf of

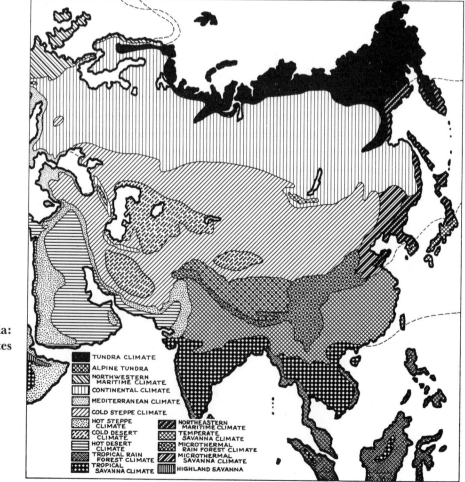

Asia: climates

TUNDRA CLIMATE
ALPINE TUNDRA
NORTHWESTERN MARITIME CLIMATE
CONTINENTAL CLIMATE
MEDITERRANEAN CLIMATE
COLD STEPPE CLIMATE
HOT STEPPE CLIMATE
COLD DESERT CLIMATE
HOT DESERT CLIMATE
TROPICAL RAIN FOREST CLIMATE
TROPICAL SAVANNA CLIMATE

NORTHEASTERN MARITIME CLIMATE
TEMPERATE SAVANNA CLIMATE
MICROTHERMAL RAIN FOREST CLIMATE
MICROTHERMAL SAVANNA CLIMATE
HIGHLAND SAVANNA

Mexico as *hurricanes*, are large (up to 200 miles in diameter) wind-whirls with clear centers, *eyes*, surrounded by inflowing air. Wind velocities are intense, rain is commonly torrential, and clouds are thick and dense around the eyes. These storms occur mainly in late summer and early fall, and are very destructive. One of the worst features is the reversal in wind direction on either side of the eye. Most of them originate on the western side of great oceans some distance north of the equator and move northwestward to about 30° N., then take a northeastward course. Many strike the Phillippines and Japan, and some reach China. Their energy comes from heat liberated when water vapor condenses, so when moisture is not available in quantity, as over land, they cease to operate. But they bring a fair amount of irregular preciptation and considerable destruction to coastal southeastern Asia as far north as Japan.

Asia extends through all the major climatic zones, as the Climates of Asia map shows, going from the tundra zone in the north to the tropical in the south. Vegetation follows climatic distribution rather closely. South of the tundra and taiga are extensive steppes of short and medium-height grass, and widespread deserts with typical Dry World vegetational characteristics. South and east of the dry climates are the plant associations of the Oriental World.

The most luxuriant forest occurs in the equatorial islands and wetter parts of southeastern Asia. This is tropical rain forest, like that of the Guinea coast or Amazon Basin. Tree growth is so dense that little sunlight reaches the ground, a fact unfavorable to smaller plants and larger mammals. Trees are mainly broad leaved and evergreen, and although they grow rapidly, they are difficult to exploit because some have no lumber value, and the variety is so great that

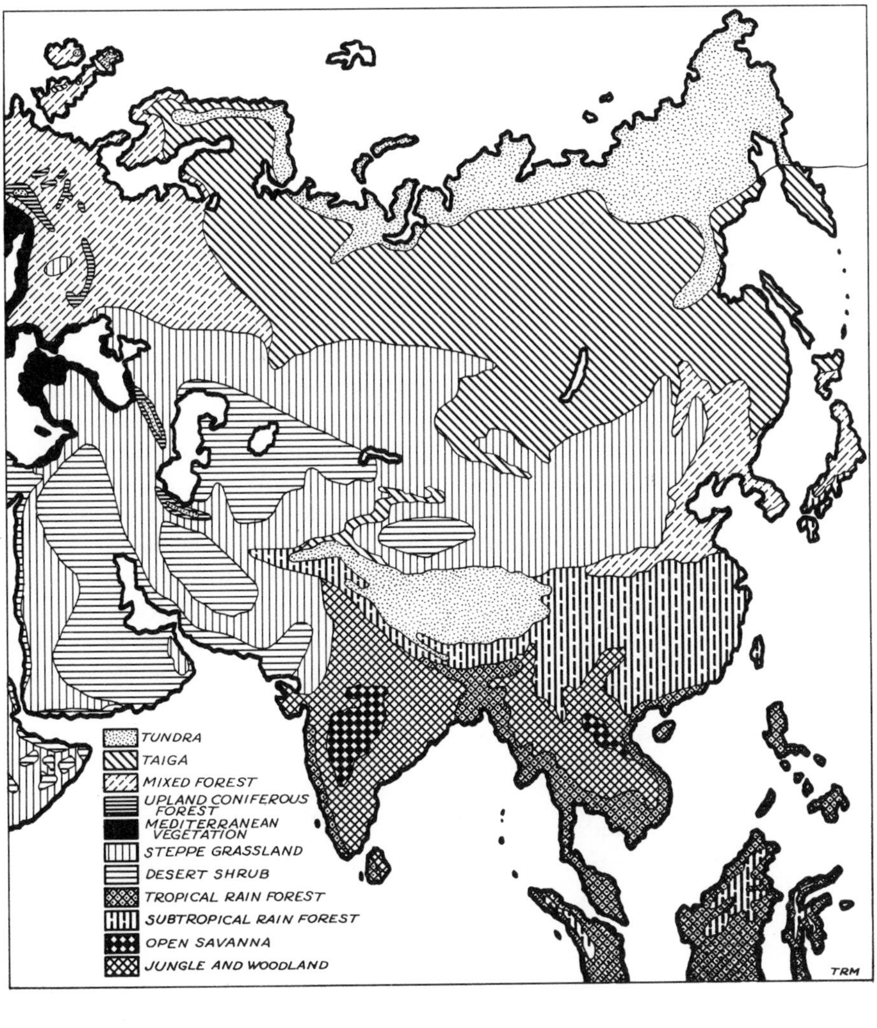

Asia: vegetation

TUNDRA
TAIGA
MIXED FOREST
UPLAND CONIFEROUS FOREST
MEDITERRANEAN VEGETATION
STEPPE GRASSLAND
DESERT SHRUB
TROPICAL RAIN FOREST
SUBTROPICAL RAIN FOREST
OPEN SAVANNA
JUNGLE AND WOODLAND

TRM

individual woods differ so much in hardness that mills have trouble getting logs that can be run at uniform saw speeds. Some trees, of course, are extremely valuable, such as ebony and mahogany. The monsoon forest, or jungle and woodland as shown on the map of vegetation, occurs where there is a distinct dry season. In summer, growth resembles the rain forest but winter finds open landscapes, when trees drop their leaves in response to dryness. Jungle is a favorable place for big game, is easily cleared for agriculture, and possesses vauable woods, such as teak and deodar, and some edible fruits and nuts. Broadleaf, deciduous forests are native to much of southern China, and to the north are mixed forests of conifers and broadleaf trees that resemble those of the European Plain. Northward, this forest grades into typical taiga. It is readily cleared and contains many useful woods, and is now greatly reduced in area. The monsoon lowlands naturally grow tall savanna grasses, such as bamboo, and a wide variety of trees along stream courses, on hills, and other places where they are not crowded out by grass. These characteristics are particularly true of India and southeastern Asia. Readily cleared and put into use, monsoon lowlands produce such crops as jute, indigo, and, most important of all, rice.

POPULATION

Most of Asia is sparsely populated, and well over half supports only nomads, or a few population knots in oases. The Polar World area of Asia is vast, but contains very few people, as do the taiga, steppe, and desert regions. Yet over half the population of the world lives in Asia. The population of the world is about 2.9 billion. In non-Soviet Asia there are 1.6 billion, and each year some 24 million are added to the total. More than one third of the world's cities of over 100,000 are in Asia, but they account for only 8 per cent of the population, for Asia is predominantly rural.

Dense populations are always supported by agriculture, and in heavily populated lands diets tend to center on cereals rather than on more expensive meat and milk. Man ordinarily adjusts himself to almost any condition that confronts him, so if an economic pattern requires him to eat cereals, he comes to regard this as virtuous and calls bread "the staff of life." Where populations are extremely dense, as in Japan, animals are a luxury, taking land that could produce more calories of energy if planted to cereals. In less populated lands animals are given a priority on space, as in Argentina where the diet of beefsteaks seems incomprehensibly large to a European or citizen of the United States. In southeastern Asia little meat is eaten, but no one feels put upon. Convenient vegetarian cults and taboos arise, such as the taboos in India against eating meat which few could afford anyway. Fish never compete with man for space, so in cults and diets they are usually highly regarded.

There are five main types of advanced Asian agriculturists: (1) the lowland Oriental World rice grower, a vegetable gardener, who is extremely skilled in conserving and enriching his soil to produce great quantities of food on small plots; (2) the oasis farmer of the dry climates who, like the Oriental gardener, practices intensive agriculture, and is skilled in the art of irrigation; (3) the marginal farmer of the steppe who follows dry farming, letting land lie fallow, then plowing and planting at just the right time to conserve limited moisture, a practice common among Europeans; (4) the Mediterranean agriculturist of Asia Minor and the Levant, a horticulturist, who uses irrigation, garden agriculture, and field agriculture; (5) the typical European field agriculturist of the Siberian Wedge of the European World, who sows broadly and farms carelessly in terms of Oriental garden agriculture. Of course there is much overlapping of these types. In addition, Asia has many forms of primitive agriculture, such as using a digging stick to grow upland rice, or the use of fire to clear fields for hoe agriculture, where fields are abandoned as soon as the yield decreases.

CONTRASTS

Asia is a continent of contrasts. It contains the highest and the lowest land on earth, the coldest

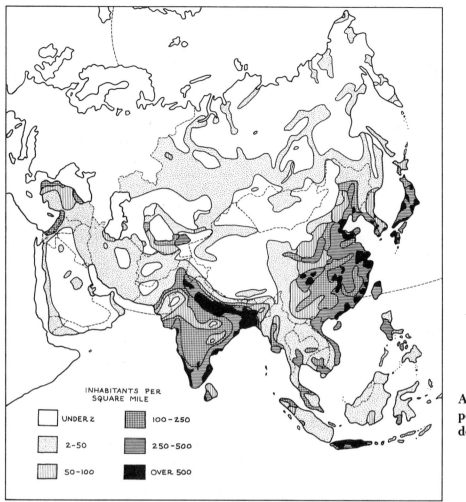

INHABITANTS PER
SQUARE MILE

UNDER 2		100-250
2-50		250-500
50-100		OVER 500

**Asia:
population
density**

part of the world in January and possibly the hottest in July, the rainiest large area on earth and the most extensive and driest deserts. Its vegetation includes tropical rain forest, extreme desert, tundra, and lands too cold to have any vegetation. Though three quarters of the continent are almost uninhabited, over half of the world's population lives on 10 per cent of the world's land area along Asia's southern and eastern coast.

From the cultural standpoint, the contrasts in Asia are so striking that it is necessary to divide the continent into four culture worlds: Polar, European, Dry, and Oriental. The first three have already been discussed. Now to the Orient.

The Oriental World extends around southeastern Asia, from Dry World Baluchistan to the Far Eastern Area of the Soviet Union, and includes the maritime southern and eastern coasts

where monsoon influences are dominant or strongly felt. The Dry World bounds most of the inner side, and it faces the Indian and Pacific oceans. Oriental World cultures extend across marginal seas to the arcuate islands from Burma to northern Japan. This World is an amorphous agglomeration of peoples, a region unified by confusion of tongues, complexity of social organizations, diversity in religions, and general absence of European types of political organization. For a brief span of years Japan has departed from the general pattern in building a nationalistic state, but no other Oriental World people has ever achieved political unity approaching that of European states. China, along with other places, has now and then been under a rule of important dynasties, but never has it become a nation of peoples who have had general awareness of being Chinese, nor the bond of a national language that could be generally understood.

The cultural distinction between Europeans and Orientals is extremely sharp. To Europeans, Oriental World peoples at times seem highly irrational. Codes of conduct, values, and ways of life are decidedly foreign, and are archaic in the eyes of Europeans. But the Oriental is likely to feel himself spiritually superior, a member of civilizations going back to antiquity, one who tolerates the ways of others but does not admire them, least of all the crude, commercial, upstart European ways. On the other hand, the European cannot understand the Oriental's willingness to give up his individuality and even his life in mass suicides or suicidal ventures, his acceptance of rigid caste systems, or a number of other things readily accepted by vast hordes of Orientals as being normal. Marriage of girls at the age of ten or less, or the arrangement of marriages by elders, without consent of the individuals, is repugnant to the European mind. Not only are the ways of life strange to Europeans, but Oriental landscapes contrast sharply with those of other culture worlds. Exotic trees and animals, bizarre architecture, and grotesque images of gods meet the eye of the European. Transportation is mainly on waterways or trails. In India man is served by awkward buffalo, inefficient humped zebus (oxen), or camels, and in China he does draft-animal chores himself. Man's implements are crude; his normal habitations are hovels. The Oriental, of course, would disagree with most of these ideas. To him his culture world is normal.

After the Voyages of Discovery, the Oriental World presented the richest of prizes to European exploiters, but the New World Revolution tactics of Europeans bogged down under well established Oriental cultures. Unlike the primitive peoples in the American or Pacific World, those of the Oriental World did not accept European ways, nor could they be exterminated. Since the sixteenth century Europeans have worked vigorously, built railroads and cities, encouraged trade, sent missionaries, established empires, policed conduct, and exploited natural resources. If they made it possible for life to be more stable or easier and more secure, native peoples simply multiplied with greater rapidity, so that more were present to resist Europeanization. The hold of western powers has relaxed since World War I, and is generally threatened throughout the Oriental World.

It may be difficult to grasp the fact that over half of the world's population lives in the Oriental World. Some appreciation of the numbers of people involved can be gained from the illustration that if the people of India were whisked past a single point at the rate of one per second, 3,600 per hour, 86,400 per day, it would take 12.5 years for them all to go by; and it would take over 20 years for all the inhabitants of China to pass at the same rate. While they were going by, of course, the populations would increase by many, many millions.

The Oriental World has three main realms, Indian, Chinese, and Malayan, with transitional territories between.

INDIAN REALM

Budh Gaya Temple
[*Government of India Tourist Office*]

18. *Indian Realm*

The Indian Realm of the Oriental World is closer to Europe in many ways than are the other realms. The majority of its people is basically Mediterranean, although Mongoloid, Australoid, and Negroid racial stocks are represented. The languages are mainly Indic, a branch of the Indo-European stem, related to Iranic tongues. Europeans have been in contact with India for well over 20 centuries. During none of this time was India a united nation. It was, and largely still is, a region of diverse peoples, large numbers of people, with many tongues, inhabiting various kinds of territory. No links existed that unified Indians in culture, tradition, history, or religion. Even the name India is of foreign origin.

When Alexander the Great conquered northwestern India in 326 B.C., he found a land with a civilization that was already old. Highly inflected languages were in use, and there was an extensive literature in written Sanskrit. Followers of Gautama, or Buddha (d. 480 B.C.), were trying to live upright, sinless lives, and seeking salvation after death; concepts that were advanced and refined in contrast to the crude and immature religions of the Greeks. Architecture was far advanced, with ornate designs requiring expert craftsmanship. The largest stone buildings on earth were in India, inhabited by monks. Europe was poor and barbarous in comparison with India, where people could make excellent fabrics, superior copper and brass wares, and fine steel. For many centuries Europe imported manufactures from India, as well as gems, spices, and oils. After the decline of the Roman Empire, Arabs took over the Indian trade to Europe, mainly with the Italian city-states. The rivalries and hostilities among the city-states cut into the Indian trade, which practically ceased when the Ottoman Turk extended his power across several East-West routes. Europe was not content to let the trade die. Tastes had been acquired, especially during the Crusades, for products and luxuries not obtainable at home, so new ways to India had to be found: hence, the Voyages of Discovery. So important was India that Columbus deluded himself into the idea of its discovery and called the American aborigines Indians.

During the Commercial Revolution, the Portuguese were first in the Indian trade, and still hold little patches of land, Goa, Damoa, and Diu, as remnants of the era. Together these have an area of 1,537 square miles and a population of 647,000, and export coconuts, fish, cashew nuts, and spices. Mormugao, in Goa, is a source of manganese. The Portuguese lost out in the Indian trade to the Dutch, who, when they began concentrating on the East Indies, lost out to the French and English. The French got into the act in the middle of the seventeenth century, but stayed only long enough to establish five stations: Chandernagore near Calcutta, Yanam, Pondicherry, Karikal, and Mahe, which they held for over a century, then yielded to India (1952–1954). In 1600 the London East India Company was formed, and it busied itself grabbing the Indian trade from France and others. It was soon bringing muslin from Dacca, dyes and spices from the Coromandel Coast, and in time, posts, or factories (depots), were established along the coasts. Sources of supply were encouraged by such practices as taking advantage of the political chaos, backing one ruler against another, bribing influential people, and sending troops to police territory where trade faced hazards. Without planning an empire, commercial control became military and, eventually, political control, and in 1877 India was declared an empire, with Queen Victoria as its Empress. Thereafter, India became a field for British investments, and Britain has been trying to protect those investments ever since.

It can hardly be argued that the British have been benefactors of India. While railroads, dams, cities, and other improvements have been numerous, these were all directed toward stimulating production and trade. Though British control began in 1813, the great majority of India's people is still in desperate need of improved health conditions, livable incomes, education, and services of all sorts. Life expectancy is shortest in the world, 32 years, and more than 85 per cent of the people are illiterate.

British India and the many native states of pre-World War II India have become two states in the Commonwealth, India and Pakistan. The latter is Mohammedan, the former is not. Pakistan consists of two widely separated parts, in the far east and the west. The Mohammedan northern state of Kashmir-Jammu was given by its Hindu ruler to India. The Indian Realm does not coincide with political India and Pakistan. Its nucleus is the lowland south of the Himalaya. Its typical parts extend south across the peninsula to Ceylon. It encounters a transition to the Dry World in Baluchistan and Afghanistan to the west, and in Kashmir, Nepal, and Bhutan to the north. Burma is transitional territory eastward into the Malayan Realm of the Oriental World. These transition lands are mountainous, and make up one of the three main divisions of India: (1) mountain borders; (2) river plains of the Brahmaputra, Ganges, and Indus; and (3) peninsular India, including

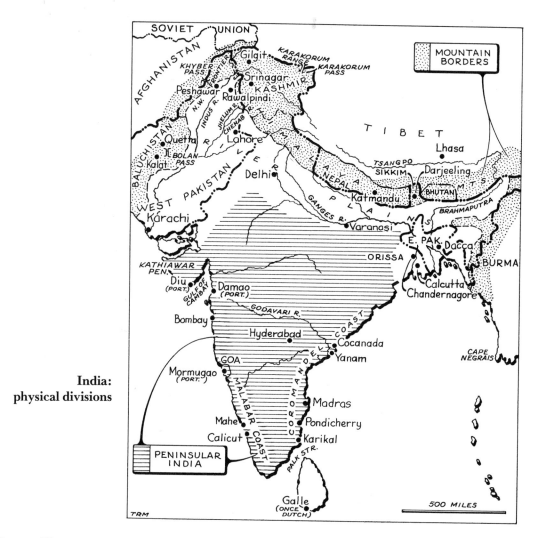

**India:
physical divisions**

the Deccan Plateau and hilly country northward to the river plains.

DRY WORLD TRANSITION

Along the western side of India the cultural transition into the Dry World lies in Baluchistan, Pakistan, where along the southern coast west of Karachi it is extremely arid. Passage is difficult, there are a few oases producing dates, and fishing is important as a source of food for the meager population and for livestock. To the north are many camel trails and a few good passes, the most important being Bolan Pass which is a railroad and highway connection from the Indus through Quetta to the west. Farther north, Afghanistan lies within the Dry World, and between it and India is a second line

of defense, the North West Frontier, a strip along the Afghanistan border and west of the Indus, where tribal organization and tendencies toward pillaging and raiding are much like those of the Afghans. Peshawar, the main city of the region, is guardian of the roads to Khyber Pass and of the upper Indus Valley.

Kashmir-Jammu, a territory about the size of Kansas, with over 4 million people, is cut in half by the deep gorge of the upper Indus. The northern part is cold and largely uninhabited Tibetan-type land, crossed by only a few difficult routes, such as that over the high, 18,000-foot Karakorum Pass to Sinkiang. These cold, remote parts of Kashmir are Dry World territory, where nomadic peoples depend on sheep, goats, and yaks for livelihood. They are surrounded by some of the world's finest alpine scenery, but their concerns are more with things they can eat. South of the Indus, especially in southwest Kashmir, are more useful parts of the territory, producing surplus amounts of silk, tea, deciduous fruits, vegetables, barley, and other crops. Centrally located Srinagar, the capital, is a center for such industries as making shawls, rugs, other woolen goods, and wood carving, and is also one of the world's finest resorts. At an elevation of about a mile, it has delightful summer climate. Elaborate house boats and skilled servants have been available to visitors at prices that seem ridiculously cheap to Europeans.

Along the Himalayan front is a mountainous and hilly belt stretching from Punjab to Assam. Vegetation is tropical and luxuriant up to about 6,500 feet, the monsoon forests containing such useful trees as oaks, magnolias, palms, and sal, and a variety of tall grasses, including bamboo, an important construction material. From about 6,500 to 11,000 feet is a "temperate zone" where such trees as maples and conifers appear in the forests. Rhododendrons and alpine plants characterize higher elevations, between the tree line and the snow line, which lies at about 18,000 feet. Various relatively pure and greatly mixed tribes of Caucasoid and Mongoloid peoples, most of them Buddhist in religion and culturally rather close to Tibetans, inhabit the Himalayan belt.

Nepal, 54,000 square miles and 8.8 million population, is an elongate kingdom along the southern watershed of the highest part of the Himalaya. Caucasoid and Mongoloid aborigines have mixed with invading Caucasoid Gurkhas from the Indus plain to form a Nepalese people who dominate the country, and who are mainly Hindu in religion. Until very recently, Nepal kept out foreigners and savored its isolation, but a new road linking its capital with India, and its membership in the United Nations, are opening its doors. Although much of the country is bleak upland or densely wooded slopes, there are fertile valleys and agricultural country toward the Ganges plain. Katmandu, the capital, lies in an attractive valley with 450,000 inhabitants skilled in agriculture. Nepalese artistic culture is seen in the palaces,

pagodas, and old Buddhist shrines. Rice is produced in surplus at lower levels, wheat, barley, and buckwheat at higher. Grain, hides, cattle, jute, herbs and drugs, along with rice, are important exports. Industries are minor and of the cottage variety. Just east of Nepal, and much like it, is the little kingdom of **Sikkim,** a 2,745-square-mile protectorate of India, with 138,000 population. It is important only because it includes the main route from Darjeeling to Lhasa. Beyond Sikkim to the east is **Bhutan,** 18,000 square miles, 700,000 population. It is a primitive, Mongoloid, Buddhist country of rugged terrain, densely forested at lower levels. From it comes a trickle of such products as lac, wax, musk, elephants, and ponies. Rice, millets, and maize are the principal foods.

The Dry World transition, in general, is recognized politically by the presence of these elongate states which have close ties to India and the British. The transitional zone is broadest in the west where it blends with the dry-

Outdoor class, Northwest Pakistan
[*Embassy of Pakistan, Washington*]

**Caucasoid girl,
northern India**
[*Government of India
Tourist Office*]

Fat-tailed sheep
[*Embassy of Pakistan, Washington*]

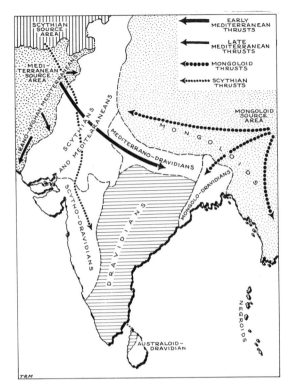

India: races and culture thrusts

climate zone. To the north it blends into a zone of nomadism resulting from extreme elevations. The dense forests along the southern slopes of the Himalaya are about as effective as the taiga as a cultural barrier. The lowland parts of such states as Nepal are culturally part of the Indian Realm, while the uplands are part of Dry World Tibet.

CULTURE BACKGROUND

India lies in the belt between Africa and western Pacific islands that was once inhabited by Negroid peoples. They were overrun by Australoids, or Archaic Caucasoids, who became the dominant pre-Dravidian population. Remnants in rather pure form are found as tribes in the most inhospitable regions of the Deccan, and in Ceylon. They are short, with little heads, triangular noses that flare into prominent nostrils, chocolate brown and darker skin, and fairly sparse, fine, wavy or coiled black or slightly reddish hair. These pre-Dravidian stocks became mixed over thousands of years with peoples from both the northwest and northeast,

and ultimately the Dravidian type developed. They are short and dark-skinned, and present many Australoid features. Later migrations into India came mainly from the northwest and resulted in the establishment of peoples who are dominantly Caucasoid across the Indus and Ganges plains and in better parts of the Deccan. These Caucasoids are Mediterraneans, closely related to people of Iran, Afghanistan, parts of Arabia, and parts of Turan. They are relatively short, slender, with skins varying from black to light brown, and heads varying from long to medium. Broader-headed peoples, Scythians, appeared later and mixed with the earlier stocks to produce the so-called Scytho-Dravidians. The very latest main groups to invade India from the northwest are distinctly Irano-Afghan Mediterraneans, with tall statures, pointed heads, and hooked noses.

The general effect of these migrations into India over the past 50 centuries has been to drive the pre-Dravidian populations to Ceylon and the worst parts of the Deccan, and the Dravidians to poor Deccan territories, and to establish purer Caucasoid peoples over the better parts of the river plains and the best soils

India: languages

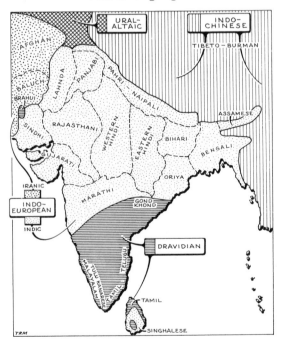

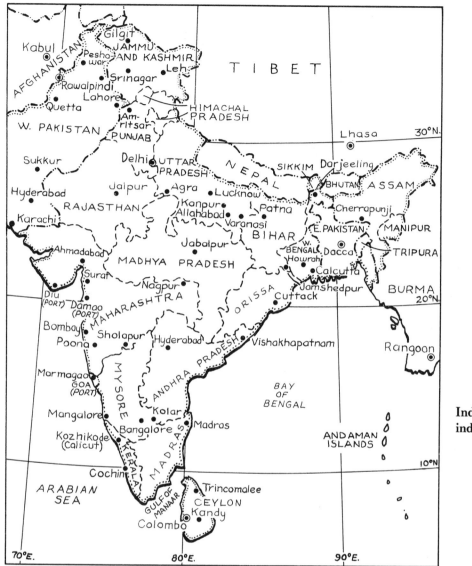

India:
index map

of the Deccan. Social distinctions arose in which the more purely Caucasoid peoples were likely to land at the top of the scale and the less Caucasoid at the bottom.

Ancestral Indo-European languages had assumed written form by at least 500 B.C. Sanskrit is kept alive by scholars, much as ancient Greek and Latin are perpetuated. The Indic tongue became extremely diversified, so today there are some 200 languages in India. Punjabi, Bengali, and several other tongues are widespread, but Hindi comes closest to being a *lingua franca* for India. Demands for political expression by some of the major language groups have resulted recently in major revisions in the boundaries of Indian states.

Traditionally India has been divided into tribal and feudal territories. Conquest had mainly come from the northwest until Europeans began arriving by sea. Punjab has been the corridor and the Ganges plains the goal of political and military invaders. Few of these had much effect on Indian cultures until a Mohammedan empire spread eastward along the river plains in the twelfth century. Then came a Mongolian conquest, the Great Moguls taking control of the river plains and much of eastern Deccan. As Mogul control waxed in the north,

Cathedral, Diu
[*Casa de Portugal*]

liefs. At the base of the social scale are the untouchables. There is no linguistic or other cultural background common to the many kinds of peoples who are Hindus. The second major religion is Mohammedanism, adhered to by about 10 per cent of the population, mainly in Kashmir and Bengal. Other leading religious groups include: 8.0 million Christians, 6.0 Sikhs, 3.0 Buddhists, 0.12 Parsees, and 0.03 Judaists. In addition, there is a wide variety of tribal religions.

Cleavages among members of the many religions, the elaborate castes of orthodox Hinduism, and the absence of clear patterns of distribution of religious groups have handicapped the rise of a coherent Indian nationalism. The separation of Pakistan from India was an effort in the direction of political unity for the areas of the two main religions. India's population is about 400 million, and Pakistan's is approximately 86 million.

HINDUSTAN

Hindustan, the river plains region of India, is a belt extending from the Arabian Sea to the Bay of Bengal between the mountain borders of the north and the hills and plateaus of peninsular India to the south. It is a lowland, some 2,000 miles long and 150 to 250 wide, consisting of active and former flood plains of the Indus, Ganges, Brahmaputra, and their principal tributaries. Occupying less than one quarter of India, Hindustan supports well over half of India's population. Much of the western part is arid, and although the Indus is fed by large rivers from northern mountains, it flows with diminishing volume through about 500 miles of its lower course, which crosses increasingly dry territory toward its mouth. East of the lower Indus is desert and steppe, the Thar, or Indian Desert, of Rajasthan. The desert and the bordering Aravalli Range separate the lower Indus from the river plains to the east.

Much land in Hindustan produces two crops a year: a winter crop of wheat, barley, or chick peas, and a summer crop of various types of millet, maize, rice, or cotton. A winter crop is possible because although this is monsoonal land

much of southern India came under Mohammedan rule. The boundaries between these main contestants for power and wealth shifted in various directions, and numerous political units appeared. The Portuguese and French did little more than establish coastal bases. The English gradually took control, but the system they imposed was about as complex and variable as that in existence before their arrival.

The complexities of racial, linguistic, and political backgrounds in India are hardly more perplexing than the socio-religious conditions. Hinduism, the religion of 85 per cent of the population, is highly philosophical, but its social system divides the population into castes, or hereditary classes. Brahmans are considered the highest caste of the 2,400 or so that exist, each with its own particular rights, taboos, and be-with nearly all the rain coming in summer, there is an inch or so in winter, just when the crops need it; the easternmost tag end of Mediterranean rainfall. More important to agriculture than the deluges of summer and the rivers produced by them in conjunction with the melting of ice and snow in the mountains, is the huge quantity of *groundwater* that seeps down into valleys and along them. This subsurface water augments river flow, appears in springs, is tapped by thousands of wells, and is vital in Indian irrigation. Another important factor in Hindustani agriculture is the high Himalaya which acts as a barricade against the cold winter air that covers interior regions. Winter temperatures in Hindustan are much like summer temperatures in northwestern Europe. This relatively cool season is short, however, and for this reason the vegetation is quite tropical. By spring, temperatures are in excess of 80° F. This hot, dry season ends with the arrival of the summer monsoon, generally in June. At least, the dry part ends, for temperature reduction is slight, and summer is a time of terrific humidity, sticky, steaming weather dragging on until the rains stop in October. High temperatures and concentration of rain in the hot season greatly reduce the value of precipitation to crops, and favor the development of soils characterized by rapid runoff with terrific evaporation losses. Under these conditions 80 inches of rain is favorable, rather than excessive, for agriculture, whereas in the British Isles half that amount is altogether too much. Places with less than 40 inches, as in the west, are deficient in precipitation in India.

The general drainage pattern east of Punjab is one in which many streams make broad turns toward the east, meeting others in junctions with narrow points of land between them. These arcuate wedges, called *doabs* (land between rivers), contain some of the main irrigated areas of India. The drainage is into the Ganges which flows along the southern side of its valley with a very gentle gradient, averaging only about 6 inches per mile from Delhi to the delta. As it leaves Bihar it makes a great bend to the south, and changes character. Upstream it is confined to a definite channel but in West Bengal its

Mosque, Lahore, West Pakistan
[*Embassy of Pakistan, Washington*]

course at first becomes meandering (swinging around in great bends) and later deltaic (dividing into various channels that run between lens-shaped islands of recently deposited sediments). The Ganges erodes its bed upstream, but deposits sediments on its flood plain and delta in West Bengal and East Pakistan, where it is joined by the Brahmaputra.

Bengal, a region containing the downstream parts of the Ganges and Brahmaputra valleys, has an area of 88,306 square miles, 33,805 square miles in the Indian state of West Bengal and 54,501 square miles in East Pakistan. The total population is about 68 million (West Bengal, 26.3, East Pakistan 42.0), and the average density is over 775 per square mile, and rises to over 1,500 per square mile in the lower delta. This density is all the more astounding because in the seventeenth century the region was sparsely inhabited. Bengal was created by the British. As in the case of most deltas, no real site existed for a commercial port until the British improved the Hooghly and established Calcutta. The conversion of swamp to cultivated land, the control of the flooding rivers, the establishment of a huge conurbation, and tremendous growth in rural population does not mean that the British made a utopia out of Bengal. It still has one of the worst climates on earth, malaria and other diseases are prevalent, earthquakes are not uncommon, and hurricanes bring high waves and floods to the lowlands.

The population of Bengal is somewhat more homogeneous than that of other parts of India. Some 90 per cent of the people understand Bengali, and three quarters are Mohammedan, although shifts in population following partition have reduced the figure to 20 per cent in West Bengal. Over 90 per cent of the people are rural. The main crop, covering 85 per cent of the cultivated land, is rice, but there is little surplus, the dense population eating most of it. In bad years there is not enough to go around, and frightful famines occur. The second important crop, the one that brings in money, is jute. Enough is produced to meet most of the world's demands for the coarse fiber used in gunny sacks, as linoleum backing, or for weaving burlap. Other food crops include pulses and grain, while sugar cane, oil seeds, tobacco, tea, and cotton are other cash crops. Aside from such places as Calcutta, Dacca, and Asansol, industry is poorly developed and largely concerned with processing products from agriculture, such as weaving textiles, milling jute, and refining sugar.

Calcutta is India's most modern and most European city. In a conurbation of some 5 million, the city accounts for 3 million. It is the financial and industrial center, and vies with Bombay for the title of India's largest city and leading port. India's greatest center of heavy industry lies in Damodar Valley and around Jamshedpur not far to the west, where abundant

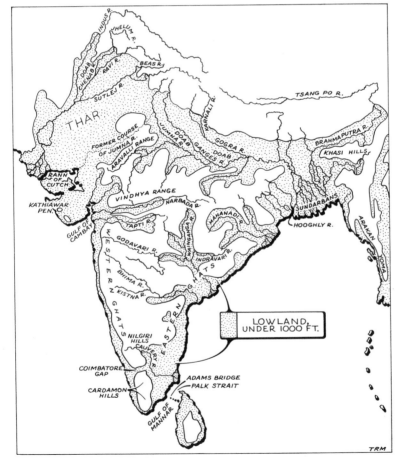

**India:
lowlands
and drainage**

**Ferry,
East Pakistan**
[*Embassy of
Pakistan,
Washington*]

iron, coal, and hydroelectric power support various iron and steel, chemical, metal, and other plants. In Calcutta itself are many textile mills, including most of India's jute mills. Dacca, 500,000, capital of East Pakistan, is in the center of the jute-growing area, and has a few industries, such as jute mills and presses, textile plants, and glass factories.

Assam, the lower Brahmaputra state, has an area of 85,012 square miles and a population of 10.9 million, or density just under 130 per square mile, so that it is about 16 per cent as densely settled as Bengal. The reason is surplus water, both in rainfall, as in the Khasi Hills, and in inundation of flats by rivers. An individual cannot cope with the situation, so most people work on large plantations reclaimed and developed under European guidance. Tea is the major plantation crop, produced mainly on the lowlands where quantities of rice are grown for food. Jute is the cash crop toward the delta. But Assam is still in a pioneer state, with less than 20 per cent in crops. Lumbering is still important. Communications are poor, and industry is essentially confined to tea packaging, lumber milling, and a few native crafts. There is minor, but locally important, development of the state's oil fields, and almost no output from its little coal deposits.

Middle India, composed of Bihar, Uttar Pradesh, and Delhi, has an area of 181,147 square miles and a population over 103.7 million, a density of more than 570 per square mile. It is the nursery of Indian culture, one of the earliest cradles of civilization, the site of India's oldest and most famous cities, as well as

**Jama Masjid,
mosque in Delhi**
[*Government of India Tourist Office*]

Parliament House, New Delhi
[*Government of India Tourist Office*]

an excellent granary. It was the goal of conquerors and its possession was the fundamental strength of the Mohammedan and Mongol empires of India's middle-ages. In modern times it maintains political leadership and supports many of India's largest cities. Because of these cities, the proportion of rural inhabitants is well below that of Bengal or Assam. Nevertheless, it is one of India's main food-producing areas. Toward Bengal the main crops are rice and various millets. To the west, where rainfall is less plentiful, the main cereal crops include increasing amounts of wheat and barley, and extensive areas are irrigated. About one quarter of all cultivated land in Uttar Pradesh is irrigated, and two crops are commonly harvested per year. Sugar cane and cotton are planted as cash crops. Oil seeds are both cash crops and a source of illumination.

Middle India is an excellent illustration of a quite general rule, that in territories richly endowed by nature, most individuals are extremely poor. Like the Po Valley, Egypt, and other fine areas, it has altogether too many people for the majority to live comfortably. Only in

rare cases is agriculture particularly profitable to the tiller of the soil. In fertile lands population increases, land holdings decrease in size, per capita yields become lower, and demands on the land are so severe that crop failures bring poverty, suffering and famine. Even in the United States the people of the barren Great Plains have higher individual incomes than those in the more agricultural states of the Southeast. The most extreme forms of poverty exist in such places as the best parts of the Yangtze lowlands and middle India. Each improvement, such as bringing more lands under irrigation, and corrective health and sanitation measures, tends to stimulate population increase and leads to increasing poverty of individuals.

For a densely populated territory, India supports an amazing number of animals which compete seriously with humans for food, and which are not particularly useful. Elephants, used in lumbering and jungle travel, are minor and not serious. There are possibly 150 million oxen, useful as beasts of burden, but consuming vast quantities of food. They are never eaten by

Buddhists and rarely by Mohammedans. Their dung, however, provides the most commonly used fuel of Indian households. There are also some 45 million buffalo, 39 million sheep, 57 million goats, and large numbers of camels to compete with man for food and space. While the European conjures schemes for improving the usefulness of Indian animals, starting dairies, improving herds, and the like, he meets utmost resistance if he tries to put his plans into effect.

The main cities of the Ganges Valley are situated mainly on the Ganges and the Jumna (Yamuna). Patna is the capital of Bihar and commercial center of the rice-raising region. Both Varanasi (Banaras) and Allahabad are religious centers that also have commercial, political, and minor industrial activities. Kanpur, the most important industrial city of middle India, is comparatively Europeanized and modern, with textile factories, flour mills, leather tanneries and factories, sugar, oil-seed, and chemical industries. Its population, 0.7 million, is rapidly expanding. Lucknow, capital of Uttar Pradesh, is a center for paper manufacturing and printing, with many agricultural industries. It has long been famous for craftsmanship, especially in gold and silver. Agra, a capital of the Mogul Empire and site of the Taj Mahal, is replacing its old crafts, such as inlaying marble and making mosaics, with modern forms of industry. But all these cities are overshadowed by Delhi, 2.0 million, capital of India, and a center of commerce and industry. Although Jumna waters have been reduced by demands of irrigation to the point where Delhi is no longer head of navigation, it remains the gateway between the mountains and the desert.

Punjab, the region west of Jumna River, includes the state of Punjab and the lowlands of the northern half of West Pakistan, and embraces an area of 117,634 square miles with a population of over 35.5 million, a density of about 300 per square mile. The plains of the Indus and its tributaries receive about 30 inches of rain toward the east and 15 or less toward the west, so most of the farm area must be irrigated. Wheat is the leading cereal crop, and millets and maize are also raised for food. Cotton, a long-staple variety, and sugar cane are cash crops. From numerous dams along the Indus and its tributaries, an intricate system of canals webs the region, which has been practicing irrigation for a very long time. These works have permitted an enormous increase in population.

The partition of India and Pakistan in 1947 not only took a major wheat producing area out of India, but started a considerable population shuffle, Moslems from India moving into Pakistan and Hindus going the other way. The people of the Punjab are more purely Caucasoid than other Indians and Pakistani. They are taller, make excellent soldiers, and, being wheat-eaters, feel superior to rice-eaters. A greater number, about 20 per cent, is engaged in industry than in other parts of the river plains, many carrying on commercial and financial activities, such as peddling and money lending. Textile making, both cottons and woolens, is the leading industry, centered largely in Lahore, 849,000. Small factories produce metal wares and tools, and from cottage industries come many rugs, leather wares, and copper, gold, silver, and brass items. Lack of skilled labor and power handicaps industrial development. There is some petroleum in Punjab, but production is small.

The **Dry West** includes the state of Rajasthan and the lower Indus plains of West Pakistan, an area of 188,674 square miles and 20.9 million population, with a density of 119 per square mile. This density is very low for India, and reflects the aridity of the Thar and the lower Indus Valley. The whole region lies beyond the northern limits of the monsoon winds that strike the west coast of the peninsula. Through this

Arid plain, West Pakistan
[*Embassy of Pakistan, Washington*]

dry, hot land, the Indus water provides an elongate oasis from Punjab to the Arabian Sea. Formerly this oasis was more important as a route than for supporting agriculture. Extensive improvements have now controlled fairly well the shifting river channels, so that here, as in the northern part of West Pakistan, there are millions of acres under irrigation. Long-staple Egyptian cotton, rice, and wheat are grown.

While the Indus provides hydroelectric power and irrigation water, it has almost no value for navigation. It carries a tremendous load of sediment that in the past was in part responsible for the Rann of Cutch, an abandoned delta of the old Jumna (Yamuna) and Indus combined. The Jumna, instead of being a main tributary to the Ganges, formerly flowed along the north side of the Aravalli Range and, with the Indus, dumped its load northwest of the uplands of Kathiawar Peninsula. Along the old course are ruins of oasis settlements dating from very early times to about 3000 B.C. As in the case of Tarim, river diversion rather than climatic change forced the abandonment of this old important route and the agricultural settle-

ments along it. Cut off from the sources of sediments, the delta continued to sink, and today much of it is submerged when tides are high or wet seasons contribute surplus waters. Karachi, 1.1 million, chief city of Pakistan, is located west of all the mouths of the Indus to escape sedimentation. Rather poor natural port facilities have been overcome by building a breakwater, so Karachi now ranks next to Calcutta and Bombay in port traffic, and is the main outlet for the Punjab. It is also a main base on air routes between Europe and Southeast Asia and Australia.

The northeast part of Rajasthan extends into steppe-climate land where rice, wheat, and cotton are irrigated. For thousands of years farming was based on water from wells, but use of water at rates greater than inflow gradually lowered the water table. Longer lifts and more expensive irrigation in time caused abandonment, and ruins of these marginal agricultural failures dot the country. Again, this is not a matter of change of climate. Even the excellent reclamation projects of recent years, the dams and ditches that render much of upper Rajas-

Karachi
[*Embassy of Pakistan, Washington*]

Golden Temple of the Sikhs, Amritsar
[*Government of India Tourist Office*]

than useful, are hardly permanent. Salts accumulate in soils, reservoirs clog with silt, and eventually areas may face abandonment.

PENINSULAR INDIA

Peninsular India was the part first touched by Europeans. It was from Ceylon and the Deccan that products first reached the Egyptians and eastern Mediterraneans. It was here that activities of the Portuguese, Dutch, and French were centered in the early days of Europe's Commercial Revolution. In the sense of contacts, then, this region can be considered as Elder India. It can also be considered Elder India in the geological sense, for the Deccan is made up of extremely old rocks, covered extensively in the central and northwestern parts by layers of rather ancient lava. These old rocks contain many useful minerals, but on the whole, India is not a mineral-rich land.

The peninsula of India is roughly an isosceles triangle with sides about 1,250 miles long and an inland base about 1,000 miles wide. This dissected plateau, over 2,000 feet high in the south and west, is tilted gently eastward, so most of its surface drainage reaches the Bay of Bengal. Two important exceptions to this general rule are the Tapti River and Narbada River which flow westward into the Gulf of Cambay. The valleys of these rivers mark the introduction of east-west lines of hills that have considerable significance as topographic barriers toward Hindustan. In the past they have served to check expansions of various national states of the river plains southward into the Deccan. Other important topographic features of the Deccan are the Western Ghats that rise abruptly from a narrow coastal plain along India's west coast to summits in excess of 4,000 feet. They catch the full brunt of the southwest monsoon and are excessively wet, receiving 200 to 300 inches of rain a year. Behind them is *rain shadow*: as winds which have dropped most of their moisture go down slope toward the Bay of Bengal, heating tends to evaporate the clouds. Precipitation of less than 40 inches is rather common just northeast of the Western Ghats. In these drier places, various millets are raised as food, whereas rice is the leading cereal in places with over 40 inches. Water on the plateau is conserved by damming thousands of small ravines and depressions to form reservoirs in which villagers water their animals, fish, wash clothes, dump refuse, and find drinking water. The Eastern Ghats, lower and more broken than those in the west, are really the scarps of the plateau. Their northern parts receive upwards of 60 inches of rain during the summer monsoon. To the south, along the Coromandel Coast, there is considerable winter rainfall from winds blowing across the Bay of Bengal.

Ceylon is a teardrop-shaped island. About two thirds of its area of 25,332 square miles is low coastal plain, surrounding the mountainous core that rises to 8,281 feet. This small, but, within the Commonwealth, independent nation houses some 9.4 million people, two thirds of whom are Singhalese, a mixed Dravidian-Mediterranean people, whose forebears invaded Ceylon in about 1,000 B.C. They are Buddhists. Hindus and Tamil-speaking people from southern India are more recent immigrants and plantation laborers. About one fifth of the island is under cultivation, mainly in plantations. Once important as a producer of coffee, it is now an important source of tea, which thrives in wet highlands, where some places receive as much as 150 inches of rain a year. Even more acreage is planted to rubber than to tea, but the monetary return is less. Cacao, cinnamon, and citronella are among the exports. Coconut palms grow on the lowlands, valuable for dried flesh, oil, and fiber, *coir*. Better lowlands produce two crops of rice, one with each monsoon. Although about a third of the cultivated land is in rice, it is necessary to import food for the fast-growing population. Two important mineral exports are natural graphite and precious stones. The export and commercial center of Ceylon is Colombo, entered by more ships than all the ports of India combined. Industries, still quite small, are concerned with wood and paper products from the evergreen forests and lowland scrub-jungle, with glass, ceramics, textiles, and fertilizers, and,

of course, with processing tea, rubber, and coconuts.

Adams Bridge is an island-chain connection between Ceylon and the mainland. It is hoped to replace the present ferry connection with a bridge to allow through passage of trains. Just to the south are good pearl fisheries. Coastal inhabitants of Ceylon are skilled seamen in outrigger canoes, similar to those of Malaya, Madagascar, and the Pacific islands.

Malabar Coast, along the west side of the southern Deccan, is wet, tropical, and, like Ceylon, was an early source of spices. Most of the area is in the new state of Kerala (previously Travancore-Cochin), where the population density is about 1,000 per square mile. A wide coastal plain produces an abundance of rice, coconuts, sugar cane, and some rubber. Millets, plantains, mangoes, cotton, tea, and spices grow at higher elevations, and higher still, are heavy forests. Many of the coastal inhabitants derive their income from fishing, or as merchant seamen. There is a considerable amount of cottage and village industry, and a number of larger factories where agricultural products are processed and where the local resources of clay and quartz sand are made into ceramic and glass wares. Some of the early centers of trade, such as Calicut (Kozhikode) and Mangalore, have declined, but Cochin, with its facilities for modern ships, continues to prosper.

North of the Malabar Coast, along coastal Mysore, Goa, and Bombay, the plain is narrower and the population less dense except around the city of Bombay. The landscapes and the activities of the people are much like those of Kerala.

Coromandel Coast, previously all within the Madras Province, is now divided on a language basis into Tamil-speaking Madras and Telugu-speaking Andhra Pradesh. Madras, 50,172 square miles, 29.97 million population, has an average population density of nearly 600 per square mile, while Andhra Pradesh, 105,700 square miles, 32.26 million, has an average density of around 300 per square mile. These figures, however, fail to show the great concentration of people on the irrigated Cauvery Delta, where densities run in excess of 1,000 per square mile. Originally this Coast was an important source of pepper, jewels, gold and silver objects, and ivory. Export of luxury items and textiles from the former French possessions, Karikal, Pondicherry, and Yanam, helped to make Paris the European fashion center. Now Coromandel Coast exports hides and leather from the plateau cattle and sheep farms, tropical woods from the extensive forests, and vegetable oils, cotton, tobacco, and sugar cane from farms in the lowlands, where rice and millets are leading cereal crops. Most of these exports, as well as imports, go through Madras, 1.4 million, India's fourth-ranking port and city. It has an improved, artificial harbor, and the city is modern and Europeanized. It is a center of textile industries specializing in cotton, and other industries for agricultural processing. As along the Malabar Coast, the east coast has few ports. Vishakhapatnam, to the north, is the best port south of the Hooghly, and has the only major shipbuilding yards in India.

Northward, the coastal plain of Orissa is narrower and more broken, except in the delta of the Mahanadi-Brahmani. In Orissa, 60,136 square miles and 14.6 million population, some 80 per cent of the people are engaged in rice cultivation. Forests cover much of the uplands. Along the coast, fishing is important, with Calcutta the main market.

Southern Interior includes the Deccan parts of the states of Madras, Mysore, Andhra Pradesh, Bombay, and all of Madhya Pradesh. Population densities run on the order of 150 per square mile in Madhya Pradesh (171,200 square miles, 26.07 million population) to 200 or 300 per square mile over much of the plateau. Large areas, especially in the south, have poor soils, leached of plant nutrients. In contrast is the *regur*, or black-soil region, that extends roughly from the Western Ghats to the Wainganga, and from the Kistna to the Narbada. Unlike the infertile *laterites*, products of the leaching of all but the most insoluble substances in rock, silicates and irons, the black soils are the result of weathering of lavas, and are rich in plant nutrients. The regur produces enormous quantities of cotton, as well as millets, wheat, oil seeds, sugar cane, and other crops. In the large valleys of the plateau are extensive irrigated areas producing quantities of rice and other cereals, and cash crops of sugar cane and tobacco. There is considerable mineral production in the Deccan, especially in the northeast section. Iron, manganese, copper, mica, and coal are mined in considerable quantity. In the south, at Kolar, is India's main gold field.

Hyderabad, 1.1 million, is the greatest city of the southern interior, and capital of Andhra Pradesh. It was the most important capital of a native state and its ruler was said to be the richest man in the world. It is a city of oriental

Ancient dance
[*Government of India Tourist Office*]

splendor, far less European than Madras or Hindustan cities. It is a center of Deccan culture and craftsmanship. Bangalore, capital of Mysore, is similar, though less magnificent in exemplifying the native architectural styles of the Deccan.

Bombay, 3.0 million, is capital of the state of Bombay (190,668 square miles, 48.3 million population), and is one of India's leading ports. The city is located on an island where congestion is unbelievably extreme. Although ceded to the British by the Portuguese in 1661 and established as headquarters of the East India Company in 1708, Bombay got off to a slow start, and had to await the building of railroads to open up the interior. The main impetus to Indian cotton raising, like that of Egypt, came with the American Civil War in the early 1860's. The opening of the Suez Canal was another boost. Today some 250,000 people work in Bombay cotton mills and tend 40 per cent of India's spindles and half of its mechanical looms. Much of the cotton comes from the regur area of the Deccan, and is easily worked in the moist Bombay air. To the north, Ahmedabad is a second Bombay in that it manufactures cotton cloth as a specialty, and like Bombay, has a variety of other industries.

ECONOMIC POSITION

The Northeastern Industrial Region lies where 90 per cent of India's bituminous coal and much of its iron occur: in the northeastern part of Deccan, about 150 miles west of Calcutta. Heavy industries are centered around Jamshedpur, where the Tata Iron and Steel Works are the largest in Asia, and around Asansol, which sits right in the middle of a large coal field. Because India is deficient in zinc, lead, and tin, and suffers from a shortage of scrap iron for making steel, there is little likelihood that it will become a great industrial country very soon, but such start as has been made is near Calcutta and densely populated Bengal.

Although the vast population of India and Pakistan is almost three times that of the United States and more than double that of the Soviet Union, per capita efficiency and output is low. About 90 per cent of the population is rural and

Village, West Pakistan
[*Embassy of Pakistan, Washington*]

about 80 per cent of all arable land is in use, 20 per cent being irrigated. Food crops of millets, rice, and wheat occupy 65 per cent of the cultivated land, yet there is not enough food to keep the people well nourished. A five-year program in India, 1957–1961, is designed to expand agriculture to help solve the food shortage, as well as to increase industry and improve communications. There is nothing close to a balance of trade where costly imports of iron and steel, machinery, fuels, quantities of food, and many other things, must be paid for by exports of tea, the main cash crop; cotton, jute, oil seeds, rubber and other agricultural products; manganese, leather and hides, and textiles.

The impact of contact with British and other Europeans has changed India a great deal in such directions as creation of trade, development of natural resources, stimulation of agriculture, and the introduction of modern industrialism, but it has not gone far in changing the medieval outlook of the great masses of the Indian people. In a thoughtless kind of way, people here and there take advantage of newly irrigated tracts of land or change their activities to benefit from new opportunities in industry or trade, but the average person has not attained a higher standard of living. The mind of the Indian is likely to be concerned more with the intangibles of religion and philosophy than with practical affairs of daily life. The barrier against Europeanization so firmly rooted in Indian mentality is the very essence of the reason why the earth is divided into cultural worlds. Indian culture traits are mainly those of southeastern Asia, territory that is very distant from the North Sea and its ideals, practices, and attainments.

CHINESE REALM

Agricultural landscape, Japan
[*Consulate General of Japan, N.Y.*]

19. Chinese Realm

The pre-1928 flag of Chung-Hua-Min-kuo, the Republic of China, had five stripes, representing China proper, Manchuria, Mongolia, Tibet, and Sinkiang. This "Greater China" has an area of over 3.8 million square miles and an estimated population of 640 million. It is highly possible that neither this estimate nor the Chinese census of 1953 bears much relation to the facts, but in any event probably something around one quarter of the world's population

lives in the People's Republic of China. China proper consists of 18 provinces with an area of about 1.9 million square miles (over half of continental U.S.A.) and a population of some 580 million. A density of population of 170 per square mile for Greater China has little meaning because of the extensive areas of mountains and Dry World territory which are sparsely inhabited. In contrast is Kiangsu, including Shanghai, with about 48.4 million people

315

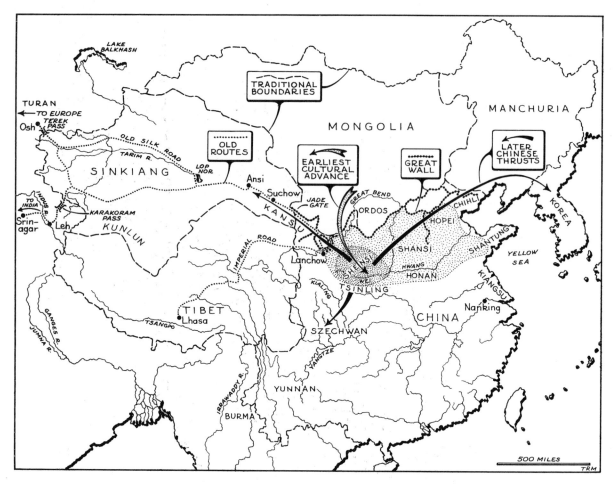

Nuclear China: routes and thrusts

jammed into less than 42,000 square miles, a density of over 1,150 per square mile.

Over half of China is unsuited to agriculture; 20 per cent is too rugged for habitation, 20 per cent is in forest, a large area has either dry steppe or desert climate, and 16 per cent has an elevation in excess of 5,000 feet. About 10 per cent is plain and a similar amount is low, hilly land. Roughly one third of China is mountainous and another third is plateau. Only one eighth of the country is cultivated, half of which is planted to rice. The average square mile of cultivated land produces food enough to maintain 3,000 people, and the finest lands can support twice that many. Under socialized, planned agriculture, the Chinese have high hopes of getting to the point where they can feed themselves, provided agricultural output increases

sufficiently fast to take care of the 5 million extra mouths added to the population each year. During the past century about 100 million have died from famines.

CULTURE BACKGROUND

Some 50 centuries ago China was probably inhabited by barbaric tribes of primitive Caucasoids from whom have descended many of the non-Chinese of southeastern Asia. Ancestral Chinese appear to have developed somewhere in the vicinity of the great bend of the Hwang Ho, north of the Ordos Desert. Legend says that the first ruler was Yao the Great, in the twenty-fourth century B.C. By the next century there were about 10,000 hsein (districts) united by bonds of common culture and religion, religion being ancestor worship. Historic time began with the Chou dynasty (1100 B.C. to 255 B.C.), during which China became 22 feudal states which covered the area of existing Shansi, Shensi, Hopei, and part of Shantung. The first serious attempt to unify China politically occured under the first emperor of the Ch'in dynasty who abolished feudalism in 209 B.C. and started the Great Wall in an effort to keep out Dry World invaders.

Chinese culture exhibits many Dry World traits, such as the cult of the family, patriarchal control, and absence of a caste system. Adaptability, keen insight as to the best use of the land, and skill in gardening suggest oasis dwellers. Excellent geographical sense in picking routes suggests the leader of the caravan who perishes if he makes a serious mistake. With minor exceptions the Chinese have failed to practice forestry, leaving the country short of fuel and other wood, for which rice straw, grass, brush, and animal dung are poor substitutes. As traders and merchants the Chinese have few peers, most of whom reside in the Dry World. Even during antiquity they were carrying goods across the dry heart of Asia or into Burma, and promoting the use of silk, their main export, among people as remote as the Romans. Al-

Chinese Realm: languages

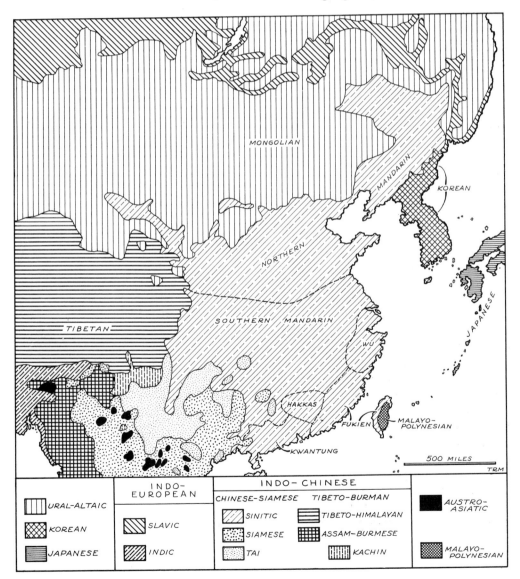

though the Chinese who came into contact with
Malay seamen took to the sea readily, most
Chinese, like most Dry World peoples, remain
pure landsmen.

Shensi, particularly the Wei Valley, was the
culture hearth of the historic Chinese. There
Ch'in grew wheat and millet, and people had
been skilled in the use of iron for many centuries. They were known to the ancient Greeks
as the producers of silk. As early as the second
century B.C. Chinese envoys had reached
Bukhara, and Marcus Aurelius sent a representative to China in A.D. 196. Chinese silk and
porcelain went westward, even to Roman
Britain, along the Old Silk Road across Tarim
Basin. By the second century B.C. the Chinese
were thoroughly established as far east as the
Yellow Sea, southward to the Yangtze, and west
to the Kialing River of Szechwan. Population
was concentrated in the Wei Valley and
Szechwan. Other parts of China proper were
only slowly occupied. Floods along the lower
Hwang Ho discouraged settlement, routes to the
basins of the Yangtze east of Szechwan were
blocked by difficult gorges and hostile aborigines, country to the west was too high and cold
for agriculture, to the north it was too dry, and
to the south the hills were inhabited by hostile
tribes of primitive Caucasoids. When Chinese
occupied new areas, it was by order of emperors,
so large groups rather than individuals were the
pioneers.

By the start of the Han dynasty in 206 B.C.,
the Great Wall was over 1,000 miles long but,
as during all later time, it was an ineffective
barrier. It took more than two centuries of
fighting people identified as Huns, similar to
early Asian invaders of central Europe, before
they were repulsed, and Kansu, Sinkiang, and
northern Korea were added to China. China
then split into three kingdoms: Shu in the west,
Wu in the center and south, and Wei in the
north. Periods of peace, prosperity, and varying
political fortunes marked the next three
centuries.

While all this was happening, China was
developing a distinctive culture in which one of
the strongest concerns of the individual was
how he could face his ancestors. Cemeteries

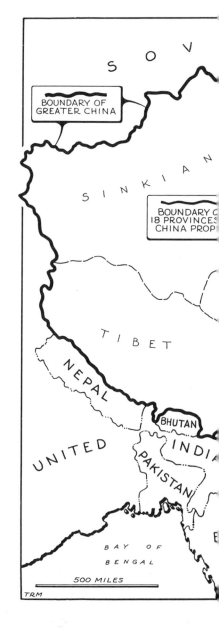

spread out over much fine land. Although all
leading religions have come from the outside,
the Chinese are inclined to blend them into
general agreement with their own ancient
philosophies of Confucianism and Taoism,
dating from the sixth century B.C. From India
came Buddhism, the most widely adopted
religion. Nestorian Christians appeared in
westernmost China in the sixth century A.D.
and are remembered chiefly for having smuggled silk-worm eggs to Europe, thus ending

Greater China: index map

China's monopoly in producing silk. Mohammedanism arrived across the Dry World, reaching the northwest, where there are some 48 million Chinese Moslems today. As a result of the efforts of Christian missionaries, there are about 1.5 million Christians, most of them Roman Catholics.

The dominant languages belong to the Indo-Chinese family, and among these Mandarin is the most widely spoken. Other languages and dialects vary so sharply that many Chinese have

great difficulty in talking with people from other districts. Curiously there is unification in the written language, an elaborate system of logograms, symbols that represent ideas. Our own numbers, such as "3," are logograms, which may be read as *three* in English, *drei* in German, or *trois* in French. Simple ideographs, pictorial logograms, appear among hieroglyphics and other picture writing, but those in China are so elaborate and symbolic that their basic elements are obscure. Some 80,000 conventional logograms have been devised, of which 50,000 are still in use, though most Chinese know only a few. A new 30-letter Latin alphabet was adopted in 1956 to replace the Chinese logograms.

China is a country of intensive agriculture, but methods are primitive. It has relatively few good roads, and these were built for facilitating army movements or the collection of tributes. The economy has not demanded much more than the trails along which the coolie with a wheelbarrow or pientan (carrying pole, balanced on the shoulder and weighted with goods at either end) trudges at the rate of about 20 miles a day. Highly localized cultures and economic self-sufficiency, such as that of old Russia, are characteristic. House types vary widely, from dwellings carved in loess to boats, or, where Malay influences are strong, houses on piles. Thatch, mud, and stones are common building materials.

Society controlled by a system of ethics, rather than by law, is one of the strongest unifying culture traits. Coupled with it is an abhorrence of foreign innovations and fear of "loss of face." The belief is general that the best life is one in which the individual walks in the ways of his ancestors. It is difficult to foresee the results of the plans imposed by the "People's Government," under which traditional ways are largely abandoned, as in the organizing of some 500 million peasants into rural districts where they live in semi-military ways.

TSINLING

The lofty Tsinling is an eastern projection of the Kunlun, and terminal prong of the great east-west Eurasian mountain barrier. Although high passes lie between its snow-clad peaks, it effectively divides China into its most distinctive parts. North of the barrier are the lands of the Seres (Ch'in), to the south those of the Sin. Southern China is a rainy land of rice, tea, tung, bamboo, and mulberry and tallow trees. Water buffalo are the beasts of burden. People are swarthy, frail and small-statured, and less purely Mongoloid than the northern Chinese. They are mentally quick, subtle in action, and

shrewd in business. Their landscapes are hilly and green. Agriculture is favored by growing seasons that last three quarters of the year. Northern China is a drier land of wheat, millet, soybeans, grass, oxen, and camels. People are taller, lighter complexioned, more robust, and of purer Mongoloid ancestry. Landscapes include extensive flats that remain brown much of the time because growing seasons last less than half of the year. Skies are at times darkened by drifting dust. Famines are common, being caused by floods, locusts, and storms.

The Tsinling has been a more effective barrier against Dry World invaders than the Great Wall. Although the Wall reached a length of nearly 2,000 miles, it was rather easily crossed by invaders such as Huns, Mongols, and Manchus. Buddhism and Mohammedanism breached the rampart readily. Cultural penetrations found more serious obstacles in Chinese conservatism, prejudices, and population density.

From their Wei Valley culture hearth the northern Chinese, staying north of Tsinling, spread to Kansu (dry place), west of the great bend of the Hwang Ho. Lands suited to agriculture, whether dry farmed or irrigated, were occupied. Lanchow became a thriving commercial center, exchanging silk, porcelain, and other products for jade, furs, and other things. To Kansu came Mohammedanism, and today about one quarter of the Moslem Chinese live there. Genghis Khan also came, in 1211, to aid northern Chinese in subduing troublesome people, but eventually took Shensi, Shansi, Honan, and Hopei into the Khan empire. Kublai Khan was one of the few conquerors who managed to cross the Tsinling, extending his domain past Szechwan to Yunnan and Burma. Under this Mongol dynasty, which ended in 1368, trade with the West was at its zenith.

RUGGED WESTERN CHINA

Cut by the upper tributaries of the Yangtze and major rivers leading to Burma and Indo-China, and crossed by magnificent high ranges, such as the Chinese Himalaya, the western part

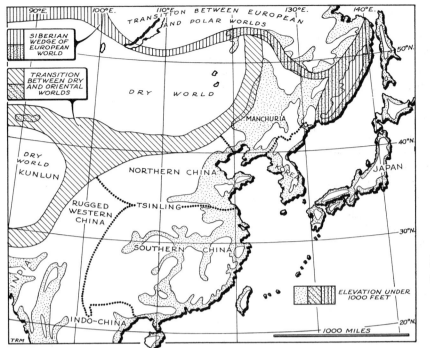

**Eastern Asia:
cultural divisions**

of China is largely a land of ups and downs. Agricultural terraces rise to elevations of 8,000 feet, where rice gives way to wheat and other cereals. Barley is harvested above 12,000 feet, and wool is produced even higher, on the pastures which extend into alpine tundra just below the snow line at 17,000 feet. Below the timber line is taiga-like forest. Kangting (Tatseinlu), at 8,400 feet, is the gateway to Tibet, the place where goods leave the backs of coolies for the backs of mules and yaks. Brick tea and other Chinese products go west along the rugged trails in exchange for musk, yak tails, and other Tibetan goods. At Paan (Batang) the main westward trail to Lhasa crosses the Yangtze on a bridge 1,200 feet above the river, which flows through a deep, narrow gorge. Branches of the main trail turn south to Burma. World War II witnessed construction of roads south of these trails, through Yunnan and Kweichow, to Chungking.

SOUTHERN CHINA

The first important migration of Chinese across the Tsinling led to the upper Yangtze basin of *Szechwan* (four streams). Here was an attractive green hilly region of about 75,000 square miles in Red Basin, about twice that of the province as constituted today. The Yangtze lowlands here have an elevation of about 1,000 feet and surrounding hills rise to 3,000 or 4,000 feet. The soils are good, precipitation is adequate, and the growing season is long, for invasions of icy, central Asian air are kept out by the Tsinling. The original forest cover was cleared away to make room for agriculture. A method of irrigation was devised, and has been successfully operated on the fertile Min flood plain for over 20 centuries. Comparative peace and prosperity reigned, and the population grew.

Szechwan now has over 60 million inhabitants, and every bit of agricultural land is in use, slopes with gradients as steep as 45° being terraced. Rice provides about half the food, followed by maize. Wheat, sweet potatoes, beans, and peanuts supplement the diet. Other crops include rape, sugar cane, tea, tobacco, fruits, opium poppies, and mulberries. Some cotton, silk, and hemp are produced. The poorer hills grow tung trees, the oil-rich nuts of which give China one of its leading exports, a drying oil for varnishes. Limited amounts of coal, iron, copper, gold, and salt are the main mineral resources. Upstream forests provide various soft and hard woods. Few regions have so many varied resources. And there are lots of people to use them. On the best lands rural densities reach 4,000 per square mile. Five or six crops may be raised each year. Landscape greenness rivals that of western Ireland.

The traditional political and agricultural center of Szechwan is Chengtu, now also a manufacturing city. To the southeast is Chungking, 1.8 million, on the site of ancient Pahsien of the fourth century B.C. Beyond the narrow lanes of the inner walled city are modern streets and industrial plants built in the last few decades. During World War II it became temporary capital of China, a function that returned to Nanking at the close of hostilities. As a Yangtze port, its interests are also commercial.

Downstream from Red Basin, the Yangtze enters a formidable gorge region, so rugged that Chinese were prevented for centuries from spreading eastward. Between Wanhsien and Ichang the river drops 300 feet in 200 miles. Within its narrow, confining walls, the level of the river varies some 200 feet, being dangerously shoal in low stage. Navigation is possible from nine to eleven months a year, during which time junks are pulled upstream by manpower. A few steamers ply the gorges in summer, but so much space is taken by their engines that little is left for cargo.

Middle Yangtze lowlands were originally occupied by peoples similar to those of Indo-China and Thailand. As early as the eighth century B.C. Chinese may have sought the excellent porcelain clay of Kaolin (high hill; now the name of a typical clay mineral), east of Lake Poyang. By the third century B.C. many Chinese were settling Han Basin lowlands. At the western end of Han Basin, Ichang is at the geographical center of China proper, and although it is 1,100 miles up the Yangtze and at 200 feet elevation, its port can take ships drawing 12 feet at all seasons. Downstream from Ichang there are extensive lakes that tend to cut down flood heights in the Middle Yangtze lowlands, but even so, floods do occur, causing thousands of deaths. The lakes lie in lowlands between natural levees of alluviating streams. Population is concentrated along these levee strips and on lands drained by an elaborate system of canals. Marginal to the lowlands are areas notable for minerals, such as tungsten, iron, antimony, copper, mercury, lead, zinc, and coal. China produces over half of the world's tungsten ore, wolfram. Hunan and Kiangsi provinces are particularly rich in minerals. Rice is the main crop of the lowlands, while maize and sweet potatoes are grown on hills. Oilseed crops and various vegetable waxes are upland products. One of the specialties is Chinese ink (India ink), produced from soot. There are extensive forests in the basins of the Yuan and Siang. Bamboo, cypress, pine, camphor, and other woods are rafted to Hankow and other cities. Hankow, Wuchang, and Hanyang constitute the Wuhan conurbation of well over 2 million people. Manufacturing includes heavy industries, wood and forest products mills, and food processing, such as making vegetable oils and brick tea. Hankow is the main port of Han Basin. Wuchang has an additional importance as capital of Hupeh.

The Yangtze Delta, east of the narrows at Anking, is culturally young compared with Szechwan and the Middle Yangtze lowlands. Shanghai was little more than a small fishing village in the eleventh century, and by the beginning of the nineteenth century it had become only a rather minor port of junks. Nanking also is comparatively young, though it was nucleus for overthrowing Mongol rule and a fourteenth century capital with walls 50 feet high. It took considerable population pressure in basins to the west to force the Chinese to reclaim their delta lands on a large scale. The Yangtze Delta is the southern end of a vast compound deltaic plain made by many rivers, but chiefly by the two dominant streams of northern and central China, the Hwang Ho and Yangtze. The plain stretches along the coast for 700 miles and inland for several hundred miles. From the cultural standpoint the Yangtze delta region extends north to the Hwai Ho and includes the southern half of Kiangsu.

The deltaic part of Kiangsu province is an Oriental World equivalent of the Netherlands, with extensive polders and a dense canal network. Agricultural productivity is immense. Two crops of rice are grown during the rainy warm season and a green crop in winter is plowed under to enrich the soil. Rice fields are flooded about half the time. Most transportation is by boat or barge. About 70 per cent of the area is cultivated, and rural population densities are over 9,000 per square mile. Drier lands and the hills to the west grow one third of China's cotton. Shanghai and other Kiangsu cities rank foremost in textiles.

Shanghai, 7.1 million, largest city on the Asian mainland and fourth largest city in the world, adds a half million to its population each year. It has a modern, European, skyscraper-dotted business district and an excellent port, which handles over half the country's foreign trade and most of its exports of silk and tea. Nearly half of China's industry lies in Shanghai, producing cotton goods, a leading item, flour, soap, chemicals, cement, paper, tobacco products, and various other commodities. Most of the city's population lives in vast, squalid settlements outside the urban nucleus. One tenth of the world's population lives in the hinterland of Shanghai, but it has little commercial importance because living standards are so low. People just manage to survive, and buy and sell very little. Inland from Shanghai, Nanking, 1.1 million, the "South Capital," long served as the capital of China. The city has tremendous political prestige, and is still considered the capital of the Republic of China, now confined to Formosa. Its political competitor, Peking, the "North Capital," is the current center of government for the People's Republic.

South China, the upland region south of the Yangtze basins, has heavy precipitation, mild winters, and widespread forests. Especially useful is a bamboo that grows over 100 feet tall. Tea, raised for more than 12 centuries, is on the decline. Rice dominates the limited lowlands, and cotton, wheat, peanuts, rape, tobacco, sweet potatoes, and sugar cane are raised above the paddy fields. Barley is the cereal crop of uplands. The densely populated lowlands grow three rice crops each year in some parts of the extreme south. The uplands are sparsely populated by non-Chinese hill tribes.

Yunnan, in the extreme southwest, is chiefly a limestone plateau. Solution (karst) topography is widely developed, characterized by steep-sided hills, numerous caverns, underground drainage, and flat-floored, sunken basins, where soils are good, and a third of the people live. Many of the people are afflicted with goiters, a malady common in limestone regions. Fully half of Yunnan's 17.5 million people are non-Chinese, the ties with Burma and Indo-China having been closer than those with China. The non-Chinese eat maize, millet, and barley. Some are primitive and Caucasoid, as the Lolos who inhabit the rough northwest country and depend on hunting, and others resemble the Thai and are more Mongoloid. Many work with the Chinese in mines, for the area has considerable mineral wealth, such as tin, copper, wolfram, antimony, iron, mercury, gold, and some coal. Exports go mainly along the railroad from Kunming, the provincial capital, to Haiphong in Northern Viet Nam. In addition to minerals, hides, furs, opium, spices, and bristles are exported.

Kwangsi and Kwantung are semi-tropical provinces, where the production of oranges, bananas, lichees, figs, sugar cane, pineapples, melons, ginger, and various fruits indicates the infrequency of frosts. All available flat country is given to rice. Rural population densities range up to 3,000 per square mile near Canton. These overcrowded lands have long been the main source of Chinese coolies, who have emigrated so widely that the Canton dialect is the common Chinese language spoken outside the country, and Cantonese food the cuisine most commonly identified by Europeans as being Chinese. Fish farming is important in providing food in Kwantung, where it is often combined with silk production, the mulberry trees around ponds supplying food for silkworms and refuse from cocoons serving as fish food. Poultry raising is also important.

Canton, 1.6 million, on the compound delta of the Si and Pei rivers, is a comparatively new Chinese settlement, but was early used by Malays and Arabs. The Chinese city grew as a congested maze of narrow lanes along which the rich were carried in sedan chairs. Wider streets were more recently added outside the old city core. The city is terminus for a main railroad trunk line via Hankow to Peking. Tea from the hills and silk from the delta have long been Canton's main exports. In the middle of the sixteenth century Portuguese were taking silk from Canton to Europe, and they acquired possession of Macao, an island at the base of the delta that once rivaled Canton, but now is decadent. It was the first European possession in China.

Hongkong, a name generally applied to the city of Victoria on Hongkong island, has the best harbor in China, and ranks high among world ports. This strategic spot was ceded to the British in 1841. Excessive precipitation and granite hills that rise 1,800 feet furnish a pure but insufficient water supply for the fast-growing population. Within the city are about 80,000 people per square mile, a congestion equivalent to Manhattan Island's. The entire Crown Colony of 391 square miles has a population of 2.7 million. About half the urban population live in Kowloon, on the mainland, terminus of a railroad from Canton. The whole population is overwhelmingly Chinese. Until the last few years, Hongkong was chiefly an entrepot and exporter of Chinese goods, which now represent only 15 per cent of its trade. Of considerably more importance are its free port activities and its own industries, such as cotton textiles, clothing, rubber, chemicals, light metals and machinery, and heavy industries including ship-building and repair, iron foundries, and mills.

Southeastern China is a hilly region served by a long coast with excellent harbors, each having only a limited hinterland. About 5 per cent of the land is flat and less than 20 per cent is under cultivation. Monsoonal conditions are well developed, most of the 80 inches of rain coming in the warm season. Typhoons are frequent and destructive. When the Chinese arrived, about a thousand years ago, they found semi-Caucasoid peoples in the hills and Malays along the coast. From the Malays they acquired many culture traits which distinguish them from other Chinese. They take readily to the sea, have developed sailing craft with speed for piracy or durability for commerce with the eastern East Indies and islands all the way to the Philippines, depend heavily on the sea for food, and,

like Malays, show a preference for living along streams. Coastal dwellers also had the Malayan experience of trading with Arabs between the eighth and fifteenth centuries. Amoy, Swatow, and other ports became important Arab outposts, and are commercial centers today, exporting handicraft products, timber, tea, salt, stones, and sea products. Foochow (Minhow) was the main base for trade with Formosa. Rice is the main cereal food and crop of the lowlands. Sweet potatoes, beans, oranges (native to this region), and other crops are grown along the valleys and lower hills. Forests cover more remote places. The hills, of ancient rocks, are sources of excellent building stones, much in demand in the cities of Kiangsu and elsewhere. They also provide soft materials, such as easily-carved soapstone. The ruggedness of the coast is an expression of the resistance of old rocks to erosion. Streams lack sufficient sediments to build deltas, so most river mouths are estuarine. Important, though undeveloped, hydroelectric potentials lie in the hills, where their association with valuable minerals promises industrial importance in the future.

FORMOSA

Ihla Formosa (Beautiful Island), the Portuguese name and Taiwan (Terrace Bay), a later Chinese name, are both appropriate for this beautiful 260-by-90-mile island, with its many cliffs and flats. Along the almost harborless Pacific shore, cliffs rise in places more than 6,000 feet above the ocean. Westward from the high, over 12,000-foot, mountain backbone, widespread flats descend like stairs to the coastal plains that are edged by mangrove swamps along Formosa Strait. Except along the west coast, agriculture suffers from too much rain, amounting yearly to over 300 inches in higher places. Typhoons are an added hazard along the east coast. About 70 per cent of Formosa is forested, and the variety of trees of tropical and mesothermal rain forest types is enormous. Cedar and other timber are exported, and the government has had a monopoly on distilling camphor, a principal export until synthetic substitutes became available in

Gathering soybeans
[*U.S.D.A.*]

World War II. Bamboo, bananas, jute, ramie, oolong tea, and pineapples are important products, as might be expected on a Pacific island cut by the Tropic of Cancer. Two rice crops are cultivated with the help of water buffalo on terraces and paddy fields on the western lowlands. All but an eighth of the crop is consumed on the island, but the crop is so large that the eighth accounts for one quarter of Formosa's exports. Sweet potatoes, peanuts, and soybeans are the main unirrigated crops. Sugar cane is increasingly important in the west and north, and is the leading export, going mainly to Japan and Southeast Asia. Tea, bananas, and pineapples are also exported in quantity through the two main ports, Keelung and Kachsiung.

Malays and Indonesian peoples, inhabitants of Formosa for over 20 centuries, are now a tiny minority of raw savages living in remote highlands. These and other semi-civilized aborigines are tribally organized and inhabit some 700 villages in the mountains, away from the changing political scene. The Dutch were the first outsiders to attempt to control Formosa, establishing a fort at Tainan. The Spaniards promptly erected two forts at the north end of the island, but were forced by the Dutch to withdraw. When the Ming dynasty fell in 1644, Chinese refugees began arriving, and soon took control from the Dutch. Japan took over in 1895 after its successful war with China, and kept control until the end of World War II when the island returned to China. After the fall of China to Communist control in 1949, Formosa remained the last territory held by the Nationalist Government. Taipei, 0.8 million, serves as capital, and like the rest of Formosa, has felt the impact of the arrival of thousands of Chinese refugees. Now well over 90 per cent of the population is Chinese, and the Amoy dialect is the official language.

Japanese control brought considerable progress. Mineral resources were exploited diligently. Considerable coal is mined on the northern end of the island, some being used to smelt bauxite from the East Indies. Gold, copper, sulphur, silver, and petroleum are produced in moderate amounts. Industries are very minor, and tend to feature consumer goods, such as textiles, chemicals, cement, and foods.

NORTHERN CHINA

All of northern China lies on the cold side of the isotherm of January 32° F. so people must dress warmly, build substantial buildings, and eat millets, barley, and wheat, instead of rice. Rivers, frozen in winter, are used as cart roads. Trees are comparatively rare. Though various mixtures occur, the population is more purely Mongoloid than that of Central or Southern China.

The Hwang Ho Delta, spread out on either side of the Shantung Peninsula, is the terminus of the long, but not very useful river, which is shoal in winter and an unruly, turbulent torrent in summer that may spread widely and destructively over the lowlands in its delta despite the artificial levees. No season finds the channel useful for commercial-size boats. Between 1192 and 1852 the Hwang discharged into the Yellow Sea, south of Shantung. A major diversion, nearly 250 miles from the coast, resulted in a channel leading to the Gulf of Pohai (Chihli), north of Shantung. In 1938 it returned to the earlier course, but in 1947 was artificially diverted toward the Gulf of Pohai. Coping with such a river was unattractive to the inhabitants of the secure Wei Valley, so they were slow to settle the lower Hwang flood plain. But now population density is on the order of 1,000 per square mile in some areas. Rice is the main crop toward the south, but northward the important crops are wheat, beans, soybeans, peas, and barley. To bring tribute in the form of rice to the northern capital, the Grand Canal was dug from the Yangtze, near Nanking, to Peking. Though in active use during much of the Manchu dynasty (1644–1911), long reaches have now silted, especially in the north.

Shantung lies between the northern and southern parts of the Hwang Ho Delta. Its peninsula almost reaches the Liaotung and Kwantung peninsulas of Manchuria. The highlands of Shantung are cut by a low gap which is followed by a railroad leading from Tientsin to the all-year port of Tsingtao. Shantung, birthplace of Confucius (about 551 B.C.), was occupied by Chinese long before they settled on the delta plains. The barren uplands, long ago deforested, are bordered by lowlands that are fertile and free from floods. Ordinary food crops are the main agricultural products, but the raising of castor beans, wax trees, and silk worms is of considerable importance. Pongee, an unbleached silk, is a manufacturing specialty. The real wealth of Shantung, however, lies in rich iron ores and excellent coal. These industrial potentials were enviously eyed by Japanese who briefly occupied the province, and by Germans who acquired Tsingtao, modernized the port and city, and lost the whole thing in World War I. Tsingtao, 0.85 million, has some industry to augment its port activities. Weihsien's coal may make it an industrial center.

The Hopei Plain is a continuation of the delta plain, but it is higher and unflooded. Winter is so cold that people must wear heavy, quilted coats. Spring is accompanied by dust storms from dry lands to the west. Summer has moderate rainfall and is warm enough to mature wheat and cotton. Rural population densities are similar to those in the Hwang Ho plain, ranging from about 450 to over 1,000 per square mile. Although farming is the main activity, Hopei is the largest producer of coal outside Manchuria, and has some iron. The leading city of the Hopei Plain is Tientsin, 3.1 million. It is the busiest port in northern China, and has one of the few good harbors of northeastern China, a region mainly of low, deltaic coasts. The icy winters make it necessary to use an ice breaker to keep the channel open. Exports include wool, raw cotton, furs, rugs, skins, bristles, eggs, and walnuts. Industries consist of flour mills, salt works, and factories that turn out rugs, carpets, cotton cloth, artificial silk, and other products. The city is the commercial capital of an agricultural region that produces a large share of China's wheat and cotton.

Interior north China really starts at Peiping (Peking), for although the city is not far from Tientsin and lies at the edge of the plain, its ties are with the inner provinces and with Mongolia through the nearby Kalgan Gate. As Yenching it was founded in 920 by non-Chinese people. Later, when it became a march-site (frontier outpost) capital for Kublai Khan, it took on the appearance of a central Asian city, with a parallelogram of high brick walls enclosing wide streets. Foreigners were not allowed in this inner city. After the fall of the Khans, Peking was the seat of the Ming dynasty until the government was transferred to Nanking. More recently it has become the capital of Communist China. Its 5.4 million people have both commercial and industrial interests. Fur, hair, wool, hides, and rugs come in from points as far west as the Kirgiz S.S.R. by camel caravan, road, and railroad, in exchange for loads of silk, brick tea, and other goods. Local coal supplies, coupled with iron ore, account for considerable industrialization. Also, next-door Shansi province has China's main iron reserves and there is abundant coal in both Shansi and Shensi. Sian, 1.5 million, in the Wei Valley culture hearth, was the largest city in China from 1122 B.C. to A.D. 1127. It often served as capital, at one time ruling lands as remote as the borders of Lake

Balkhash. In the Golden Age of Chinese literature (Sung dynasty, 960–1126) it stood foremost in education. Sian was the terminus of the Imperial Road to Lhasa and the Old Silk Road to Samarkand, or to India. It still has similar importance, for roads from Sian lead to Szechwan, Tarim and Turfan in Sinkiang, and the Dzungarian Gate to the Soviet Union. It is a leading commercial town in a district producing large amounts of wheat, barley, millet, and cotton, and some silk. Industrialism is growing, but lags behind Shensi's potentialities.

Kansu shades off into the cold Dry World. Wheat, millet, vegetables, melons, apricots, tobacco, and other crops are grown by irrigation or dry farming. Oil fields at Yumen produce most of China's natural crude oil, and oil-shale deposits are also productive. Copper mines yield both ore and sulphur. Although timber is available for building materials, the people of the loess hills of northern Kansu prefer to dig their dwellings into hillsides because such homes are cheap and well insulated against summer heat and winter cold. Of course, they may collapse during an earthquake, such as that in 1920 when a quarter million people lost their lives. The Moslem stronghold of Lanchow boasts a steel bridge across the Hwang Ho, lies on the main road west from Sian, has some industry, and does a considerable amount of commerce in exchanging Dry World products for those of China.

URBANIZATION

The traditional Chinese city has always functioned primarily as a commercial center. Prior to 1841 most large cities were in the interior serving provincial trade needs, or those of foreign commerce. Sian, Lanchow, and Chengtu were trade centers along routes to the west. In 1842–1843, the British gained rights to use the ports of Canton, Hongkong, Amoy, Foochow, Ningpo, and Shanghai. Then came the impact of the Commercial Revolution and the development of a new overseas commerce, with British and American ships arriving in large numbers and offering high prices for impressive quantities of tea, silk, opium, and other products. Seaports, rather than the age-old interior cities, became the main commercial outlets. Although Chinese statistics are notably unreliable, they reported in 1957 that 13 cities, including two in Manchuria, had over one million population each. Of these, Shanghai, Peking, Tientsin, Nanking, and Hongkong were the leading cities, and their huge populations were recent developments, largely a result of overseas trade. Results of the Industrial Revolution are also seen in the smelters and heavy industries of Peking, Wuhan, and other places, and the textile factories of Shanghai, but Chinese cities are still mainly commercial. Although industry and commerce attract increasing numbers to the cities, less than 15 per cent of the population are city-dwellers. Communications are so poorly developed that no city is very important as a route center. In recent years a few roads and railroads have been built, but the total mileage is still low.

MANCHURIA

For centuries Chinese have been slipping into the former Manchu state of Manchuria, the more than 400,000 square miles of territory now comprising the northeastern provinces of China. Although their entrance was officially opposed until the middle of the nineteenth century, Chinese farmers arrived in such numbers that today the Chinese are dominant among the 50 million or so inhabitants of the Manchurian plain. They have completely overwhelmed the native Manchurian, a descendant from Tungus-like people, racially Mongoloid and speaking a Ural-Altaic language.

Manchuria has felt Russian influences for the past three centuries. First came the fighting, exploring, and trapping Cossacks, reaching the Amur Valley in 1644 and establishing a brisk fur trade. Then came the branch of the Trans-Siberian Railroad across Manchuria to Vladivostok, which caused Harbin to become a Russian stronghold. To overcome the disadvantage of Vladivostok's being icebound in winter, the Russians developed Port Arthur. These holdings have been in and out of Russian hands several times, and although the Soviet

Union is very influencial in Manchuria, technically these Russian developments are controlled by China.

British capital built the important railroad between Peking and Mukden, and the Japanese built most of the other lines. Railroads in Manchuria are especially important. They handle most of the commerce, and play a dominant role in developing and policing the country, locating sites of towns, and exploiting resources. They made it easy for Japan to gain control of Manchuria in 1931 to set up the puppet state of Manchukuo. During Japanese rule a semblance of law and order was brought to Manchuria, industries were established, and natural resources vigorously exploited, but few Japanese could be induced to colonize.

The most extensive lowlands follow a northeastward trend from the Gulf of Pohai toward the Amur River. Moderately arid lands to the west rise to increasingly higher levels, culminating in the Great Khingan on the boundary of the Dry World. East of the lowland are several ranges which are wet enough to bear extensive forests. About half of Manchuria has somewhat arid climate and steppe vegetation, a region of pastoral nomadism. About a third of the country could be cultivated, and nearly that amount is plowed, although the growing season is short, between the late arrival of summer rains and the early arrival of killing frosts in fall. Winters are dry, and winds from the Polar-Siberian air mass at times bring intense cold. Forests cover about one quarter of the land, both the mixed forests at lower elevations and the taiga-like forests being of considerable value.

The fertile soils of the plains, developed under natural grassland conditions, produce millets in sufficient quantity for a surplus to be sent to Korea, and large harvests of wheat, especially near Harbin. Barley grows in higher and drier places. A single crop of rice or maize can be grown in parts of southern Manchuria. Vegetables, sugar beets, tobacco, hemp, and soybeans are common crops. The soybean is particularly versatile, being used as human and animal food, a source of oil for illumination, a fuel, and an ingredient of artificial silk. It is a leading Manchurian export.

Mineral wealth is considerable, and is being increasingly exploited. Coal reserves, especially those in the south, together with abundant but low-quality iron, are the basis of China's main iron and steel industry, located in and around Anshan, just south of Mukden. Fushon, a few miles east of Mukden, is a center of shale oil and synthetic crude oil produced from coal, and of aluminum production using local bauxite. Lead, copper, gold, manganese, and other metals are also mined. A considerable amount of heavy industry and production of textiles, machinery, and processed food is conducted in Mukden (Shenyang), 2.9 million. Its spectacular growth from an old Manchu capital took place in the last three decades, mainly after the Japanese built a modern commercial and industrial district outside the old walled city. Increased production in Mukden means greater traffic through ice-free Dairen-Port Arthur, 1.1 million.

KOREA

Korea (Chosen, Calm Dawn Land) is the hard-luck nation of the Chinese Realm; like Belgium, it has been the theater of many wars. Its most recent history includes annexation by Japan in 1911, post-World War II occupation by Soviet and American troops north and south of the 38th parallel, creation in each section of an independent republic, and invasion by the Communist Republic of the Republic of South Korea, which was resisted by United Nations forces.

Korean woman preparing soybean flour
[*U.S.D.A.*]

The Koreans are modified Tungus, predominantly Mongoloid, with some Caucasoid showing up in their lighter skins and brown hair. Fears, taboos, and extreme conservatism make it difficult to assist them in raising living standards. As in China, much fine land is occupied by cemeteries. Agriculture follows primitive practices, and this is all right with Koreans, who are easy-going to the point of shiftlessness. Naturally, they did not take kindly to changes brought during Japanese occupation, such as improving farming methods, modernizing communications, and initiating industry. They had good reason for resentment, for all the benefits went to Japan, and although food production was doubled, Koreans went hungry.

Korea's area of 85,266 square miles (38,542 in South Korea, 46,814 in North Korea) supports an unevenly divided, predominantly agricultural population of 32 million (23 million in South Korea, 9 million in North Korea). Most of Korea is rugged and forested; only 20 per cent is cultivated. The country is essentially a dissected plateau that rises toward the north, has a steep scarp on the east and a more gentle slope on the west. Productive lowlands lie to the west and south, those in the south having a climate about like that of New Jersey except that monsoon influences concentrate rain in summer. In the north winters are severe. Rice covers 40 per cent of the cultivated land, irrigated paddy fields being concentrated on the southern lowlands. Barley, the chief item in Korean diets, is the second-ranked crop. Other crops include millets, wheat, soybeans, maize, potatoes, cotton, tobacco, hemp, and fruits. Double cropping is limited to the extreme south. Along the south and west coasts fishing is important.

Mineral resources include gold, silver, copper, graphite, and lead. North Korea has iron and petroleum, and South Korea has coal and tungsten. Industries are mainly devoted to textiles, light metals and machinery, food processing, and cement.

During antiquity Korea vied with the Wei Valley for intellectual leadership in the Oriental World. Much of the culture of the early Japanese came from Korea and to Korea went Japanese and Chinese for education. But continued ravages at the hands of foreigners turned Koreans into isolationists. The Yalu River became a sharp cultural boundary against Manchuria, a political line that persists today, although Yalu hydroelectric power is feeding both Manchurian and North Korean industries. Isolation failed to bring peace, for the country was too attractive as a source of raw materials to be passed up by aggressive nearby Japan. The capital of the south, Seoul, 1.8 million, vies as a political and industrial center with Pyongyang, capital of the north. Pusan, 1.1 million, is the main port for commerce with Japan, the United States, and the United Kingdom. North Korea trades mainly with China and the U.S.S.R.

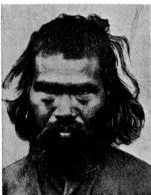

Ainu
[*from E. A. Hooton,*
Up from the Ape,
© 1946, The
Macmillan Company]

JAPAN

Japan proper extends northeastward across latitudes from 30° to 45° N., equivalent to those from New Orleans to Minneapolis. On the four main islands, Honshu (89,000 square miles), Hokkaido (30,000), Kyushu (16,000), and Shikoku (7,000), and on a number of small islands nearby, live 92 million people. The average density is over 600 per square mile, but more significant is the fact that there are more than 3,000 per square mile of cultivated land. More than 300 million people were included in the pre-World War II Japanese Empire, which encompassed Korea, Manchuria, parts of China, and some 1,700 Pacific islands. Losses in that war included all occupied mainland areas, southern Sakhalin, Kuril and Ryukyu Islands, and the former German mandated islands in the Pacific.

Cultural Background. Japan's earliest inhabitants were proto-Caucasoid peoples, who now show up in only a tiny minority, the Ainus, but who have left their place names over much of Japan. The dominant Japanese stock comes from Mongoloids, peoples of northeastern Asia. Around the Inland Sea these developed into the Yamato people, with short, thickset, slightly bowed legs, and large heads, that became the main Japanese strain. The sheltered, beautiful Inland Sea, with over 700 miles of shoreline between the three main southern islands, became nuclear Japan. The people acquired skill in boat handling and fishing, and a taste for raw fish, unlike most other Oriental World peoples. As population grew they turned to rice cultivation.

It took many centuries for the Japanese to dislodge the Ainus from parts of Honshu northeast of Biwa Lake, but by the eighth century they held most of the island and were in firm possession of the Inland Sea. By this time Japan had begun to assume a place in the Chinese Realm, chiefly through adoption of mainland culture traits. Confucianism, Buddhism, logograms, and various arts appeared. On the fighting front developed military rulers, the Shoguns, who later plunged Japan into a Medieval period from which it did not emerge until the Emperor Meiji took over in 1868. Although Portuguese, Dutch, and other outside influences penetrated Japan's isolation during Shogun rule, modern times appeared with great suddenness after the Meiji Restoration. Renaissance, Commerical and Industrial revolutions, Westernization, Empire, and World War II appeared with a rapidity equivalent to compressing the history of Europe since the fourteenth century into less than 90 years.

Like Great Britain, Japan has enjoyed insularity and proximity to a highly civilized continent from which it could borrow what it chose, has fought its wars on foreign soil and escaped invasions (until World War II), had its culture hearth in an excellent agricultural tract, and is much interested in seafaring and fishing. Unlike Britain, Japan under Shogun rule went through a long period of isolation designed to preserve its culture by prohibiting people from

Japan: index map

leaving the country, and cutting off trade and other contacts with outsiders.

Physical Background. Japan is one of a series of island festoons partially enclosing large seas along the east coast of Asia. These island arcs and adjoining deep troughs in the sea bottom are still in process of formation, as evidenced by numerous earthquakes and intense volcanic activity. Japan rises as a high, complex mountain mass above a floor more than two miles below sea level in the Sea of Japan and a trough more than five miles deep in the Pacific. The ranges paralleling the coast contain many active faults. Tokyo feels an earthquake on the average of every third day, and though most of the shocks are slight, some are disastrous. In 1923, 143,000 deaths were attributed to an earthquake near Tokyo, which set off fires and brought with it a great sea-wave resulting from crustal adjustments below the ocean surface. In addition to earthquakes, another sign of Japan's current geologic growth is the number of volcanoes, totaling some 500, of which possibly 25 are more or less active today. Most of the volcanoes lie along the east coast. Best known is Fujiyama, famed for the symmetry of its cone, which rises over 12,000 feet, just southwest of Tokyo.

Japan is so mountainous that it is hard to find even reasonably flat lands, and many of these are useless stony valley floors and wet coastal marshes. Less than one fifth of the area is potentially agricultural and only 16 per cent is cultivated. Swift streams cutting through the rough terrain are commercially navigable for only a few miles near the coast. Roads through such country are winding, and costly to build and maintain, but despite this, the railroad system is excellent. Although the swift streams and mountainous terrain are hard on transportation, they are a fine source of hydroelectric power, an increasing amount of which is being harnessed. A large share of the power is used industrially, augmented by electricity generated from coal. Widely scattered small hydroelectric plants supply local needs, so that possibly no other country has so great a proportion of wired rural homes.

Japan has a great variety of mineral deposits, but not in amounts sufficient to meet its needs. Copper is the most abundant metal. Sulphur and pyrites, important in the chemical industry, are fairly abundant, but there is an insufficiency of chromium, zinc, manganese, tin, iron, and lead. Both silver and gold are also mined. Coal deposits are widespread and of poor quality, but they meet about 90 per cent of the domestic requirements. Coking coal has to be imported. About 10 per cent of the country's petroleum needs are supplied mainly from fields of Honshu.

Dividing Japan about in half is the isotherm of January 32° F. Temperatures to the north are similar to those along the Atlantic coast from New Jersey to Maine, and those to the south resemble seaboard temperatures extending into Florida. Precipitation is heaviest in the south, over 100 inches in some places, and decreases northward to about 30 inches in the Hokkaido lowlands. Drought is practically unknown. Well-developed monsoonal influences are exhibited in summer maximum rainfall brought by Pacific winds blowing toward Asia and a winter maximum along the west coast of Honshu from winds moistened during their trip across the Sea of Japan. On the whole, Japan

is wetter and colder than other islands in its latitude. The west coast is cool and cloudy much of the time. The south coast is regularly hit by typhoons, such as the one in 1959 that left 5,000 dead or missing, 400,000 homeless, and caused $750,000,000 damage. Northern Honshu is beyond most storm tracks, which recurve northeastward, and is a territory of fog.

Over half of Japan is forested, including mesothermal rain forest, mixed forest, and taiga. Conifers dominate about half Japan's forests. These forest resources have given prominence to wood and paper industries, and have made Japan a land of wooden buildings and fire hazards, where old structures are rare. Domestic heating is dependent on oak and pine charcoal, burned in braziers. In spite of its lumber industry and supplies of such woods as pine, Japan cedar, and cypress, timber is regularly

Komagadake volcano, Japan
[*Consulate General of Japan, N.Y.*]

Gen-ya, Japan
[*Consulate General of Japan, N.Y.*]

imported, and reforestation is diligently pursued. About 15 per cent of the country is covered with coarse grass, the most striking being bamboo. Some 8 per cent is rough, stony land, *gen-ya.*

Agriculture. About 40 per cent of the population is engaged in agriculture, working small plots which average only 2.7 acres. Over half of the tilled land is in rice, almost all irrigated, and each acre produces about twice as much as in Java, where productivity is high for the Orient. In Kyushu, two crops are raised each year. This tremendous rice crop is consumed at home, augmented by rice imports. Wheat, rye, barley, oats, maize, and a variety of vegetables are widely grown food crops. About 6 per cent of the arable land is in industrial crops, such as mulberries, tea, tobacco, flax, hemp, and pyrethrum. Tobacco-raising centers near Tokyo, and tea-raising is concentrated on the slopes between Yokohama and Nagoya. Other tree crops include oranges, mandarin oranges, peaches, plums, cherries, persimmons, pears, and apples.

Japan comes closer than the United Kingdom to providing its own food, in spite of great population density and large proportion of non-agricultural land. Little cultivable land is used for nonessentials, houses, towns, and roads being located on stony or barren areas wherever possible. Not much land is given over to animals, for although in recent years the cattle and sheep population has increased to provide needed milk and wool, animal raising is not popular because the food value of grain is far greater than the value of milk produced by feeding the grain to a cow.

Fishing. Protein needs of Japan are supplied mainly from the sea. In prewar years the Japanese empire accounted for one third of the world's fish catch, and some 20 per cent of the population was directly or indirectly supported by fishing. Postwar years have seen a reduced annual catch, but it still amounts to about 4.5 million metric tons, one of the largest in the world. A large share of the catch comes from local grounds along the west coast north of 37° N., where cold and warm ocean currents meet. In cold water are sardines, the leading catch, herring, cod, sea trout, and halibut. In warm water are tunny, sardines, albacore, tuna, mackerel, sailfish, and swordfish. In addition to local fishing, floating canneries go north after crab and salmon, and whalers and factory ships go to Antarctic waters, bringing back oil, meat, leather, and fertilizer. Squid and octopus supplement diets, as do various seaweeds which are also used for making paper, glue, and for iodine.

One of the interesting occupations along the coast is raising cultured pearls by putting a tiny foreign particle between the flesh and shell of an oyster-like mollusc and waiting four years or so for a pearl to grow. Cultured pearls are a major export.

CULTURAL LANDSCAPES

Prior to the fall of the Shoguns Japan was a land of local economy, subsistence agriculture, and factories without mechanical power. Following the restoration of the Emperor Meiji the feudal system was abolished and lands of the nobility were parceled among the tenants. Shinto ("way of the gods"), an ancient religion, took on new vigor as nationalistic propaganda. Its many gods and its doctrines of conservatism, simplicity, cleanliness, and reverence for the emperor, heroes and other great people, tended to stress the greatness of Japan and the Japanese. Over 100,000 Shinto shrines spread throughout the country, where there was a like number of Buddhist temples, for Buddhism ("belief in the future") combines nicely with Shinto ("belief in the past"). The Buddhists actively supported education, arts, and crafts. Christianity ranks far behind the two main religions in numbers of followers. Almost in the class of a religion is the matter of face, an oriental form of prestige that is unable to bear acknowledgement of mistakes.

The end of feudalism saw a change in the highly restrictive educational policies. Leading scholars were imported from Europe, along with many skilled technicians, who soon taught their specialties to the Japanese. Knowledge was quickly absorbed and passed on to others, so that soon an educational revolution was under way such as no other country has experienced. No other part of the Oriental World approaches Japan's literacy. Its great universities have produced many outstanding scientists.

Unique among Oriental World countries in willingness to adopt Occidental ways, Japan rapidly made commercial and industrial gains that placed it on a par with European nations. But only the government had sufficient capital to establish European-type industry, so manufacturing became a kind of regimented feudal-ism, where the former peasant left the noble's land to work in the factory of a government employee of "rank." The first modern industries were textile mills, match factories, cement plants, shipyards, munition works, and porcelain works. Once these enterprises were firmly established, the government sold out to private interests, but although the prices were absurdly low, few "families" had sufficient capital to take over. Thus developed the *Zaibatsu*, or financial clique which gained control not only of almost all important industry but also of practically all banking, shipping, and commerce. Between this wealthy class and the common people was a gap equivalent to that between noble and serf.

Specific milestones in Japan's Industrial Revolution include a great boom in the textile industry following the Chinese War in 1895, a similar boom in chemicals and machinery after the Russian War, a tremendous increase in shipping after World War I, and a large upswing in metal industries and shipbuilding after World War II. Although Japan's overseas commerce using its own ships only started in the late nineteenth century, its merchant marine now ranks sixth in world tonnages. Japan leads the world in shipbuilding, which provides its

Intensive cultivation, Japan
[*Consulate General of Japan, N.Y.*]

Fishing village, Japan
[*Consulate General of Japan, N.Y.*]

second most important export. Cotton and rayon textile industries account for almost a third of Japan's exports. Silk fabrics and yarn are specialties of importance. The iron and steel industries also felt a postwar boom, and supply the country with its third most valuable export. The tempo of increased industrial production is shown by the fact that in 1957 the manufacturing output was 70 per cent higher than in 1953. A large share of the manufactures comes from family workshops, the typical factory of the Oriental World.

Kinai Plains. Unlike England, where industrialization resulted in development of a new part of the country and shifting of areas of greatest population density away from the agricultural culture hearth, Japan's culture nucleus became its leading manufacturing center. The Kinai Plains, a lowland extending from the Inland Sea toward Biwa Lake, became one of the world's great population nodes, with more than 9 million people. Two thirds of the residents are engaged in industry or commerce. Osaka and Kobe dominate the southern part of the plain. Osaka (2.7 million), both the "London" and "Manchester" of Japan, has long been a leading political, educational, and commercial center. One quarter of Japan's factory workers turn out one third of the country's industrial products in Osaka's factories. There is considerable ship building, and production of iron and steel, machinery, glass, chemicals, cotton textiles, paper, celluloid, rubber goods, and toys. Agricultural processing includes refining sugar, brewing sake, and preparation of many foods. Extensive slums have grown and a pall of smoke lies over this port and city. Fifteen miles west is Kobe (1 million), "Liverpool" of Japan, a busy entrepot, leading port, and center of ship building and of the manufacture of steel products, industrial machinery, and small items, such as matches, toys, and rubber goods. The main interests, however, are commercial.

The Kinai Plains lead inland through agricultural lands that produce large quantities of rice, vegetables, and, in the low, wet places, reeds used for making the mats that floor Japanese homes. At the head of the plains is Kyoto (1.2 million), capital for 11 centuries, with strong political and religious, as well as industrial interests.

Elder Japan. Kyushu is a rugged, partly forested, volcanic island whose steep, terraced slopes and limited lowlands produce rice, bananas, sugar cane, beans, taro, and sweet potatoes. Nearness to Korea, China, and, via the Ryukyus, to Malaya brought early foreign contacts to the Satsuma culture of Elder Japan that developed here, and still acts as an agricultural and conservative influence. The southern part of the island retains its rural ways, with villages tucked in deep valleys as protection against typhoon damage, thatched huts strung along trails or primitive roads, and little urban centers near wall-encircled old castles. Completely different is the industrial belt along the northwest coast, where blast furnaces, rolling mills, shipyards, cement and glass plants make use of the abundant coal in the Chikuho Basin for power. The Moji-Yawata industrial district, an unattractive concentration of coal docks, ore piles, and smoky factories, is connected with Shimonoseki by tunnels. Although nearly 10 per cent of Japan's industrial output, especially pig iron and steel, comes from northern Kyushu, the cities are not large, only Fukuoka having as many as 550,000 people. Even Nagasaki, long the main port for trade with China, has only 304,000 people.

Shikoku is a rugged island, and like southern Kyushu it contains extensive forests, produces copper, and is mainly rural, although fishing and paper making are important. Across the Inland Sea, along the coast of Honshu, is rugged country with only small hinterlands for its cities, such as Okayama and Hiroshima. The latter was rapidly rebuilt after having been the first atomic-bomb target in World War II.

Central Honshu. In the sixteenth century Edo was a small fishing village and primitive Shogun stronghold in backward territory, where winters were a bit cold for the Japanese and earthquakes altogether too frequent. After the Shogun period, Edo became Tokyo (Eastern Capital). When population

ELEVATION LESS
THAN 1000 FEET
• GIANT CITIES

HOKKAIDO

38°N

BIWA
LAKE
Kyoto

KWANTO PLAIN

Tokyo
Yokohama

CHIKUHO
BASIN

NOBI PLAIN
Nagoya
KINAI
PLAIN
Osaka
SHIKOKU Kobe

KYUSHU

500 MILES

Japan: lowlands and cities

pressure forced people from the Kinai Plains and other parts of Elder Japan into territory east of Biwa Lake, the Kwanto Plain—Japan's most extensive lowland—began to develop agriculturally. There are now more than 15 million people living on its 5,000-square-mile surface. The Plain is relatively fertile and produces a large share of the food, especially rice and barley, needed locally.

Tokyo and Yokohama assumed commercial significance after 1858, when Admiral Perry had managed to open some Japanese ports to foreign ships. Tokyo grew rapidly, becoming headquarters of the Zaibatsu, hence commercial capital, as well as the leading educational center and chief node in the railroad network. The old Shogun castle became the royal palace. Partly as a result of being half-destroyed in the earthquake of 1923 and bombed during World War II, many of the buildings are new and modern, streets are wide to prevent the spread of fire, and its whole appearance makes Tokyo the most European city in the Oriental World. Greater Tokyo has an area of 223 square miles and a population of 9.1 million. It is outranked among world cities only by the interstate conur-

bation centering in New York. Until the mid-nineteen-thirties it was a city of small factories, but when it was apparent that the disadvantage of earthquake hazard was outweighed by the advantage of central location, huge mills and factories were built, which now make use of Honshu and Hokkaido coal and nearby hydroelectric power sources, to turn out quantities of pig iron, steel, machinery, ships, railroad equipment, electric goods, silks, and a number of smaller manufactures. Nearly 30 per cent of Japan's industry is concentrated in the Kwanto Plain. As capital and educational center, Tokyo is foremost in in printing and similar trades. Yokohama (1.2 million) is Tokyo's modern port, with excellent wharves and extensive warehouses.

The Nobi Plain, extending inland from Ise Bay, is separated from both Kinai and Kwanto plains by hills that make communications difficult and expensive, so Nagoya (1.4 million) developed quite independently as a commercial center. The plain supports over 5 million people. The uplands, especially those between Nagoya and Tokyo, are a source of tea, including the green tea sent to the United States. Central Honshu also produces about three quarters of the world's silk. Harbor improvements permitted Nagoya district to become a leading Japanese port, in addition to its prominence as a center of textiles, cheap pottery and good porcelain, and more recently, aircraft manufacturing. It also makes tools, machines, metal wares, lacquer wares, and chemicals.

Northern Honshu. Landscapes characteristic of central Honshu, with rice on flats, tea and mulberries on slopes, and a wide diversity of crops, gradually lose their subtropical forms northward, where little double cropping is possible, summers are foggy, and the growing season is reduced to as few as 160 days. Japanese adjusted themselves slowly to this northern territory; much of the cultivated land has been in use less than a century. Precipitation is excessive, 80 to 100 inches, except in sheltered places. Sidewalks of many towns are covered, houses have wide, snow-shedding eaves, and railroads wind through wooden tunnels, snow sheds. Much of the land remained in large

Temple dating from 8th century, Japan
[*Consulate General of Japan, N.Y.*]

Urban landscape, Tokyo
[*Consulate General of Japan, N.Y.*]

estates and was relatively unproductive prior to World War II. Common people found difficulty in making a living. Many turned to the sea, so long fishing villages parallel the coast. Others sought better conditions elsewhere, in Hokkaido or foreign countries. Redistribution of land during the occupation has given a new impetus to agriculture. Population is increasing rapidly. Rice is raised wherever it will grow, but much of northern Japan is given to potatoes, beans, cereals, and orchards. Horses are pastured on lands unsuited to cropping. Copper, lead, zinc, silver, manganese, chromite, coal, petroleum, and hydroelectric power are produced. A little industry has developed at Sendai and Kamaishi. Tourism provides important income, for the mountainous scenery is magnificent.

Northern Islands. Hokkaido is still in a pioneer stage of development. It is the home of the surviving Ainu, and would be more attractive to Scandinavians or Chinese than it is to Japanese, for it is cold, the temperature in the interior at times dropping to —40° F., the growing season is short, and taiga covers most uplands. These coniferous forests are the source of much of Japan's timber and pulp. Mixed forest is widespread in the southwest, where the relative mildness of the climate is indicated by the fact that rice occupies one quarter of the cultivated land. Beans, however, rank first, and farming incomes are supplemented by sugar beets, potatoes, and peppermint. Oats and hay support horse and dairy farms. Cherries, apples, and pears are the main orchard crops. Farms average well over 10 acres in size, are rectangular, and usually have log cabins and large barns. Fishing is an important occupation. Hokkaido's main industries are canning, food-processing, and lumbering, and its resources of coal, iron, manganese, and chromite are the basis for heavy industries around Sapporo and the main port, Hokadate.

Karafuto, the portion of the island of Sakhalin south of 50° N., extending to within 30 miles of Hokkaido, has been the subject of dispute between Japan and Russia since the sixteenth century. In 1875 the Japanese withdrew, in exchange for clear title to the Kuril Islands. In 1905 Sakhalin was divided between the two nations, Japan getting the part with coal and Russia getting the part with petroleum, reputed to be the largest reserves outside of the Caspian Basin in Soviet Asia. After World War II the Soviet Union claimed the whole island. Essentially; all its prewar inhabitants were Japanese, with a handful of Ainus and Koreans. In this snowy, taiga and tundra region, the little land that can be planted is in oats, fodder, potatoes, and peas. Logging is the winter occupation. The value of forest products exceeds that of fishing,

Tea plantation, Japan
[*Consulate General of Japan, N.Y.*]

the summer occupation. Since there are so few farmers, most of the people live in the scattered towns. Industries center on forest products and fishing. Salmon and crab meat are canned and other fish dried, salted, or processed for oil or fertilizer. In the northern part of the island, interest centers on petroleum production.

The Kurils, now part of the Soviet Union, are a chain of volcanic, fog-shrouded islands that stretch for more than 700 miles from Hokkaido to Kamchatka. Aside from naval and military personnel, their prewar population consisted of a few Ainus, Kamchadals, and Japanese. There are practically no agricultural possibilities on these bleak islands, except on Kunashir, where some beans are raised. The chief occupations are hunting, fishing, and mining iron, copper, and sulphur.

Electronic industry, Japan
[*Consulate General of Japan, N.Y.*]

URBANIZATION

Japan has six cities of over a million: Tokyo, Osaka, Nagoya, Kyoto, Kobe, and Yokohama. These giants manufacture goods for foreign trade and perform commercial and political functions for the islands as a whole. It is notable that there are so few cities of intermediate size; only one with a population between 500,000 and one million, and only 2 in the 400,000 class, and 5 in the 300,000 class. These lesser cities serve limited agricultural areas or industrial districts near coal. The giant cities are those characteristic of a world power. The absence of a reasonable number of smaller cities is an expression of the mountain block topography where lowlands form insufficient hinterlands for more than large towns. Nevertheless, the number of urban dwellers, like the population itself, is growing at spectacular rates. The number of people engaged in agriculture remains about constant. The change from being predominantly rural to predominantly urban, accompanied Japan's intensified Industrial Revolution and was equally swift.

The major cities are Europeanlike, but other cities and towns are low, crowded places with unpainted wooden buildings. Here and there an attractive temple or shrine rises above the thatched roofs of plain one-storied buildings.

Nucleated settlement is the rule, except on Hokkaido. Most rural houses are hidden by bamboo or other hedges, or lie behind fences. A tendency to raise structures on stilts may be an expression of Malay influence. Outside the towns, the rural landscapes are typically Oriental: few roads, narrow lanes winding to fields separated by hedgerows, dikes or ditches, almost no mechanical equipment, few teams of animals, and an occasional ox or horse hitched to a plow. Forests are important, and unlike the Chinese, the Japanese are interested in forestry and have planted a large share of the trees now growing.

POPULATION PRESSURE

After remaining stable at about 30 million for over a century, Japan's population climbed to 60 million between 1840 and 1925, rose to over 73 million by 1940, and is about 92 today, with an annual increase of over 1 million. The result, of course, is that Japan cannot feed itself, even though the land is used with great skill. Human excreta, fish guano, wood ash, rice straw, and soybean fertilizers are used to increase crop yields, but there is still not enough food, although some experts think yields could be increased by 20 per cent. Income from manufacturing, shipping, foreign investments, tourists, and other sources help fill the gap by paying for food imports, but diets of the masses are meager.

It is incorrect to blame population pressure for Japan's becoming a world problem; taking lands of others has been a habit for centuries. As early as the fourth century Japanese embarked on a program of taking Korean and Chinese lands when there was certainly no population pressure at home.

The Ryukyu Islands were objects of the first major aggression. They belonged to China until Japan conquered the Okinawa Group in 1609. Okinawa is relatively large and densely populated, its main town, Naha, having a population over 65,000. It was the scene of great and bloody battles during World War II, and is now administered, together with the other southern Ryukyus, by the United States. Altogether, the islands and reefs of the Ryukyus, which stretch from Kyushu to Formosa, have an area of less than 1,000 square miles and a population of nearly 850,000. Japan used the islands as stepping stones to Formosa, its next main acquisition, in 1893. Had it not been for European intervention, Japan would at that time have also kept several places on the Chinese mainland.

After the Russo-Japanese War of 1904–1905, Japan carried on aggressions against China by shadow-boxing with Russia, and after a number of incidents in the nineteen-twenties showed that the Soviet Union was unwilling to go to war, Japan took over Manchuria (1931), and later swept through most of eastern China during the nineteen-thirties. Although Japan had played almost no part in World War I, it profited enormously and ended up in control of the former German islands in the Pacific. The ease of these gains undoubtedly promoted more aggressive plans that were finally halted by World War II.

Population pressure has not been reduced appreciably either by Japanese aggression or by emigration. Colonization schemes have not lured many Japanese to Hokkaido, Formosa, Brazil, Peru, Philippines, or other places which offered higher standards of living. There are some 185,000 Japanese in Hawaii and about 142,000 in the rest of the United States. Many reasons are offered why so few Japanese have gone into conquered lands or places to which they can emigrate freely. The most probable is simply that they prefer to remain at home. Shinto and other influences have instilled in them a love of fatherland that is rarely seen elsewhere.

MALAYAN REALM

Mosque, Kuala Lumpur

[*Perutusan Tetap Persekutuan Tanah Melayu Ke-Pertubohan Bangsa² Bersatu*]

20. Malayan Realm

Less Caucasoid than the Indian and less Mongoloid than the Chinese is the Malayan Realm of the Oriental World, a region of islands centering in Indonesia, or the East Indies. Included are a small part of the mainland of Asia, the Malay Peninsula south of Kra Isthmus, and the Philippines, but excluded is New Guinea, which is in the Pacific World.

The central part of the realm is geologically a stable region, a partially submerged plateau that extends from the Malay Peninsula and Indo-China across shallow seas to the limits shown on the map. In an arcuate pattern be-

yond this quiescent core is one of the world's most complicated folded regions, where earthquakes are frequent and many volcanoes are active. On the convex fronts of the arcs are some of the world's great ocean deeps, Sunda Trough and Philippine Trough, including the 34,440-foot Mindinao Deep. The realm centers on the equator, which bisects Sumatra and Borneo. It is thus almost seasonless, rain falling at any time and lowland temperatures seldom departing from 80° F. Significantly cooler weather occurs at higher levels. Tropical rain forest is the natural vegetation cover of most lowlands,

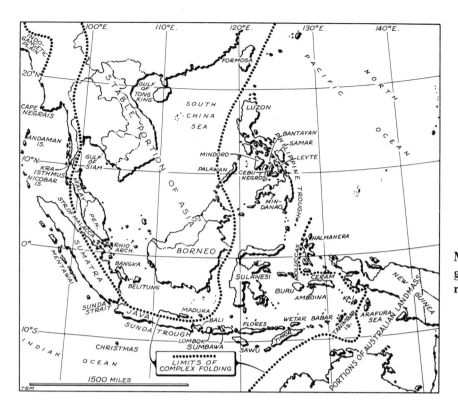

Malayan Realm: geological relationships

varied only by open forests and grasslands in the rain shadow of mountains.

The Malays are a mixed stock, predominantly Mongoloid, but with some Archaic Caucasoid physical traits and evidences of a Negroid strain. The original Negrito inhabitants, members of a group that once extended from Africa across southern Arabia and India to the Pacific, mixed with arriving archaic Caucasoids, resembling the Bushmen of Australia. Mongoloids were the last invaders to become thoroughly entrenched. In his culture hearth, which extends from Sumatra to Sumbawa, the Malay evolved as an aristocratic, good-natured little Mongoloid who is an excellent seafarer, pirate, fisherman, and trader. He cultivates land because the chore is unavoidable. As a plantation hand he is ordinarily unreliable. In a position of some authority he may become extremely faithful. He is instinctively polite and, according to European appraisal, occasionally capable. He is now dominant along the coasts eastward into Flores and other islands as far as Timor, while various primitives occupy the interiors. Some Malays found their way west to Madagascar and north to Japan, settling wherever they went and be-

coming significant strains in surviving populations. The realm has served as an earlier home of populations that spread eastward into Pacific islands, the Melanesian, Micronesian, and Polynesian all tracing their migrations back to the Malayan Realm, where they acquired their languages and basic culture traits.

Some 250 Malayo-Polynesian languages of the Austronesian family are spoken. Except for Javanese and a few other highly cultivated tongues, the languages are easy to learn because they are simple structurally and have small vocabularies. The so-called Trade Malay, a pidgin language, is widely understood in the East Indies and Pacific islands. Indonesian is being created as a more formal variant of Malay.

The most widely adopted religion is Mohammedanism, introduced by Arab traders at an early date and enforced by conquests of the thirteenth and fourteenth centuries. Arabs, on the whole, are a wealthy class, and are respected as spiritual and intellectual leaders of the Moslems. Hinduism, dating from the sixth century, and Buddhism, from the eighth century, have only minor followings today. There are some 3 million Christians in Indonesia and four fifths of the Filipinos are Roman Catholic. Paganism is widespread among tribes in the interiors of larger islands.

Most Malays depended on subsistence agriculture until Europeans introduced modern farming. The earlier objective was to provide food for the traditional two meals a day, one before and the other after the period of greatest heat. The primitive digging stick is still in use in upland, unirrigated rice areas. On lowlands wooden plows are dragged by water buffaloes across irrigated rice fields. In the interiors *fire cultivators* still carry on a shifting agriculture in which plots are burned to leave wood ash on the surface, a fertilizer sufficient to raise three crops or so before activities must move to a new site. In sharp contrast to these smallholders are the large scientifically run plantations or estates, which until recently produced more than half of the agricultural exports although they occupy only a tiny fraction of the cultivable lands.

Malaya has been exploited by Arabs, Chinese, and Europeans. Arabs still comprise one of the wealthy groups in Java, Chinese are in control of most of the business, and Europeans, now in decreasing numbers, have in the past made vast fortunes out of East Indian products, but at the same time, Europeans were industrious workers, developing plantations, promoting commerce, and carrying out governmental assignments. Europeans also assisted in maintaining and making prosperous the sultans, rajas, and other native princes who occupy the apex of the economic and social pyramid.

European contacts really started during the Voyages of Discovery, which brought Magellan to the Philippines in 1521 in search of spices. His trip was more than paid for by cloves and other spices brought to Europe by the single surviving ship. Spain promptly took possession of the Philippines. Spice-laden galleon fleets used Pacific waters, rather than routes disputed by Portugal. Goods went from Philippine Manila to Mexican Acapulco, then overland to Veracruz, thence across Spanish waters to Europe. The Portuguese also arrived in the sixteenth century to enter into trade, especially with the Moluccas, where now a number of very Mongoloid people retain Portuguese names and family traditions. The Dutch and British arrived later, and in time the Dutch managed to squeeze the British out. They were wise enough to concentrate their activities in places that were culturally advanced through Indian and other contacts, and where Arabs had established trading habits among the natives. The Dutch East India Company was in control until rule was assumed by the Crown in 1798. Eventually the Dutch consolidated their holdings into an empire extending across a length of 3,100 miles and comprising an area of 735,000 square miles. The United States entered the colonial picture in 1898 by taking over the Philippines from Spain.

In 1946 the United States voluntarily gave up its richest colony, the Philippines. Three years later the Dutch recognized the independence of the Republic of the United States of Indonesia, retaining only a portion of New Guinea. These new countries, inexperienced in self government, are having the same sort of internal turmoil that followed the attainment of independence by the United States. Of Portuguese possessions, only the eastern half of Timor remains. The British retain only a part of Borneo, a few small islands, and Commonwealth ties with the mainland part of the Malayan Realm.

The islands of the East Indies ordinarily supply the world with 90 per cent of its quinine, 85 of pepper, 80 of cocaine, 65 of kapok, about one third each of rubber and sisal, one quarter each of copra and palm oil, one fifth of tea, one sixth of tin, one twentieth of coffee, and one fiftieth of petroleum. The islands contain largely unexploited resources of hardwood, iron, gold, and other minerals. The leading exports are rubber, petroleum, bauxite, copra and coconut products, sugar and sugar products, timber, tin, and tea.

There are astounding differences among population densities of various islands in the East Indies. Java and Madura have 57 million inhabitants in an area of about 51,000 square miles, a density of over 1,100 per square mile. The rest of Indonesia has 30.1 million on 685,000 square miles, a density of over 40. In the Philippines, Cebu has a density of 630, but Mindanao has less than 50. Many islands are sparsely inhabited, with densities of about 5.

JAVA

With an area of 48,500 square miles, Java is the smallest of the Greater Sunda Islands (Celebes or Sulawesi, 73,000; Sumatra, 182,800; Borneo, 290,000; New Guinea, 316,800). The population of Java and Madura increased from fewer than 5 million to over 28 during the nineteenth century, and has doubled in the first half of this century. It had the advantages of an early start in cultural development under Hindu rule, dating from the sixth century, and in commercial activities resulting from Arab contacts. Mohammedan conquest destroyed most Hindu temples and brought widespread conversion to Islam. The Dutch began by making an alliance with the Sundanese Sultan in western Java, which led eventually to control of the island. Dutch colonial policy was considered enlightened because some concern was given to the natives; Europeans could not usurp native lands, and villages were left in the control of their elected officials. Nevertheless, few benefits accrued to Indonesians, little love was felt for the Dutch, and the native population thoroughly resented European control.

Among East Indian islands Java is favored by having extensive areas of fertile, lava-derived soil, only limited swamps and broader areas of healthful territory, a variety of climates as a result of its topographic irregularity, and an annual rainfall of from 60 to 100 inches on most of the lowlands, although parts of southern Java receive more than 300 inches. The original vegetation of tropical rain forest in the west and south, and forests and grasslands in the northwest, have been cleared to an elevation of 4,000 feet, except on very steep slopes. As a result, nearly half of Java is cultivated, two thirds of which is in manioc, rice, or maize. About half the tilled land is irrigated, producing two rice crops and one other crop each year. Peanuts and soybeans are other important food crops.

Eighty-five peaks rise above 6,000 feet, the highest to over 12,000. Of over 100 volcanoes, about half have been active during historic times, Krakatao in Sunda Strait being a spectacular example, with its eruption in 1883 which brought death to 36,000, drowned in the resulting sea-wave. But the prospect of being blown into eternity rarely prevents farmers from ascending the slopes and spilling over into favorable craters to take advantage of fertile volcanic soils. So, up the wet slopes of western Java are grown sisal, rubber, tea, and cinchona, the latter growing best above 5,000 feet. The most extensive and productive lowlands lie north of Java's volcanic backbone. Here sugar cane, coconuts, various palms, and kapok are grown. Two important starch crops are sago and manioc (cassava) for tapioca. In central and eastern Java, tobacco is an important crop.

Most of the export crops, rubber, sugar, tea, cinchona (quinine), and tobacco, came from European-managed plantations, but on Java and even more noticeably on other islands of Indonesia, war and occupation damage, fluctuating world prices, and governmental policies, such as expropriation of Dutch-owned business and expulsion of Dutch nationals, have resulted in an increasing proportion of agricultural production for export coming from small farms. The average farm size on Java is about 2 acres. The export of food crops, of course, has been greatly reduced because the fast-growing population consumes more and more of the produce.

Rural scene, Malaya
[*Federation of Malaya, Mission to United Nations*]

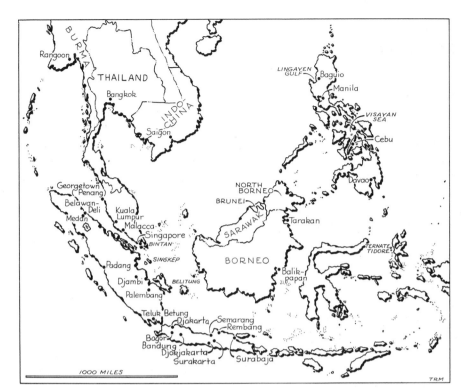

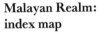

**Malayan Realm:
index map**

The surprise is that until recently this most densely populated island was able to feed itself. Its protein needs were filled, not from its water buffalo that slosh about in the rice paddies, but from fish, both from the sea and ponds. Fish farming is a secondary occupation in paddy fields.

Java is rather lacking in mineral resources, although petroleum occurs near Rembang, natural gas is found west of Surabaja, and sulphur and manganese are mined extensively. About two thirds of all East Indian industry is concerned with making products by hand, for local needs. Only one third involves factories with power, and consists chiefly of agricultural processing, such as sugar refining, preparing quinine or tobacco, and making leather goods. Cement, brick, tile, small metal wares, furniture, plaited goods, soap, ice, paint, and paper are manufactured. Although hydroelectric potential is great, only a small fraction has been utilized. Communications, however, are well developed, with roads and railroads to all principal places, and good air and sea connections with Europe, which have encouraged a growing tourist trade.

An increasing number of people are living in the cities, creating problems of housing and sanitation. Djakarta, formerly Batavia, the capital, is a seething confusion of 3 million people living under dreadfully crowded conditions, made even more uncomfortable by the uniformly high temperature, always near 80° F., and the heavy rainfall, 72 inches. Bogor (Buitenzorg), in the foothills nearby, has a better climate and is a secondary business and residential center. Other cities with populations approaching one million are Bandung, a center of native crafts and small manufactures, Surabaja, a modern port and center of the petroleum industry, and Djokjakarta (Jogja), an interior commercial center. In all the urban centers, it is the Chinese who tend to control business and commerce. Although the population is predominantly Malay, fewer than half are Javanese, who live mainly in the central part of the island. To the west are Sudanese and to the east are Madurese, who, with the Javanese, are ordinarily quiet, peaceful people. With the growth of nationalism, there is an increasing dislike and suspicion of anything that appears to be foreign influence.

EASTERN ISLANDS

Nusa Tenggara, or Lesser Sunda Islands, which extend from Bali to Timor, are volcanic, and are progressively drier toward the east. Bali is wet and naturally forested, but barren steppe covers much of Wetar, north of Timor. The Moluccas, Halmahera, New Guinea, and islands to the east are detached fragments of the Australian continent, which resembles in stability the western portions of the Malayan Realm. In these less-volcanic islands, soils are relatively infertile, population is less dense, and cultural attainments less advanced than in the islands to the west, such as Bali and Lombok, which so closely resemble Java.

Outstanding, at least in the matter of size, are Sulawesi (Celebes) and Borneo. Sulawesi, a spiderlike island larger than North Dakota, consists of several rather narrow mountain-chain peninsulas, which radiate from a central hub. Cones of extinct volcanoes rise to heights of 10,000 feet. Old rocks in the north and southeast contain valuable deposits of nickel, gold, and silver, but there is little economic development. Rainfall is excessive in most places except in the southwest, where there is something of a dry season in summer. Chief money crops are coffee and nutmeg in the north, and kapok toward the south. The population of nearly 7 million is mainly Indonesian, with a few Chinese. In the interior are some wild Malays who practice head hunting and have few outside contacts. The coastal and urban inhabitants are mainly Mohammedan in the south and include many Christians in the north.

All but 79,000 of Borneo's 290,000 square miles were in Dutch hands. The smaller share includes Sarawak, North Borneo, and tiny Brunei, all politically British. The mountain arrangement is something like that of Sulawesi, but lowlands extend from range to range, like the webbing of a duck's foot. The most valuable resource is petroleum, found in Brunei and at Balikpapan and Tarakan in Kalimantan (Indonesian Borneo). Some rather poor coal has been mined in the southeast. Rubber is a leading crop, and is exported along with timber, sugar, copra, and other tropical products.

Business and local trade are monopolized by Chinese, who comprise less than 10 per cent of the 4.8 million population.

WESTERN MALAYA

Sumatra is much larger than Java, being about twice as long and twice as wide, but in most respects it is less developed than its eastern neighbor. It retains most of its forest and has a population of only about 14 million. Along the southwest side of the island rises a chain of volcanic peaks, several projecting over 10,000 feet. Some coal is mined in this section, but considerably more important are the petroleum deposits near Medan, Palembang, and Djambi, all on the eastern half of the island. This part of the island also contains the most extensive lowland, but agricultural development has been retarded by the presence of infertile, lateritic soils, and broad swamps. Rice is widely grown. Rubber is the leading crop at elevations of less than 300 feet, the center of production being Medan. Tobacco is grown in the same general region. Limited amounts of cinchona, tea, coffee, and pepper are other crops, produced largely on plantations. Most of the modern agriculture is a product of British capital and Chinese labor. Extensive rain forests remain hardly-touched homes for orangutans and playful gibbons. A highly diversified fauna includes elephants, rhinoceroses, tapirs, wild pigs, deer, tigers, monkeys, powerful python, and vicious crocodile.

The islands of Belitung, Bangka, and Singkep supply one fifth of the world's tin. Bintan, in the Rhio (Riouw) Archipelago, just south of Singapore, supplies one sixth of the world's bauxite. Aluminum ore is also mined on the Mentawai and other islands off the southwest coast of Sumatra, where the natives are not Malays, but speak primitive Indonesian tongues. Tiny Christmas Island, inhabited mainly by Chinese, and long governed by Straits Settlements, is now Australian. The Nicobar Islands, northwest of Sumatra, are administered by India. About 12,000 Malays raise a few coconuts on their 625-square-mile surface. Seventy-five miles to the north are the Andaman Islands, over 200 bits of land with a combined area of about 2,500 square miles. These are also administered by India. In their extensive forests are some of the world's most primitive Negritos who, like their Pygmy relatives, are experts with spear and arrow. Some 20,000 Indonesians live along the coasts, and make a living from timber, coconuts, coffee, rubber, and rice.

The **Malay Peninsula** barely escapes being an island. Its tenuous connection with the mainland of Asia, the Kra Isthmus, is the northern limit of the Malayan Realm. Political and cultural boundaries fail to coincide. Thailand (Siam) projects well into Malay territory.

Most of the interior of the peninsula is rough country, where peaks attain elevations of about 7,000 feet, the highest being toward the west. Limited coal reserves along the west coast supply the needs of local railroads. Excellent iron ore to the south, bauxite toward Singapore, and manganese to the north were developed by the Japanese, for export to the homeland. Tungsten ore is mined near Kuala Lumpur. The greatest metal resource of all, however, is tin, abundant in stream gravels in the western foothills. Chinese began working Malayan tin as early as the fifteenth century and they constitute about 80 per cent of the miners today. Dredges and hydraulic mining yield most of the ore, the main workings being just southeast of Penang. About a third of the world's supply of tin comes from these mines. Most of the Malayan ore is refined in Penang and Singapore.

The peninsula has a hot, wet climate, not much different from that of a hothouse. Yearly rainfall averages over 100 inches, and up to 300 inches in the uplands, and temperatures hover between 75° and 85° F. In many places the tropical rain forest is too dense for people, but tigers and monkeys abound. Forests cover 70 per cent of the peninsula and are more of a barrier to travel than are the mountains. The west coast is barricaded by mangrove swamps, while clean-sand beaches face the South China Sea.

Of the total Federation of Malaya population of about 6.5 million, 50 per cent are Malays, 37.5 Chinese, and 11 Indian. Chinese are miners, foresters, plantation owners, and city dwellers. As proprietors they own most of the businesses, produce a large share of the tin and rubber, and they constitute four fifths of the industrial population. The Indians, principally cultivators of rubber, are mainly Tamil-speakers from Madras. Like the Indians and Chinese, most of the Malays live in the west, where they tend paddy fields and small plots planted to rubber, although a considerable number follows these pursuits along the northeast coast. Being in political control, their language is the official one, although English and other languages are widely spoken. In addition to Malays, Chinese, and Indians, there are a few more-or-less Caucasoid aborigines living in a primitive way in the more open forests, some Pakistani, and a few Europeans and others.

About 15 per cent of the land is cultivated and rice is the main food crop, but the peninsula is unable to feed itself. Concentration on export crops makes it necessary to import two thirds of the needed food. Sixty per cent of the cultivated land is in rubber, about half the area being in large plantations. Seeds smuggled from Brazil and raised near London became the parent stock for rubber, which the British introduced into Malaya in 1877. About one third of the world's natural rubber now comes from the peninsula. Trees, thriving where the rainfall is in excess of 80 inches with no dry season, are planted mainly below 1,000 feet, where the temperature is highest. Most of the rubber is produced along the west coast, where there are also considerable plantings of palms for oil and copra. Pineapples are grown mainly to the south, and the output ranks second only to Hawaii. Some coffee and tea are raised on uplands.

In 1957 the Federation of Malaya came into being as an independent country in the British Commonwealth. Prior to that time the British had controlled the various states through local sultans and rajas, and complex political ties, largely with the Straits Settlements. Straits Settlements, a British Crown Colony from 1867 to 1946, was composed of Penang and Malacca, now part of the Federation, Singapore, now a separate state, and several other places along the

Government Offices, Kuala Lumpur
[*Department of Information, Federation of Malaya*]

Strait of Malacca. Penang, where the British East India Company established a depot in 1786, is a free port, an entrepot for the Federation, and center of tin smelting and fishing. Malacca, also a port and fishing center, is just south of the modern capital, Kuala Lumpur, which, like Ipoh, is a collection center for tin and rubber. Kuala Lumpur and Singapore differ notably from most Malayan towns, which are rather run-down and helter-skelter in appearance.

Singapore (1.5 million) is one of the world's most strategic "south tips." It has been a British possession since 1819. About 75 per cent of its population is Chinese, 13 Malay, and 9 Indian. The city is on a 224-square-mile island, tied to Johore by a causeway. Heavily fortified and considered the greatest naval base in Asian waters, Singapore proved vulnerable to attack from the rear and fell to the Japanese, who occupied it from 1942 to 1945. It is the busiest entrepot in the tropics, carrying on 70 per cent of Malaya's trade. Its main interests are commercial, but there is some industry, mainly concerned with rubber. Of less importance is tin smelting, cement making, and processing of palm oil, coconuts, pineapples, spices, and timber. Petroleum is refined and stored. Excellent dry-dock facilities and coal docks serve ships of all nations. Various airlines connect its busy airport with Europe, the Far East, East Indies, and Australia.

PHILIPPINE ISLANDS

The Philippines lie somewhat over 200 miles due south of Formosa, well to the southeast of any part of China and about 700 miles east of Indo-China. Island chains on either side of the Sulu Sea almost reach Borneo. The entire group consists of some 7,000 islands, of which over 1,000 are inhabited and nearly 500 have areas in excess of one quarter mile. The combined area is 115,600 square miles, with Luzon (40,420) and Mindanao (36,537) constituting two thirds of the area. A population of 24 million is more than twice that of 1898, when the United States obtained possession from Spain.

Stretching for 1,200 miles across latitudes from 4°40′ to 21°20′ N., the Philippines are somewhat less equatorial than other parts of the Malayan Realm, and have a somewhat better climate, being a little less rainy. The northwestern islands actually have a winter dry season. The northern islands suffer severe and all too frequent damage from typhoons. Forests cover just over half the surface, and include many commercially useful species. About 2 billion board feet of timber are annually cut and sold. Tropical rain forest covers most uncleared lowland and mesothermal rain forest is typical of uplands. Mangrove swamps are common along many coasts. About 18 per cent of the area is in grass, some of it coarse and useless. About 20 per cent is farmed, and another 10 per cent is potentially cultivable. The finest agricultural lands are in central and southern Luzon, southern Panay, Cebu, western Negros, and Leyte.

The four main types of natives are Negritos, Igorots, Moros, and Filipinos. Only the former are non-Malay, and they are few in number, living in a primitive fashion in remote forests. Igorots is the collective name given to some 80 tribal groups descended from Early Malays. There are some 40 ethnic groups represented, and they speak 87 different languages. They have in common the fact that they are mountain tribes, although they started on the coasts, and are physically similar, being short and stocky, with powerful limbs and flat noses. They have remarkable physical endurance, as was demonstrated when they assisted American forces during World War II. They are intelligent, but normally have little opportunity for education. Most are pagans, living in constant fear of taboos. Some still engage in head hunting, others are savage warriors, while others are peaceful farmers. Their engineering skill in constructing terraces is most impressive.

Moros are Later Malays, physically similar to Filipinos, but culturally different in such aspects as being fanatical Moslems, filing their teeth to points, and chewing betel nut, which blackens the teeth. Some Arab blood and many Arabian culture traits help differentiate the group, and explain their name—Moro meaning Moor in Spanish. They are capable fighters, skilled pirates and boatsmen, and completely unconcerned with modern politics and economic problems, wishing only to be let alone. Filipinos are also Later Malays, with a strong Chinese strain. They farm, rarely engage in business, and are politically minded. Almost all inherit Christianity from Spanish days. Their leading languages are Tagalog, which has been adopted as the national tongue, Ilocano, and Visayan. Spanish is widely spoken among the upper classes, although English has largely taken its place in business and government. As a group Filipinos are the most Americanized, and most aware of the need for American help if their republic is to survive. They possess the best agricultural lands.

The main food crops are rice, maize, yams, and sweet potatoes. Rice occupies about half of the tilled land in use for growing food, and a fair share of the crop is raised by Chinese. Food crops, including a variety of vegetables and warm-climate fruits occupy three fourths of the farmed land. Only about one quarter of the cultivated land is irrigated and about one twelfth is double cropped. Most of the farms are small, the average size being about 8 acres. Plantations, mainly Filipino-owned, are devoted largely to commercial crops, such as coconuts, sugar, hemp, tobacco, and pineapples. Two thirds of the national income is derived from coconuts, sugar, and hemp. Despite an active program to increase food production, 15 to 20 per cent of the food has to be imported. The biggest buyer of the commercial-crop products, embroideries, and gold is the United States, with which the Philippines have a trade agreement for reduced duties on imports into both countries.

Industry is largely a home affair, where embroidery, hats, mats, pottery, and some cloth are produced. Textiles include *pina*, a pineapple cloth, and *husi*, a Panay banana fiber blended with silk. An increasing number of factories are making their appearance, and they deal largely with processing coconuts and rice, making cigars and cigarettes, manufacturing leather and rubber shoes, and refining sugar.

Mineral resources are abundant. Gold, mined mainly in northern Luzon, constitutes about 30 per cent of the value of metals produced. About equal in value is the copper production. Good iron ore is mined in Luzon, Samar, and Mindanao. Coal and petroleum reserves appear to be inconsequential, but there is a large, although almost undeveloped, hydroelectric potential. Chromium and uranium, late discoveries, are possibly the most valuable of the mineral resources. Minor amounts of silver, bismuth, mercury, platinum, nickel, zinc, lead, and manganese are mined, and considerable quantities of cement and salt are produced. All the natural resources are the property of the Republic.

Luzon, about the size of Kentucky, has fine food-producing lands, extending from Manila Bay to Lingayen Gulf, and mainly planted to rice and sugar. Toward the north, tobacco is grown, and coconuts are produced to the south of the island. Much of Luzon is mountainous, volcanic peaks rising over 9,000 feet. Perched on a high tract is Baguio, "summer capital." The official capital is Quezon City, a suburb of the old capital, Manila, where most of the government offices are located. Manila, 2.0 million, is principal port and main center of education, commerce, and industry. On the delta of the Pasig River, it became the site of a Spanish walled city surrounded by a moat, in sharp contrast to the modern wharves and buildings of new Manila. Under the Spaniards Manila gave its name to the fiber (Manila hemp) that became world famous for its qualities of strength and resistance to salt-water

deterioration, and to a variety of cigar tobacco. Under American direction Manila became the healthiest lowland city in the tropics.

Some of the islands around the Visayan Sea, such as Bantayan and Cebu, are more densely populated than Luzon. Cebu is particularly favorable for crops, its lowlands having only moderate rainfall. Maize, rather than rice, is the leading crop. The city of Cebu is the commercial center and main port for inter-island trade. To the south, the large island of Mindanao remains comparatively undeveloped, although more and more lands are being cleared of forests and brought into cultivation. The forests are an important reserve of hardwoods, especially Philippine mahogany, valued as a cabinet wood. Cattle range in open territory. Coconuts, hemp, rubber, bananas, pineapples, and coffee are lowland crops. Copra and hemp are leading exports, going mainly through Davao, located at the foot of Mt. Apo, highest peak in the islands. About half of the Japanese population of the islands live in and around Davao, where they are industrious farmers and skilled fishermen. Throughout the islands fishing is an important activity.

INDO-CHINESE SHATTER BELT

21. Indo-Chinese Shatter Belt

Between the three culture realms of the Oriental World is a transition zone, a cultural shatter belt, that politically includes a small part of India, all of Burma, most of Thailand (Siam), and all of Vietnam (north and south), Cambodia, and Laos. Like the European Shatter Belt, this "Farther India" has been invaded by widely diverse peoples, with the result that fragmental remnants of many different cultures now live in rather close proximity. It is less densely populated than lands to the east or west; some 87 million people live on 750,000 square miles, or about 115 per square mile. In general, these people are conservative. They trust the old ways and are skeptical of new crops, new implements, or other changes. As true Orientals they are also concerned with loss of face. About 90 per cent are peasants, living relatively simple lives. Houses need only protect against rain and sun, clothing can be minimum, and health and sanitation arouse little interest, despite the high death rates from malaria, typhoid, smallpox, cholera, and dysentery. Among the rest of the population are the business men, largely Indians and Chinese, and the revolutionary leaders who spearheaded the intense nationalistic movements that led to independence of most of the countries in the years following World War II. Throughout the Shatter Belt there are strong anti-colonial feelings and distrust of Europeans as long-time exploiters of these lands. Until the nineteen-fifties the western lands were controlled by Britain and the eastern lands by France, with Thailand an independent buffer state in the middle.

Physically the Indo-Chinese region is characterized by north-south mountain trends. Cultural and economic contacts follow valleys of the Irrawaddy, Salween, Menam, Mekong, and other streams along the lowlands of the regional grain. Separated by high mountains, these lowlands—deltas and flood plains—tend to become ethnic, political, and economic units. Rugged barriers become retreats of primitives. Climates are more or less monsoonal, and vegetation varies from open to dense forest in most uncleared land.

Many of the primitives are strongly Caucasoid. Originally they occupied lowlands, but as wave after wave of increasingly Mongoloid invaders appeared, the aboriginal inhabitants were crowded into hill and mountain refuges. Among the partially Mongoloid early invaders were people resembling Early Malays, thought to have come from Central Asia. Tibeto-Burman and Mon-Khmer speakers come later, the former being an important element in the west, the latter in the east. Many of the latest pre-Commercial Revolution invaders came from southwestern China. Later Malays crossed from Sumatra into the Malay Peninsula, where they inhabit a small part of Thailand. In coastal Burma and fringes of Indo-China, Trade Malay and other forms of Malayo-Polynesian are spoken, but the dominant language family in the Shatter Belt is Indo-Chinese, composed of

355

many tongues. Geographical distribution of these tongues is about as complex as that in the European Shatter Belt, and for quite similar reasons.

BURMA

Burma was administered as part of India from 1826 to 1937, when it became a "self-governing" commonwealth. In 1948 it severed all ties with the British and became independent. Its 262,000 square miles contains some 20 million people, a density of 76 per square mile, which is low compared with India, China, or Java, and which belies the fact that the density in the Irrawaddy Valley is over 250 per square mile.

The country has a pronounced regional grain (belted topographic pattern). A narrow coastal plain lies west of Arakan Yoma, a range that provides some protection from excessive precipitation for the main lowlands, which lie along the Irrawaddy, and, beyond the Pegu Yoma, along the Sittang and Salween rivers. Part of the upper Irrawaddy is aligned with the Sittang, so that easy communication exists between the main valleys of central Burma; the railroad from Rangoon to Mandalay, both on the Irrawaddy, follows the Sittang. The long coast south of the Sittang, like that to the west of Arakan Yoma, is flanked by relatively little lowland. The short central coast is a deltaic plain, built by the large south-flowing rivers, and is the key to the lowlands where most of the people live. Remote from these lowlands in terms of cultural or political ties is northeastern Burma, the Shan States, which lie on the westward extension of the Yunnan Plateau. In these and other remote places are found the old Caucasoid inhabitants of Burma, pushed there by Mongoloids. In general, there is a transition in which cultures are progressively more and more advanced toward the lowlands. Racially the series ordinarily runs from most Caucasoid in the mountains to most Mongoloid on the rice-producing lowlands.

Lower Burma, chiefly the flood plains along the Irrawaddy and Sittang rivers, is relatively homogeneous, racially and linguistically. About 85 per cent of the people are Buddhists, and a slightly smaller proportion speaks Burmese or one of its variants, while English is taught as a second language. Burma is the most literate nation in southeastern Asia. Politically, educationally, and in terms of production and population, lower Burma is the heart of the country. Behind the fringe of mangrove swamps lie excellent rice-growing lands, developed almost wholly during the last century. The coming of cheap transportation made raising of a money crop possible and established lower Burma as one of the world's most important granaries. About 90 per cent of the flat land in the deltaic plain is planted to rice, which is a main export item. Most of the rice is raised by tenant farmers and by Tamil-speaking Indians brought in from Madras. Many of the Indians were sent home in the mid-thirties when the worldwide depression caused a serious drop in the price of exported rice, a situation which was locally blamed on the Indians, but which really was the natural result of extreme specialization in one crop, making the country completely subject to fluctuations in world markets.

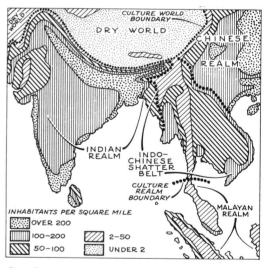

Southeastern Asia: culture boundaries and population density

Rangoon, 0.8 million, is capital and main commercial center, terminus of river steamers and all railroads, and the spout of a funnel through which most of the foreign trade must flow. Some petroleum arrives by a pipeline from Chauk, but most comes on barges, to be refined or exported as crude oil. Industries are concerned almost entirely with rice, lumber, especially teak, and petroleum. In addition to these, other exports are metal ores, hides and skins, tobacco, cotton, and vegetable oils. About half of the people and 70 per cent of the skilled laborers are Indians. Health conditions are poor, malaria is prevalent and so is tuberculosis.

Various towns up the Irrawaddy are known for their native crafts, such as wood and ivory carving, jewelry, bronze work, and lacquer wares. New "oil towns" around the fields contrast sharply with the primitive native villages. The main oil fields lie 100 to 150 miles southwest of Mandalay, the old capital and leading city of upper Burma. Its surroundings are much drier than those of Rangoon, and although some rice is raised, the chief food crops are beans, millets, and sesame. Tea, oranges, cotton, and tobacco are important cash crops, along with lac, tung oil, peanuts, and sugar cane. This diversity provides more economic stability than that experienced in lower Burma. Both Rangoon and Mandalay are important Buddhist centers. Spired sacred buildings, many of which suggest Chinese pagodas, give Burmese urban landscapes a distinctive, thoroughly Far-Eastern, look.

The Shan Plateau is inhabited largely by descendants of peoples driven from southern China during the last 20 centuries. The Shan, closely related to the Thais, engage in agriculture, have developed minor industries, and exploit the mineral resources. Silver, lead, zinc, and copper are abundant, as are gem minerals, such as rubies, sapphires, and lapis lazuli. North of the Shan States, the uplands are inhabited by Kachins and other non-Burmese peoples, who remain tucked away in isolated valleys separated by steep slopes. Monsoon jungle forest and shrub extend up to about 3,000 feet, above which are dense rain forests. The rain-drenched uplands rise above 10,000 feet. Millets, maize, and upland rice are raised by primitive methods. Elephant capturing and training is a specialty in the lower, more open forests.

The southern tail of Burma stretches some 500 miles south of Moulmein, port for rice and timber exports from the Salween Valley. To the south, Mergui exports coconuts, rubber, and locally mined tin and tungsten ores.

On the whole, the cultural landscapes of Burma are those of a young country and exhibit many pioneer characteristics. Only about a quarter of the cultivable land is planted, and even these lands could produce considerably more than they do. Population densities are low for the Oriental World. Lumbering, mining, petroleum exploitation, grazing, and hunting occupy a relatively large part of the population. Manufacturing has gone little farther than processing agricultural products, and native crafts are too unorganized to be classed as industry. Both rural and urban populations have increased rapidly in the last few decades, but the country could support many more people, particularly if agrarian reforms and better farming methods were adopted.

THAILAND

Thailand, the ancient and official name of the country long known as Siam, is essentially the drainage basin of the Menam, with a southern tail down the Malay Peninsula. Politically it has been a buffer state that neither the British nor the French cared to fight over. This constitutional monarchy covers an area of 200,000 square miles and has a population of 21 million, an average density of 105 per square mile. Included are about 600,000 Malays, largely in the southern provinces, and possibly 3 million Chinese, mainly in Bangkok and other cities.

The country is divisible into several parts, which differ in physical characteristics and peoples. Northern Thailand, a hilly region, is commonly known as western Laos. Its Laos-speaking population is strongly Mongoloid. Both Chiengmai and Nan are heads of navigation, the former being a center of caravan trade with Soviet Asia and western China, and the latter, a center for curing fish that are stranded when the river stage drops suddenly. From the forested hills come many valuable woods, including teak, rosewood, ebony, and boxwood, although the main stands are now fairly depleted. Crop raising is handicapped by leached soils and winter drought, but some upland rice is grown along with a diversity of other crops similar to those of upper Burma. Fowls and pigs contribute heavily in maintaining the population. Incomes are supplemented by mining.

Lamphun, sixth-century capital of the Laos and Thais, lies on the northern edge of the fertile central plains of the Menam, where two crops a year of rice, peanuts, tobacco, and other products are grown with the aid of extensive irrigation. It was a march site, a western outpost of the Laos and Thais as they spread southward from southern China, pushing ahead of them the Mon-Khmer-speakers who eventually sought refuge in the uplands and in Cambodia. By 1350 the Laos and Thais of the lowlands had been fused into a single group, the Thais, and had adapted the Khmer alphabet, based on ancient Sanskrit of India, to the Thai language, which also contains many Chinese forms. As invaders from hilly lands they brought no experience in raising lowland rice, but that crop now occupies over 90 per cent of lower Thailand's agricultural lowlands and furnishes the country with its chief export. About 80 per cent of the population is agricultural, and almost everyone fishes, although full-time fishermen account for only a small percentage of the population.

The lower Menam and delta are slowly getting rid of malaria and the threat of summer floods. Although roads are few, an excellent irrigation system of canals serves not only to irrigate and drain rice fields but as avenues of communication as well. Ayutthaya, capital of Thailand for over 400 years, has become an important railroad junction, with lines radiating to Chiengmai, northeastward to Laos, and south to Bangkok. With almost two million inhabitants, Bangkok is the one large city and only real port for international trade, serving Laos as well as Thailand. A walled, inner, brick city with the old royal palace and official buildings, is surrounded by an extensive, low, wooden native residential district, many of the houses resting on piles and along raft streets. Huge tonnages of rice, fish, teak and other lumber, rubber, coconut products, tobacco, pepper, and cotton move outward through the port past the incoming manufactured goods, machinery, chemicals, and the like. Bangkok is a political and commercial city, not an industrial center.

The long southern arm of Thailand reaches into purely Malayan territory. A railroad tends to bind it economically to Thailand, but the tie is weaker than the linguistic, ethnic, and trade ties with Malaya and Singapore. The narrow Kra Isthmus has potential value as a canal site which would shorten the sea distance from Calcutta to Hongkong by 600 miles. But its immediate value is in rubber production, accounting for a fifth of all exports, in timber and rice, and in tin, mined near Phuket. Tin is the only metal exported in quantity from Thailand, a fact largely responsible for the country's political hold in Malayan territory.

INDO-CHINA

Far less homogeneous than lower Burma, or even than Thailand, Indo-China consists of several contrasting parts, each of which is inhabited by a distinctive population. Cambodia is almost wholly a vast lowland that drains hesitantly into the lower Mekong, whose delta lies in a region known as Cochin China, the southern part of Viet Nam. To the north and northwest, a chain of mountains divides Laos on the western slopes from the Annam region on the slopes toward the South China Sea and Gulf of Tong King Tongking (Tonkin) region in North Viet Nam (Vietminh) centers along flood plains of the Hong Ha (Red) and Da (Black). Its heart is the deltaic plain.

The lowlands of Cochin China have an average temperature of about 80° F. and an annual rainfall of about 80 inches, with a summer maximum. The highlands are excessively wet, and toward the north they receive precipitation with both the southwestern and northeastern monsoons. The Mekong Valley of eastern Cambodia is somewhat drier and receives its rain during the southwest monsoon, April to October. The interior basins of Laos, in the rain shadow, are comparatively dry. Health conditions are ordinarily good where there is a dry season, and extremely poor where there is none.

The original agriculturists of Indo-China were Khmer and related Cham peoples, who possessed the lowlands. Angkor, deep in the deadly, steaming, and musty lowlands of Cambodia, was one of their ancient capitals and the site of magnificent temples, such as Angkor Vat. These earlier inhabitants were forced into uplands and remote places by invading Annamese, culturally similar to southern Chinese. Laos and Thais came in from southwest China, some remaining in Indo-China, others going on to Thailand. The modern immigrants are Chinese, totaling over a million, three fourths of whom are in Viet Nam. A variety of languages and dialects is spoken, Annamese being among the most popular, but communication is difficult, especially since French has been dropped as the official language.

After a number of fruitless attempts to gain a foothold in China proper, the French turned to Indo-China, occupied Cochin China, and made it a colony, with Saigon as the capital. Cambodia, Laos, Tonkin, and Annam were made protectorates. In 1941 Japan occupied all of Indo-China and used it as a base for southward aggressions. At the end of World War II, a shaky form of French control was resumed. In 1955 both Cambodia and Viet Nam broke with France and became independent. The northern section was relinquished to the communist-controlled Vietminh government. Laos is independent, but vaguely tied to the French Community.

Some 33.5 million people occupy Indo-China's 290,000 square miles, but the density varies from an average of 19 per square mile in Laos to over 600 in most rice-raising lowlands, and 1,800 in Tongking. About half of the cultivated land, some 10 per cent of the whole area, is planted to rice, and this important food crop could be greatly expanded to support considerably more people. Surpluses of rice are exported from all countries except Laos. More people could also be supported if transportation facilities were improved sufficiently to allow the exploitation of mineral resources, such as the iron ores of Cambodia. At present, Tongking exports tin, tungsten, zinc, silver-bearing lead, and iron ores, although all in considerably smaller amounts than the exports of coal which come from fields west of Along Bay. Practically all these Tongking exports go through Haiphong, which, although on the flood-ridden and rapidly alluviating Red River delta, is the main port for Vietminh. It has rail connections, through Hanoi, the capital, to tin-producing Yunnan and southern China, and southward along the coast to Saigon.

Laos is a rather poorly developed hinterland which might be served by Haiphong, but which actually looks south, floating its logs down the Mekong and sending its few meager products, including opium, out through Vientaine, the capital and main trading center at the head of the rail line from Bangkok. Cambodia is considerably more productive, for in addition to quantities of rice, cotton, silk, tobacco, oil seeds, and pepper are raised. Pnom Penh, the capital, is the center of the silk industry. To the north is Tonle Sap, a huge lake and curious inland center for fishing.

The mountains of Annam produce cattle, cinnamon, silk, tea, and various drugs, and spices. Sugar cane is important at lower elevations to the east, and much rice is raised along the coast, where fishing is the main non-agricultural occupation. In the invigorating climate of the southern parts of the mountains are several resorts, "hill stations," which serve the more prosperous residents of Saigon.

Saigon, 1.8 million, capital of Viet Nam, is the largest city in Indo-China. It is located to the left of the Mekong delta, where dike-protected fields produce surpluses of rice and quantities of sugar cane, bananas, tobacco, pepper, and sweet potatoes. North and east of Saigon, rubber is the important cash crop. The busy ports of Saigon and Cholon, important entrepots for Cambodia, have large Chinese populations, and a little industrial activity, mainly along the lines of preparing agricultural products for use and export.

It may be expected that control of such diseases as malaria, improved sanitation, reduction in death rates, and use of less primitive farming methods will lead to enormous population increases in Indo-China and lands west to Assam. It is likely that the Chinese will become the dominant lowland population, but the non-Chinese will certainly maintain themselves as cultural units. As the Indo-Chinese Shatter Belt gradually becomes incorporated into surrounding culture realms, probably three quarters will go to the Chinese Realm, and a small portion will become Indian Realm territory.

PACIFIC WORLD

Teoh
Nov. 21 '81

Atoll, Caroline Islands
[*official U.S. Navy photograph*]

22. *Pacific World*

The Pacific World, made up of the thousands of islands dotting the water hemisphere plus the island continent of Australia, falls into four major parts: Australia-New Zealand, Polynesia, Melanesia, and Micronesia. All have cultural roots in Southeast Asia, and all were unknown to civilization until the Age of Discovery. The encroachment of European culture met little resistance, for the island peoples had no militant religion such as Mohammedanism to fortify them, no strong political loyalties to native rulers or states to unify them, and an easy-going way of life that did not secure them from change. Throughout the Pacific World, the typical pattern of the New World Revolution was followed: discovery, exploitation, colonization, and then political domination by Europeans. In general, the New World Revolution is far from the end of its course in the Pacific World.

PHYSICAL BACKGROUND

Literally tens of thousands of islands are strewn across the huge Pacific, whose area of some 69 million square miles is equal to half the

363

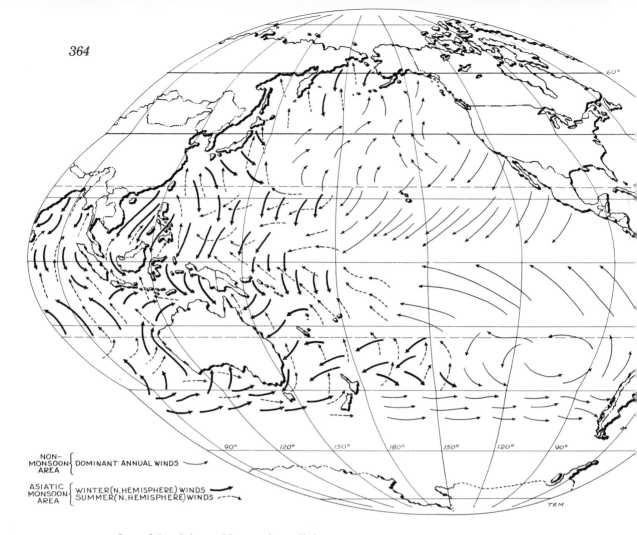

NON-MONSOON AREA { DOMINANT ANNUAL WINDS ——→

ASIATIC MONSOON AREA { WINTER(N.HEMISPHERE) WINDS ——→
SUMMER(N.HEMISPHERE) WINDS ---→

TRM

water surface of the globe and larger than all the land masses combined. Along the western side of the Pacific basin are trenches exceeding six miles in depth, the deepest places being in the Marianas Trench near Guam where soundings show a depth of 35,958 feet, more than a mile deeper than Everest is high. Rimming the whole Pacific are young, actively growing mountains. Many of these are volcanic, as are a considerable number of the Pacific islands. Most of the small islands are ancient volcanoes whose present shape is largely due to coral growth. The only active volcanoes among the eastern islands are those of the Tonga and Hawaiian islands. The western islands are generally larger and contain a number of active volcanoes. The largest of the western islands are really part of the Austral-Asian continent, and are products of diverse geological forces, such as folding, faulting, uplifting, and volcanic activity.

Warm clear waters and shallow depths around islands are ideal living conditions for many lime-secreting organisms. In clear ocean water that is not cooler than 68° F. and at depths less than 120 feet, both corals, with their rock-like skeletons, and algae that secrete cementing substances, thrive, and are responsible for the reefs that fringe many of the volcanic islands, and for the atolls. An *atoll* is a coral reef, with emerged or partly emerged islets, irregularly surrounding a shallow lagoon. The size and shape of the islets vary, but in general those on the windward side are most continuous, highest and widest. The outer beach is of coarse coral rubble, while the beach on the lagoon side is finer material. Navigable openings to the lagoon, if any, are on the leeward side of the ring. Maximum elevations are the summits of coral-sand dunes, rising a few feet above sea level.

Pacific Basin:
wind system

In a world that is predominantly water, such phenomena as ocean currents, water temperatures, tides, prevailing winds, and destructive storms take on special importance. Essentially, all the islands of the Pacific World except New Zealand and part of Australia lie within the tropics. Thus the general pattern of air circulation is toward the equator, the northeast and southeast trade winds blowing toward a central belt of calms, which seasonally shifts between 2° and 10° north of the geographical equator. The large land masses in the western Pacific upset the trade wind system. During northern hemisphere winter, air moving out from Asia brings "northwest trades" or monsoon winds to islands south of the equator. In northern summer the movement is reversed, reinforcing the southeast trades, which then extend far north of the equator. The western islands are also most subject to damaging typhoons. These and other

tropical storms originate between 8° and 15° both north and south of the equator, and move along an arcuate path, first westward and poleward, then eastward and poleward. Along the equator is a belt that is virtually free of destructive storms. Although typhoons are frequent in the western Pacific north of the equator, less ferocious storms can devastate the small atolls.

Less dramatic than tropical storms, but more persistent in their influences on life are the ocean currents. The gross pattern is two gigantic whirls, one in the north Pacific, one in the south. Waters move clockwise in a northern whirl and counter-clockwise in a southern whirl, so that along the equator of the currents, which like that of the winds lies north of the geographical equator, waters move eastward. Between these two eastward moving currents is a counter current, flowing toward the west. It has recently been discovered that below the eastward South Equatorial Current is a faster-moving westward current. All these currents are significant for the role they have played to aid or retard the diffusion of plants, animals, and man himself.

Vertical view, active volcano, Marianas Islands
[official U.S. Navy photograph]

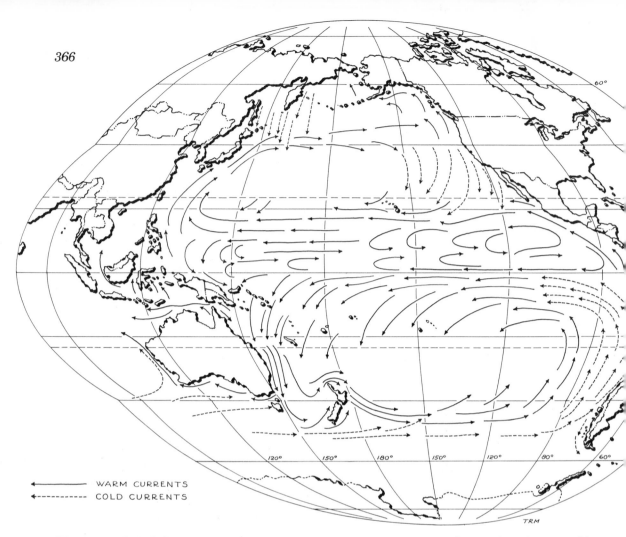

WARM CURRENTS
COLD CURRENTS

They have little influence on Pacific temperatures or precipitation, simply because they are warm currents in a region that is climatically warm, and so do not produce the abnormalities in weather, such as were described along the southwest coast of Africa.

Tides are important in sea-conditioned lands. Among the smaller Pacific islands the tidal range rarely exceeds 4 feet. In the larger continental islands the range is much greater, reaching over 40 feet in Australia. Even slight tidal range is significant on low islands. Ebb tide exposes shellfish and other edibles, and may make it possible to get to islets that are isolated during flood tide. High tide may provide the depth of water necessary to sail over a reef. While lunar tides have these useful aspects, tides and swells produced by strong winds, as those in some tropical storms, may wash completely over an atoll. Similar in effect are the

sea-waves accompanying earthquakes caused by displacements of the earth's crust on the floor of the sea. These, like the wind tides with typhoons, can be very destructive.

The climate of the Pacific World exhibits less than normal variations because low-latitude position and dominance of the sea make for a uniformity of atmospheric conditions. Only Australia has climatic variation on a continental scale. Its climate and that of New Zealand will be discussed later. Among the tropical islands local variations in climate reflect elevation, size, and direction of dominant winds. Temperatures are steady and relatively high, truly high temperatures being found only in interior or leeward places on the larger islands, as New Guinea. The growing season is year-round; cool weather relating to elevation rather than season. Because rainfall is a matter of exposure to prevailing winds, elevated, windward places are the most of them play an important part in aboriginal economy, and a considerable number of the so-called native plants and animals were actually carried to the islands by migrating peoples. The distinctions between native Asian and Australian plants and animals were noted in the middle nineteenth century by the English scientist, Wallace, who drew the famous Wallace's Line through Indonesia, to mark the separation of the two life zones. The faunal and floral differences were interpreted to mean a separation between the Asian and Australian continental masses at an early date in the history of life. West of the Line Asian mammals include the tiger, rhinoceros, wild buffalo, deer, and wild pig, while in New Guinea, for example, the only indigenous mammals are *marsupials* or pouched mammals, and the primitive *monotremes*, who both lay eggs and suckle their young. New Guinea's eucalyptus and nettle trees belong to the strange flora found east of the line. Surprisingly, however, the land mollusks of New Guinea are Asian species. Further study added refinements to Wallace's Line, for Sulawesi (Celebes) exhibited both Asian and Australian species, so Weber's and other "lines" have been drawn to indicate a rather broad transitional belt which may be called "Wallace's Zone."

Oceanic islands, that is, those never part of a continental land mass, occupy the greater area of the Pacific World, and their flora had to come from continental sources, whether through

Pacific Basin: ocean currents

rainiest. Near 5,000-foot Mt. Waialeale, Kauai, in the Hawaiian group, the annual rainfall is over 450 inches, while a leeward location just 15 miles southwest receives less than 20 inches. Similar contrasts are common on all the mountainous islands; for example, on New Guinea, Port Moresby annually receives an average of 40 inches while mountain peaks 75 miles away average close to 250 inches a year. Low coral islands or reefs may remain quite rainless, even though subject to constant winds, but commonly they receive precipitation benefits from convectional showers, frontal disturbances, and tropical storms. In general, the Pacific World has adequate to abundant precipitation, with considerable local range in amounts, and with no marked seasonal dominance.

Flora and fauna of the Pacific World have both academic and practical importance; many are different from those associated with Asia,

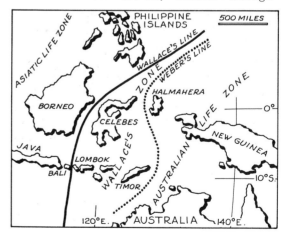

Contact of Asian and Australian life zones

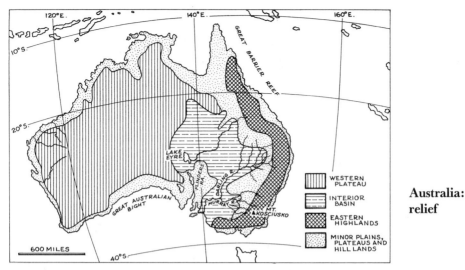

Australia: relief

natural or human agencies. Imperfect as knowledge is regarding the sequence and manner of spread of plants and animals to these islands, two generalizations seem safe: the number of species declines eastward; their sources, with exceptions for Hawaii and Easter Island, are New Guinea and the East Indies. And what a fine source region it is, with luxuriance and variety of plant growth, and abundant and varied fauna! Tropical rain forests dominate the lower elevations, fringed by the coconut palm and pandanus or screw pine along the beaches, mangrove at river mouths, brackish swamps of nipa palms, and fresher swamps of sago palms. Bamboo thickets spring up in forest clearings. Bananas grow wild in colonies on more open hillsides, along with orchids and ferns. The source area has a wide array of wild birds, mammals, reptiles, amphibians, and insects, but, more important, it provided domesticated animals that could be transported great distances in small boats: the dog, fowl, and pig. It is entirely possible that some small animals were carried to distant islands on rafts of debris, and certainly such natural agencies as wind, currents, and birds brought coconuts, pandanus fruit, and seeds to the oceanic islands. Storm winds could blow insects, land birds, and bats to these islands.

By the time that man entered the picture it is likely that the coconut and pandanus were already widely distributed, even to the low atolls unfit for most plant growth. The most distant volcanic islands appear to have had a luxuriant, if specifically limited, plant cover. In general, plants were spread by natural agencies far more widely than were animals, insects, and land birds. With man came additional plants and animals. Polynesians brought taro, yams, breadfruit, bananas, sugar cane, and possibly a sweet potato to the mid-Pacific islands. They intentionally introduced the dog, fowl, and pig, and accidentally brought along rats, mice, and lizards, who traveled as stowaways. To the pre-European list have been added many plants and animals. From America came papaya, guava, arrowroot, cassava, tobacco, and pineapple, to mention a few that now seem thoroughly "native."

Less confined in their movements are the sea birds. Albatrosses, petrels, and terns may be encountered anywhere in the Pacific. Snipes, sandpipers, and other shore birds nest on the northern margins of the basin and winter in the islands. While gulls always stay close to land, the golden plover regularly migrates in fall from its nesting places around Bering Sea to the Tuamotus in the South Pacific, and returns in the spring. It is believed that these regular mass flights guided the Polynesians on their journeys between Tahiti and Hawaii.

The tropical waters of the Pacific support a tremendous variety of life, even if the total amount is less than in colder waters. The fisheries are not commercial, but are very adequate sources of local food. Sea life is particularly abundant on the reefs and in the lagoons, where quantities of edible fish, snails, clams, squids, eels, crabs, crayfish, and oysterlike clams that carry gem pearls are found. Hovering around in search of an easy meal are predatory sharks and barracudas, and in the open sea are swift-moving fish, such as the tarpon. Both sea turtles and the eggs they deposit on beaches are welcome foods.

Australia, with its nearly 3 million square miles, may be considered the world's largest island or the least of the seven continents. It is large enough to have a continental variety of climates and a topography no simpler than that of Africa. The relief pattern suggests a huge platter, rimmed about the edge. The coast has a number of indentations that are useful harbors except along the shore of the Great Australian Bight, whose smooth outline results from abundant beach-forming sand. The western three quarters of the continent is a plateau, 600 to 1,500 feet high, with isolated ranges in the interior and along the western rim rising over

4,000 feet. The rocks are generally old, highly altered, and rich in gold and other minerals. East of the plateau is a low, interior basin, about half of which drains into salty, seasonally-dry Lake Eyre, while the southeastern half drains through Australia's only important river system, the Murray-Darling. The two parts of the basin are separated by Flinders Range, old rocks that are a source of copper. The sedimentary rocks of the northern part of the basin provide artesian water to a land climatically dry. Rimming the eastern margin of the continent is a thin band of mountains, low and broken in the north and higher in the south, culminating in Mt. Kosciusko, 7,328 feet, Australia's highest peak. The highlands have metalliferous sediments and coal measures.

The Great Barrier Reef, though hardly a physiographic region, is nevertheless an important feature, stretching along the east coast for some 1,250 miles north from latitude 24° S.

Australia: climates

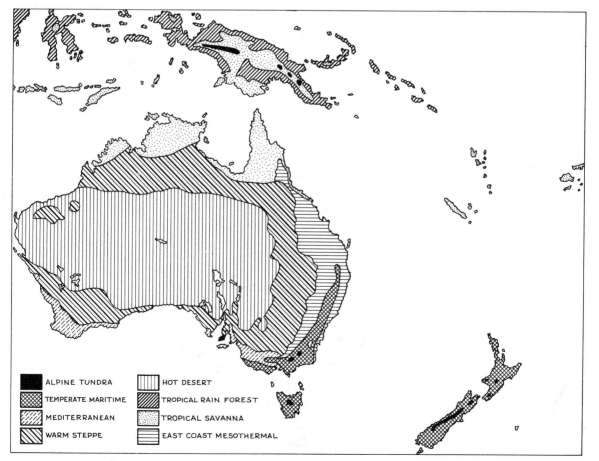

ALPINE TUNDRA		HOT DESERT	
TEMPERATE MARITIME		TROPICAL RAIN FOREST	
MEDITERRANEAN		TROPICAL SAVANNA	
WARM STEPPE		EAST COAST MESOTHERMAL	

The 35-mile-wide coral reef gives a measure of protection to the lagoon lying between it and the mainland. The deep, wide lagoon has long been used for coast-wise and deep-water shipping.

Australia's climatic variety is suggested by the range of annual precipitation, from over 80 to less than 6 inches; and annual temperatures, from 85° F. to less than 50°. Killing frosts are few, but permanent snow is found in highland Tasmania. The weather is affected by trade and westerly winds, the monsoon, and polar air from Antarctica. Although several kinds of climate occur, most of the continent has arid conditions, and is classed as steppe or desert. The eastern and northern margins are Australia's only humid regions. Between the million-square-mile interior desert and the humid and less-arid margins of the continent is a zone of transitional steppe.

Most of the Australian desert is reg, not unlike the vast gravel surfaces of the Sahara, with areas of hammada and erg, and numerous wadies. Xerophytic, or drought resistant, acacias are the dominant plants in the scanty vegetation cover. The sharp desert landscape gives way to softer profiles in the flanking steppe areas, the acacias, eucalypts, and salt bush yielding to a solid expanse of grass on the moister margins. Toward the wetter northern coasts, in the tropical savanna climate, woodland takes over from the grassland. The east coast of Cape York Peninsula receives sufficient rainfall to support true rain forest. Along the east coast is a broad band of Carolina-type or east coast mesothermal climate, with 30 to 60 inches of precipitation distributed throughout the year, mild winters, and warmer summers. The area contains a valuable temperate forest composed largely of species of eucalypt. The higher mountains in the southeast have a temperate maritime climate, with seasonal temperatures slightly lower than those of the east coast mesothermal climate, and 30 to 40 inches of precipitation without a pronounced dry season. Part of the area is humid grassland, but its temperate forest includes Australia's finest eucalypts. The two other humid regions, one east and one west of the Great Australian Bight, are Mediterranean in climate, with 15 to 40 inches of winter rain, moderate summers, and mild winters. The vegetation ranges from forest through woodland and grassland to maquis.

Australia's flora and fauna are characterized

Australia: vegetation

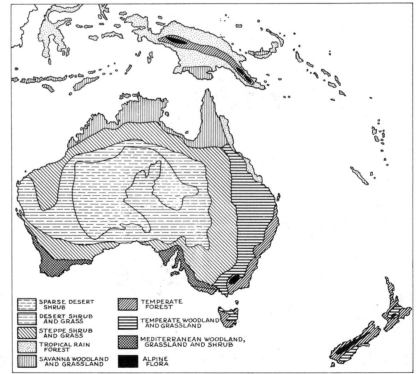

SPARSE DESERT SHRUB

DESERT SHRUB AND GRASS

STEPPE SHRUB AND GRASS

TROPICAL RAIN FOREST

SAVANNA WOODLAND AND GRASSLAND

TEMPERATE FOREST

TEMPERATE WOODLAND AND GRASSLAND

MEDITERRANEAN WOODLAND, GRASSLAND AND SHRUB

ALPINE FLORA

High volcanic islands, Truk group
[*official U.S. Navy photograph*]

by numerous species and few genera. The great bulk of Australia's trees are of but two genera, eucalypt and acacia, each represented by nearly 400 species. Similarly, marsupials and monotremes dominate the mammals, and most of them have names associated only with Australia: kangaroo, wallaby, duck-billed platypus, and spiny anteater. Birds are numerous and varied, particularly migratory waterfowl. Reptiles are represented by crocodiles, lizards, snakes, and turtles. The "wild" buffalo and wild dog or dingo were probably brought in by man, who may also be credited with some rather unfortunate importations, such as the prolific rabbit and the fast-spreading, useless prickly pear cactus.

Tasmania, with its 26,000 square miles, is a small, detached fragment of Australia. Structurally, climatically, and in other natural aspects it is a southward extension of the mainland from which it is separated by 150-mile-wide Bass Strait. Above its 4,000-foot central plateau rises Mt. Ossa, 5,309 feet, the highest peak on the island. Around the highlands are coastal lowlands, widest in the north. The uplands are cut by deep canyons, and their sharp crests and lakes are evidence of past glaciation. Waterpower and mineral resources are great. Tasmania's insularity gives it a remarkably even climate. Prevailing westerly winds reinforced by polar air bring rainfall of well over 100 inches to westward exposures, while lee locations receive as little as 18 inches. The wetter slopes are densely forested with gums, ferns, and beeches. Park landscapes are typical in the rain shadow.

New Zealand, with an area of over 103,000 square miles divided mainly between North and South Islands plus a few smaller ones, is quite distinct from Australia, which lies a thousand

miles to the west and north. On attenuated North Island, ranges occupy the center, active volcanoes are conspicuous to the west, and lowlands are most extensive on the long northern neck of the island. South Island is dominated by a long, regular range along the western two thirds of the island, which restricts the major lowlands to the east coast. A number of peaks are over a mile high; the tallest, Mt. Cook, reaches 12,349 feet. The still-active glaciation here is in striking contrast to the active volcanoes and thermal springs of North Island. Lakes, waterfalls, cirques, matterhorns, and even fiords on the southwest coast make for scenic grandeur but obstruct access to a variety of mineral deposits.

New Zealand is cool for the average of its latitude, having temperate maritime climate. Precipitation is well distributed seasonally, and

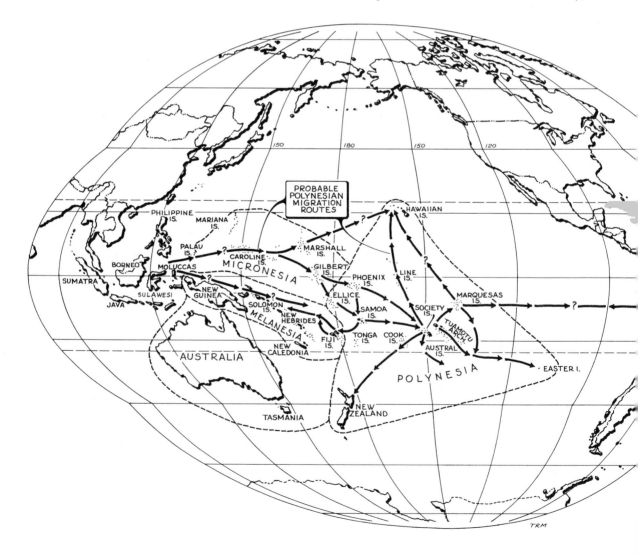

varies in amount from over 120 inches annually along the southwest coast to less than 30 inches in lee locations, but everywhere it is adequate. Dense forests are original cover on all but the higher or drier lands, and are composed mainly of indigenous plants, with some Asian conifers and South American hardwoods, but no common Australian trees. The fauna is rich in birds, many of them flightless varieties found nowhere else. Bats are native, but indigenous land mammals and snakes are lacking.

New Guinea, westernmost of the larger islands of the Pacific World, has an area of 316,860 square miles. Although most of the island lies within 10 degrees of the equator, the peaks of the central range that runs the length of the island are so high, well over 15,000 feet, they are permanently snow-clad. North of this range is a plateau, deeply cut by major streams, and be-

**Pacific World:
pre-European realms
and Polynesian migration**

[*routes after Weckler*]

Taro, Ponape
[*Trust Territory photograph*]

yond is a coast range with peaks reaching over 6,000 feet. The main lowlands are on the south side of the island. New Guinea's shape and location let it benefit from moisture-bringing southeast trades in winter and northwest and northeast winds in summer. Abundant precipitation, combined with an average annual temperature of over 80° F. for the lowlands, produces a hothouse climate, dense forests, and a lushness of life, very important in the diffusion of plants and animals to the oceanic islands lying to the east.

NATIVE PEOPLES

Just as many plants and animals spread from Asia eastward and southward through the islands, so did man. Asia's racial diversity is reflected in the Pacific World, where the three great races, Caucasoid, Negroid, and Mongoloid, and even far older peoples, are all represented among the pre-European inhabitants. This diversity is shown in the following table of racial composition of Pacific peoples:

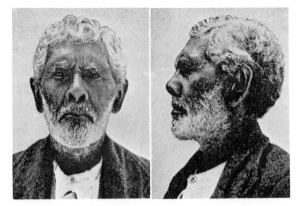

Australian aborigine

[*from E. A. Hooton,* Up from the Ape, © *1946,*
The Macmillan Company]

TABLE 8

Racial classification of the Pacific World

[*after Hooton*]

Primary Race: Negroid
　Primary Subrace
　　Negrito
Composite Race (predominantly Negroid): Melanesian-
　　Papuan
　Secondary Subraces
　　Papuan
　　Melanesian
Composite Race (predominantly Negroid): Tasmanian
Composite Race (predominantly White): Australian
Composite Race (predominantly White): Polynesian
Composite Race (predominantly Mongoloid): Indonesian-
　　Malay
　Secondary Subraces
　　Malay-Mongoloid
　　Indonesian

Negroid and predominantly Negroid peoples occupy Melanesia and the now extinct aborigines of Tasmania were of Negroid stock. The purest racially of the Oceanic Negroids, the Negritos, or Pygmies, are found only in interior New Guinea. They are similar to and possibly of the same origin as those of Malaya and central Africa. Papuans are distinguished from Melanesians partly because they are more Negroid, but mainly because they speak a variety of unrelated tongues, while Melanesians belong to the widespread Malayo-Polynesian linguistic family. Papuans are largely restricted to western and southeastern New Guinea. Melanesians, whose racial characteristics suggest Polynesian or Indonesian admixture, occupy the rest of New Guinea and the islands east to Fiji.

Caucasoid characteristics show up in the Australian aborigines who exhibit traits similar to those of the Ainu of Japan and the pre-Dravidians of Ceylon. Considerably more Caucasoid are the Polynesians, big, broad-headed people, with wavy hair and light-brown skins. They are primarily Caucasoid Mediterraneans, with some Mongoloid and Negroid admixture. They occupy the islands within the great triangle between Hawaii, Easter Island, and New Zealand. Their language, called Sawaiori or Mahori, belongs to the Malayo-Polynesian family.

Inhabitants of Micronesia do not constitute a distinct racial group, but tend to be like adjoining groups. In the east they are similar to Polynesians, in the south they show a Negroid strain, and in the west the Indonesian subrace is dominant. Throughout Micronesia, Malayo-Polynesian tongues are spoken.

Asia was a reservoir big enough to furnish the varied racial elements contributing to the primitive peopling of the Pacific World. First came the Negritos, occupying New Guinea and pushing south to Australia and Tasmania. Then came archaic Caucasoid Australians, some mixing with the Negritos of New Guinea to give rise to the Papuans, and others going to Australia to overwhelm racially its Negroid peoples. Much, much later, about

Australian aborigine hunting equipment

[*Australian News and Information Bureau*]

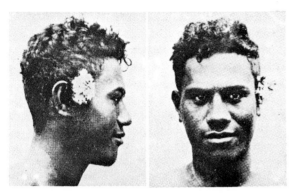

Polynesian
[*from E. A. Hooton,* Up from the Ape, © *1946,*
The Macmillan Company]

the time of Christ, Polynesians began sailing eastward from the East Indies. Their routes are a matter of debate, but whether they went through Micronesia or through Melanesia, by about A.D. 700 they had firmly established Tahiti as the center of the Polynesian region. From here colonists spread to every habitable island in Polynesia, reaching Hawaii probably in the middle of the thirteenth century, and New Zealand and Easter Island a century later. During this time, Micronesia and eastern Melanesia also were populated.

NATIVE CULTURES

Information on which to base descriptions of Pacific cultures prior to the time of the first contacts with Europeans in the sixteenth century is fragmentary and of varying reliability, being derived almost wholly from such records as were kept by early explorers. Using all possible evidence, including biologic, linguistic, cultural, and areal considerations, the major cultural divisions can be distinguished: Polynesia, Melanesia, Micronesia, and Australia.

Polynesia. Within the Polynesian triangle, as shown on the map on page 372, there are less than 125,000 square miles of land, and of this amount New Zealand accounts for over 100,000. An estimate of 1.1 million for the sixteenth-century native population allows an average density of 9 persons per square mile of land area, but the fact is that the population was quite unevenly distributed, being most dense on Hawaii, Samoa, the Societies, the Marquesas, and New Zealand. The Polynesians had visited and possibly lived on most of the habitable islands, deciding to abandon some, as in the case of the Phoenix group and Pitcairn, and never permanently occupying others, as Midway. In general through trial and error they found that their stone-age culture involving both fishing and agriculture fared better on volcanic islands than on coral atolls. Both might provide excellent fishing, but the higher volcanic islands supplied fresh water, good agricultural soils, stones for tools, useful wild plants, forage for pigs, and abundant wild fowl, all limited or lacking on atolls.

The favored sites of dwellings were in the valleys on volcanic islands, where water and arable land were available, and on lagoonal shores of atolls. Individual dwellings were dispersed or nucleated in strongly defended villages, depending on the nature of neighboring

Boat landing, Bounty Bay, Pitcairn Island
[*official U.S. Navy photograph*]

Stone images, Easter Island
[*official U.S. Navy photograph*]

covered with leaves and earth, to let the food steam for several hours.

The sea was as important as the land to the Polynesians who used traps, baskets, weirs, spears, nets, rods and lines, trolling, and poisons to take a variety of sea foods from the reef and open sea. Fishing meant boats, the family-size outrigger dugout and the built-up outrigger for use in the open sea. But neither of these approached in size or seaworthiness the vessels used for long inter-archipelago voyages. Some of these were 100 feet long and carried up to 60 passengers. The keel was hewn out of a single log, and the sides were built up with carefully fitted planks sewed fast with coconut fiber. A smaller boat of the same type served as the steadying outrigger. A platform between the two hulls, sheltered by a thatched housing, had ample space for sufficient supplies to last for several weeks. That such boats were built clearly indicates that the long voyages of Polynesians were intentional and not mere accidents.

On the margins of Polynesia there developed modifications of the central culture pattern. Lower temperatures and an abundance of wood encouraged the New Zealand Maori to build wooden houses, bring wood carving to a high art, substitute woven cloth for tapa from the missing tropical mulberry, dispense with outriggers on broad-beamed dugouts, and emphasize sweet potatoes rather than more tropical crops. In Easter Island the scarcity of wood permitted the Polynesians to work strikingly in stone.

Although many of the pre-European-contact ways of life are gone, and described here in the past tense, there are still a good many Poly-

peoples. Houses were expertly built thatched structures, oval shaped in western Polynesia and rectangular in the east. In central and eastern Polynesia there were built a few stone platforms and pyramids, used as altars, tombs, and temples. Near the houses were fields or patches of taro, yams, sweet potatoes, and sugar cane, and groves of coconut, banana, and breadfruit trees. Pigs were often fattened in pens, while dogs and fowls were free to forage. From wild or cultivated plants came kava root for making a ceremonial drink, mulberry bark to be pounded into tapa cloth, and various fibers for woven mats. Knives were of bamboo or of stone, as was the blade of a wood-working adze. Lacking pottery, cooking was done in an earth-oven, an excavation which was lined with hot rocks and filled with vegetables, meat, and fish, and

Main Street, Puka Puka, Tuamotu group
[*official U.S. Navy photograph*]

Micronesian outrigger canoe, Yap
[*Trust Territory photograph*]

nesians on more out-of-the-way islands who follow the old traditional culture patterns.

Micronesia, meaning small islands, is an apt term for the five major island chains lying west of Polynesia and north of Melanesia: Palaus, Marianas, Carolines, Marshalls, and Gilberts. The total land area is only some 1,200 square miles, with no great discrepancy in size among the islands, such as there is in Polynesia. An important distinction, however, is that between high volcanic islands and atolls. Micronesia is overwhelmingly composed of low coral islands, the only volcanic islands being Yap, Truk, Ponape, and Kusaie in the Carolines, and Guam in the Marianas. Simply because they are so numerous, it must be assumed that the coral islands held the bulk of the 100,000 or so Micronesians of the sixteenth century. Those who lived on the volcanic islands benefited from the abundant plant and bird life, and were able easily to grow taro, breadfruit, and other foods, as the rice found on Guam. There was leisure to construct great stone platforms and figures like those of Polynesia. Yap islanders imported large limestone disks of stone money from the Palaus.

A few atolls have sufficient soil to support a luxuriant vegetation, but most have a sparse plant cover. The coarse, easily dried-out soils made agriculture a really difficult task. Taro could be raised only by laboriously digging pits into which brackish water could filter to the growing plants. Only two trees grew fairly well, pandanus and coconut palm, the latter providing a wide variety of foods and materials. Drinking water came from the green nuts, thatching and mat and basket material from leaves, cordage and thread from husk fiber, meat and oil from ripe nuts, intoxicating drink from fermented flower-stalk sap, and from the trunk, planks for boats and timber for houses. The pandanus was also fully utilized; the fruit was eaten, the pounded seeds provided flour for long sea voyages, and the leaves were used for thatch and fiber. Versatile as the use of these trees was, they and the resources of atolls provided only a very limited number of material things. Skillfully woven fiber cloth had to take the place of tapa cloth because there were no mulberries. No clay meant no pottery. Scanty food supply meant few or no domesticated animals. Lacking volcanic rock, all tools, weapons, and utensils had to be fashioned from shell and wood.

Micronesian houses were thatched, but differed from those in Polynesia in that they were always built on platforms of stone or wood, were rectangular, with high, steep gables, and had a roof that dipped almost to the ground. The little villages stretched along lagoonal beaches, a sensible location in view of the fact that fishing was the most important economic activity. Fishing methods and catch, boats, and seamanship were similar to those in Polynesia. Long voyages were undertaken, sometimes with the aid of crude maps made from the midribs of palms.

The atoll was a poor setting for a primitive self-contained economy. It is a tribute to the industry and resourcefulness of the Micronesian that he got along as well as he did. It is not sur-

ticularly heavy toll, nor has the population recovered to the extent that it has in Polynesia and Micronesia. The trend of decline ties in with the fact that culturally the Melanesians are far less changed than the other two groups. Even today there are stone-age people living in New Guinea.

The dominant island of Melanesia, New Guinea, is sufficiently large and well-endowed by nature, and has been exposed to outside culture influences long enough for three main cultures to develop. These cultures are similar in

**Village
on coral island,
Caroline Islands**
[*official U.S. Navy photograph*]

prising that he accepted eagerly the devices of civilization that were adaptable to his habitat.

Melanesia, "black islands," has a total land area of about 400,000 square miles, of which New Guinea constitutes over 300,000. The remainder is unequally divided among the islands of the Bismarck Archipelago, the Solomons, Fijis, New Hebrides, and New Caledonia. They are largely high, volcanic islands, some of the volcanoes being active. The population density was much greater than in the other two island groups, estimates for the sixteenth century being some 3 million. Introduced diseases took a par-

distribution to the three major groups of people: Pygmy (Negrito), Papuan, and Melanesian. Pygmies, living in isolation in the central mountain chain, have a culture that is completely stone age in character. They are hunters, trappers, and collectors of all kinds of animal life. They lack pottery, use the earth-oven, and practice a shifting agriculture, planting bananas, sugar cane, taro, and sweet potatoes in clearings that must be changed every two or three years. In their small villages, their widely spaced houses are walled with split slabs of wood and roofed with thatch.

**Thatched house,
Marquesas**
[*official U.S. Navy photograph*]

**Earth oven,
Marquesas**
[*official U.S. Navy photograph*]

**Outrigger canoes,
French Oceania**
[*official U.S. Navy photograph*]

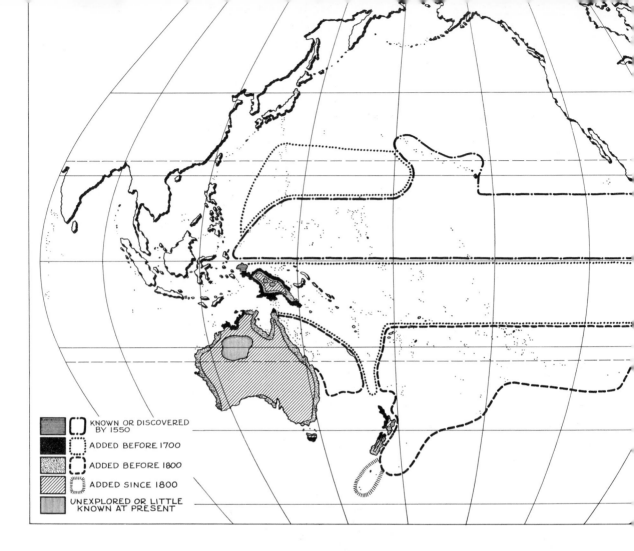

KNOWN OR DISCOVERED BY 1550

ADDED BEFORE 1700

ADDED BEFORE 1800

ADDED SINCE 1800

UNEXPLORED OR LITTLE KNOWN AT PRESENT

The Papuans (Malay for "wooly hair") adjoin the Pygmies in interior New Guinea and also occupy the whole western part of the island and the south coast. They too live in the stone age and lack pottery. They hunt and fish, those on the south coast being skilled boat-builders and seamen, and carry on a limited cultivation of bananas, sweet potatoes, taro, and sugar cane. The coconut and sago palm supplement the diets of coastal and lowland dwellers. A number of tribes regard human flesh as the choicest of all meats. Houses vary in shape and size, but walls and roofs are generally of palm leaves, matting, or bark, and floors are packed earth, or of wood when the house is built on piles.

The culturally distinct Melanesians reached New Guinea from the north and east at a comparatively late date, occupied the northern and eastern coasts, and pushed on to the lesser islands. From them the primitive inhabitants of New Guinea got the bow and arrow, domesticated pig, betel-nut chewing, and seagoing boats. Melanesians were a seafaring people, ardent traders, and fishermen. In other respects too, Melanesian culture parallels that of Micronesians and Polynesians. But there were differences; Melanesians were expert wood carvers, had pottery, did loom weaving, and in New Caledonia used bamboo pipes to irrigate terraced garden plots. Their houses resembled the thatched rectangular ones in Micronesia and western Polynesia, except for the round, bee-

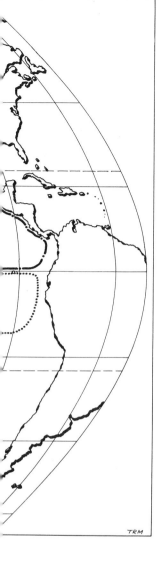

**Pacific World:
European exploration**

but skillfully made. They had a great fund of practical knowledge that enabled them to track animals, locate water holes, and find edible plants and insects. A surplus of food meant gorging, for there was little effort to store against future need, so life was a sequence of feast and famine. Being nomadic, their houses were just crude windbreaks. Even in cold weather the naked aborigine preferred to sleep on the open ground between fires.

Today the native Australians number about 80,000, including many half-castes who live like Europeans. Although enormous areas are inhabited exclusively by natives, their numbers are dwindling.

Tasmania was inhabited by a culturally distinct and very primitive people. They lacked agriculture, pottery, domesticated animals, true clothing, the fishhook, boomerang, bow, and spear thrower. Their chief weapon was simply a sharpened pole. They also made a combined club and throwing stick of wood, baskets, and string nets. The 2,000 pre-white inhabitants were divided into a number of tribes, each with a defined territory. For these hunters and collectors no form of animal life, dead or alive, large or small, was too repulsive to be eaten. Like the Australians, the Tasmanians never stored surplus food, and their dwellings were mere wind breaks. They moved from inland summer locations to the seashore in winter, and though they were familiar with the sea, they were never boat-builders, using only bundles of bark for rafts. The last survivor of these primitive people died in 1876.

NEW WORLD REVOLUTION

The search for a better route to the Indies and for riches brought Spanish, Portuguese, Dutch, English, and French explorers to the Pacific World. First came Magellan, who in 1521 stopped at Guam on his voyage westward to the Philippines and who opened the route used for 200 years by galleons between the Philippines and Mexico, bring the Spanish in touch with the main islands of Micronesia. Other discoveries by Spanish and Portuguese soon followed: New Guinea, the Hawaiian Islands, Ellice Island, the Solomons, Marquesas, Tuamotus, and New

hive-like dwellings of New Caledonia, the large communal houses of New Britain, and pile dwellings built over the sea found elsewhere.

Australia, when the Europeans arrived, had some 300,000 aborigines, but these were split into 500 tribes with languages so different that signs were used for communication. Although there was some variation in attainment, in general the culture was so primitive that it lacked agriculture, domesticated animals, clothing worthy of the name, pottery, and the bow and arrow. The native peoples were hunters and collectors, who fished when they had an opportunity. They were nomadic in that they moved when necessary to secure food. Their tools, weapons, and utensils were few in variety,

Hebrides. About the middle of the seventeenth century Dutch navigators, already familiar with the western coast of Australia, ventured to within sight of Tasmania and New Zealand, and sailed on to Tonga. Later they discovered Easter Island and western Samoa, and still later, the French reached Tahiti, Samoa, and the New Hebrides. The Englishman, James Cook, greatest of the early scientific explorers, reached Tahiti in 1769, sailed around New Zealand, demonstrating it was not part of Australia, landed at Botany Bay on the east coast of Australia, then sailed through Torres Strait. In 1774 he added New Caledonia to the list of known islands, and rediscovered Hawaii in 1778. With Cook's passing the great discoveries were over, and the Pacific World was easily accessible to Europeans of quite different character.

The New World Revolution followed the same sequence in the Pacific World as in Africa and the Americas. The Pacific World, however, did not offer the prizes found in Africa and the Americas. It lacked ready wealth to satisfy early exploiters, and missionaries were handicapped because the natives were so dispersed, although in time they managed to convert virtually all Polynesians and Micronesians at least nominally to Christianity. Traders fared better, profiting from such items as tortoise shells, pearls, sandalwood, trepang, and later, coconuts and copra. Agriculture for profit began early on Guam and spread widely to other islands, sugar, coconuts, tropical fruits, cattle, and even cotton becoming important commercial crops. The search for minerals was finally rewarded by finds of gold in Australia and New Guinea, and chromite and nickel on New Caledonia.

The European impact, in the early phases of the New World Revolution in the Pacific, was important to the extent that it changed economic practices and determined vital trends. New needs were created, as for the steel axes, guns, cloth, tobacco, mirrors, and glass beads introduced by traders, and European-type clothing approved of by missionaries. Horses, cattle, and other domesticated animals were widely introduced, as were many useful and weed plants. The native was forced to change from a subsistence to a commercial economy if he wished a share of the new goods. Many had to learn a pidgin language to enter the world of trade. The vitality of the native population, as usual, declined, for they had no immunity to the introduced diseases, such as smallpox, cholera, tuberculosis, dysentery, influenza, or even the common cold. Many were killed in bloody conflicts with Europeans, and thousands, particularly Solomon Islanders, were kidnapped into virtual slavery to work on the guano islands off Peru, in the cotton fields in the Fijis, or on the sugar plantations in Australia. It is estimated that by 1900 the original 1.1 million Polynesians had been reduced to 180,000; Hawaiians, specifically, from 200,000 to 40,000. The Tasmanians were exterminated, and the Australians declined to a fraction of their former numbers. The 1 million Melanesians are about a third of their original figure. While for Micronesia and Polynesia there is now a general increase among the native peoples, new racial mixtures are emerging.

The next stage in the New World Revolution, European political domination, followed the usual patterns. Discovery, seizure, purchase, treaty, war, and colonization all have contributed to make the complex political map of the Pacific World. While Spain's claim to Micronesia dated back to the seventeenth century, the major parceling of the islands among European powers took place during the nineteenth century, much of it contemporary with the final partition of Africa. In this grand shuffling of islands, some were occupied, others were "protected," many were bought and sold, and a good number changed political hands in other ways. Micronesian ownership offers an illustration of the general practice. With the exception of the Gilberts, all island groups were discovered and held by Spain until 1898. Then Guam was ceded to the United States and the remaining islands sold to Germany. Following World War I the German-owned section was made a mandated territory of Japan. After World War II these islands, the Territory of the Pacific Islands, became a United Nations trust, administered by the United States.

The present distribution of political controls

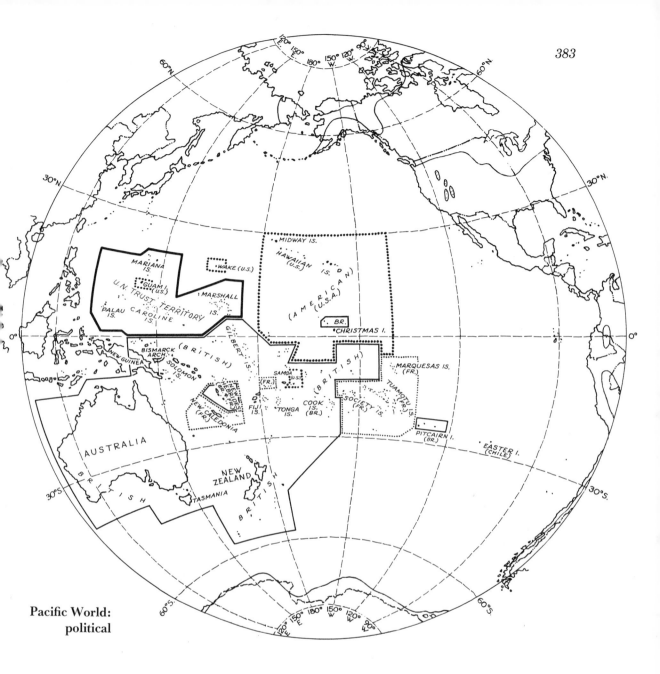

Pacific World:
political

follows no regular pattern. Areally the British are far in the lead, but the areas shown as British on the map are actually split among the United Kingdom, Australia, and New Zealand. France is well represented across the South Pacific, and the United States has most of the North Pacific, including the state of Hawaii, and strategically important Wake and Guam. Another American nation, Chile, owns lonely Easter Island. It should be noted that for Aus-tralia and New Zealand, the New World Revolution is in its final phase, for they are both independent and self-governing, voluntary members of the Commonwealth of Nations.

European colonization proved one of the surest ways of gaining and holding political control. Starting late in the eighteenth century and continuing through most of the nineteenth century, Europeans came or were brought as convicts to the islands. Today there are two

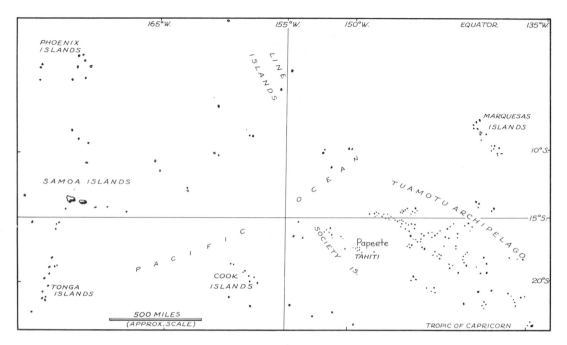

Southern Polynesian: index map

"white" countries in the Pacific World: Australia and New Zealand. In Australia, Europeans number 9.9 million and natives and half-castes about 80,000; in New Zealand, 2.1 million, and 150,000. Nowhere else are Europeans in the majority, although in New Caledonia they number 24,900 as compared with 36,700 native Melanesians; in Samoa, 6,000 to 116,000 Polynesians; in the Societies, 14,000 to 40,000; and in Hawaii, Europeans comprise about one quarter of the 640,000 population. These are all the places where Europeans are numerically important. In addition to natives and Europeans, there are a number of other peoples in the Pacific World: Filipinos, Indonesians, Indo-Chinese, Japanese, Koreans, and everywhere, the Chinese traders.

The New World Revolution has brought profound changes in the population composition of the Pacific World. It seems certain that, with the exception of Australia and New Zealand, the future lies with people of non-Caucasian stock, but it is equally clear that the cultural pattern will be that designed in Europe.

MODERN LANDSCAPES

On the dual basis of the character of surviving aboriginal cultures and the degree of change caused by the New World Revolution, the Pacific World may be divided into four modern realms: Polynesia, excluding New Zealand; Micronesia; Melanesia; and Australia and New Zealand.

Modern Polynesia. Of the six large groups of Polynesian islands, only one, the Hawaiian Islands, lies north of the equator. The southern islands are least changed culturally and racially. The land remains mainly in Polynesian hands, and the economy is largely subsistence farming and fishing. Copra is the main export, and imports are few. Possibly least changed are the hurricane-swept Tuamotu atolls, occupied by some 8,000 Polynesians and a few Chinese traders and French administrators. Pearls and pearl shells are the primary contribution to commerce. The volcanic Marquesas support about 4,000 natives who produce small surpluses of sugar, cotton, and copra. The Samoa and Tonga islands have over 180,000 inhabitants, almost entirely Polynesians. Copra and bananas are important exports, but as in the other southern islands, the main activities are the cultivation of home-consumed crops and fishing. Somewhat more commercialized are the Society Islands, especially Tahiti. Its chief town, Papeete, is administrative headquarters for the

77,000 people in French Polynesia, and processing and export center for copra, sugar, phosphates, and pearl shells.

The Hawaiian Islands are very different from the southern groups. They contribute 6,400 square miles of land to the 11,000 total for Polynesia, and contain two thirds of the total of 930,000 inhabitants, but unmixed Polynesians account for only 12,000 of the new state's total population of 640,000, almost 80 per cent of which is on Oahu. Less than one quarter of the population is Caucasian. The fact that over one third are Japanese, and that among the remainder are numerous Chinese, Filipinos, and other Asians, is a result of the importation of plantation labor necessary because Polynesians took unkindly to the drudgery of regular work. Highly commercialized and mechanized plantations produce tremendous amounts of sugar and pineapples, which provide 85 per cent of the agricultural income. Manufacturing is largely a matter of agricultural processing, plus the production of a few items needed on plantations and articles to sell to tourists and the Armed Forces, the latter numbering 10 per cent of the population. Tourism and military personnel lead all other sources of income for the state. Honolulu, commerical and tourist center, is a hustling city of over 300,000. The predominant modern attributes of the Hawaiian Islands lift them out of the Polynesian realm to the south,

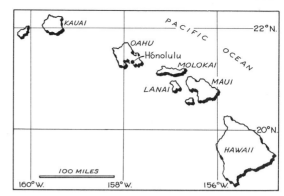

Hawaiian Islands: index map

and place them in the New World of Australia, New Zealand, and mainland United States.

Modern Micronesia. Between World Wars I and II Micronesia felt the influx of large numbers of Japanese, concerned almost wholly with construction of military bases. After the latter war, which while expelling the Japanese brought heavy destruction to so many islands, the natives slowly reestablished their old economy, subsistence farming and fishing. Among the 45,000 inhabitants of the Gilberts and Marshalls, the 40,000 Carolinians, and the 7,000 inhabitants of the Marianas (excluding Guam) there is little commercial production beyond a few trade items. Exceptions to this general picture are few but important. Eniwetok and Bikini have been cleared of natives so the atolls can be used for testing atomic bombs. Quite different are Nauru and Ocean, little islands that are important centers of phosphate production, and that number among their 7,000 population more than 500 Europeans and 800 Asians, mainly Chinese. Guam is not only the largest of the Marianas Islands, with an area about equal to all the rest combined, but its population of 38,500 is five times that of all the other Marianas. In addition, there are some 20,000 nonresidents, Armed Forces and their families. It is also the most productive, with exports of coconuts, sugar, rice, coffee, cacao, and other crops. Nearly half the island's population lives in Agana, a leading city of Oceania, and an interesting mixture of old and modern, Spanish and native architecture.

Micronesian house, Yap
[*Trust Territory photograph*]

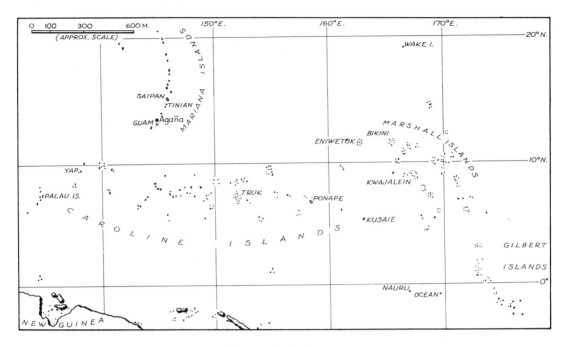

Micronesia: index map

Modern Melanesia. The population composition of Melanesia grades from being most mixed in the east to most pure in the west, and, of course, the degree of commercial development follows the same gradation. Less than half of the 361,000 inhabitants of the Fijis are natives, and they prefer subsistence agriculture and fishing to work on the plantations, which produce exportable amounts of sugar and copra. The 16,000 Europeans and part-Europeans direct the plantations and the manganese and gold mines, and the workers are mainly drawn from the 180,000 Indians. Of the 38,000 people in the main city, Suva, about 4,000 are Europeans. About half of the 73,000 people on mountainous New Caledonia are Melanesians, but they take little part in the important chrome, iron, nickel, and manganese mining, and in commercial agriculture. Noumea has more than 15,000 Europeans among its 23,000 inhabitants. The 80 high islands making up the 5,700 square miles of the New Hebrides are inhabited by 50,000 Melanesians and some 4,500 Europeans and Asians, the non-natives being responsible for the plantation production of copra, cacao, and coffee. Toward the west, even fewer non-natives are found; fewer than 2,000 among the 165,000 Solomon Islanders, and

about 5,400 among the 150,000 inhabitants of the Bismarck Archipelago and Admiralty Islands. On these large, mountainous islands, plantations, restricted to the coasts, produce enormous quantities of copra and coconut products. New Guinea is the far end of Melanesia, geographically and culturally. Administration is divided between the Netherlands and Australia, but among the 2.3 million population, only the tiniest fraction is European. Coastal plantations produce coconuts and copra, rubber, hemp, cacao, and coffee, and

Cacao harvest, Ponape
[*Trust Territory photograph*]

petroleum is exported from the eastern part of the island, while much of the interior remains a stronghold of stone-age culture.

Australia and New Zealand. In these two countries the New World Revolution is virtually complete, aboriginal peoples and cultures are reduced to insignificance, the population is overwhelmingly Caucasoid, and commerce, industry, and urbanization are well advanced. Development to the present status was slow in starting and progressed in irregular spurts, mainly because of the remoteness of these lands from the British center of Empire. British North America had been colonized for 200 years and an independent United States born before any European settlement was made in Australia, and that settlement, because of remoteness, was a penal colony.

Australia. During the first half of the nineteenth century several centers were founded,

Perth, Melbourne, and Adelaide, but expansion of settled areas was slow and uncertain. The well-watered coastal areas were occupied first, and only gradually did sheepherders and adventurous farmers move toward the ever drier interior. It was not until near the end of the century that all the usable pastures around the edges of the deserts were being nibbled by sheep, and wool production was then at its zenith. Meanwhile, other changes were taking place: coal was being mined at Newcastle, dry farming was proving a successful way of raising wheat and other grains in the steppe plains, sugar cane was introduced in coastal Queensland, wells were being drilled in the great artesian basin of south interior Queensland and adjacent states, doubling its stock-carrying capacity, and irrigation was initiated in the Murray River Valley, eventually to produce cereals, alfalfa, fruit, and vegetables.

The growth of population, overwhelmingly of British stock, to its present size of 10 million,

Australian and Melanesian realms: index map

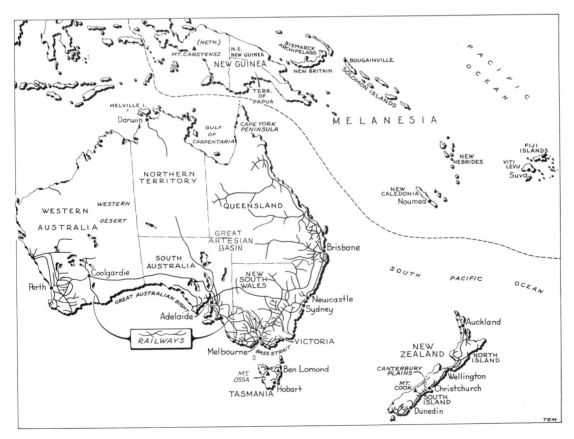

was largely sporadic, waves of immigrants coming in response to sudden increases in economic opportunities, such as the 1840 land boom based on the prosperity of the wool producers, the 1851 discoveries of gold west of Sydney and in central Victoria, the mining boom in the eighteen-seventies in Queensland, railroad expansions, and discovery of tin and gold in Tasmania. The big gold strikes in Western Australia, which marked the opening of the rich Coolgardie deposits, brought many hopeful immigrants. Well over a million have arrived since World War II.

The distribution of population is striking. Outside the eastern and southern marginal humid strips the country is extremely sparsely populated, as few as 4 per 100 square miles in Northern Territory, in contrast to over 3,000 in Victoria. This clustering of the population on coastal and near-coastal lands is largely a matter of climate. It is estimated of the total continent that 21 per cent is temperate crop land, 3 per cent tropical crop land, 26 per cent

Silver-lead-zinc-copper mine, Mt. Isa, Queensland

[*Australian News and Information Bureau*]

good pastoral land, 27 per cent fair to poor pastoral land, and 23 per cent desert. Where the good lands are, so are the people. Equally striking is the fact that almost 80 per cent of the population is urban, and that half of the population lives in the six state capitals: Sydney, 2.0 million; Melbourne, 1.7; Adelaide, 0.59; Brisbane, 0.54; Perth, 0.38; and Hobart, 0.1. The country's capital, Canberra, ranks very low, with only about 40,000 inhabitants. Each major

Australia and New Zealand: population density

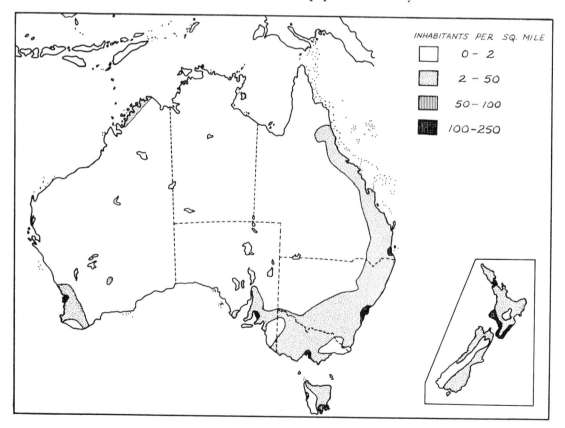

INHABITANTS PER SQ. MILE

- 0 - 2
- 2 - 50
- 50 - 100
- 100 - 250

city has a productive hinterland. The southwest region around Perth produces wheat, oats, apples, vegetables, and grapes, some with the aid of irrigation, while the back country supplies sheep, gold, coal, silver, and other ores. From the South Australia hinterland around increasingly-industrialized Adelaide, come wheat, barley, oats, hay, grapes, cattle, and, of course, sheep. Melbourne's surroundings are even more productive and varied, including fine wheat lands, excellent pastures for beef and dairy cattle, and the irrigated Murray Basin, which produces grapes, vegetables, and other crops. Tributary to Melbourne is Hobart's hinterland, Tasmania, which specializes in apples and hops, and also supplies other fruits and vegetables, wool, copper, zinc, and timber. Sydney and its heavy-industry partner, Newcastle, are about at the dividing point between temperate and subtropical crop zones in New South Wales, noted as a producer of minerals, wheat, cattle, dairy products, and timber. Potatoes and deciduous fruits are produced to the south, and rice, sugar cane, and bananas appear to the north. Queensland also produces cattle and wheat, and along the coast north of Brisbane sugar cane is the main crop, with lesser plantings of pineapples, bananas, and cotton.

The clustered pattern of population is paralleled by that of transportation facilities. The tightest network of roads and railroads is in the southeast. Queensland is tied into the system by a coastal road and a mid-state highway. From Darwin through sparsely populated Northern Territory to Adelaide is a highway-railroad connection, but in the Territory, as in Western Australia, the best way to get around is by plane. The transportation network in the southeast is connected to the lesser one around Perth by a single railroad. The use of the railroad system is greatly handicapped because there are three different gauges, but plans are underway for standardization.

Australia's high degree of urbanization lacks a reasonable explanation, except possibly in the nature of the immigrants who, coming from

Parliament House, Canberra
[*Australian News and Information Bureau*]

industrialized, urbanized Western Europe, found the isolation of rural life too appalling. Highly urbanized countries are generally highly industrialized, entering world trade with manufactures. While it is true that the value of Australia's manufactures is equal to that of all its other products combined, and more than twice that of pastoral and dairy production, all the iron and steel, metals, machinery, automobiles, aircraft, and other similar products of industry are for local markets. Australia's exports are headed by wool, and range through wheat, meats, butter, hides, and other pastoral and agricultural products. Processing raw materials for export obviously supports some industry, but neither this nor manufacturing for home markets is sufficiently great to explain urbanization.

New Zealand. While New Zealand belongs in the same realm of the Pacific World as Australia because of its similar cultural heritage and present development, it is distinct, not only by being a thousand miles from the larger land to the west, but also by virtue of the fact that its mild, humid marine climate, active volcanoes, and high, glaciated mountains bear little natural resemblance to Australia. Politically, it is an independent member of the British Commonwealth.

New Zealand broke into the commercial

Shearing sheep, New South Wales
[*Australian News and Information Bureau*]

world when sealers, traders, and whalers began to frequent its waters and coasts in the late eighteenth century, but it was not until 1840, after France had shown an interest in the islands, that the British formally annexed them and made the first settlement, at Wellington. Additional colonies were soon established. In contrast to early colonization of Australia by convicts, two of the first three New Zealand settlements were church-sponsored. Arriving colonists preferred North Island, which the native Maori also favored, so a series of bloody wars ensued. The Maori were all but obliterated, but today they number over 147,000 in New Zealand's 2.3 million total population.

The early settlers brought English grains, sheep, and cattle, and were soon exporting wool and wheat. Toward the end of the nineteenth century, when competition for world markets for these items became too great for New Zealand, it switched to the export of frozen meats. In the twentieth century, New Zealand has also become an exporter of dairy products. As there are no unoccupied farm lands, the lowland landscapes are pastoral. The rural landscape is strikingly English, with trees and grasses imported from the British Isles, European breeds of sheep and cattle, and English-type houses. Well-tilled fields produce mainly feed for stock. There are apple orchards and vegetable gardens, but largely for home consumption.

New Zealand's economy is almost entirely agricultural and pastoral. Mining is unimportant. Although some coal is mined on South Island, power needs are most easily satisfied by the high hydroelectric potential of the island. Industry is mainly concerned with processing, packing, and shipping dairy and pastoral products. Such manufacturing as exists is devoted to making farm implements, clothing, and other locally used items. Yet, over half the population is urban. Auckland, in the midst of the nation's most productive agricultural district, is the largest city, with over 400,000 inhabitants. Christchurch with half that number is next largest. Wellington, the capital, has more than 140,000. A dozen other cities have populations in excess of 20,000.

AMERICAN WORLD

Sierran landscape, Mt. Whitney
[*U.S.D.A.*]

23. *Physical and Cultural Background*

Just as southern Africa, Australia, and New Zealand are deeply involved in the New World Revolution, so is the American World. In fact, the term New World is most commonly associated with the Americas, although it as surely encompasses these other areas as well. Many New World characteristics are displayed in the American World. For one thing, native cultures have been all but extinguished. During the past 400 years, arriving Europeans, steeped in their own cultures, have almost entirely submerged the aboriginal inhabitants of the American World, absorbing them or pushing them aside. Another characteristic is the general attitude that natural resources are endlessly exploitable, an attitude that only recently has been modified, and then only in certain areas. Throughout the period of the expansion of European settlement, and to a discouraging and dangerous degree even today, soils, forests, wildlife, and minerals have been used with lavish waste. Part of this attitude is based on the fact that there remain areas in the American World that are sparsely populated, so there is little pressure for careful,

393

POLAR WORLD

ANGLO-AMERICAN
REALM

REGIONS:
1 – Northern forest
2 – Alaska
3 – Eastern maritime
4 – St. Lawrence Valley
5 – Central manufacturing
6 – Coastal Plains
7 – Piedmont
8 – Appalachians
9 – Prairie Plains
10 – Ozark-Ouachita
11 – Great Plains
12 – Rocky Mountains
13 – Plateaus
14 – Pacific Northwest
15 – California

60°N.

30°N.

0°

30°S.

LATIN–AMERICAN
REALM

REGIONS:
1 – Mexico
2 – Central America
3 – West Indies
4 – Northern South America
5 – Central South America
6 – Southern South America
7 – Brazil

90°W.   60°W.   30°W.   TRM

conservative use of the resources. These and other evidences of the course of the New World Revolution are found in differing degrees throughout the vast American World.

Progress along the course of the New World Revolution also varies widely from country to country within the American World. Essentially, all parts are independent and politically sovereign, there being only a few remnants of European empires left in the American World. Since this is one of the criteria indicative of the culmination of the Revolution, much of the American World appears to be approaching the end, and the course has been run in the United States and Canada. But on the basis of other criteria, such as economic and political stability, and full participation in world affairs, a number of Latin American countries must be judged as still being involved in the New World Revolution, albeit in possibly the terminal phases.

Although it is customary and reasonable to consider North and South America as two separate continents, the truth is that they are parts of a single, continuous land mass that stretches some 9,000 miles from 72° N. to 54° S. The widest parts of both North and South America exceed 3,000 miles, and the narrowest place is the Isthmus of Panama, where its 30-mile width and favorable natural conditions made possible an artificial severance of the northern and southern parts of the land mass.

While the Panama Canal is an acceptable dividing line between the two continents, it is unsatisfactory from the cultural viewpoint. Cultural distinctions within the American World rest upon differences in the European backgrounds of the settlers. The culture traits of the United States and Canada reflect those of northwestern Europe, while those from Mexico southward are similar to the cultures of southwestern Europe. The dividing line between the two main culture realms of the American World is thus the southern boundary of the United States. To the north is the Anglo-American Realm, where English is the common tongue, the dominant religion is Protestant Christianity,

(*opposite*)
American World: realms and regions

and political, social, and economic practices are similar to those of northwestern Europe. Mexico, Central America, the islands of the Caribbean, and all of South America lie in the Latin-American Realm, where Spanish and Portuguese are the dominant tongues, Roman Catholic Christianity is the major religious faith, and laws and customs resemble those of southwestern Europe.

SPACE RELATIONS

Although the American World is strongly bound by culture ties to western Europe, it is fairly remote in terms of miles from the Old World. New York is some 3,000 miles from Europe, San Francisco is 2,300 miles from Hawaii and 5,200 miles from Yokohama, Panama is 5,000 miles from Gibraltar, and South America and Africa approach each other no closer than 1,750 miles. A glance at the map shows that most of South America lies east of North America; a line drawn due south from Florida approximates the westernmost point of South America. Thus, the east coast ports of South America, south of the bulge, are closer to Spanish ports than they are to New York. Routes from the west coast ports to New York, via the Panama Canal, are shorter than routes to San Francisco.

North America ranks third in size among the continents, with its 9,300,000 square miles, exceeded only by Asia and Africa. Its length is some 5,300 miles, extending from 8° N. in Panama to 84° N. at the northern tip of Ellesmere Island, Canada. The great bulk of the continent lies in the middle latitudes, and exhibts the natural conditions inherent in such a position. Its northern, Polar World parts almost touch adjoining land masses to the west and east. The Bering Strait between Alaska and Siberia is only 36 miles wide, and even less distance separates Ellesmere from Greenland. Southward from these points, on either side of the continent, the water bodies widen, so that the main part of North America lies thousands of miles from the land masses of Asia and Europe. The shoreline of the continent is sufficiently irregular to provide an abundance of excellent harbors. The greatest irregularities in shape occur in the northern part of the continent, where the severity of high-latitude climate restricts or prohibits their use as harbors or waterways. The pattern of interior, continental waterways is relatively simple. The major continental water divide follows the crest of the Rocky Mountains, separating the continent into two drainage areas of unequal size. The smaller, relatively rugged section drains westward into the Pacific through the Yukon, Fraser, Columbia-Snake, Sacramento-San Joaquin, and Colorado rivers. The broad eastern, largely plains section drains into the Arctic Ocean through the north-flowing Mackenzie, into Hudson Bay and the North Atlantic through the Saskatchewan-Nelson and St. Lawrence rivers, and into the Gulf of Mexico through the Rio Grande and the gigantic Mississippi-Missouri-Ohio system.

The 6,800,000 square miles of South America place it fourth among the continents. It spans the latitudes from 13° N. to 56° S., a distance of some 4,750 miles. Its widest part lies between the equator and 20° S., and is thus tropical, a marked contrast with North America. Also, unlike that of North America, the outline of South America is exceedingly regular, so there is a general scarcity of good, natural harbors. Only the fiorded coast of southern Chile provides fine harbors, but the area is sparsely populated and largely unused. Even more than in North America, the great continental water divide, the crest of the Andes, lies close to the western margin of the continent. All the major streams and plains lie to the east. The Amazon river system drains more area than any other river system in the world, over 2 million square miles. It dwarfs all others on the continent, just as the Mississippi system does in North America. Through the Amazon and other river systems, such as the Parana and Orinoco, most of the continent drains into the Atlantic. In the narrow band west of the water divide, rivers are short, of small volume, and many flow through very dry country which further reduces their size. Neither an eastern nor a western stream is the Magdalena, which flows between the forked ends of the northern Andes northward into the Caribbean.

MAJOR SURFACE FORMS

In broad plan there is striking similarity in build between the two American continents. Both have a western cordillera, ranges of high, still actively changing mountains. Both have old, worn-down, comparatively stable uplands to the east. And both have lowlands of intermediate geologic age lying between the mountains and uplands. These broad similarities, however, tend to get lost in the maze of differences in detail. For convenience in describing the more detailed surface forms, the American World is divided into three major parts: northern North America, Middle America, and South America.

In northern North America, north of Mexico, there are two well-defined mountain systems in the west and a lesser one in the east. Of the western systems, the Rocky Mountains are dominant, stretching from New Mexico northward through the United States and Canada to the Brooks Range of northern Alaska. Parallel to the coast, and never far from it, is the Pacific mountain system, a series of ranges that extends from southern California to the Aleutian Islands. In its southern half the Pacific mountain system is split into two belts, the lesser Coast Range of California, Oregon, and Washington, and the more impressive inner belt, the Sierra Nevada and Cascade mountains. Between these belts is a series of valleys and depressions which are of great importance agriculturally because they occur in a region where a coastal plain is essentially nonexistent. In the broad corridor between the Rockies and the mountains of the Pacific system are a number of plateaus: the Colorado Plateaus and Great Basin in the south, and the Columbia, Yukon, and other plateaus to the north.

The character of the land east of the Rockies is very different. Plains extend from the mountains to the Atlantic, interrupted only by the Appalachians, and from the Arctic Ocean to the Gulf of Mexico. The plains are comparatively flat, with low relief. Individually they vary from the high plains just east of the Rockies to the lowlands of the Mississippi basin, and from the glaciated ancient land mass of the Canadian Shield to the young, nonglaciated Gulf and

American World: natural features

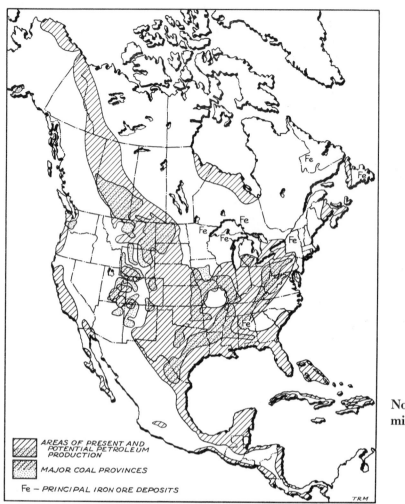

North America:
mineral deposits

AREAS OF PRESENT AND
POTENTIAL PETROLEUM
PRODUCTION

MAJOR COAL PROVINCES

Fe — PRINCIPAL IRON ORE DEPOSITS

Atlantic Coast Plain. The interrupting Appalachians are in general far more subdued and softer in contour than the western ranges. The only sharp-peaked, truly rugged mountains east of the Rockies are the glaciated mountains of northern Labrador.

The diversified geologic history of North America is reflected in mineral resources that for variety and abundance probably entitle the continent to first rank. The supply of minerals essential to modern industry, such as coal, iron, petroleum, silver, gold, zinc, lead, copper, and nickel, is ample. Only tin, bauxite, and some of the rarer metals are missing. Deposits of coal and petroleum are generally associated with the sedimentary rocks of the plains areas, and so are most abundant east of the Rockies. Gold, silver, and copper come from the western mountains and from the old rocks of the Canadian Shield, the major source also of iron, nickel, and radium ores.

In Middle America, Mexico as far south as the Isthmus of Tehuantepec is mainly a plateau bounded on the east and west by somewhat higher mountain ranges. The plateau is divided into a number of basins and rough hilly uplands. Separated from Mexico's northwest mainland coast by the shallow depression occupied by the Gulf of California, is the rocky peninsula of Baja California. Southward from the Isthmus of Tehuantepec to the Nicaraguan lowlands, the structural trend is east-west. This trend is apparent on the Caribbean coast, for here valleys and ranges plunge under the sea to reappear in the Greater Antilles. On the Pacific side the underlying structure is obscured by a thick mantle of ash and volcanic flows, forming a high plateau in which valleys and basins nestle among volcanic peaks. Lowland plains are small or lacking, with the single exception of the low, featureless, limestone plain of the Yucatan Peninsula. Lowlands continue to be scarce southward from Nicaragua to the continent of South America. This region of rough terrain is dominated by a series of northwest-southeast-trending folded mountains, surmounted at intervals by active volcanoes.

The east-west structures of Middle America that reappear toward the east are responsible for the Greater Antilles, considered to be the exposed tops of mountain ranges whose bases lie far below sea level. The Lesser Antilles are an arc of volcanoes, some actively building, others eroded or submerged. The southernmost islands of the chain, notably Trinidad and Tobago, are structurally part of South America. An interesting feature of all the islands of the Caribbean Sea and most of the continental shores that adjoin it is the extensive growth of coral.

The southern part of Middle America is marked by three comparatively easy natural passes between the Atlantic and Pacific. The northernmost is the Isthmus of Tehuantepec, only 130 miles wide and with a maximum elevation of about 800 feet. To the south, in Nicaragua, a low passage follows the San Juan River upstream to Lake Nicaragua, with an elevation of only 108 feet. Westward, narrow low passes lead to the Pacific. So impressive was this route that in 1916 the United States gave Nicaragua $3,000,000 for the option on the canal route, and for a naval base on the Pacific coast and some islands off the Caribbean coast, islands that the United States still claims. The most significant of the three passages is across the Isthmus of Panama. Here the width is less than 50 miles and the maximum elevation is under 300 feet, a situation appreciated ever since the days of Balboa. Transportation by mule was succeeded in 1850 by a railroad. In 1914 the Panama Canal was opened, offering tremendous savings in distance over the Cape Horn route.

Portions of Middle America are heavily mineralized. Mexico was one of the original *El Dorados* of the Spanish conquerors, and it continues to yield quantities of gold and silver, as well as copper, mercury, and petroleum. Similar mineral resources are generally present in the other Middle American countries, but coal is a major deficiency, just as it is in South America.

South America, with its young mountains, plains, and old-rock shields, resembles the conditions described for northern North America. Considerably more spectacular than the North American mountains, however, are the Andes, for no other mountain system extends so far at such constantly great height. Many of the peaks rise above 20,000 feet, and even the passes reach 10,000 feet. The slopes to the lowlands are abrupt and steep. The Andes, rarely a single chain, vary in width and are broadest in Bolivia. The Southern Andes are fairly narrow and compact, with one main range that has the highest individual peak and the lowest average elevation of the entire system. The southernmost mountains are heavily glaciated, exhibiting both glaciers and the fiords, lakes, sharp peaks, and other features resulting from ice sculpture. The central Andes consist of numerous ranges, frequently enclosing high plains or plateaus, knots of volcanic and other peaks, and deep canyons cut by eastward-flowing streams. To the north the Andes chain narrows, and then in southern Colombia it splits into three ranges,

Andean landscape, Venezuela
[*Venezuela Ministry of Development*]

the valleys between them being occupied by the northward-flowing Magdalena and Cauca rivers. The eastern prong again splits as it goes on either side of the Maracaibo basin, the eastern range continuing along the northern edge of Venezuela, finally to end in the low range in northern Trinidad.

Because the Andes hug the western margin of the continent, the coastal plain is narrow or entirely missing. The central and southern Pacific coast of South America is strikingly similar to the west coast of North America. Both have low coast ranges, important interior valleys, and a scarcity of good harbors in middle latitudes. Southern Chile resembles the rough, irregular fiorded coast of British Columbia and Alaska.

East of the Andes are the major lowlands, covering more than half of the area of the continent. In general they are low in elevation and

South America: mineral deposits

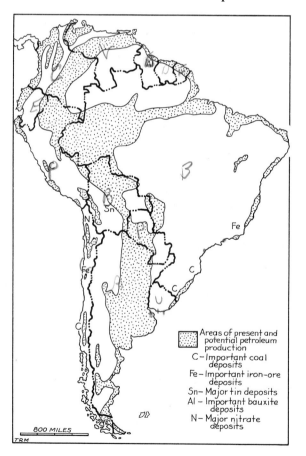

have little relief. To the north are the low plains or *llanos* and the delta of the Orinoco. This basin is separated by an almost imperceptible divide from the vast Amazon basin which, at a distance of 2,000 miles inland, attains an elevation of only 350 feet. Most of the innumerable streams in the basin are subject to seasonal flooding. Another low divide separates the Amazon basin from the plains drained by the Parana-Paraguay system. The plains of the upper Paraguay are almost featureless and poorly drained; in the rainy season they are broad swamps, but in the dry season water is difficult to find. Farther south lie the *pampas*, thousands of miles of grass-covered plains, with low relief, poor surface drainage, and dotted with numerous small, shallow ponds.

Bordering the eastern margin of the continent are three highland areas: the Guiana Highlands, the Brazilian Highlands, and Patagonia. Seaward from these old-rock areas are discontinuous and fairly insignificant coastal plains. The little-known Guiana Highlands are essentially a plateau with ragged remnants of ancient mountains, bordered on the east by a steep escarpment, or cliff, down which plunge a number of streams, producing scenic waterfalls and wild rapids. To the east lies the lowland of the Guianas, the most extensive coastal plain of the continent. The Brazilian Highlands are similar to those of Guiana, being made up of a series of plateaus intermingled with the protruding roots of old mountains, and averaging some 2,000 feet in elevation. The tablelands of Patagonia average about a mile in height, and are composed of older rocks, lavas, and younger sediments. Eastward-flowing streams have cut deep valleys whose bottomlands offer far more habitable sites than do the broad, barren, windswept surfaces of the upland plateau.

Except for a deficiency of coal, South America is amply provided with minerals. From the Guiana lowlands come quantities of bauxite, while the Highlands are important sources of gold, diamonds, and iron. The Brazilian Highlands also produce gold and diamonds, as well as copper and iron. The Andean regions yield tin, copper, silver, lead, zinc, gold, platinum, iron, and other important minerals. The desert

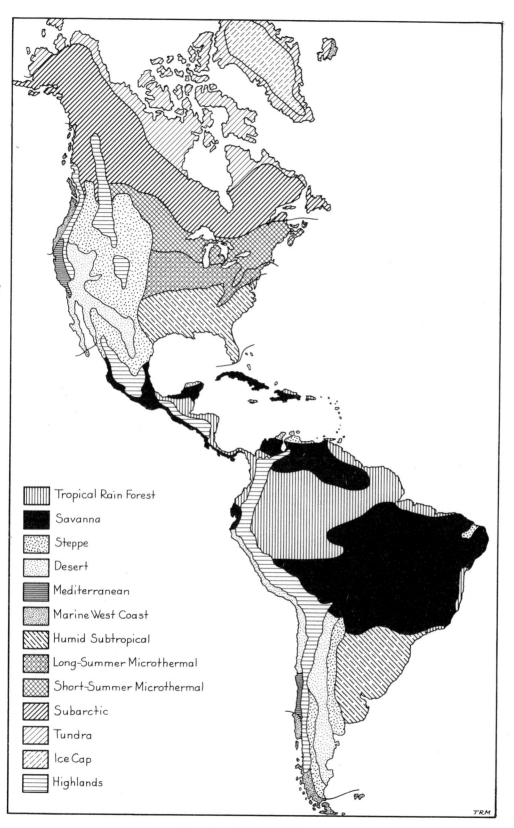

Tropical Rain Forest	
Savanna	
Steppe	
Desert	
Mediterranean	
Marine West Coast	
Humid Subtropical	
Long-Summer Microthermal	
Short-Summer Microthermal	
Subarctic	
Tundra	
Ice Cap	
Highlands	

TRM

American World: climates

of northern Chile has excellent natural deposits of nitrates. Venezuela ranks second only to the United States among petroleum-producing countries of the world. Some oil fields have been discovered in the lowlands lying east of the Andes, and experts predict that many more will be found.

CLIMATE AND VEGETATION

In a most general way, the climatic and vegetational zones of the American World follow similar patterns to the north and to the south of the equator. Only in the higher latitudes do the greater breadth and farther poleward extension of North America introduce conditions which are not matched in South America.

Tropical, that is, winterless, climates occur over most of the area lying between the tropics of Cancer and Capricorn. The central core is the tremendously large area of tropical rain forest astride the equator in the Amazon basin. The American rain forest, like that of Africa, has a climate marked by high annual temperature and high annual precipitation, with almost no seasonal variation. The natural vegetation is a broad-leaved evergreen forest, whose dense foliage allows little light to reach the ground, thus inhibiting the appearance of undergrowth. A number of domesticated plants, such as bananas, cacao, and rubber, thrive under rain-forest climates. These rain-forest conditions, while most widespread in the Amazon basin, also occur in poleward extensions along the eastern continental margins to the very limits of the tropics, as the maps of climates and vegetation illustrate. These extensions are in places exposed to prevailing trade winds, especially where highlands force the moist air upward.

On either side of the rain forest are the savanna climatic and vegetational zones, centering on the llanos of Venezuela and the campos of Brazil. Savannas also appear on the Pacific side of mountain barriers in Middle America and on windward coasts where lands are low. These regions are still winterless as far as temperature is concerned, but savannas have less rainfall than do rain forests and the winter

season is dry. The natural vegetation is semi-deciduous forest, open woodland, or grassland, depending upon the amount of precipitation. Savanna climatic conditions favor the production of coffee, sugar cane, cotton, and other crops that need a dry season in which to mature and be harvested.

A welcome interruption of tropical climates is produced by the highlands of Middle and South America. These highlands have played a very important part in human developments, being the sites of advanced Indian cultures, and providing favorable conditions for European settlement. From the Spanish-speaking inhabitants of these areas come a series of names that are applied to the various climatic zones that occur up the tropical highland slopes. Up to elevations of 2,000 or 3,000 feet, where lowland temperatures and rain-forest plants are encountered, the zone is called *tierra caliente*. Above this, to elevations around 6,000 feet, is *tierra templada*, where temperatures average between 65° and 75° F., and coffee, maize, and cotton are typical products. The *tierra fria* zone extends upward to about 10,000 feet, has temperatures that average between 55° and 65° F., experiences occasional frost and snow, and is suitable for the growing of wheat, apples, barley, and Irish potatoes. Still higher is a tundra-like zone to which is given a variety of names, such as *puna*, or *paramo*. Here temperatures average below 50°, too low for agriculture or forest, but useful in a limited way for grazing. Above 14,000 feet are barren areas of permanent ice and snow.

Lying only partially within the tropics are the steppe and desert regions, places deficient in precipitation. As on other continents, arid climates are present on the west coasts of the Americas, extending toward the equator from latitudes of about 30 degrees. In North America the region of steppes and deserts includes most of the intermontane plateaus of the United States, and the Great Plains northward to the Saskatchewan River. In South America, the coast of Peru and northern Chile is arid, and so is much of western and southern Argentina, where the desert and steppe of the Patagonian plateau mark one of the rare instances of dry climates occurring on the east coast of a conti-

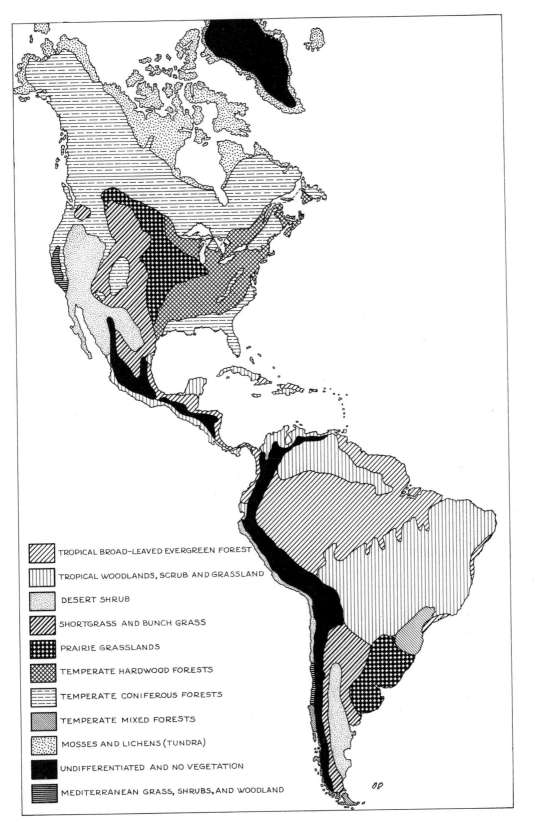

TROPICAL BROAD-LEAVED EVERGREEN FOREST

TROPICAL WOODLANDS, SCRUB AND GRASSLAND

DESERT SHRUB

SHORTGRASS AND BUNCH GRASS

PRAIRIE GRASSLANDS

TEMPERATE HARDWOOD FORESTS

TEMPERATE CONIFEROUS FORESTS

TEMPERATE MIXED FORESTS

MOSSES AND LICHENS (TUNDRA)

UNDIFFERENTIATED AND NO VEGETATION

MEDITERRANEAN GRASS, SHRUBS, AND WOODLAND

American World: vegetation

nent. The reason here may be the rain-shadow effect of the high Andes in an area where the land is narrow.

The American deserts and steppes exhibit the features typical of these regions everywhere. The deserts are characterized by interior drainage, extensive alluvial fills, sharp contrasts in slope where bedrock is exposed, and scant, highly specialized vegetation. They offer limited grazing, and an oasis agriculture where water and arable soils happen to coincide. Steppes are normally grasslands, varying from abundant short grass on the humid margins to bunch grass near the desert limits. They provide range grazing, and, particularly in the middle latitudes, a rather risky extension of the great cereal-producing belts.

Poleward of the dry climates in middle Chile and in California are two small but significant areas of Mediterranean climates. Summers are hot and marked by dryness and prevalent coastal fogs, and winters are mild and fairly rainy. Subtropical crops, such as olives and citrus fruit, can be grown successfully despite occasional frost. The characteristic natural vegetation cover is grass with widely spaced trees, commonly found in the valleys, and chaparral, or maquis, on the drier hillsides.

Extending poleward from the Mediterranean areas to the southern tip of South America and nearly to 60° N. in North America are marine west-coast climates, characterized by cool summers, mild winters, and heavy precipitation, which is favored by the windward exposure and the mountains that rise abruptly from the coast in both areas. At the higher elevations precipitation comes in the form of snow which, because of the cool summers, gives rise to extensive accumulations of glacial ice. On the poleward margins of both areas glaciers discharge directly into the sea. Fiords and other evidence of ice action indicate that glaciers were even more extensive in the past. These areas are heavily forested with excellent timber trees, the North American area being the chief source of commercial timber for the continent.

The humid subtropical is the remaining climatic type common to both North and South America. In North America it is present in the region lying south of the Ohio River and east of the 100th meridian, while in South America it occurs in the humid pampa of Argentina, Uruguay, southern Brazil, and part of Paraguay. This climate is distinguished by long hot summers and mild winters, conditions that are highly favorable to a great variety of crops, from citrus fruits, sugar cane, and cotton, to maize and wheat. The climate also favors forest growth, although grasslands are prominent, especially in the South American section. Some people believe that the grasslands are the result of annual burning of the region by the aboriginal Indian hunters.

Missing on the southern continent are those climatic zones lying between humid subtropical and tundra in North America, for they develop only on extensive land masses. Their great seasonal extremes of temperature can occur only beyond the reach of the tempering influence of the sea. Of particular importance in continental climates is the varying length of the growing season, and on this basis three types of continental climates can be differentiated in North America: long-summer microthermal, short-summer microthermal, and subarctic. The belts of these climates are shown on the map.

In the zone of long-summer microthermal, summers are warm to hot, the growing season lasts some five months, winters are mild to cold, and precipitation is both adequate and fairly well distributed throughout the year. The natural vegetation is forest of broad-leaved deciduous trees, although at the time of settlement by Europeans the western part of the belt was covered with tall grass. It is still a question whether the prairie was natural or induced by Indian burnings. However that may be, this prairie portion, frequently called the Corn Belt, is agriculturally the most productive extensive area in the Americas. The southern boundary of the long-summer microthermal is the effective northern limit of cotton cultivation, while its northern boundary approximates the poleward limit of maize and the vine.

The short-summer microthermal is distinguished from the preceding climate chiefly by its longer and colder winters, with a growing season diminished to only a hundred or so days.

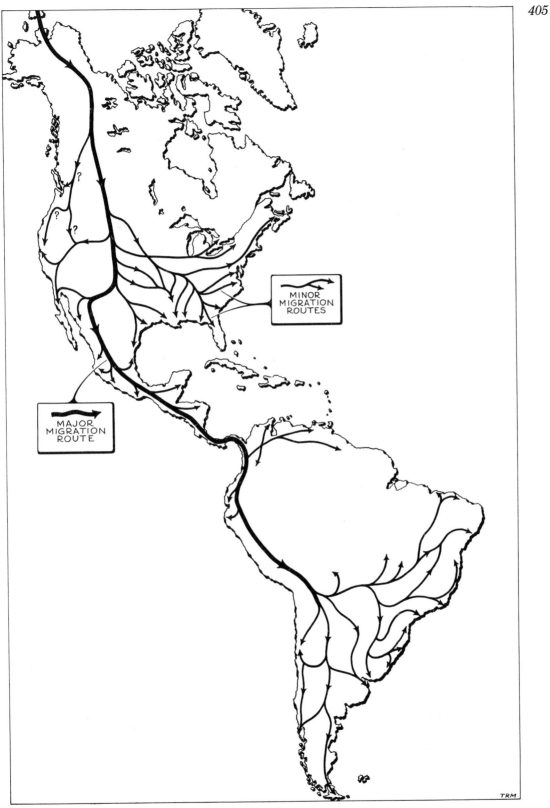

Indian migration routes
[*after Sauer*]

Precipitation is reduced in amount, but is fairly evenly spread over the year. The natural forest cover of broad-leaved deciduous trees gives way to tall-grass prairie west of Lake Superior, in what is called the Spring Wheat Belt. Because of the shorter growing season, hay, root crops, and small grains are the major crops.

The subarctic reaches northward to the poleward limit of trees, the southern boundary of the Polar World. This climate is characterized by reduced precipitation, long and very cold winters, and a short growing season, which decreases from around a hundred days in the southern parts to about thirty days along the tundra border. Killing frosts may occur in any month. Needless to say, this climate is hardly a boon to agriculture, which can be successfully pursued only in a very limited number of places. On the other hand, the taiga thrives under these conditions. These extensive forests of pine, fir, and spruce have commercial importance along the southern borders, but toward the north the trees decrease in size and density as the region of true polar climates is approached.

CULTURAL BACKGROUND

When Europeans "discovered" America in the latter part of the fifteenth century, they found the two continents occupied by peoples whom they promptly lumped together under the label of Indians, although in fact these peoples were of diverse origin and had already developed fundamental cultural differences. No major section of the new lands was without inhabitants, but the most densely populated areas were in Mexico, Central America, and Andean South America. Estimates of the size of the existing Indian population at the time of Columbus vary from 8 to 50 million, and wherever between these extremes the true figure lies, it is certain that the Indian population of Latin America far exceeded that of Anglo-America, which probably had around a million inhabitants.

Present evidence indicates that the Indians originated in Asia and had reached the Americas some 20,000 to 30,000, possibly even 40,000, years ago. The first comers are thought to have been simple gatherers and hunters, so poorly equipped that they lacked even the bow. Their point of entry to the American World seems to have been Cape Prince of Wales, Alaska, where the crossing from Asia was no problem, even for a primitive people. It is probable that at the time much of Alaska was ice-covered, but since the central portion of the Yukon Plateau escaped glaciation, it very likely was the route to the interior, where the western margin of the Great Plains provided a corridor to the south. It should be realized that this was not a planned migration of peoples to settle a new land. It was a slow, probably seasonal movement of small, unorganized groups.

The main route, as shown on the map, swung around the southern end of the Rockies and southward along the western margin of the plateau of Mexico and along the highlands of Central America to the Andes, from which point penetration of both the northern and southern parts of the continent was possible. All along the way there were divergent paths, minor migration routes, that brought the peoples to most parts of the two continents. The time involved in this spread of peoples was certainly a matter of thousands of years.

American Indians were a mixture of a number of ancient and modern racial stocks. It is doubtful that there were many Mongoloids among the early migrants, but there are suggestions of primitive Caucasoid, Australoid, and even Negroid strains. Arriving somewhat later were the Asian peoples who gave to most American Indians the straight coarse hair, prominent cheek bones, and dark skin typical of Mongoloids. Whatever their racial background, the Indians, at the time of Columbus, spoke a wide variety of languages, none of which has a known relation to any Old World tongue. This suggests both a great antiquity for the American Indian and a long period during which there was no important migration from the Old World.

While the cultural equipment of the first migrants was exceedingly primitive, later migrants and Asian contacts brought a growing list of new equipment and traits. The dog, spear thrower, bow, and techniques for grinding stone to make implements appeared. The presence in northern North America of such elements as the dog sledge, snowshoe, tailored skin clothing, and tipi, is paralleled in northern Eurasia, suggesting long, continuous contact. But when all the imported items are added together they amount only to the equipment of a primitive people, so the fact that the American Indians advanced beyond the simple way of life must be credited to their own initiative and inventive genius.

At the time of Columbus' discovery, the Valley of Mexico and the highlands of Peru were the centers of the most advanced Indians, living under highly organized social and political systems, and supported by well-developed sedentary agriculture. Particularly in Peru, among the Inca, the degree of material advancement was high. Maize, Irish potatoes, and quinoa, a grain, were raised on the highlands. Irrigation, terracing, and soil-fertilization were common practices. On high grassy areas, too cool for agriculture, grazed llamas and alpacas, domesticated animals that provided meat, wool, and transport. The Incas had constructed excellent roads to the various parts of their empire, and had erected buildings of huge dressed stones. Metallurgy had advanced to the making of bronze, and fine cloth was woven of wool and cotton.

Elsewhere in South America the cultural attainments were considerably less than those of the Inca. The Chibcha Indians of Colombia practiced metallurgy and sedentary agriculture, but otherwise were behind their Peruvian neighbors. Still farther behind were the inhabitants of the Amazon basin, who engaged in a shifting agriculture, mainly the raising of manioc, and in hunting and fishing. Similar activities were pursued by the West Indian tribes, who, in addition, were skilled in the use of boats. In the Argentine grasslands agriculture was subordinate to hunting and gathering. The pampa Indians took readily to the horse when it was introduced by Europeans. Like their North American counterparts in the Great Plains they became thoroughgoing horsemen, migratory hunters, and fierce fighters against the European invaders.

In North America the culture focus was the Valley of Mexico, a center of intensive agriculture that extended intermittently northward to the Pueblo tribes of Arizona and New Mexico, and southward through the highlands of Middle America. Maize, peppers, beans, and cacao were raised, but there were no domesticated animals comparable in importance with the llama and alpaca. Despite the magnificent pyramids and temples built of stone, the range of material development seems somewhat inferior to that of the Inca area. On the other hand, the Maya excelled in at least two nonmaterial accomplishments: the development of a calendric system and of writing.

The Pueblo tribes marked the northern limits of the aboriginal cultures whose major economic activity was an intensive agriculture. Their substantial stone villages and floodwater farming placed them well ahead of other Anglo-American Indians. Throughout the eastern half of the United States, however, the Indians practiced some farming, mainly the raising of maize, along with hunting, gathering, and fishing. The abundance of bison in the Great Plains made hunting the most attractive and easiest way of life, especially after the introduction of the horse. West of the Pueblos, throughout most of present-day Nevada and California, the Indians were wild-seed gatherers, and to a lesser extent, hunters and fishmen. Northward along the coastal belt the wealth of sea life made possible a near-sedentary existence, with large, well-built wooden houses, and encouraged an extensive and skilled use of dugout boats. Inland from this region of fishermen, and extending in a wide band across the continent, roughly corresponding with the zone of subarctic climate and forest, is the caribou area, the northernmost Indian area. To some extent this was a meeting place of Indian and Polar World Eskimo, but the Eskimo preferred the tundra and the Indian was more at home in the forest, where he was a hunter of land mammals, fisherman, and gatherer. The Indians made extensive use of birch-bark for canoes, containers, and shelters. Snowshoes and toboggans were used to traverse deep winter snows.

These, then, were the general pre-Columbian

Indian ways of life, and in a very restricted sense they still persist in such remote places as parts of the highlands of Mexico, Middle America, and the middle Andes, and in such, to Europeans, unattractive places as the Guiana Highlands, parts of Amazonia, and the subarctic of North America. Although these isolated groups of Indians still living by their ancient methods are interesting, of more importance in understanding the present culture landscape is the number of items the Europeans borrowed from the Indians and incorporated into their own culture. Among the borrowings were the canoe, snowshoe, and maple sugar. Place names of Indian origin are numerous. But these and many other culture traits are insignificant compared with the list of cultivated plants taken from the Indians. Most of these plants are now so thoroughly a part of modern economy that their domestication by Indian horticulturists is forgotten. Among the more familiar and important are maize, Irish and sweet potatoes, tomatoes, tobacco, cacao, long-staple cotton, pineapples, red peppers, beans, and squashes. To these should be added rubber, cocaine, and quinine, all in use by the Indians before Columbus arrived. The preparation of dishes, such as hominy, grits, and succotash, are related borrowings.

Not only was there a wealth of useful culture traits available to the invading Europeans, but the natural resources of the American continents remained essentially untouched. The Indians had caused very little alteration in the natural landscape, and had left the vast mineral and forest resources largely undisturbed.

BEGINNINGS OF EUROPEAN SETTLEMENT

The claim that Columbus discovered America is really supportable by the fact that when he landed on the island of San Salvador in 1492 he initiated a movement of Europeans to the new continents that has continued to the present time. Although other Europeans had preceded him by some 500 years, their discoveries brought no such movement. Right behind Columbus came explorers, adventurers, and fortune hunters from many lands, for it was quickly realized that the route west from Europe led not to the Indies but to new lands, free for the taking. The seafaring nations of western Europe: Spain, Portugal, France, Holland, and England, saw the fine new opportunities, and hastened to establish claims of ownership.

In addition to the four exploratory voyages of Columbus, Spain also sent forth Balboa, Magellan, Cortez, Pizarro, and a number of others. By the middle of the sixteenth century Spaniards were established in western South America from Venezuela to Chile, had followed the Amazon from Peru to its mouth, and had opened the Parana route from Peru to the La Plata estuary. By the end of that century, they had determined the general configuration of all Latin America, had recognized the great river systems, were making regular use of routes across Middle and South America, and, as a result of the explorations of DeSoto, Coronado, and others, had a fairly good picture of southern Anglo-America.

The Portuguese in 1500 had sent Cabral to have a look, and on the basis of his purported sighting of the coast of Brazil, Portugal claimed the area. At the same time the English and French were busy along the north Atlantic coast. The English Cabots cruised the coast from Hatteras to Hudson Strait, and a little later Cartier went up the St. Lawrence to the site of Montreal, establishing the French claim to that excellent route to the interior of the continent. Many details were added to the picture by Hudson who discovered Hudson and James bays, and by Champlain who directed visits to the upper Great Lakes.

At the beginning of the seventeenth century the exploration of the interior of Anglo-America was in its infancy, but nevertheless a new epoch was ushered in by the establishment of settlements by both English and French on the Atlantic seaboard. Here, as in the matter of exploration, the Spaniards were far ahead, their first settlements being already a century old.

EARLY SPANISH SETTLEMENTS

The first Spanish settlement was on the island of Hispaniola, and from here settlements spread to Cuba and other West Indian islands. But the

Spaniards were seeking neither new homes for landless peasants nor sanctuaries for the persecuted; their purposes were to fill the depleted Spanish treasury, to obtain personal wealth, and, incidentally, to convert Indians to Christianity. For these purposes, they particularly sought places with an abundance of precious metals. If these metals were already being mined, so much the better. Another valued asset was a dense, docile Indian population which would produce food for the conquerors, and provide labor for the mines and converts to the Christian faith. These conditions were met perfectly in two areas: the Valley of Mexico and Peru. In both places a handful of technically superior Spaniards defeated the native rulers after sharp conflicts. The well-disciplined Indian populations readily accepted new masters, became at least nominal Christians, and to some extent took over European crops and domesticated animals. The horse, sheep, cattle, and wheat became part of the new scheme of life, but on the whole, Indian existence continued to be based on a sedentary subsistence agriculture, with maize the common crop. Changes of a different nature were brought about by the depletion of males used to work the mines, and by the introduction of new diseases.

Mexico and Peru were the two great centers of colonial times. Mexico City was built on the site of Montezuma's capital. In Peru, Pizarro chose a coastal location, Lima, rather than Cuzco, the old Inca capital in the highlands. Mexico City and Lima established the urban pattern for Spanish America: a square or plaza containing the cathedral and public buildings, and about it a rectangular pattern of streets. The dense Indian populations and mineral wealth that gave rise to the two cities were the model whose possible duplication drove Spanish adventurers on their far-reaching explorations.

Wherever the Spaniards found mineral wealth or dense Indian population, or preferably both, they took over control and established settlements. They found little that was attractive in such places as the non-mineral-producing grasslands of Argentina, sparsely populated by fierce nomads, so the area's only function was to supply cattle and mules for Peru. Places that lacked minerals but had dense native agricultural population were considered valuable because individual Spaniards could obtain grants to large estates and set up a feudal system wherein Indian tenants served Spanish lords. The pattern of the large estate was widely extended over Latin America, while the production of specialized commercial crops reached even broader limits. In time, the Spaniards recognized the value of areas that possessed agricultural possibilities, even though the areas lacked abundant natives. To solve the labor problem, Negro slaves were imported, or in rare instances, the Spaniards themselves became peasant farmers. The institution of Negro slavery spread throughout the islands of the West Indies and extended to the low tropical lands bordering the Caribbean and the northern Atlantic coast of South America.

EARLY PORTUGUESE SETTLEMENTS

In 1494 the Treaty of Tordesillas between Portugal and Spain assigned to the former all territories lying east of about the present meridian of 50° W. This gave to Portugal the eastern bulge of South America. Preliminary exploration revealed no great amount of gold and silver, and showed the Indian population to be sparse and poorly adapted to steady labor in mine or field. As a result, Portugal turned its interest to more profitable holdings in India and the East Indies, until the Spanish and French began to encroach on Portugal's American claim. Then, settlement of Brazil was vigorously fostered. The coast was divided into a number of districts, each independently administered by its appointed leader. Inept leadership, among other causes, brought an end to many of the settlements, but others hung on and became nuclear centers of Brazil's growth. The outstanding survivors were Salvador, founded in 1502, Recife, 1561, and highland São Paulo, 1554.

The northeastern coastal section around the centers of Salvador and Recife showed the first signs of energetic development, starting with the export of dyewood. The large estates soon began planting tobacco for export, but shortly turned to sugar cane, an introduced crop quite familiar to the Portuguese. So favorable were the natural conditions and so excellent were the returns

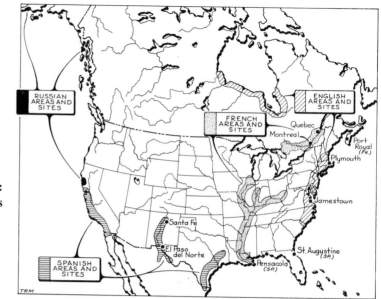

Anglo-America: colonial settlements

from sugar, that in 1538 Negro slaves began to be imported to supplement the labor supply. Thus the pattern was set: large estates operated by slaves and owned by a proud aristocracy, a pattern that was reinforced and expanded when the zenith of the sugar production period was reached in the late sixteenth and seventeenth centuries. In such a pattern there was no place for poor white settlers, so some of them moved inland, there to develop a pastoral and small-agricultural economy, quite different from the coastal system.

The history of early settlement in Latin America provides an insight into the origin of economic patterns and attitudes that prevail even today. A common attitude is the hope of obtaining wealth and position, whether they come from minerals or from large-scale mining of the land for crops of sugar cane, coffee, or wheat. Even the mestizo (mixed European and Indian) or mulatto (mixed Caucasian and Negro), struggling to live, is not free from grandiose aspirations. All too rare is concern for wise use of the resources. While it can hardly be said that the remnant sedentary Indians are ardent conservationists, at least their use of the land causes little destruction. Their crops are not for sale, so they see little purpose in owning vast tracts, nor do they desire a place in the world of commerce.

EARLY ANGLO-AMERICAN SETTLEMENTS

The first permanent settlements in Anglo-America were established by Spaniards, as northern outposts of their vast empire. All but one of their four northern settlement areas were designed to ward off aggressive thrusts by other nations. In Florida, Pensacola, occupied intermittently after 1559, and St. Augustine, established in 1565, were directed mainly against British and French encroachments. Twelve missions established in southern Texas between 1690 and 1731 were less concerned with converting Indians than with preventing aggressive moves by the French who were attempting to occupy the lower Mississippi Valley. Similar threats, only in this case from the Russians, brought about the establishment of the chain of missions in California during the latter third of the eighteenth century. The only northern outpost that was unrelated to settlements of other nations was the series of missions along the Rio Grande, the northernmost, Santa Fe, founded in 1609. These missions were in fact for the purpose of converting the Pueblo Indians.

These Spanish extensions into Anglo-America were, at best, only tenuous holdings, completely dependent upon the maintenance of long routes to the south. They brought about neither con-

Louisiana-French plantation house
[*U.S.D.A.*]

centrations of Europeans nor intensive use of the land. As a result, they were easily taken during the westward expansion of the Anglo-Americans, but despite this they left a significant mark on the culture of the conquerors. Place names, terms, the details of the range cattle industry, architecture, and the citrus fruit and vine of California became integral parts of the varied Anglo-American way of life.

Meanwhile the French and English were active in the northerly portions of the Atlantic coast. After a number of failures, they finally managed in the early seventeenth century to establish three nuclear settlements, the French on the St. Lawrence, and the English in Virginia, and in New England. Each developed along separate lines, but together they dominated the settlement character of Anglo-America.

The French had been maintaining summer fur posts along the lower St. Lawrence and had been fishing on the banks off Newfoundland for over half a century before they got around to establishing settlements. Their first, founded in 1604 by Champlain, was at Port Royal, now Annapolis, Nova Scotia, but although the site was good agriculturally, it was off-center with

respect to the St. Lawrence and the major French interest, beaver. The real founding of French Canada came with the establishment of Quebec in 1608. From this base the French went out in search of new sources of fur. Barred from going directly south by the enmity of the Iroquois, they went west along the Ottawa River to the upper Great Lakes. Attempts to expand their fur domains toward the north ran into conflict with the English Hudson's Bay Company, which in 1670 had been granted exclusive rights to a vast tract of northern territory. The French then turned south, along the Ohio and Mississippi, eventually establishing control all the way to the Gulf coast. So ardent was the search for fur that agriculture got a late start in the St. Lawrence Valley, beginning only in about 1700 with the arrival of peasants sent from France for that purpose.

The vast American empire of France, which at its height extended as far west as the Rocky Mountains, collapsed in 1763 with the defeat of France in the Seven Years' War, the American part of which was named the French and Indian War. The British acquired all lands lying east of the Mississippi, while French Louisiana west of the Mississippi went to Spain, only to be returned to the French in 1800 and sold to the United States in 1803. Although politically France was pushed off the continent, French influences and French ways were not, and throughout Quebec and in parts of Louisiana they persist today.

Unlike the extended French settlements, those of the English in Virginia and New England were compact agricultural colonies, though they differed from each other in development. At the first permanent English settlement, founded at Jamestown in 1607, the introduction of tobacco in 1612 as a commercial crop set the pattern of development. To solve labor needs, Negroes were brought in as early as 1619, first as indentured servants, later as slaves. During the seventeenth century the economic and social lines were being drawn. At the top was a small class of wealthy planters living on large plantations worked by the group at the bottom of the pyramid, the indentured servants and Negro slaves. In the middle were the small-scale

Fishing harbor, Peggy's Cove, Nova Scotia
[*Nova Scotia Film Bureau*]

Anglo-America: territorial growth

farmers who worked their own lands. The tremendous expansion of both plantations and slavery in the eighteenth century forced the middle-class farmers to accept one of three possibilities: to become small planters, to migrate, or to remain and constitute part of a new class of "poor whites." Those who chose to migrate went to Pennsylvania, or across the Blue Ridge to the Great Valley, or to newer lands even farther west.

The New England settlements began with the landing of refugee Pilgrims at Plymouth in 1620. After a number of years of struggle to exist and several unsuccessful experiments in growing commercial crops of rice, indigo, and cotton, all unsuited to the environment of New England, they finally gained experience in the kinds of crops that could survive in the climate and would grow on the stony, rough terrain. Natural conditions favored an agricultural system of small subsistence farms worked by the owners. There was little surplus for cash sale, and there was no place for slave labor. To many colonists this system was unacceptable, so they turned to the exploitation of other resources. From the banks off the coast they obtained exportable amounts of codfish. The mixed forest provided pine for masts, oak for the frames of ships, and

nuts on which to fatten pigs for export. Ice taken from frozen ponds in winter could be sold in the tropics at all seasons. New England vessels, carrying such cargoes as molasses, rum, and slaves, or engaging in whaling, created fortunes for their owners. The wealth so evident in the fine houses in the seaport towns of colonial New England was certainly not a product of the soil. But the social and economic system that developed, while it encompassed the wealth of the great families, did not deny a place to a substantial middle class, nor did it degrade through slavery the position of the small farmer.

The influences of these two significant and different nuclear British settlements spread westward in the expansion of the new nation. In general the traditions of Virginia were dominant in the South; those of New England, north of the Ohio River. Further westward movement brought strong dilution of the ways of the Atlantic seaboard. The grasslands demanded special cultural adaptations. Spanish American influences were met in the Great Plains. Mining, range grazing, irrigation, dry farming, and Mediterranean crops had few if any antecedents in early New England and Virginia. The varied cultural landscape of Anglo-America is really a product of a great many factors.

ANGLO-AMERICAN REALM

Quebec
[*Canadian National Railway*]

24. Anglo-American Realm

Anglo-American consists of Canada and all the United States (except Hawaii), exclusive of the areas that lie in the Polar World. Because of the vastness of the Anglo-American Realm, it is convenient and reasonable to divide it into geographic regions. These regions are drawn with no regard for political boundaries, for in this Realm they have almost no importance.

The basis for regional division is man and the imprint on the land indicative of his manner of living. Since neither the distribution of people nor the kinds of activities they engage in are affected by the political boundaries, they can be ignored in the regional descriptions. The regions themselves have traditionally been assigned names, some of which refer to natural condi-

415

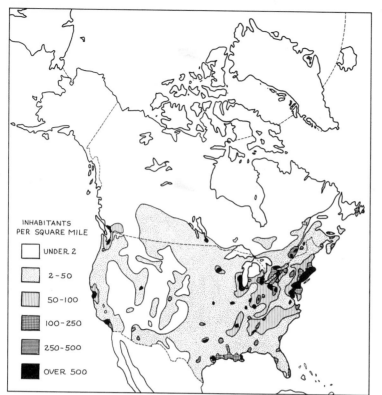

INHABITANTS
PER SQUARE MILE

	UNDER 2
	2–50
	50–100
	100–250
	250–500
	OVER 500

(*opposite*)
**Northern Forest;
Alaska; Pacific Northwest:
index map**

**Anglo-American
Realm:
population density**

tions, such as plant cover, climate, or relief, or to the main human activity, and others are locational. But irrational as the naming may seem, the regional divisions are based consistently on distinctions in man's way of life.

THE NORTHERN FOREST

The Northern Forest, as the index map indicates, is a vast region extending across Canada from Newfoundland to the Rocky Mountains. It is a land of little relief, bare-rock surfaces, countless lakes, and clear, rapid, patternless streams, all products of continental glaciation. Its surface is covered with swamps, muskegs, and a largely coniferous forest. The climate is continental, with bitterly cold, long, snowy winters and a short summer growing season. Culturally, the region is characterized by a sparse population whose major economic interests are furs, mining, and timber. There are no truly large cities, nor is there much in the way of railroad and highway development.

The Indians of pre-European days were hunters and fishermen who wintered in small groups on the family hunting grounds and met in summer rendezvous to transact tribal affairs.

The system was hardly disturbed by the coming of European fur traders who established posts throughout the Northern Forest region, usually at the summer gathering places. The Indians brought in furs, at first mainly beaver, to exchange for the traders' goods, which arrived by canoe brigades from Montreal or Hudson Bay ports. Heavy trapping in the more accessible places soon brought a decline in beaver, but other pelts and trapping in more remote areas kept the fur trade lively. The advance of civilization in the form of mining and lumbering during the last hundred years has led to the abandonment of posts at the south, as the center of fur production has been pushed northward.

Commercial logging of white pine began in Maine, and by the last third of the nineteenth century was underway in Quebec, Ontario, and the Upper Lake states. In less than 50 years the United States had chopped down its white pine, and the last stands are now being logged in western Ontario. Other species are being cut for lumber or pulp-wood, but, as with furs, the center of this major industry gradually moves northward.

Mining got off to an enthusiastic start with the exploitation of the copper deposits in the

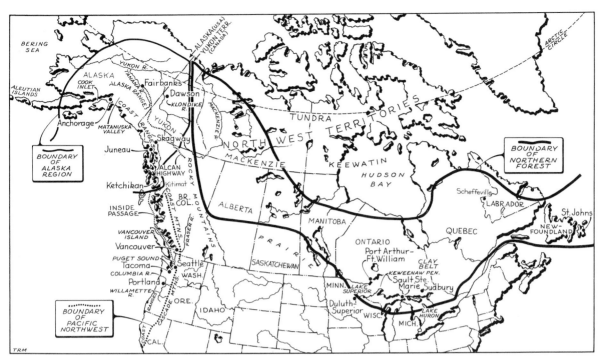

Keeweenaw Peninsula. Large-scale operations began in the eighteen-forties and in ten years were important enough to cause the opening of a ship canal around the rapids at Sault Ste. Marie. In less than 100 years these copper deposits were essentially exhausted. Of somewhat longer duration are the iron ore deposits first mined in Michigan at about the same time as copper. Mining spread westward into Wisconsin and Minnesota, and for many years these three states have produced a major part of the world's iron ore. The end of the best ores is in sight, but others less rich are still extensive.

The major Canadian mining district is in Ontario, north of Lake Huron and east of Lake Superior. This section, centering around Sudbury, is the world's leading producer of nickel, and in addition, gold, copper, uranium, iron, and other ores are mined. This mining section extends into neighboring Quebec, which is also an important producer of gold, copper, zinc, and lead, and which shares with the Labrador part of Newfoundland the important iron deposits near Schefferville. The exploitation of these iron deposits had to await the completion in 1954 of a railroad from the Gulf of St. Lawrence, whereas similar deposits near St.

Johns that lie at tidewater have long been mined. There are a number of other mining areas within the Northern Forest, such as that along the border between Manitoba and Saskatchewan, centering around Flin Flon, where nickel and gold occur in association with copper, silver, zinc, and other minerals. But all these mining areas are outshone in terms of the value of production by the Sudbury district, although the frantic search for minerals is uncovering more and more deposits, and improved transportation is allowing more of them to come into production.

The expansion of what should logically be the fourth form of land use, agriculture, has been slow and uncertain. Following the lumbering operations, optimistic settlers cleared the land with little regard for its agricultural possibilities. Very few were successful. Climate, soils, and distant markets preclude the general development of anything more than subsistence farming. With the possible exception of the French Canadians of the Ontario-Quebec clay belt, Americans are not satisfied with such an existence.

Industrialization and accompanying urbanization have made but slight imprint on the scene. Lumbering towns come and go, and to a lesser extent, so do mining towns. Permanent-type industry has not located within the region, but rather, the Northern Forest region has shipped its mineral and timber products outside its boundaries to be manufactured or used. Consequently, large cities are missing from the region, and such cities as it has are located near the southern border. Of these, the largest is Duluth-Superior, contiguous cities at the western tip of Lake Superior, whose chief function is transshipment of bulk cargoes: iron ore and wheat from rail to ship, and coal from ship to rail. Lesser cities are Port Arthur-Fort William, a wheat-shipping point; Sudbury, specializing in mining and smelting; and St. Johns, a base for fishing and sealing off the Labrador coast.

ALASKA

The Alaska region does not entirely coincide with the new State. The tundra margins on the north and west are excluded because they lie in the Polar World. The Canadian part of the drainage basin of the Yukon is included because it shares with the rest of the region a common culture and a background of exploitation of natural resources, fisheries, minerals, and furs. Within this region are two very different parts, coast and interior.

Coastal Alaska has a marine climate, that is, winters are mild and summers cool. Precipitation is heavy and there is no marked dry season. Dense coniferous forests, mainly of spruce and hemlock, clothe the land, which is extremely rugged and highly sculptured. There is little level land on the islands or among the fiords and sharp peaks, remnants of the period when ice carved the landscape. Even today, glaciers are still extensive, and in a number of places they reach from the mountains to the sea. This rough land is rich in minerals ranging from copper, gold, silver, and lead, to coal and petroleum. Streams, plunging down from the mountains, have enormous hydroelectric potential. Also, these streams and the near-shore waters are among the world's best fishing grounds, with abundant salmon, halibut, herring, and other excellent food fish.

Interior Alaska lies north of the coastal moun-

tains, and is essentially the plateau drained by the Yukon River and its tributaries. Here the climate is continental, with long severe winters, and summers that are punctuated by occasional hot spells. Precipitation is considerably less than along the coast. The plateau, averaging about 3,000 feet in elevation, slopes down toward the west, and is deeply cut by streams. In the valley bottoms are woodland patches of spruce, birch, and willow, but the interstream ridges rise above the cold timber line. Inhospitable as the plateau may seem, it escaped glaciation during the Pleistocene, and thus could have been attractive as a route for incoming Asian migrants. Its glacer gold and coal have continued its attraction right to the present.

European interest in Alaska started in the middle of the eighteenth century when Bering, a Dane employed by Russia, brought back reports of the abundance of excellent furs. The Russians promptly established fur posts along the coast as far south as Fort Ross, California. Their fur trade was largely with China, which offered an accessible and ready market. The Russians did not penetrate the interior, nor did they come in sufficient numbers to establish permanent settlements. Unable to utilize the fisheries and unaware of the value of its mineral wealth, Russia, faced with a declining fur trade, sold Alaska to the United States in 1867 for the bargain price of $7,200,000.

Americans at first took little interest in Seward's "ice box." Seasonal salmon fisheries and trivial placer-gold finds brought a few people to the coasts, while furs attracted some to the interior. By the 1880's enough placer gold had been found in the interior to tempt prospectors into further search which was rewarded in 1896 by the discovery of rich gold deposits on the Klondike, a small tributary to the Yukon. During the rush that followed, thousands of hopeful gold seekers poured into the region. Dawson became a city of 30,000 within a matter of months. Spurred by success, the prospectors continued the search, making a number of other discoveries, the most important being in the vicinity of present Fairbanks. The last big stampede came about 1915, and it now seems unlikely that any large, rich body of placer gold remains undiscovered. But none of these great

Northern Forest outpost, Port Arthur

[*The Photographic Survey Corporation, Ltd., Toronto*]

influxes of people brought any sense of permanence or stability to Alaska, which is still largely in the frontier stage of development, with most of its activities directed toward exploitation of natural resources. Sedentary agriculture has yet to prove it can become widespread.

The Alaska region is about a fifth the size of the fifty States, while the state of Alaska contains over 586,000 square miles and 167,000 people. The region includes about the same number of people as the state, of which less than 20,000 are native Indians. The bulk of the population and major economic activities are concentrated in the coastal section. Here are the fisheries, lode mining, lumbering, tremendous waterpower, magnificent scenery to attract tourists, and one of the few successful agricultural ventures, in Matanuska Valley. Interior Alaska is still largely concerned with mining which in the placer areas is now a large-scale operation of huge dredges, drag lines, and bulldozers, requiring relatively few employees. Agriculture utilizes perhaps 10,000 acres, mainly in the vicinity of Dawson and Fairbanks. Admitting that crops of grain, roots, and hay can be successfully grown, the absence of large markets points toward a subsistence rather than a commercial agriculture. Fur yield is declining, mainly because of the lack of sound regulation. All in all, it is difficult to see a future for the interior that differs in any marked way from the present pattern or intensity of utilization.

Despite the tremendous increase in population during the last decade, urbanization is still in its infancy, and so is transportation development. There are less than 1,000 miles of railroad, and only about three times that mileage in surfaced roads. Only one city, Anchorage (about 80,000), has over 15,000 population, and it serves as the entrepot for Matanuska Valley and interior Alaska, being the terminal of the railroad to Fairbanks. From Fairbanks there is a road connection to the navigable Yukon River, and to Whitehorse and other southeastern points along the Alaskan Highway. Fairbanks is also at the crossroads of air routes, and in the midst of a mining area and the most extensive interior agricultural district. Neither Juneau, the capital of Alaska and the center of lode mining, fisheries, and timber, nor Ketchikan, a fishing center, approaches 10,000 in population.

EASTERN MARITIME REGION

The Eastern Maritime region includes the six New England states and three provinces of Canada, as shown on the index map. The term maritime is locational rather than indicating either the climate or culture, for interior New England has a continental climate, and Prince Edward Island, although surrounded by sea, has no background of notable maritime achievements. The region's meager natural endowments made life difficult for the early European settlers, who tried to make the best of its raw, disagreeable climate and its few, scattered areas of arable land. Mineral wealth is limited to coal found in Nova Scotia, and building stones. The only really valuable assets are the excellent fishing grounds nearby, the abundance of good harbors, and, formerly, the fine forests.

The early economic development was the same throughout the region: limited agricultural possibilities causing attention to be turned toward fishing, merchant marine, and lumber-

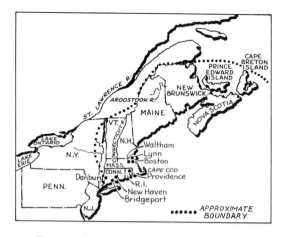

Eastern Maritime Region: index map

ing activities. After the exhaustion of the forests and the decline of the merchant fleets, the development of the Canadian and New England sections followed different courses. The waning of New England's merchant marine activities with the Civil War resulted in the acceleration of developments long underway, manufacturing and accompanying urbanization. No such shift in economic endeavor occurred in maritime Canada, nor in the adjacent parts of northernmost New England.

New England manufacturing has always been notable for its diversification, perhaps because it lacked an abundance of any particular natural resource on which to specialize. There were, for example, no deposits of iron and coal as the basis of heavy industry. But what New England lacked in natural resources it made up in its location. Numerous harbors allowed the cheap import of seaborne raw materials and immigrant labor. At an early date Boston and other growing urban centers provided good nearby markets for a wide variety of consumer goods. With adequate water power, cheap imported raw materials, sufficient labor, and good local markets, it is not surprising that a diversity of industries was established. This industrialization led Rhode Island, Massachusetts, and Connecticut to become three of the four most densely populated states in the United States, although New England contains only one city, Boston, that ranks among the first ten in population in the United States. Nevertheless, there

are a number of areas of essentially uninterrupted urban development, as between Boston and Providence, and between New York and New Haven. In these densely settled urban areas there is a preponderance of peoples of foreign birth or recent foreign extraction.

In contrast, the rural population is still largely old-American stock, a reflection of the fact that New England agriculture attracts very few newcomers. The trend is actually in the opposite direction, people leaving sterile hill farms to move to the cities or to better western lands. Aroostook potatoes, Cape Cod cranberries, New Hampshire dairying, and Connecticut Valley tobacco are a few of the bright spots in an otherwise dark agricultural picture. A more profitable use of the land is the entertainment of tourists, an endeavor yielding an income second only to that from manufacturing. Recent years have seen summer vacationers and winter skiers arriving in increasing numbers.

In the three Canadian maritime provinces and in northernmost New England, substantial agriculture is restricted to better lands: dairying on Prince Edward Island, and apple orchards in Nova Scotia, for example. The forests that cover the land have been cut over at least once. Fishing is important, especially in Nova Scotia. Missing from the scene are the industrialization and urbanization characteristic of southern New

Covered bridge, Vermont
[*U.S. Forest Service*]

Rural landscape, Cornwallis Valley, Nova Scotia
[*Nova Scotia Film Bureau*]

England. The lone important representative of manufacturing is the iron and steel industry of Cape Breton Island, fostered by the local occurrence of coal and the availability of Newfoundland iron ore.

Boston, in urbanized southern New England, is the one great city of national prominence. It is the core of a tightly packed conurbation of about 2.5 million people. Its industrial output is enormous, but no one product is dominant. It possesses an excellent harbor, but its hinterland is restricted to New England. In addition to its industry, Boston is a financial and an educational center. As a commercial center, it is a major distributor of textiles, shoes, furniture, and fish and other sea food. Included in the conurbation are Lynn, famous for its shoe production, and Waltham, long a watch center. Other southern New England towns are diminished by comparison with Boston, yet they are nevertheless important. Among these are New Haven, a manufacturing center and home of numerous insurance companies; Bridgeport, a hardware producer; Providence, a trade center and producer especially of metal and rubber goods; and many lesser industrial centers such as Hartford, Lowell, Fall River, and Worcester.

ST. LAWRENCE VALLEY

The St. Lawrence Valley region is topographically the long, narrow depression lying between the harder, higher Laurentide Mountains to the north and the Adirondacks and New England uplands to the south. Culturally, it is the heart of French America, the nucleus of a distinct people and a distinct way of life. The region is more than a museum of curiosities to be enjoyed by the touring Anglo-American. It exerts an influence both in Canada and in neighboring New England. Canadians of French descent number over 4.5 million, and constitute about a quarter of Canada's total population. French-Canadians are numerous in New England and in the Lake States, and were pioneers in the Clay Belt and northern frontiers of the Canadian prairies. Everywhere they go, their culture goes with them.

Preoccupation with the fur trade resulted in a late start for agriculture in French Canada, but once it was established it became and remains the economic base for the region. Its pattern is one of small farms growing oats, hay, and roots, and pastures and dairying. Its expression on the landscape is distinctive. The land is divided into narrow strips extending back from the river, with the dwellings facing the road along the river bank. Along the road creak two-wheeled carts, still common in the French-American scene. The road, dotted with religious shrines, leads to the small, white village, dominated by the church.

The farms are commonly divided into narrower and narrower strips as the land is inherited by generation after generation. Since the division cannot go on indefinitely to accommodate the numerous progeny, some of the younger people are forced to migrate to other

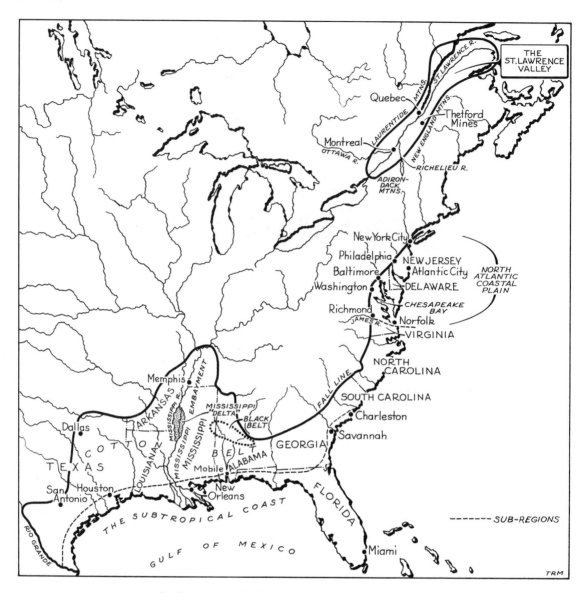

St. Lawrence Valley; Coast Plain: index map

regions or to work in the small factories within the region that manufacture such articles as shoes and cloth. Some employment is found in the Thetford Mines, which produce most of the world's supply of asbestos. But timber and waterpower combine to provide most employment. Trees are cut in winter, and in spring the logs are floated down the streams to mills located near their mouths on the St. Lawrence. The streams provide power to change the logs into pulp and paper. Surplus hydroelectric power has resulted in the erection of smelters to convert imported ores into aluminum to be manufactured elsewhere.

Two cities dominate the region. Quebec is the city of tradition, the only walled city in Anglo-America. Picturesque buildings face narrow, crooked streets, a few leading precipitously down the bluff to the warehouse-lined waterfront. Quebec's commercial importance is restricted to its immediate hinterland. In contrast is Montreal (1.7 million), the commercial center of the whole country. It is Canada's largest city, port, and railway center. Until 1959 it was at the head of deep-water navigation on the St. Lawrence, but with the opening of the St. Lawrence Seaway, it now stands at the entrance to that important series of locks and canals that allows ocean-going vessels to reach Great Lakes ports. To some extent this may reduce Montreal's function as a handler of wood pulp, newsprint, and grain from western Canada, but it will continue to be a center of finance, commerce, education, and industry.

CENTRAL MANUFACTURING REGION

The Central Manufacturing region is the great industrial area that extends from the lower Great Lakes to the Ohio River and from Pittsburgh to St. Louis. It is a region of diversified manufacturing, ranging from basic iron and steel to the processing of agricultural products. Within it are huge industrial cities and small towns boasting of but a single factory. The whole economic structure, however, rests on a sound and substantial agricultural base.

Most of the region was part of the French colonial domain, and so was largely unavailable to the English colonists. Even after the French lost the area in 1763, the British authorities tried to reserve it for the Indians, a plan that was swept aside after the American Revolution by a flood of settlers. Initially the Ohio River was the main route of ingress, and from it settlement moved up the north-bank tributaries. Many of the early settlers came from Virginia, bringing a decided southern character to the landscape. The easier route along the Mohawk was opened after the War of 1812, letting in a new flood of settlers, mainly of New England origin. Their influence can still be seen in the architecture and folkways of the northern margin of the region.

Early agriculture provided cash returns from corn, hogs, wheat, tobacco, and their derivatives, such as whiskey, bacon, and flour. At first the products went down the Mississippi to New Orleans. Then, after the building of canals and railroads, the cities of the eastern seaboard began to draw the bulk of the produce of this rich agricultural region. General farming is still the pattern, with medium-sized farms producing corn, grains, hay, and livestock. The production

of fruit in Michigan, Ontario, and New York is one of numerous specialties reflecting particular advantages of location or natural conditions.

Manufacturing first gained impetus after the Civil War when there was a general expansion of economy, population, and transportation facilities. The early industrial enterprises met with success, so more and more industries were attracted to the region. The region is well endowed for manufacturing. It has coal, petroleum, limestone, and cheap iron ore from the Lake Superior areas. Transportation facilities on the rivers and lakes have always been good, and are now augmented by excellent railroads and highways, and by the St. Lawrence Seaway, which brings ocean transports to the Great Lakes ports and generates hydroelectricity for the eastern part of the region. With these assets, industry thrives and population continues to increase at a rapid rate, providing ample labor supply and good markets as well.

Urbanization has kept pace with the expansion of industry. Within the region are some 45 cities each with more than 100,000 people in their metropolitan areas. A dozen of these are in the half-million and over category, and two are real giants, Detroit (3.0 million) and Chicago (6.4 million). Such concentrations of population were a natural consequence of the early manufacturing processes which called for all parts of a single machine or vehicle to be made in one plant or in plants in the near vicinity. Now it is both technically possible and desirable to decentralize manufacturing, and the trend is for small plants to be established in towns or villages to gain the advantage of a local labor supply, low overhead costs, local tax structure, or any number of other benefits. This tendency may call a halt to the tremendous growth of great urban centers.

Although industry is widespread in the region, in few places is it continuous over long distances, but rather, it is interrupted by agricultural countryside. Nor is the nature of industry uniform throughout the region, so it is most conveniently described in terms of subregions, differentiated on the basis of their dominant industrial activities. (Note: in this section and

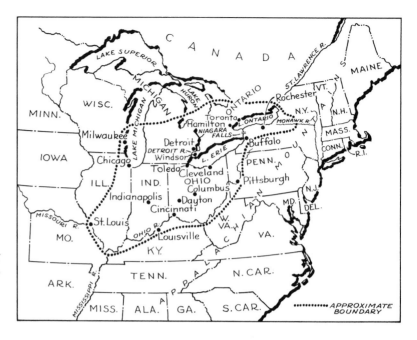

Central Manufacturing Region: index map

all the following descriptions of Anglo-American urbanization, population figures are given for the standard metropolitan area because they are more indicative of the size of the agglomerations than are the figures for the city units based on political boundaries.)

The **Niagara District** surrounds the western half of Lake Ontario, and has the advantages of excellent transportation facilities, both rail and water, and proximity to a source of hydro-electric power, Niagara Falls. Diversity of manufactures is the keynote, the range including optical goods in Rochester, iron and steel in Hamilton, flour milling in Toronto, and chemical and metallurgical industries on both sides of the border. The leading cities, Toronto (1.4 million) and Buffalo (1.1), are much alike in their activities, which include both heavy and light metal industries, milling, and a number of other manufacturing enterprises.

The **Pittsburgh Steel District** centers on Pittsburgh (2.5 million), but includes nearby parts of Pennsylvania, West Virginia, and Ohio. It is the leading iron and steel producer of the nation, and is also important in the manufacture of machinery, tires, glass, and ceramic wares. Included both in this district and in the Automobile District is Cleveland (1.6 million), which in addition to manufacturing iron and steel, automobiles, heavy machinery, and many

metal wares, is a Lake Erie port, receiving iron ore and limestone, and shipping coal.

The **Automobile District** includes southern Michigan and adjacent parts of Ohio, Indiana, and Ontario, The United States has 70 per cent of the world's passenger cars and over half the world's commercial vehicles, and a large share of these are produced in the Automobile District. Although most of the concentration is on the production of automotive vehicles, the district also produces farm equipment, heavy machinery, metal wares, and other manufactures. While such cities as Windsor and Toledo are important, they are completely overshadowed by the foremost motor car producer, Detroit (3.0 million), which pioneered in the production of automobiles as an outgrowth of its even earlier manufacture of carriages and marine engines.

The **Middle Ohio River District** is oriented toward the Ohio River rather than toward the Great Lakes, but makes more use of its fine rail and highway connections than of river transport. The district is characterized by its diversity of manufactures, for although it does not produce basic iron and steel, it is an important supplier of a wide range of articles, such as tools, refrigerators, computing machines, engines, radios, clothing, whiskey, and beer. The cities are all of comparatively moderate size:

Cincinnati (0.9 million) is the largest, and Indianapolis, Louisville, Columbus, and Dayton each have over a half million population.

The **St. Louis District** coincides with a concentration of population and industry on the Mississippi at the mouth of the Missouri and near the mouth of the Ohio. There is also a convergence of railroads and highways. Among the varied manufactures are airplane and machinery parts, chemicals, drugs, shoes, electrical equipment, engines, and beer. The single large city is St. Louis (1.9 million), founded by the French, and true to its tradition it remains a fur-marketing center, as one among its many distributing and manufacturing activities.

The **Chicago District** centers around the southern end of Lake Michigan, and profits from excellent transportation facilities and proximity to coal, petroleum, and the highly productive Corn Belt. Industry ranges from iron and steel, through machinery, electrical equipment, farm implements, and railroad cars, to publishing and meat packing. Both of the two large cities in the district, Milwaukee (1.0 million) and Chicago (6.4 million), participate in all these industries, but in terms of production, Chicago is by far the leader. Chicago is the second largest city and the major railroad center of the United States. In addition to its iron and steel, farm equipment, and other manufactures, it is also a major grain center, and has huge meat-processing establishments, but many of these are becoming obsolete and costly to operate, so the slaughtering and meat packing business is abandoning the plants and moving closer to the sources of supply.

COAST PLAIN

As a natural feature the Coast Plain is a belt of lowland lying between the sea and a clearly defined inner boundary marking the ascent to higher and older lands. It stretches from New York City to and beyond the Rio Grande. (See index map of St. Lawrence Valley and Coast Plain.) The average width along the Atlantic seaboard is about 100 miles. To the south the plain broadens along the Gulf of Mexico and

extends inland as the Mississippi Embayment to the mouth of the Ohio. Throughout, it is characterized by low elevation and low relief, adequate to abundant precipitation, hardwood swamps and sandy pine uplands, and, girdling the coast, a band of marshes and an outer line of sandy barrier islands. The young sedimentary rocks yield a variety of mineral wealth, petroleum, gas, salt, sulphur, and phosphates.

As a cultural region the Coast Plain possesses no high degree of unity. Agriculture is the common form of land use, and on the immediate coast are such varied activities as commercial fishing, recreation, and the handling of maritime commerce in port cities. Beyond these general similarities the cultural activities and patterns are such as to necessitate the division of the Coast Plain into three subregions: the North Atlantic Coast Plain, the Cotton Belt, and the Subtropical Coast.

North Atlantic Coast Plain subregion extends from New York City to the southern boundary of Virginia, but does not include the Fall Line cities of New York, Philadelphia, Baltimore, Washington, and Richmond, which lie in the Piedmont Region. The coastline is deeply indented by bays, estuaries, and tidal rivers that carry deep-water ships to its inner margin. The land itself is rather poorly endowed by nature, lacking good soils, forests, and mineral wealth. The natural assets are a comparatively long growing season, excellent fisheries, and attractive sandy beaches.

Culturally the subregion embraces tidewater Virginia, with its aristocratic tradition of one-crop plantations, and a portion of the originally non-English, peasant-artisan middle-Atlantic area. Despite these differences in culture background, the whole subregion can be uniformly characterized by a sparse, declining population, absence of great cities, and the recent emphasis on the production of vegetable crops. The decline of the area was due largely to soil depletion. It was apparent in tidewater Virginia even in colonial times. The abolition of slavery further contributed to the decay of the old plantation system. The raising of general crops became concentrated on the better lands, but something of the old ways was preserved, as in the use of Negro labor and in the maintaining of an unbridged gap between large and small landowners. Parallel changes in the northern section saw the abandonment of thousands of acres of marginal land and the rise of a class of backwoods "pineys."

The unifying development of vegetable production came largely after 1920, and was favored by an early growing season and proximity to large urban centers. The distinctive land use pattern is that of small, intensively cultivated fields; packing, canning, and freezing plants; and fast, modern means of transportation. Even so, all the older traditions have not been entirely obliterated, for in the southern section Negroes are still the main labor supply, and life moves in a leisurely fashion.

Independent of agricultural changes and developments are the fisheries. Leader among these is Chesapeake Bay, in which are caught a variety of food fish and rough fish for fertilizer, and which is the nation's leading producer of oysters.

The North Atlantic Coast Plain is lacking in great cities, and even the urban centers that it has are not the products of the subregion itself. Atlantic City is almost purely a resort city, drawing tourists from all parts of the country. Norfolk-Portsmouth is the largest of a cluster of three ports lying near the mouth of the James River at the lower end of Chesapeake Bay. Newport News is a large ship builder and exporter of coal, and, with the port of Hampton Roads, is connected by tunnel to Norfolk, which is concerned largely with loading ships with coal brought by rail from west of the Blue Ridge. Norfolk is also a major naval base, and like the other ports, is engaged in processing agricultural products and imports.

The Cotton Belt includes the remainder of the Coast Plain except for a narrow strip of subtropical coast. The climate, optimal for the growing of cotton, is characterized by a growing season of 200 or more days and a dry fall. These climatic conditions are also found outside the Cotton Belt in parts of the Carolina Piedmont and the interior plains province of Texas and Oklahoma, where cotton is also grown. Within the subregion, the dominance of cotton as a cash crop came with the invention of the gin and a tremendous demand for the newly cheap textile fiber. Other crops were abandoned in favor of cotton. The need for labor gave slavery new economic importance, and the plantation pattern became firmly established in areas of better soils, such as the Black Belt of Alabama, and later, the "delta" lands of Mississippi. These plantations, along with the smaller farmers in the poorer sections, overwhelmingly dominated world cotton production at the time of the Civil War. But that war marked a turning point in the economic well-being of the Cotton Belt. The substitution of sharecropping for slavery accelerated soil wastage. The imposition of high import tariffs on manufactures from Europe in an effort to foster northern industry greatly reduced Europe's ability and interest in buying southern cotton. The spread of the destructive boll weevil in the twentieth century was but an added push down the road of decline. The social results were poverty and rural slums as bad as those of any city.

Slowly the area is recovering, but cotton is no longer dominant, for it now shares the land with corn, tobacco, soybeans, sweet potatoes, peanuts, rice, peaches, and pecans; with livestock and pastures; and with forests which produce pulp for the new paper mills, lumber, fuel wood, and naval stores. Crops vary in kind, not only on those individual farms which practice crop rotation, but from one place to another within a region. Long-abused soils are being reclaimed, and to an increasing extent farming is becoming mechanized. There are still many problems, of course, but the approach is sane and fairly systematic.

Many regard industrialization as the cure of all the ills of the Cotton Belt, which offers several advantages for manufacturing, such as abundant labor supply, mild winters, natural gas, and raw materials, including petroleum, timber, and cotton. On the other hand, there are drawbacks, such as the distance from the richest markets, absence of coal, long hot summers, and lack of technical skills. Despite these handicaps, industry has expanded rapidly in recent years, with the steady addition of plants and factories involving petroleum, chemicals, paper, textiles, aluminum, synthetic rubber and tires, and tractors.

Cotton Belt home, Louisiana
[*U.S.D.A.*]

Urbanization has as usual accompanied industrialization, and both are recent. As late as 1870 there was no Cotton Belt city with a population in excess of 100,000, and now there are nearly a dozen cities that exceed that figure. Dallas, San Antonio, and Memphis, each with a half million or more population, are among the many modern, bustling metropolitan centers that are a far cry from the courthouse towns of the traditional Cotton Belt.

The Subtropical Coast differs both naturally and culturally from the other subregions of the Coast Plain. As the name indicates, the climate approaches that of the tropics in length of growing season and mildness of winter temperatures. The coastal location means low elevation and relief, extensive swamps and marshes, sandy barrier beaches, and generally abundant precipitation. Culturally the subregion has been marked by erratic and special utilization, with port cities of a size quite out of keeping with the meager endowments of their hinterlands.

The early founding of such ports as Charleston, Mobile, and New Orleans fostered local experiments with various commercial crops, such as indigo, rice, sugar cane, and cotton. Of these, rice and sea-island cotton became established crops on the Georgia-Carolina coast, and sugar cane became important in southern Louisiana, where, later, technical advances in refining led to rapid expansion of sugar plantations in the rich delta lands. Over most of the Subtropical Coast, however, population remained scant and utilization was limited, for even such activities as fishing, cattle grazing, and the extraction of naval stores did not reach very large proportions.

Especially in the last 50 years the Subtropical Coast has expanded greatly in population and commercial activity. Part of the growth rests upon the rehabilitation or extension of old enterprises, and part is the result of the introduction of new activities. The present pattern of agriculture finds sugar cane still dominant in coastal Louisiana, with a recent extension into Florida. Southwestern Louisiana is now devoted to rice. Florida, delta Louisiana, and the lower Rio Grande Valley produce citrus fruits and early vegetables. Scientific forestry, tung-oil trees, and pecan groves are making use of worn-out soils. The beef cattle industry has been revived with the assistance of tick-fever control and improved breeding.

The extractive industries have kept pace with the growth of agriculture. Carefully planted and tended forests keep one of the subregion's oldest occupations faintly alive, that of extraction of naval stores, now mainly turpentine and resin, and foster a fairly new activity, pulp production. The whole coast produces fish of choice quality. Waters around the mouths of the Mississippi are the leading source of shrimp and important for oyster production. The Louisiana marshes continue to yield the bulk of the continent's muskrat catch. But all these combined are insignificant in comparison with the wealth of minerals produced in the subregion: phosphates in Florida, salt in Louisiana, sulphur in Texas and Louisiana, and above all, petroleum and natural gas. The latter are new activities that began during this century. Producing oil fields now dot coastal Texas and Louisiana, even in the offshore areas, and promise to extend eastward. Nothing else has done so much to alter the landscape or to lend momentum to industrial enterprise.

Manufacturing is about in the same stage as in the Cotton Belt, and only recently has gone beyond processing the yield of extractive industries and agriculture. Lumber, naval stores, meat, hides, furs, sugar, and shellfish have been supplemented by pulpwood, paper, salt, and sulphur, but present-day manufacturing expansion rests mainly on petroleum and natural gas. From the modern refineries come not only gasoline and lubricating oil, but also the ingredients of synthetic rubber and a variety of chemicals, plastics, and detergents. Natural gas supplies the needed industrial power, and is abundant enough to support iron and steel plants in Houston.

Many of the old port cities have lost out in the race for urban-industrial growth. Charleston, Savannah, and Mobile have risen only to the 200,000 population class, but New Orleans, an important port for 200 years, has kept the pace, its 0.8 million population being only recently topped by the 1.2 million of Houston. New Orleans owes its significance to its control of the Mississippi Valley route to and from the continental interior, and so its chief function is that of an entrepot. The growth of its chief rival, Houston, began with the construction of a ship canal to the Gulf of Mexico early in the twentieth century. The new port drew cotton, wheat, and petroleum for export. The city is today the most thriving industrial center of the Subtropical Coast, specializing in oil refining, chemicals, and milling of rice and flour, among a number of other industries. Of a completely different nature is Miami (0.8 million), whose sole function is catering to tourists, an industry reflecting mild winters and sandy ocean beaches. Many other expanding resort centers dot the Florida, Mississippi, and Texas coast.

THE PIEDMONT

The Piedmont borders the inner Coast Plain for about a thousand miles, from New York City to central Alabama. To the west is the Blue Ridge, and to the east, the Fall Line, a boundary that is at tidewater as far south as central Virginia and rises to 500 feet in Georgia. The region is hilly, with streams rather deeply cut, particularly in the southern portion. Soils are generally of limited productivity due to their shallowness. Mineral resources are unimportant, and so is water power in general. Culturally, on the basis of patterns of rural living and degrees of industrialization and urbanization, the region tends to be divided into two parts: Northern Piedmont, extending from New York into northernmost Virginia; and Southern Piedmont, including the remainder of the region.

The Northern Piedmont is a land with con-

Piedmont landscape, North Carolina
[*U.S.D.A.*]

siderable agriculture practiced by small farmers who are largely of non-English origin. The crops are varied: wheat, corn, tobacco, and potatoes; with special products such as milk, butter, eggs, and poultry especially for the nearby dense urban populations. A highpoint in the rural landscape in terms of productivity, tidiness, and careful farm practices is in the Pennsylvania "Dutch" area, centering on the limestone soils of Lancaster County.

Agriculture, however, is certainly not the basis for the high degree of urbanization represented by New York, Philadelphia, Baltimore, and Washington. The first three owe their growth to extra-regional relations which got off to early starts. Washington, D.C., (1.9 million) is a purely political creation, as the nation's capital.

New York City is the world's largest city and numbers within its metropolitan area over 14.4 million people. It is the focus of population, finance, and industry for the country and the western hemisphere. Its population is largely recent-American in composition. To feed the enormous concentration of people in Manhattan alone it is necessary to import daily 15 million pounds of fresh fruits and vegetables, nearly 6 million pounds of meat, and almost a million quarts of milk. They keep warm in the winter on a daily import of 2 million gallons of fuel oil. New York dictates styles of living and thought, and sets urban standards with its tall buildings, subways, and other transportation facilities. The skyscrapers of its Wall Street financial district, with an area of only one third square mile, have a daytime population of over 1.5 million, and a night population of some 2,000—which conjures up a picture of the terrific rush-hour traffic. As the country's chief industrial center, New York anomalously lacks basic iron and steel production.

As a city, New York long ranked behind Philadelphia and Boston, for it lacked the excellent agricultural hinterland of Philadelphia,

major role in the growth of New York, but even should the relative value of its location change, as with the opening of the St. Lawrence Seaway, which might attract traffic from its port, it seems unlikely that it will lose its preeminence because its highly organized financial and commercial activities have a position too entrenched to be dislodged.

Philadelphia (4.2 million) and Baltimore (1.6 million) differ from New York in degree rather than in kind. Each tried by means of rail and canal construction to match New York's com-

Urban landscape, New York
[*Belgian American Educational Foundation*]

and was unable to match the maritime interests of Boston. Its march to outstanding dominance began in the first third of the nineteenth century with the building of the Erie Canal and New York Central Railroad along the best route to the interior of the continent. The development of the trans-Appalachian West found New York at the small end of the funnel through which most traffic flowed. Location thus played a

mand of traffic with the interior. Each is today an important port joining rail and ocean shipping, and each has varied industry and manufacturing. Unlike New York, both Philadelphia and Baltimore have access to iron and steel production, Philadelphia with Bethlehem, and Baltimore with Sparrows Point.

The Southern Piedmont is part of the South. Although the tidewater plantation system never

Piedmont: index map

dominated the Piedmont, it has its quota of landed gentry, small farmers, rural Negroes, and "poor white" sharecroppers. These elements are unevenly distributed, and change progressively from north to south with transitions in crops and levels of living.

Southward to middle Virginia is an area of commercial apple orchards and livestock, where land is carefully managed, and living standards are comparatively high. In the central section, from middle Virginia to central North Carolina, tobacco is the main commercial crop, while farther south cotton is important. Both the central and southern sections are alike in their wastage of land through soil depletion and erosion, and in the widespread poverty and deficiency diseases of their inhabitants. In contrast to the rural poverty in the southern two thirds of the Piedmont Region are the attractive, modern cities that have grown in company with the development of industry. This district is first in the country in the manufacture of cigarettes and cotton textiles, and produces a significant amount of furniture, knit-goods, rayon and other synthetic fibers, fertilizers,

pulp, and paper. This industrialization has taken place largely in the last 50 years. The district offered a number of attractions to capital and industry: local production of cigarette tobacco, cheap hydroelectric power, low-cost land, mild winters, tax concessions, and, above all, an abundance of cheap, unorganized labor provided by poverty-stricken sharecroppers and mountaineers. Although the latter advantage has essentially disappeared as a result of wage increases, industrial expansion continues at a rapid rate.

So far, industrialization in the Piedmont has produced no great urban agglomerations, because the individual factories tend to be dispersed rather than concentrated. Modest-sized Winston-Salem, the cigarette-manufacturing capital of the nation, and Charlotte, a leading cotton-textile center, are the largest cities of the new industrial district, but neither metropolitan area exceeds 0.250 million. Richmond (0.4) is much older in its industrialization. Its manufactures range from tobacco products to locomotives. It is a minor port and important railroad center. Atlanta (0.9), the largest city in the southern Piedmont, is a product of the railroad age, for it is situated at the crossroads of lines from the northeast and northwest where they converge as they swing around the southern end of the Appalachians. It is primarily a commercial city, but also has a variety of manufacturing industries.

THE APPALACHIANS

West of the Piedmont lies the largest area of hills and mountains in eastern Anglo-America. It includes, from east to west, three distinct natural units: Blue Ridge, Folded Appalachians, and Appalachian Plateaus. Common to all three units are such natural characteristics as steep slopes, heavy forest cover, and abundant precipitation. Here and there are limited areas of good soils. Coal, petroleum, and iron ore, the most important minerals occurring in the region, are unevenly distributed.

Culturally the region is united only in broad terms. Old-stock Americans are numerically dominant, but recent immigrants are well represented in the northern sections. Agriculture is the most widespread occupation, but mining and manufacturing are important. The nature of the agriculture, however, is of more cultural significance than the fact that agriculture is a major activity. The raising of wheat, corn, apples, and livestock distinguishes Appalachian agriculture from that of adjoining lowlands, where cash crops of cotton or tobacco are dominant. With these Appalachian crops goes a pattern of small, owner-operated farms, with a relatively small number of Negroes and tenant farmers, and subsistence agriculture at a maximum for the nation. Within this general cultural framework there is considerable local variation, which is most conveniently described on the basis of the three natural units, even though it is recognized that cultural similarity has limited respect for natural boundaries.

The Blue Ridge is the highest and roughest part of the Appalachian Region. The mountains are mantled by a heavy forest that obscures all but the steepest slopes. Level ground is rarely encountered, and almost as scarce are mineral deposits of any commercial value.

Into this land of natural beauty and limited resources came English small farmers who found no place for themselves in the plantation-slavery system developing on the Coast Plain. They were joined by Scotch-Irish, Germans, and Huguenots from the stream of migrants descending the Appalachian Valley. Isolation welded these diverse elements into a homogeneous group having a folk pattern reminiscent of that of their British ancestors. Speech, the feud, song, story, dance, arts, and crafts are about the same now as at the time of the retreat of these peoples into the mountains. The economic base was, and continues to be, subsistence agriculture: corn, wheat, apples, sorghum, and livestock, with corn whiskey the nearest approach to a cash crop. The farmers were also artisans and craftsmen, at least to the extent of supplying their own needs. These self-sufficient, independent, conservative mountaineers liked their way of life, even when it became precarious. A high birth rate combined with a reluctance to leave the mountains caused the spread of agriculture to every bit of flat land and to slopes too steep for permanent cultivation. Resulting erosion and declining agricul-

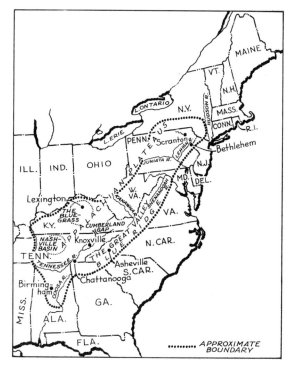

Appalachian Region: index map

tural yields brought poverty matching that of the southern Piedmont, but the Blue Ridge had no mineral industry or manufacturing to provide relief.

Today the Blue Ridge is a major problem area in terms of both land and people. Families are still large and mere existence is increasingly difficult. But the mountaineer clings to his land and his culture patterns, and only the greatest needs force him to move to the mill cities of the Piedmont.

Although attractive naturally and interesting culturally, as a living museum of old Americana, there is nothing in the Blue Ridge to promote urbanization. Only in the south where the mountains broaden to a plateau is there reason for even a moderate-size city. Asheville is primarily a summer tourist center with modest industrial development.

The Folded Appalachians are a belt of alternating ridges and valleys extending from the Hudson River to central Alabama. Almost continuous throughout the length of the region is the Great Valley, which locally bears the name of the stream that occupies it, such as Coosa,

Tennessee, Shenandoah, or Lehigh. The Great Valley lies on the eastern or Blue Ridge side of the Folded Appalachians. It owes its position to a concentration of folded limestones whose comparatively rapid weathering formed the valley and floored it with productive soils. West of the Great Valley is a series of sandstone, shale, and

Appalachian Plateaus landscape, New York
[*U.S.D.A.*]

conglomerate ridges separated by lesser limestone and shale valleys. Unlike the Blue Ridge, the Folded Appalachians belt has industrially significant mineral deposits of iron ore, anthracite coal, and, of course, limestone.

The Folded Appalachians became culturally important when settlement pushed west of the Piedmont and Blue Ridge. The Great Valley became a main route of land seekers. From it distributary routes led up the Juniata or down the Kanawha to the headwaters of the Ohio, or through Cumberland Gap to the Bluegrass and Nashville basins. Some settlers turned eastward into the Blue Ridge, and others pushed on to the Piedmont. Because the broad opening to the Valley is in Pennsylvania, where the Blue Ridge peters out, Scotch-Irish and Germans landing in Philadelphia followed the obvious path, to contribute greatly to the character of the new settlements. Aside from the function of the Great

Valley as a corridor, it and other parts of the Folded Appalachians were also places of settlement. Some people chose to establish themselves in the productive limestone valleys, while others, oddly enough, seemed to prefer the sterile shaly ridges. Agricultural development, needless to say, reflects these differences. A further contribution to the variety of occupance patterns comes from the exploitation of minerals and from industrialization, both of which are areally restricted.

Agriculture is the most widespread use of the land. In the Great Valley it is successfully commercial. On the ridges and in the poorer valleys it is similar to the impoverished subsistence farming of the Blue Ridge. Most common is the growing of wheat, corn, livestock, and hay, but some places have specialties, such as apples in the Shenandoah Valley and dairying near cities. Cotton as a cash crop appears only in the extreme southern part of the subregion.

Industrialization and urbanization have developed extensively only at the two ends of the Folded Appalachians, and even there the cities are not notable for size. Birmingham (0.6) is the largest, and owes its development to the happy coincidence of coal, iron ore, and dolomite. It produces steel, iron, pipes, and other metal manufactures. At the northern end of the subregion is Scranton (0.2), near the continent's only important anthracite coal deposits. At Bethlehem are the largest iron and steel works east of Pittsburgh, with the advantage of huge markets nearby. In the Lehigh Valley of Pennsylvania, limestone is the basis of an old and still-important cement production. Of special interest is the industrial development in connection with the Tennessee Valley Authority, a government project primarily concerned with flood control and navigation improvement, but at the same time producing an abundance of cheap electric power. This power has made possible a variety of industries concerned with chemicals, textiles, and metallurgy, such as are found in the growing industrial districts of Knoxville and Chattanooga, and is important to Oak Ridge, a center of atomic-energy research.

The Appalachian Plateaus subregion extends from the Lake Erie plain to northern Alabama, and from the Folded Appalachians to the upper Ohio Valley and central Tennessee. Excluded are the northern plateau margins which, because of their industrialization, are parts of the Central Manufacturing region. The natural unity of the Appalachian Plateaus consists of such widespread characteristics as a high degree of dissection and deeply entrenched valleys, steep slopes, heavy forest cover, abundant precipitation, and excellent resources of coal and petroleum. Beyond these generalities there is great variation: glaciated and non-glaciated sections, sharp stream divides and broad flat ones, mild and cold winters. Culturally there is unity in an unsuccessful attempt to foist on a rough country a system of agriculture adapted to flat lands, in the coal-mining towns dotted over virtually the whole subregion, and in the absence of urbanization and industrialization. Man has fared none too well in the Appalachian Plateaus and the land has suffered under his administration.

Agriculture is at its best in the New York section, where there are vineyards, apple orchards, general farming, and dairying. From New York to northeastern Kentucky general farming leads to decreasing yields and abandoned land. Here too is the densest grouping of coal-mining towns, providing the miners with little that is better than the farmers get from the unproductive soils. Recent years have seen a worsening of the lot of the coal miners. Mechanical coal-mining devices have reduced the need for large numbers of miners, and at the same time the coal market has shrunk as a result of the conversion of railroads to the use of diesel oil-burning locomotives, and of householders to the use of fuel oil for heating. Nor do things get better farther south in the "mountains" of Kentucky and central Tennessee, for here the impoverishment of the land and people matches that in the Blue Ridge. Little relief is offered by mining and lumbering, nor do these or any of the economic activities of the Appalachian Plateaus offer any basis for urbanization, which is almost wholly lacking.

In contrast to this picture of a poor land bursting with an excess of poor people who must struggle to secure a poor existence out of a reluctant soil, is the opulence of the Bluegrass and Nashville basins. The original settlers of the

plateaus and these basins were of the same stock, but the excellence of the soils and the comparative flatness of the basin slopes made possible a standard of rural living that is hardly exceeded anywhere else in the country. The basin cities of Lexington and Nashville are prosperous, refined, and fairly free of the evi-

Appalachian landscape, Maryland
[*U.S.D.A. Photography by Roth Stein*]

dence of human poverty. The contrast between upland and lowland is an illustration of man's failure to alter his traditional ways in the face of unfavorable natural conditions.

OZARK-OUACHITA REGION

The Ozark-Ouachita region of highlands is essentially a cultural outlier of the Appalachians, separated from it by the Mississippi Embayment. Its rough, eroded terrain; poor, unproductive soils; cut-over forests; widespread subsistence agriculture; and mining activities, are all strikingly similar to those of the Appalachians. On the better soils dairy and beef cattle are raised, and some fruits and berries are grown. Mining is concerned mainly with lead and zinc, with some iron. As in the Appalachians, tourism provides a source of income.

Forest and Alpine landscape, Cascade Mountains
[*U.S.D.A.*]

25. *Anglo-American Realm*

(Continued)

PRAIRIE PLAINS

The Prairie Plains region is the agricultural heart of the continent, extending from central Texas to the Northern Forest and lying generally east of the 100th meridian, as shown on the index map. The region possesses unsurpassed advantages for agriculture. The surface is mostly flat, and in places this flatness extends for miles without a significant break. The soils are of excellent quality. Rainfall is adequate and well distributed seasonally. In the northern section winters are sufficiently severe to check erosion and halt leaching. In addition to these endowments for agriculture, the region has resources of petroleum, gas, and coal, abundant in the southern section.

Agriculture overwhelmingly dominates the man-made landscape. One cultivated field lies next to another in a seemingly endless succession. Crops are uniformly luxuriant. Thorough and orderly care of the land conveys the impression of solidity and richness. Orderliness is really a pervasive characteristic of the landscape, expressed in many ways. Roads, oriented in strict north-south, east-west directions, delimit rectangular farms or fields. A cluster of buildings borders the road about every quarter mile, and they too stand square with the compass. Barns are large, substantial, and painted red. The houses ordinarily are designed for utility rather than for beauty. Trees are restricted to small orchards, wood lots, or windbreaks guarding the buildings. A sea of corn is broken by islands of grain or hay, and by feed lots occupied by fat beef cattle or fatter hogs. Every few miles there is a crossroads village.

This type of occupance pattern is most frequently seen in Iowa, the heart of the Corn Belt, which extends into the surrounding states. Beyond this corn-hog economy is dairying in the northeast, wheat-raising in the north and west, and cotton to the south. But these crop changes do not affect the essential cultural unity of the region. There is a sameness, a uniqueness that transcends even the common natural base and finds explanation only in history. When settlers from the forested seaboard reached the grasslands they were faced with problems for which they had no traditional solutions. Furthermore, they entered a country where the new square township survey had been applied to favorable terrain. The need to devise new ways, combined with isolation, encouraged a break with eastern traditions. The result was the creation of a largely new, distinctively American pattern of living. Although the northern part of the region received a large immigration directly from Europe, weak ties with the Old World and deep loyalties to the new are everywhere evident. The region expresses itself not only in the material pattern of a remunerative agriculture practiced on flat, rectangular fields, but also in a minimizing of social distinctions, and a leaning toward smug political isolationism.

Industry and commerce in the Prairie Plains are concerned primarily with the needs of agriculture. Essentially everyone not directly engaged in agriculture is employed in supplying the farmer's requirements and in handling and processing crops and fattened livestock. An important exception is the considerable number of people employed in the coal-mining and petroleum industries. Large-scale manufacturing for national markets, while present, is relatively unimportant. Accordingly, urbanization lags. In Iowa, for example, the largest city is Des Moines, but its metropolitan area includes only 0.3 million people. A number of other cities in the Prairie Plains fall in this general class, such as Wichita, Lincoln, and Sioux City, each with less than 0.4 million population. About in this class is Winnipeg, a railroad center for lines fanning out to the wheat-producing prairies to

Prairie Plains; Great Plains; Ozark-Ouachita: index map

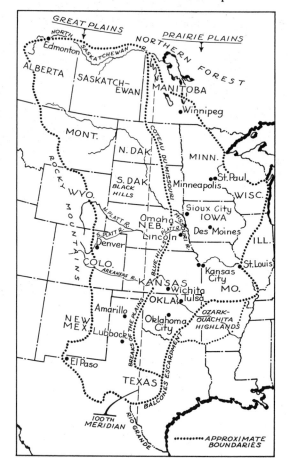

the west and northwest. Omaha and Kansas City are larger railroad centers, both specializing in meat packing and flour milling, although Kansas City also produces a number of other manufactures, such as automobiles, clothing, and steel articles. The largest urban center in the Prairie Plains is Minneapolis-St. Paul (1.4), at the head of navigation on the Mississippi, and with excellent rail connections in all directions, making it a commercial as well as an agricultural-processing center. Flour milling, machinery, instruments, plane and vehicle assemblying, and food-processing are among its important industries. In the southern part of the region, Oklahoma City has a variety of activities, including flour milling, meat packing, cotton-seed oil production, and petroleum refining. Its multiple economic interests give it a fair lead over its rival, Tulsa, a city whose growth is almost wholly due to the petroleum industry.

GREAT PLAINS

The Great Plains region, extending from the Northern Forest south to the Rio Grande, lies between the Rocky Mountains on the west and the Prairie Plains on the east. A satisfactory eastern boundary is difficult to select, and rather arbitrarily the abrupt rise in elevation westward that approximates the 100th meridian is chosen. This break in the plains has a number of names, as indicated on the index map. But the exact boundary is of no great consequence. The main point is that the heart of the Great Plains is different from Iowa. Westward elevation increases until it is about a mile at the base of the Rockies. The stream pattern grows coarser. Trees get scarcer until there are none. Tall-grass prairie yields to plains short grass and bunch grass. Precipitation decreases from 35 inches to half that figure. Buttes, mesas, badlands, sand hills, canyons, and other landmarks of an arid climate interrupt the flat or rolling surface. The isolated Black Hills, with their conspicuous cover of western pines, serve as an introduction to the Rocky Mountains. The color of the soil changes from black through chestnut and brown to gray, with increasing aridity westward. Widespread are the deposits of coal,

petroleum, and gas, and locally there are salt, potash, and gold. Combined with these physical changes are equally distinct cultural changes. Population density declines toward the west, while the occupance pattern is on an ever-enlarging scale. Dry farming, irrigation, and range grazing are activities foreign to the Corn Belt, and common to the Great Plains. Industrialization and urbanization are still in their infancy.

When the western movement of Anglo-Americans brought them to the Great Plains, they found the region occupied by bison-hunting Indian tribes who fiercely resisted the notion of giving up their lands. The Indians stood firm, despite the incursions, first by trappers in the eighteenth century, and then by wagon trains of settlers and traders moving along the Santa Fe Trail, opened in the eighteen-twenties, and the Oregon Trail, opened in the eighteen-forties. Fear of the Indians and the rigors of the land moved these wagon trains hurriedly through the region. The Indian menace ended in the eighteen-seventies when the government, torn between respecting the Indians' rights and protecting its own trespassing citizens, decided to forsake the Indians and opened the land for settlement.

The end of the Civil War found south Texas overrun with wild longhorn cattle, which had to be gotten to the eastern markets if they were to bring a profit. Some were shipped by water, but larger numbers were driven overland along trails that became well established. As the railroads pushed west of the Mississippi, the dis-

Old routes to the West

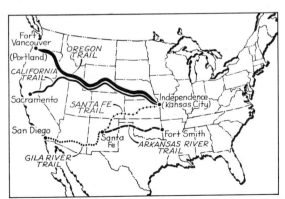

tance of the drives was reduced, profits were increased, and the cattle business expanded. An increasing market and the elimination of Indian and bison brought new herds to the grazing lands of the more northerly Great Plains. Cattle and ranching methods, borrowed directly from Spanish Mexico, were introduced as far north as Alberta. But unregulated open-range grazing and overstocking soon brought calamity: cattle could not find enough to eat and the weak ones died in the severe winters. The bonanza period was over and the grazing industry was forced to change its ways, particularly in the face of a new rival for the land.

Hard on the heels of the railroads came farmers. They tried to apply traditional methods of agriculture to these semiarid lands, and were successful only when the cycle of precipitation was on the high side, with above-average amounts of rain. The dry part of the cycle saw thousands of farmers trudging eastward, discouraged and penniless. In time, experience showed that milo maize (grain sorghum) did better than Indian corn, dry farming assured better yields than did constant cropping, and irrigation could solve the worst drought problems. But still the agricultural difficulties of the Great Plains were not, and are not, solved. Tempted by periods of rainy years and good markets, farmers plow and plant marginal lands, only to be faced with crop failure and complete loss of income during a cycle of dry years, which may bring such disasters as the Dust Bowl. All the evidence indicates that

Calgary
[*R.C.A.F. photo, Canadian Information Service*]

Great Plains farming methods must be sharply altered, or agriculture abandoned entirely in favor of grazing, except in irrigable areas.

From the series of successes and failures, and experiments with new and old ways, have come the rural patterns of the Great Plains. Along the indeterminant zone joining Prairie Plains and Great Plains is the primary wheat-producing area of the continent, resembling somewhat the patterns of the Corn Belt, but on a larger scale. Farms are still rectangular, but cover 500 to 1,000 or more acres. Houses and roads are thus farther apart. Complete mechanization has eliminated the horse and most of the hired help, so farmsteads are simpler and barns less prominent. More numerous in the landscape are the clusters of metal structures built to house the surplus grain, which is bought and stored by the government. Towns are few and barren, visible from a distance across the treeless land because of the row of tall grain elevators along the railroad siding or a prominent water tank. The grain elevators and agricultural atmosphere are missing from the small towns to the west, where the rougher, drier country is dominantly range-grazing land for cattle, sheep, and goats. Here the land units are still larger, from several thousand to more than a hundred thousand acres. Corrals, haystacks, windmills, barbed-wire fences, and other signs of the livestock industry make the scene distinctive.

Irrigated areas in the drier parts of the Great Plains are green oases amid drab surroundings. Here success is more certain, cultivation more intensive, and hand labor more required in the growing of the dominant crops: cotton, alfalfa, sugar beets, fruits, and vegetables. The main irrigated areas are along rivers originating in the Rocky Mountains, such as the Arkansas, North Platte, and upper tributaries of the Missouri River. These areas are characterized by denser populations, pleasanter towns, and a concentration of activities that are foreign to the grazing and wheat-growing sections of the Great Plains.

Totally unrelated to the agricultural and grazing activities are the imprints on the landscapes from the exploitation of minerals. Oil and gas fields dot the whole region, bituminous coal is mined in a number of places, and gold is produced in the Black Hills. The petroleum, natural gas, and coal reserves are known to be enormous, and there are large deposits of potash and phosphates.

The general sparsity of population and the absence of intense industrialization leave little reason for the growth of large cities. Denver (0.8), the region's largest city, was founded to serve mining activities in the Rockies, and still serves that function, as well as being an important meat-packing, commercial, transportation, and tourist center. Some examples of other Great Plains cities are: Edmonton, originally a fur post on the North Saskatchewan River, and now the center of the northern Canadian wheat area; Amarillo and Lubbock in the Texas Panhandle, with early and continuing interests in livestock and agricultural activities, but whose growth is due largely to petroleum production; and El Paso on the old Spanish route to the upper Rio Grande Valley, concerned mainly with livestock and irrigated agricultural products, and with smelting imported ores.

ROCKY MOUNTAINS

The Rocky Mountains region extends from the Sangre de Cristo Mountains in New Mexico to the Cassiar Mountains in southern Yukon. To the east are the Great Plains and the Northern Forest, and to the west is a series of plateaus. Physiographically the region is made up of several units. The Southern Rockies, from New Mexico to Wyoming, consist of two major systems of ranges and intervening basins or "parks." Just to the north is the Wyoming Basin, providing an easy route between the Great Plains and the Plateaus. Beyond the Basin, the Northern Rockies are a number of irregularly oriented ranges in Wyoming, changing to a pattern of parallel mountains and trenches in Montana and Idaho, a pattern that continues to the northernmost part of the region. The natural landscape of the whole region is in sharp contrast with the regions on either side. The Rockies are well watered in the midst of the surrounding aridity. In them originate major streams flowing east and west of the continental divide. The vegetation is dominantly coniferous forest, covering a span of elevations that are limited on the low side by dryness and on the high side by cold. In contrast to the flanking regions, there is a minimum of flat surfaces. Steepness of slope and sharpness of outline become more and more pronounced toward the north, with the increasing dominance of ice sculpture. It is a region of scenic grandeur and cool summers in contrast to the hot summers and monotonous landscape of adjacent regions, except in the Northern Forest. Man's activities that show up in the landscape of the Rockies are concerned with mining, grazing, agriculture, lumbering, catering to tourists, and attempting to solve the difficult transportation problems in this land of steep slopes. Urban manufacturing has yet to appear in the landscape.

In the seventeenth century, Spaniards from Mexico had reached the upper Rio Grande Valley, had established permanent settlements, such as Santa Fe, their capital, and had pioneered in irrigation agriculture and livestock ranching. Santa Fe became the mecca of traders venturing across the plains early in the nineteenth century, just as Taos, to the north, became a favorite rendezvous of American trappers who roamed the whole region. Starting in the eighteen-forties, these trappers put their expert knowledge of the countryside to use in establishing trails and leading settlers to Oregon and California. Some of the settlers who never go to their destinations, and some disappointed prospectors, opened the Rockies mining era in the eighteen-fifties. Denver came into being and grew in pace with the mining developments. In 1862 a rich placer-gold strike at Alder Gulch, Montana, started a stampede of miners northward. A series of gold discoveries followed, each more tempting to the prospectors than the last, so towns mushroomed and were deserted, sometimes within a matter of a few months. In time, the industry settled down to less-dramatic, more-stable lode mining. Gold was largely replaced in importance by silver, copper, lead, zinc, and more recently, molybdenum, chrome, tungsten, mercury, and fluorspar.

Livestock ranching and agriculture are older than mining, but their development lagged in competition with the more alluring search for

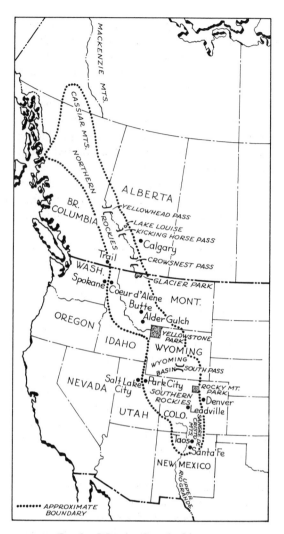

Rocky Mountains: index map

gold. Now, however, grazing is the dominant form of land use where natural conditions preclude agriculture, and farms occupy most arable lands. Both dry farming and irrigation are practiced. Lumbering is of primary commercial importance only in the Northern Rockies, where timber is of excellent quality and easy to log. Much of the timbered area is in National Forests, which assures a regulated supply of lumber for the future. To preserve places of particular scenic beauty, a number of national parks have been established, such as Rocky Mountain, Yellowstone, Glacier, Banff, and Jasper parks. Tourists flock to these parks, and to the dude ranches, winter-sports resorts, and camping areas, providing an important source of the region's income.

Scenic as they are, the Rocky Mountains offer difficulties to transportation. Railroads and highways are highly restricted in their choice of passes across the mountains. Only three passes through the Canadian Rockies are used by railroads: Yellowhead, Kicking Horse, and Crowsnest. Three lines cross the mountains in Montana and Idaho. A railroad and highway make use of the easiest route, across the Wyoming Basin. To the south, the expensive Moffat Tunnel gives Denver direct rail connections with Salt Lake City, and two pairs of railroads and highways laboriously climb over the Southern Rockies. The railroads pioneered the way, so highways tend to follow the same routes. Location on a natural crossing of the mountains is by itself responsible for none of the major cities of the region, although such a location has aided city growth where other factors are favorable.

Neither of the two major cities of the region, Butte and Santa Fe, exceeds 50,000 population, but it should be remembered that many of the commercial and industrial urban functions for the Rockies are performed by cities lying just outside the region, such as Calgary, Denver, Salt Lake City, and Spokane. Butte is a somewhat declining copper-mining center, which prides itself on the preservation of many of the old traditions of a western mining camp. Santa Fe, a center of agricultural and grazing industries, is attracting a profitable stream of tourists by its pleasant climate and its picturesque old Spanish-American qualities.

PLATEAUS

Between the Rockies and the Pacific Mountains is the Plateaus region, a series of well-defined physiographic areas: the Colorado Plateaus, the Basin and Range Province, the Columbia Plateaus, and the Interior Plateau of British Columbia. Each of these plateaus has a relatively flat surface, cut by deeply eroding rivers, such as the Colorado River that forms the Grand Canyon in the Colorado Plateaus,

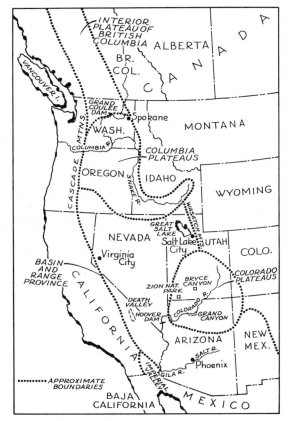

Plateaus: index map

and the Snake and Columbia rivers of the Columbia Plateaus. The Basin and Range Province is composed of irregular ranks of parallel rocky ranges and wide intervening alluvial basins. Climatically the region has a wide variety of temperatures, but is uniform in its scantiness of precipitation, averaging annually less than 20 inches. The natural vegetation shows the varying efficiency of the precipitation, an efficiency that varies with temperature, and thus with elevation and latitude. The bottom of the Grand Canyon, for example, has desert plants, while the plateau rim a mile above it supports an open pine forest. The ranges and higher surfaces of the northern plateaus are forested, while the lowlands are typically sagebrush covered. To the south the forests of the highlands give way at lower elevations to drylands vegetation dominated by the cresote bush and cactus. Even this sparse vegetation is lack-

Orchards, Okanogan Valley
[*Canadian Pacific Railway*]

ing in the driest, hottest basins that are expanses of alkali and salt flats.

The most striking feature of the occupance pattern is the spotty distribution of a sparse population, a result of the uneven availability of water. For most of the region rainfall is far too slight for agriculture without irrigation, and lack of water prevents the use of some otherwise good grazing lands. Only mining shows a measure of independence from local water supply, the activity being sufficiently rewarding to afford the high cost of imported water.

The first agriculture in the region was the floodwater farming of the Pueblo Indians. The initial Anglo-American experiment with irrigation was conducted by the Mormons on the alluvial piedmont flanking the Wasatch Mountains. Their success in creating the economically sound Salt Lake oasis encouraged similar attempts, some of which prospered, but many failed for lack of experience or capital. Increasingly the national government undertook the sponsorship of irrigation-hydroelectric power projects because of the great costs involved, as in the building of Hoover Dam on the Colorado and Grand Coulee Dam on the Columbia. Although today irrigated areas dot the region from the Gila and Salt rivers of Arizona to the Okanogan Valley of British Columbia, they account for less than five per cent of the total acreage of the Plateaus. Crops are varied, de-

pending upon latitude, transportation to markets, seasonal opportunities, and other factors. Crops range from apples in British Columbia, Washington, and Oregon, through potatoes in Idaho, sugar beets in Utah, and cotton, lettuce, and cantaloupes in California and Arizona. Common characteristics of all the areas are intensive cultivation, high degree of mechanization, and an assured harvest.

Quite different from the rural pattern of the irrigated oases is that of the large dry-farming area of Washington and Oregon. This has long been a major wheat-producing area. Here the farms are measured in thousands of acres. The intensity of irrigation agriculture is missing, as is the assurance of harvest, for variations in precipitation are matters of real concern. Wherever it is possible, dry farming gives way to irrigation.

The grazing industry was introduced by the Spaniards, who converted the hunting-gathering Navaho Indians into thoroughgoing pastoralists. Cattle ranching by Anglo-Americans spread from Texas to Arizona, and up through the plateaus to Washington. The pattern was similar to that of Great Plains ranching, and, as in that region, grazing suffered from inroads of agriculture and from its own errors, such as overgrazing. Nevertheless, grazing remains the most widespread and least intensive use of the land. It involves cattle, sheep, and even goats. The pattern varies from the 16,000,000-acre open range of the Navaho sheepherders, through the traditional cattle ranches of the Colorado Plateaus, to isolated ranches hidden along the fronts of desert ranges in Nevada. Pastoralism seems assured a long life in this region of limited possibilities.

Early mineral discoveries came as an aftermath of the California gold rush. Placer-gold finds extended from Oregon to Arizona, but the real bonanza came with the discovery of the Comstock Lode in 1859 at Virginia City, Nevada. The Lode produced first gold, then an abundance of silver. By the end of the century, the Comstock Lode had been exhausted, and Virginia City was deserted by miners seeking other opportunities. In time, of course, the mineral industry settled down to the large-scale exploitation of rather lean ores. Although silver is still produced, copper is today the chief mineral, with Arizona the leading producer, Utah second, and Nevada fourth, behind Montana. Since 1957, however, oversupply and a decrease in demand have caused curtailment of production. Among the other products of this mineral-rich region are lead, manganese, molybdenum, iron, vanadium, and, as a result

Mediterranean landscape, California
[Soil Conservation Service]

of many hopefuls ambling around with clicking geiger counters, uranium. Salt, potash, phosphates, borax, and petroleum are also produced.

Only three of the region's cities exceed 0.250 in their metropolitan areas, and these cities illustrate the major reasons for urbanization in the Plateaus. Spokane (0.279) is the chief city of the "Inland Empire," comprising Oregon and Washington east of the Cascades, and Idaho. It is a focus of transportation routes, and a commercial and industrial center for a hinterland that produces wheat, lumber, and minerals. Salt Lake City (0.370) is the chief commercial city for a large part of the middle Plateau and central Rocky Mountain regions. Within the city's immediate sphere are the Salt Lake agricultural oasis, copper mines, ore smelters, basic iron production, sugar refining, flour milling, and sheep and cattle ranges. Phoenix (0.549) is the urban center for the productive Salt River oasis, a popular winter resort, and, like Salt Lake City, is state capital.

PACIFIC NORTHWEST

The Pacific Northwest region is a narrow, mountainous strip extending from northern California to the southern boundary of Alaska. Its eastern limit is the crest of the Cascades and the Coast Mountains of British Columbia, a barrier so effective that only two major streams cross it, the Columbia and the Fraser. Rimming the seaward margin are the less-impressive Coast Ranges of the United States and the large islands flanking the coast of British Columbia. Between these margins in the southern part of the region is a belt of comparatively level land in the Willamette Valley of Oregon and the Puget Trough in Washington. The coast line south of Puget Sound is broken only by minor irregularities, while to the north the mainland is indented by innumerable fiords between mountainous headlands. The islands along the coast provide protection for the "Inside Passage."

The region enjoys mild winters and cool summers, with a remarkably long growing season for these latitudes. Precipitation is heavy, with a winter maximum that covers the mountains with snow. The climate favors the growth of magnificent coniferous forests, which include such important commercial species as redwood in California, Douglas fir in Oregon and Washington, and spruce and hemlock in British Columbia. Abundant precipitation, mild winters, and steep slopes combine to give the region an unexcelled water-power potential. The innumerable clearwater streams are the spawning grounds of salmon, while the coastal waters yield halibut, herring, shellfish, and other commercially important varieties of fish. Only in the matter of known mineral resources does the region appear to be poorly endowed.

Culturally the Pacific Northwest is distinctive in its isolation and its preoccupation with lumbering and fishing. Agriculture is both limited and specialized. Agriculture was initiated by the first settlers, New Englanders, who came in the early eighteen-forties to support American claims to the disputed Oregon country. In their wake came a stream of settlers along the Oregon Trail to establish farms in the hospitable Willamette Valley. So great was the influx of settlers that by 1846 the British were willing to accept the present international boundary, and the Valley was sending an overflow of immigrants to California. Agriculture expanded from the Willamette Valley to other valleys and the Puget Trough, but it still occupies only a small

Drying apricots, California
[*U.S.D.A.*]

percentage of the region's area. For the most part it is general farming, with crops of hay, grains, berries, tree fruits, nuts, bulbs, and flowers, but of prime importance is dairying. The production of cheese, milk, eggs, and poultry ranks high.

Commercial lumbering also began with the first settlers, and by the first quarter of this century the region had become the continent's prime producer. Logging and sawmilling are now highly mechanized so the depletion of the forest goes at a frightening rate. Increasing efforts are being made to farm rather than mine the forests, and now a number of lumber firms engage in selective logging to leave seed trees, and in reforestation, the actual planting of seedlings.

The region's basic industries are concerned with the processing or manufacturing of the products of forest, fishery, and farm. The excellent harbors encourage commerce, and even shipbuilding, which boomed during World War II, as did the aircraft industry. The abundance of hydroelectric power, and the availability of cheap ocean transport favor industries that otherwise would be out of place in the region, such as the aluminum smelters of Kitimat, British Columbia, which use ores from Jamaica and British Guiana. Industrialization is on the increase despite the handicap of distance to big markets, although the three main population centers, around Portland, Seattle, and Vancouver, provide a growing number of consumers.

Each of the three large metropolitan areas of the Pacific Northwest is a port and each shares the general background of lumbering and fishing. In addition, each exhibits local specialization and has distinctive extraregional relations. Vancouver (0.7), the third-largest Canadian city, is terminus of transcontinental railroads and of steamship lines to Alaska and Asia. In addition to its commercial activities, it conducts a wide range of industries, such as the making of pulp and paper, furniture, plywood, and veneers, the packing of fish and meat, and the processing of dairy and poultry products. Oil for its refineries comes by pipeline from Alberta, and nearby are important coastal coal mines.

California: index map

Seattle (0.9) is the center of Puget Sound urbanization. It combines among its activities, trade with Alaska and the Orient, the manufacture of aircraft, ships, aluminum, machinery, and clothing, the milling of flour, and food processing. Portland (0.9) has the advantage of being the natural outlet for the Willamette Valley and for interior Washington through the Columbia gorge, the easiest route through the Cascades. In addition to its importance as a commercial and transportation center, it has shipyards, an aluminum smelter, flour mills, lumber mills, furniture and paper factories, meat-packing plants, and a well-established wool-manufacturing industry.

CALIFORNIA

California as a region is somewhat smaller than the state, since excluded are the northern coast ranges that are part of the Pacific Northwest, and the dry country east of the Sierra Nevada belonging to the Plateaus. The region includes four well-defined units: the Sierra

Nevada, the Valley, the Coast Ranges, and Southern California. The Sierra Nevada, the region's eastern wall, is a 400-mile-long tilted block whose steep face is toward the east. In the south many peaks rise above 12,000 feet, with Mt. Whitney, highest peak outside of Alaska in the United States, attaining 14,496 feet. The northern portion is famous for its Mother Lode, source of the gold that brought the rush in 1849. The western slope is well timbered between 1,500 and 9,000 feet. Deep winter snows feed perennial streams that flow westward to the Valley, a 50-mile-wide depression between the Sierra Nevada and Coast Ranges. The north end of the Valley is drained by the Sacramento, the south end by the San Joaquin. The two rivers join at about the midpoint of the Valley to discharge into San Francisco Bay. The Valley is low, seemingly flat, and mantled with productive alluvial soils. The climate is characterized by very hot summers, mild winters, and very little rainfall. A low to moderate amount of rain falls on the Coast Ranges, a series of low, parallel ridges and valleys, frequently shaken by earthquakes. Winters are mild and summers cool to warm, but dryness prohibits the growth of much more than scrubby chaparral. This type of vegetation continues into Southern California, which is climatically Mediterranean, verging on steppe.

Neither the natural attractions of California nor its Indian inhabitants were sufficient cause for Spanish settlement. Missions were established in the late eighteenth century to ward off the Russians, who were setting up fur posts on the north Pacific coast. The line of missions and the roads connecting them followed Coast Range valleys from Southern California to San Francisco Bay. The mission inhabitants were never very numerous, nor did they wander very far, but they did introduce range grazing and Mediterranean agriculture.

The gold rush brought a great influx of Anglo-Americans to the Mother Lode and the northern Valley. San Francisco became an enterprising, bustling city, while Los Angeles remained a sleepy, Spanish-American town. Incoming Anglo-Americans, bent on farming, moved into the Valley to raise wheat and cattle. The pattern changed very little until the last quarter of the nineteenth century when rail connections with the East were improved, bringing a new flood of settlers, mainly to Southern California. Profound changes in agriculture followed. Large-scale irrigation was applied to the Valley, Southern California, and Coast Range valleys, reducing the acreage of grazing and dry-farm lands. Today this garden region has an almost unbelievable record for farm production, and although it contains only 3 per cent of the nation's acreage, it accounts for 10 per cent of the harvest. It is a leading producer of cotton, fruits, nuts, vegetables, sugar beets, and is the exclusive producer of commercial lemons, nectarines, dates, almonds, olives, and prunes. It produces over 90 per cent of the American grapes, and four fifths of the wine. It has a near monopoly on the canning of olives, peaches, figs, apricots, and mixed fruits.

Another milestone in economic development came with the discovery of petroleum at the beginning of this century. The southern part of the Valley and Southern California combine to rank next to Louisiana and third among states in petroleum production. Not only does petroleum support a tremendous industry, but it encourages, along with the climate, the use of automobiles: there are only six states that have more automobiles than Los Angeles County.

The region's industries are varied, including a number concerned with the products of farm, ranch, oil field, forest, and fishery, and many that are attracted by the salubrious climate, such as the aircraft and electronic industries, motion picture industry, and the enormous tourist industry. Others, such as automobile assemblying, rubber and tire production,

clothing, and construction, came in response to the demands of the local market, which increases at the rate of 1,500 people a day. The population has doubled every 20 years for the past century, and the rate of growth is still increasing.

Although the region has a number of agricultural and market towns, such as San Jose, Fresno, San Bernardino, and Sacramento, the capital, with metropolitan-area populations in excess of 0.3, urbanization is largely concentrated in two districts, centered about San Francisco and Los Angeles. San Francisco (2.7, including Oakland) is the chief unit of conurbation on magnificent San Francisco Bay. It is a major Pacific port and airline terminus located at the natural outlet of the Valley. It is a cosmopolitan city of old traditions, combined with varied industrial interests, including oil refineries, shipyards, automobile assembly plants, steel and other metal fabrication, printing and publishing, and food processing. It ties its conurbation together with two of the country's largest bridges, the Golden Gate and San Francisco-Oakland bridges. Los Angeles (6.2) is the center of a conurbation that extends to San Diego. This is the center of the aircraft industry, which includes missiles and electronics. Its artificial port handles an enormous volume of traffic, as does its busy airport. Among the major industries, in addition to aircraft, are processing Mediterranean agricultural products, production of motion pictures and radio and television programs, clothing and fashions, oil production and refining, automobile assembly, metal fabrication, tires, and furniture. Its rapid industrialization all but obscures the old traditional Spanish-American ways, although it still maintains an air of leisure.

LATIN AMERICAN REALM

São Paulo
[*Consulate General of Brazil, N.Y.*]

26. *Latin American Realm*

Latin America begins at the southern border of the United States and includes all the countries and islands to the south. Many of these countries or political units are also cultural units, mainly because population throughout the whole realm tends to be clustered into nuclei of high density, and these nuclei are separated by areas of low density. The nuclei are largely confined to distinct political units, and many are the outgrowth of original settlements, which in Latin America were hundreds of years earlier than European settlements in Anglo-America.

MEXICO

In a general way, Mexico is a good illustration of Latin American characteristics, for it exhibits clustering of population, a city too large for its hinterland, the importance of subsistence agriculture and the extractive industries, a coarse network of railways and highways, limited industrialization, dominance of the rural village over isolated farmstead, im-

portance of Indian blood, expression of religion in the landscape, and a gap between landed gentry and impoverished peon. As in the rest of Latin America, and indeed throughout the world, the years since World War II have seen a great increase in the urban population, and the growth of industry, but with all this, Mexico remains dominantly an agricultural country. Two thirds of its 32.4 million people are rural. Most of the population is of mixed blood, heavily Indian.

Within Mexico's 760,400 square miles, the population is notably concentrated in the Valley of Mexico and adjacent plateau basins. The center of the cluster is Mexico City (3.3 million, 4.5 million in the Federal District), sixth among the largest cities in the world, a sophisticated, increasingly industrialized, cosmopolitan city. It lies in the midst of a band of dense population that stretches across the country from Veracruz, leading east coast port, to Manzanillo, a lesser port on the west coast. The band includes the manufacturing city of

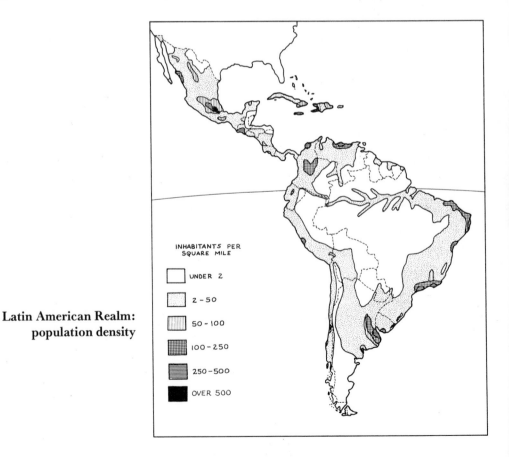

Latin American Realm: population density

INHABITANTS PER SQUARE MILE

- UNDER 2
- 2 - 50
- 50 - 100
- 100 - 250
- 250 - 500
- OVER 500

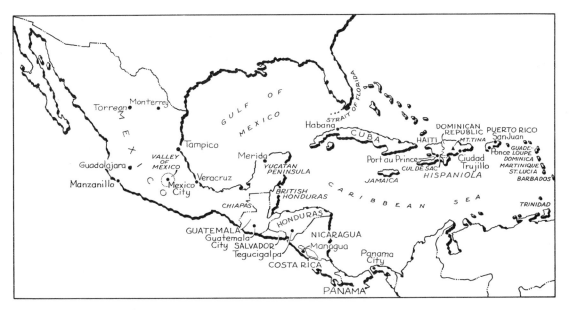

Middle America: index map

Guadalajara (0.590) and Puebla (0.309), a near neighbor of Mexico City. The density of population decreases rapidly toward the north, reaching a minimum along the desert boundary with the United States, except for the concentrations around Torreon (0.2) and Monterrey (0.564), local centers of trade and industry. Most of the Yucatan Peninsula is sparsely populated, although its leading city, Merida, approaches 0.2 million population.

The pattern of rural occupance is a mixture of Indian and European, the Indian showing up in the communal holdings around the villages, where small plots are planted in corn, beans, peppers, and tomatoes, while more European are the *ranchos* of several acres cultivated by the owner who comes daily from the village to raise the same subsistence crops. Until recently *haciendas* were an imposing aspect of the landscape, but most of these large estates have been broken up. Increasing in number are the areas of irrigation, especially in the north where wheat and cotton are important crops, the cotton being mainly an export crop. From the southern half of the country come the other export crops: coffee, cacao, sugar, bananas, and, from Yucatan, sisal. Everywhere possible, the leading food crop, maize, is grown. Livestock

raising is an important activity in the north, and fishing provides another source of food along the coasts.

Although Mexico is dominantly agricultural, it depends on its extractive industries for the bulk of its exports. Mexico continues to be a major source of silver, accounting for over half of the world's production. Other important minerals are gold, copper, lead, zinc, manganese, and petroleum. The country is a leading producer of sulphur. Until recently, most of the mines and oil fields were foreign owned, and so of limited benefit to the country. Nationalization of the petroleum industry caused a temporary slump in production because of a lack of trained people, but the industry is recovering.

Mexico, like other Latin American countries, is an exporter of raw materials and an importer of manufactured goods. There is a long history of small, localized industries, such as the making of saddles and other leather goods, cotton textiles, coarse clothing, sandals, pulque, and tequila. The recent acceleration of industrialization has been largely the centralizing, modernizing, and intensifying of these old light industries, which use Mexican labor and raw materials, and cater to the Mexican market. New to the scene is heavy industry, such as that at Monterrey, where Mexican coal and iron ore are used to produce iron and steel for the foundries and machine shops of the city. The trend toward industrialization and urbanization, common in Mexico and all of Latin America, tends to widen the gap between the dweller in the modernized city and the agricultural Indian in his little-changed village.

CENTRAL AMERICA

Six independent countries and a British possession occupy the narrowing body of land between Mexico and South America. As Table 8 shows, they vary in size and population, but in each country there is a nucleus of comparatively dense rural population surrounding the capital city. There is also a much larger back country of very low density, except in Salvador, where there is only minor departure from the average density of 290 per square mile.

TABLE 9
Central American Countries

	Areas (sq. miles)	Population (millions)
Guatemala	42,042	3.5
Honduras	43,227	1.8
Salvador	8,259	2.4
Nicaragua	57,143	1.4
Costa Rica	19,690	1.1
Panama	28,576	1.0
Panama Canal Zone	648	0.04
British Honduras	8,867	0.08
	208,452	11.32

The clustering of population stems from both natural and historic factors. Along the western part of the Central American plateau, heavy deposits of lava and ash in the basins and valleys have been weathered into fertile, productive soils. Rainfall is generally adequate and the climate of the plateau is considerably less tropical than that of the rain-soaked, narrow coastal lowlands. The fever-ridden coastal plains were avoided by mineral-seeking Spaniards, but they scoured the plateau in search of ready wealth. A few of the unsuccessful ones turned to the other alternative, land and the Indians to work it. Nuclear settlements were established in the basins of the western plateau,

and today, all the capitals of the republics, except Managua and Panama City, are located in highland basins. Nicaragua is distinctive in that original settlements were made in the tropical lowland that crosses the country. Panama is unique in that its population cluster is fixed by the crossing of the isthmus.

Although less than 10 per cent of the area of Central America is cultivated, two thirds or more of the people are engaged in agriculture, mainly on a subsistence level that has changed very little since before the arrival of the Spaniards. At the same time, the countries depend upon commercial agriculture for their prosperity. Cacao, wheat, indigo, sugar cane, and cattle were all tried with varying degrees of success until the middle of the nineteenth century, when coffee became the dominant commercial crop. The tropical coast remained little used and sparsely populated until the coming of banana plantations late in the nineteenth century. Promoted by large United States corporations, the new industry spread along the Caribbean coast from Panama to Guatemala. The forest was cleared for plantations, sleepy ports were awakened and modernized, railroads were built, and Negro laborers were imported from the West Indies, to remain, multiply, and become the dominant racial group in the Caribbean lowlands.

Coffee and bananas remain the leading cash crops. On the plateau coffee is king, whether it is produced by peasant farmers in Costa Rica or by Indian laborers on the plantations of Guatemala. Such other sources of income as balsam in Salvador, cotton and gold in Nicaragua, and cattle, sugar cane, and palm oil elsewhere are but minor hedges against possible disaster to the one-crop economy. Bananas faced just such a disaster in the form of plant disease, which caused the abandonment of large sections of the Caribbean coast, and a shift of the industry to the disease-free Pacific coast, leaving behind the Negro laborers. The east coast shows modest activity in timber cutting, chicle gathering, an expansion of subsistence agriculture, and the production of cacao.

The marked changes in agriculture and the growth of population have not destroyed the old nuclear pattern of settlement nor have they altered the racial composition of the plateau. Guatemala is overwhelmingly an Indian country of villages, subsistence maize agriculture, and ancient markets, with little concern for modern world commerce. Honduras, Salvador, and Nicaragua have fewer Indians; they are predominantly *mestizo*, that is, mixed European and Indian, and thus are more European in culture. Highland Costa Rica is populated by the descendants of Spaniards who had no Indian laborers, and so is almost entirely European. Panama remains what it has long been, a significant crossroads, with the racial heterogeneity expected in such a situation.

Commercially Central America is an exporter of raw materials and an importer of manufactures. Its infant industry boasts only a few sugar refineries, cotton gins, tanneries, and sawmills, with an occasional plant producing textiles, cigarettes, or beer. Where there is so little industry it is difficult to explain the high degree of urbanization. Each capital has a population in excess of 100,000, Guatemala City having 0.375 million, and there is a long list of cities with populations of 10,000 or more.

Banana harvest
[*U.S.D.A.*]

WEST INDIES

The West Indies are a chain of islands that swings east and south from the mouth of the Gulf of Mexico to South America, marking the limit of the Caribbean Sea. The four large islands along the northern part of the chain are the Greater Antilles: Cuba, 44,204 square miles; Hispaniola, divided into Haiti, 10,712, and the Dominican Republic, 18,700; Jamaica, 4,411; and Puerto Rico, 3,423. The Lesser Antilles, making up the eastern part of the chain, range in size from Trinidad, 1,864 square miles, to tiny coral reefs. Of the larger islands, Guadeloupe and Martinique are departments of France, and Dominica, St. Lucia, Barbados, and Trinidad are British. In 1958 all the British islands, except the Virgin Islands, officially became part of the West Indies Federation, a unit in the British Commonwealth.

Structurally, the Greater Antilles are extensions of Central America, and are mountainous, with the exception of Cuba, whose extensive plains are similar to those of Yucatan, Florida, and the Bahamas. The Lesser Antilles are the product of vulcanism, embellished by coral growth, except for Trinidad, which is structurally part of South America. Throughout the chain the climate is tropical, although temperatures and precipitation vary with elevation and exposure. The lee sides and rain-shadow parts of the islands are likely to semiarid.

The West Indies are culturally a distinct region because they possess unique cultural attributes. They all have long histories as political colonies, have long been a bulwark of tropical plantation agriculture, and are racially more Negro than Caucasian, Haiti's culture being considerably more African than European. Rural population densities reach a maximum for Latin America, as in English-speaking Barbados whose 166 square miles support 0.230 million, a density of 1,400 per square mile.

The islands were the sites of earliest European settlement in the Americas, but since they lacked ready mineral wealth, the Spaniards moved on to Mexico and Peru, keeping only outposts, such as Habana, to protect their treasure fleets sailing for Spain through the Strait of Florida. Unoccupied islands made fine

Fishing pier, Margarita Island, West Indies
[*Venezuela Ministry of Development*]

bases for pirates who attacked the fleets and raided settlements. There was some production of food and commercial crops by the Spaniards along the coasts, and the island interiors were divided into large estates for grazing. The Indians were virtually exterminated within 50 years after Columbus arrived, so Negro slaves were imported for labor. The demand for slaves grew to tremendous proportions when, in the middle of the seventeenth century, commercial sugar cane cultivation had spread to the Lesser Antilles from Brazil. With it came the system of large estates, a few Europeans, and many Negro slaves. By the eighteenth century the wave of sugar prosperity had reached the Greater Antilles. The sugar bonanza waned in the nineteenth century when beet sugar and the abolition of slavery sharply reduced profits. Nevertheless, the growing of sugar cane continued, experienced a twentieth-century boom centering in Cuba, and remains the most widespread activity, together with its companion pursuit, rum making. Of lesser commercial importance are coffee, cacao, coconuts, tobacco, cattle, sisal, bananas, timber, citrus fruit, and cotton.

The West Indian islands differ enough from each other culturally to make generalization difficult, and to warrant description of each of the four major islands as examples.

Cuba is a world leader in sugar production, and sugar is the island's major economic pursuit, although the acreage planted to cane is matched by that devoted to grazing and forage crops. The pattern of the big sugar *central* is striking, with its village cluster of refinery, houses, store, school, and church, surrounded by vast fields of cane. Of lesser importance are tobacco, bananas, citrus fruits, and vegetables. Among the other exports, largely to the United States, are chrome, manganese, copper, nickel, and iron. But food must be imported to feed the 5.8 million population. A fifth of the total population lives in metropolitan Habana (Havana), largest port city in the Caribbean, and political, commercial, and transportation center of the country. This modern city attracts many United States tourists, whenever the volatile politics make this possible.

Haiti is a French-speaking, densely populated Negro country. The rural pattern, strongly similar to that of West Africa, is one of thatched houses clustered in a village about which are patchy fields of cassava, yams, plantains, sugar cane, and maize. In contrast to this hoe-agriculture scene are the irrigation projects and commerical-crop areas, where coffee, sisal, bananas, cotton, tobacco, and rice are produced mainly for export. A French atmosphere is retained only in the capital, Port-au-Prince, Haiti's main city.

The Dominican Republic presents a different picture: dominantly mulatto, that is, mixed Caucasian and Negro; Spanish language; and a culture that is Latin American rather than African. More significant is the matter of population density, 144 per square mile as compared with Haiti's 327. Dominican fear of the more numerous neighbors led to a massacre of some 10,000 Haitians in 1937, and has made the Dominican Republic receptive to European immigration. Population is densest in the northern and southern lowlands, which produce the bulk of the export crops: sugar cane, cacao, and tobacco, as well as maize and rice. The highlands yield coffee and gold, copper, and iron. Petroleum resources are being developed. Grazing is widespread. The capital and principal city, Ciudad Trujillo (formerly

Santo Domingo), is interesting because of a few old buildings that have survived earthquakes and hurricanes, and because of its associations with Columbus.

Jamaica is dominantly Negro, and its 1.6 million population has an average density of 362 per square mile. Pastures for livestock grazing occupy the greatest amount of land, but of more commercial importance is the land planted to sugar cane, bananas, pimento, coffee, and citrus fruits, the leading cash crops. Considerable income is derived from the export of alumina and bauxite.

Puerto Rico, with its 2.3 million inhabitants, has the highest average density in the Greater Antilles, 672 per square mile. It has more acreage devoted to agriculture than do the other islands, farming is highly commercialized and mechanized, and, as is not the case in the rest of the West Indies, more income is obtained from manufactures than from agriculture. The fast-growing population is increasingly more Caucasian than Negro. Tremendous strides have been made since the days when Puerto Rico was a fairly prosperous, and then a neglected, sugar-cane and coffee producing Spanish colony. Its acquisition by the United States in 1898 was the signal for the expansion of plantation agriculture, the modernizing of the country, and a rapid growth of population. Since 1952, Puerto Rico, as a Commonwealth associated with the United States, has adopted its own constitution and flag. It clings to Spanish as its language and supports a national lottery.

Complete dependence on sugar plus minor exports of tobacco, citrus fruits, coconuts, and coffee, has been offset in the last decade by the growth of industry, mainly small plants scattered about the island to make use of local labor supplies to produce textiles, glass bottles, chemicals, clothing, electrical and electronic equipment, and other manufactures. The population is becoming increasingly urban, with more than a dozen towns in the 10,000 and over category, led by San Juan (0.4 including Rio Piedras).

NORTHERN SOUTH AMERICA

Colombia, 439,520 square miles; Venezuela, 352,143; and Ecuador, 116,270, comprise the Greater Colombia formed in 1819 by Simon Bolivar. Colombia has the largest population, 13.2 million, followed by Venezuela with 6.2,

Caracas
[*Venezuela Ministry of Development*]

South America: index map

and Ecuador, 3.9. The racial elements are about the same in each country, but the proportions differ. Venezuela and Colombia are predominantly mestizo, while Ecuador is strongly Indian. Negroes are an important element in each country. There are few persons of unmixed European origin. The population tends to cluster in the highlands, around three separated nuclei, which in part explains why Bolivar's plan for a Greater Colombia would not work.

The Spanish approach to the region was from the Caribbean. Along the Venezuela coast they founded Cumana in 1523, then Coro, and when they got to Lake Maracaibo, the pile-dwellings of the Indians inspired them to name the country Little Venice or Venezuela. Moving inland, the discovery of placer gold resulted in the founding of Caracas in 1767. Meanwhile, Santa Marta and Cartagena (1533) had been established near the mouth of the Magdalena River in Colombia. Search for gold took the Spaniards into central Colombia, where they found the Chibcha Indians advanced in metallurgy, and a dense agricultural population in the highlands, in the midst of which they founded Bogota in 1538. In highland Ecuador they seized Quito, capital of the northern part of the Inca empire, and made it the seat of a Spanish presidency. Thus the three major nuclei were established, and in 1831 the three old cities of Caracas, Bogota, and Quito became the capitals of independent countries.

The search for precious metals never ceased, but the results could not support a mining economy, so the Spaniards divided up the land and introduced cattle to the hitherto unused high pastures of the Andes and the savanna llanos of Venezuela. Native maize remained the most widespread subsistence crop, somewhat augmented by wheat and other European food plants. Commercial agriculture experimented with native crops, such as cacao, tobacco, and indigo, and in time sugar cane and coffee became well established. The plantations, mainly on the accessible lowlands, soon exhausted the scant supply of Indians, and turned to imported Negro slaves, who became a significant element of the humid lowland population. In the remoter highlands, however, the denser Indian

populations retained their racial dominance and preserved their culture.

The persistence of the oldest European interest, mineral wealth, is responsible for the latest significant economic development. Colombia has experienced a marked revival of mining, but it is unimportant compared with petroleum production in Venezuela. As a major world producer, Venezuela's interests have so centered on petroleum that agriculture has been neglected. These latest developments tend to accentuate old distinctions among the countries.

Colombia remains agricultural, with most of its population clustered in the mountains and transmontane plains, and a secondary center on the combined delta of the Cauca and Magdalena. An indication of the nation's commercial activities is found in a list of its leading exports: coffee, bananas, cacao, hides, gold, platinum, emeralds, and petroleum. Maize is the dominant food crop, and much of the agriculture is of the subsistence variety. Industry is still in a very youthful stage and is handicapped by lack of adequate transportation. The three largest cities are located in the highlands. Bogota (1.0 million), capital and largest city, lies in a high valley of the eastern Andean range, and is reached by uncertain river transport on the Magdalena and by difficult road and rail connections to Cali and Buenaventura, the main Pacific port. Bogota is a cultural center for much of northern South America, but its commercial importance is limited, its hinterland being occupied largely by a dense population of Indians engaged in subsistence farming. Of more commercial importance is Medellin (0.6), a banking, transportation, and manufacturing center whose hinterland includes coffee raising and mining. Cali (0.3) is the center of population in the upper Cauca Valley, a sugar-cane producing area. Its growing list of industries includes paper, cement, and pharmaceuticals. Barranquilla (0.4), located at the mouth of the Magdalena, is both a seaport and a river port, with a hinterland that produces sugar cane, cotton, and bananas.

Venezuela has several natural parts: Maracaibo Basin; the lower, fragmented extension of the Andes; the extensive plains or llanos forming part of the basin of the Orinoco River; and an equally large area of Guiana Highlands. Each has a distinctive place in the economy of Venezuela. The Andean part has always had the main clusters of population, had an early start in commercial agriculture using Negro slaves, and still is a center of production of coffee, cacao, tobacco, and cotton and sugar cane at lower elevations. Livestock and subsistence agriculture also occupy much of the land. In this area are to be found not only the densest population and largest city, Caracas (1.16 million), but also the major evidences of modernization, such as railroads, highways, cotton textile factories, breweries, and other signs of industrialization. The sparsely populated llanos have been primarily a cattle producing area since Europeans brought in cattle in the middle of the sixteenth century. The discovery of petroleum along the northern side of the Orinoco basin, and of mineral deposits in the northern Guiana Highlands, have brought some changes to the llanos and to Ciudad Bolivar, the region's main city and port on the navigable Orinoco. The Highlands are the least known and least populated part of the country. Extremely valuable deposits of gold, iron, manganese, and diamonds are being mined, but other minerals remain undeveloped, as do the opportunities for agriculture and grazing. The discovery of petroleum in Maracaibo Basin changed the outlook of the whole country, and transformed sleepy little Maracaibo into a modern city of 0.4 million, but left unchanged its hot, sultry climate.

The dominance of Venezuela's economy by petroleum has meant that agricultural production has declined to the point where food and meats must be imported, at prices hardly within the reach of laborers. Peasants flock to oil fields and cities, where Europeans tend to hold the main jobs. For the most part, the new industries, such as steel, petrochemicals, glass, and others, only increase the gap between the urban and rural populations.

Ecuador is culturally part of both the Highlands and the Coast. The Highland section of basins and valleys surrounded by volcanic peaks unequaled elsewhere in the Andes, is densely

Rice threshing, Ecuador
[*U.S.D.A.*]

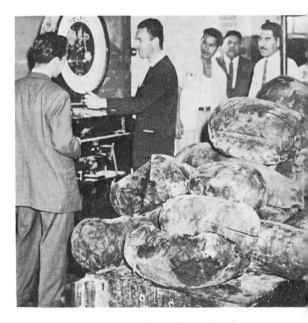

Rubber "pigs" from Peruvian Amazon
[*U.S.D.A.*]

Sugar cane harvest
[*U.S.D.A.*]

Stripping cinchona bark
[*U.S.D.A.*]

populated with agricultural Indians. In part they work on large estates and cattle ranches, but dominantly they are communal subsistence farmers who produce some cattle for sale. In one of the mountain basins is Quito (0.3), capital and leading Ecuadorean city, connected by rail to Guayaquil on the coast. In contrast to the Highlands, the Coast is tropical in climate and vegetation, contains most of the non-Indian elements of the population, and has the major commercial center of the country, the port city of Guayaquil (0.3). In the coastal section originate most of the nation's exports: cacao, bananas, rice, kapok, rubber, coffee, vegetable ivory, and fattened cattle, all from large estates; balsa wood, petroleum, gold, and "Jipijapa," better known as "Panama," hats. Expanding industries include the production of textiles, chemicals, edible oils, cement, and beer.

The contrast between subsistence-farming Indian and commercially minded European or mestizo is not peculiar to Ecuador. It extends throughout the highlands from Mexico to Peru and Bolivia.

CENTRAL SOUTH AMERICA

Central South America includes Peru, 514,000 square miles, and Bolivia, 416,000 square miles. Their respective populations of 10.2 million and 3.2 million are about 50 per cent pure Indian, 25 per cent mestizo, and the remainder is largely European, with some Negroes and Asians in Peru. The two countries have long been associated. They shared the pre-Inca cultures centered around Lake Titicaca that straddles the present boundary, were parts of the Inca empire, and remained united under Spanish rule. The modern boundary cuts across topographic features and through a dense, homogeneous Indian population, politically dividing an old major nucleus, but not interrupting the culture pattern and ways of life, which are the same in Andean Peru as in highland Bolivia.

Structurally, Andean Peru is similar to Bolivia, although there are differences in detail. In Peru, two mountain ranges, paralleling the coast, lie on either side of a broad, high plateau, which contains a number of basins. The western range is the water divide, and eastward-flowing streams have cut valleys in the plateau that become increasingly steep-sided and deep until they finally reach the Amazon lowland. These stream valleys contain the only moderate elevations encountered, for much of the plateau lies above 12,000 feet, and above it is a majestic array of 20,000-foot snow-capped peaks. The Peruvian plateau continues into Bolivia as the Altiplano, a mountain-rimmed plain 500 miles long and 80 miles wide, having an elevation of about 12,000 feet. It too is divided into a series of shallow basins. Again, the water divide follows the crest of the westernmost range, but only part of the drainage goes to the Amazon. A part flows into the Parana-Paraguay system, and the remainder never reaches the sea, for it flows into Lake Titicaca, which discharges southward into Lake Poopo and a region of undrained salt marshes.

The basic element in the highland occupance pattern is subsistence agriculture practiced by the dominant Indian population. The holdings are communal, individual plots are small, terracing and irrigation follow old practices, and methods are primitive. The crops are maize, and at higher elevations, Irish potatoes and quinoa. Native domesticated animals are grazed on high pastures, the llama being a beast of burden and source of meat, and the alpaca yielding fine wool. To the native plants and animals are added a few European introductions: wheat, barley, and sheep at higher elevations, cattle and sugar cane in the valleys. Superimposed on this pattern of Indian agriculture is a highly restricted, unevenly distributed system of large estates, owned by Europeans or mestizos, worked by Indians, and operated for profit. Cattle, sheep, sugar cane, coffee, wheat, and fruits are grown, mainly for local markets, such as the mining communities. None of the highland agricultural products ranks high among the exports of either country.

The commercial interest of the highlands is mining, an industry dating back to pre-Columbian Indians who mined and smelted gold, silver, copper, and tin, and mixed the latter two to form bronze. The Indians, how-

ever, did little to change the landscape as compared with the discordant elements introduced by mining operations of large foreign companies. At such centers as Cajamarca and Cerro de Pasco in Peru and Oruro in Bolivia, not only are there structures, machinery, and dwellings directly associated with mining, but also local commercial agriculture and modern communication with coastal ports. Highland-produced minerals dominate Bolivia's exports and are important among Peru's. Bolivia normally supplies about 15 per cent of the world's tin, and quantities of antimony, tungsten, wolfram, silver, lead, zinc, copper, and gold. From highland Peru come vanadium, copper, silver, gold, lead, and zinc, with a total value about equal to that of the petroleum produced on the coast.

There are many towns in the highlands, but few cities. Those founded by the Spaniards have a set form: a square or plaza around which are the church and government buildings; streets are lined with adobe houses, the more pretentious ones with a patio, and, if two-storied, with a high balcony. The largest of the cities is La Paz (0.4 million), the seat of Bolivia's government, and the country's commercial center, with rail lines to the free port of Arica, Peru, and Antofagasta, Chile, the main entrepots of this land-locked country. The industry of La Paz includes the manufacture of matches, shoes, beverages, tobacco products, leather goods, and woolen textiles.

Although the highlands are the real heart of Bolivia, containing three quarters of its population, and are one of two culturally important parts of Peru, both countries include large sections east of the mountains, in the continental-interior lowlands. Much of the eastern section is rain forest, both on the Andean slopes and the plains, but part is savanna, and to the south, in the Chaco, the climate is steppe. Very few commercially minded farmers have ventured into the lowlands because of the difficulties of getting products out and supplies in. A more common invader is the exploiter of wild rubber, coca, and cinchona trees, and the searcher for petroleum. Attempts to raise cattle and to conduct plantation agriculture have shown that it is possible to grow a variety of crops, but development has been held back by poor and expensive transportation. To help open up this rich section, Peru built its first trans-Andean highway in 1943, and in 1953 Bolivia completed a road to Santa Cruz, rail-head of a line to São Paulo, Brazil. These roads provide the eastern section with outlets, both across the barrier of the Andes and along navigable tributaries of the Amazon. As important as the roads, and perhaps of more significance in the development of this eastern section, is the discovery of promising oil fields.

Lacking a seaboard, Bolivia has no counterpart to coastal Peru, which is the modern Peru of Europeans and mixed-bloods. It has the largest cities, produces the major commercial crops, and contains the country's industry, aside from that connected with highland mining. This cool, desert coastal region was not especially attractive to the pre-Columbian Indians, although they did establish a few agricultural oases where rivers emerged from the mountains. The importance of the coastal region started with Pizarro who made Lima the capital of the empire that replaced the old Inca empire with its capital at Cuzco. Lima became and remained the great center of the Spanish possessions in America. At first the Spaniards simply took over some of the irrigated oases, discovered that their animals could find enough to eat in the vegetation of the fog-drenched coast and on the mountainsides, and learned that guano deposits make excellent fertilizer, but their interests were mainly in mining, and agriculture was restricted to the production of needed food crops.

Commercial agriculture began only in the late nineteenth century, and was initiated with sugar cane. Its success led to other crops, notably cotton, which now leads the list of agricultural exports. Maize remains the staple food crop, supplemented by rice. Expansion of the irrigated agricultural oases on the coast has reached the point of complete utilization of the available water, from both rivers and wells.

The coast has produced petroleum since 1880. The fields, all in the section bordering Ecuador, provide Peru with half of its mineral exports, and although local consumption now takes some 70 per cent of the production, exports remain high. Petroleum has introduced its own peculiar modifications to the landscape in the form of oil fields, refineries, pipelines, and industrial settlements.

Little villages dot the coast, in support of the active fishing industry which is now freezing and canning a considerable portion of its catch. But completely overshadowing these little ports is Callao, the country's chief entrepot. Like other Pacific ports of central and northern South America, it is essentially an open roadstead, somewhat protected by a breakwater. The port's hinterland includes the highland mining sections and the agricultural coast, but most important, it includes Lima (1.2 million), Peru's capital and chief center of commerce and industry. Lima is a pleasant mixture of the old, as typified by the venerable San Marcos University, and the new, seen in the factories producing sugar, cotton textiles, shoes, chocolate, and flour. North of Callao, at Chimbote, is Peru's first iron and steel mill, opened in 1958 to produce pig iron, wire, and sheet metal. At the southern end of coastal Peru is Arequipa, an export center for highland wool, hides, and other articles.

SOUTHERN SOUTH AMERICA

Included in this region are Argentina, 1,084,120 square miles with a population of 20.3 million; Chile, 286,397 square miles and 7.1 million population; Paraguay, 157,000 square miles and 1.65 million; and Uruguay, 72,172 square miles, 2.7 million population. Regional unity, both natural and cultural, is limited. Within the region, however, are most of South America's temperate climates, and the continent's one major expanse of highly productive plains. Racially the region is overwhelmingly European and mestizo, pure-blooded Indians being unimportant socially and economically, and Negroes and other elements being few. Argentina is the most European, while the other three countries are dominantly mestizo.

Chile is isolated from the other countries by the Andean barrier, and is remote in historic aspects, its settlements having little in common with those to the east of the mountains. The structure of this stringbeanlike country, 2,600 miles long by 40 to 250 miles wide, is similar to that of the Pacific Northwest region of North America. Between the Andes to the east and the much-lower coast ranges is an interior valley. From Chile's northern boundary south to about 30° S., both valley and mountains have extremely dry climates, barren surfaces, and only an occasional oasis. The section is Chile's major source of mineral wealth. South of the desert is a belt of Mediterranean climate, and here the interior depression, the Vale of Chile, is the nuclear area of the nation. From 36° southward the forest is heavier and rainfall more abundant. At about 42° S. the central valley gets lost in a maze of islands and arms of the sea. The irregular glaciated coast provides innumerable harbors, in contrast to the unbroken northern coast.

East of the Andes are plains and basins that extend to the Atlantic and stretch from Bolivia south to the Rio Negro, where they meet the barren bleak Patagonian plateau. They experience a considerable seasonal range of temperature, and are well watered only where streams emerge from the mountains. From the desert and steppe in the south, the plains become humid grasslands toward the northeast. These plains have local names: Gran Chaco in Paraguay and northern Argentina, Entre Rios between the Parana and Uruguay rivers, and Pampa in central Argentina. The grassy Pampa continues into southern Uruguay, but to the north the surface is rougher, and is an extension of the uplands of southern Brazil. Inland, the Brazilian plateau extends into Paraguay, to end abruptly before reaching the Paraguay River. Where the Paraguay and Parana rivers meet, the plateau gives way to a low marsh and swamp. West of the Paraguay is the nation's much fought-over section of the Chaco, newly important because of petroleum developments.

Chile felt the influence of the Inca empire, was early settled by Spaniards who founded Santiago in 1541 and Valparaiso two years later, and long remained, in its nuclear central valley, a land of large feudal estates owned by mestizos and worked by mestizos and Indians, where cattle grazed and crops were grown by irrigation agriculture. A wide gap developed between the wealthy few and the impoverished mass of peon laborers, who formed a steady stream of migrants to Argentina. It was not until the nineteenth century that the economy was broadened. First came a group of German settlers who went into the stubbornly-resistant Araucanian Indian country south of the Vale of Chile, cleared the forests, set up small, owner-operated farms, and introduced crafts, such as iron and wood working, and the making of shoes, all of which served as examples for the landless Chilean peasants. The second series of developments came with minerals, and involved the sparsely settled desert section of northern Chile.

In the middle of the nineteenth century important finds of silver and copper were made, copper becoming a permanent industry and a leading Chilean export. At about the same time, the demand for nitrates caused a boom in production. Chile continues to supply a large share of the world's nitrate for fertilizer and the by-product, iodine. Sulphur is abundant in the north also. Excellent iron ore from the southern part of the desert section, and quantities of rather poor-quality coal found in coastal middle Chile, combine to foster a growing iron and steel industry near Concepcion. While mining broadened the national economic base, its unpredictable fluctuations did not contribute to economic stability, a stability that may be achieved by the current surging expansion of manufacturing.

While old nuclear middle Chile remains the center of the old system of grazing and irrigation agriculture on large estates, it also contains the most evidence of industrialization and the largest cities. Santiago (1.6 million) and Valparaiso (0.3) are centers of an industrial area producing such items as wine, beer, flour, textiles, chemicals, canned food, furniture, sugar, leather, and shoes. From the big refinery just north of Valparaiso comes most of the petroleum Chile uses, although part of the crude oil is imported. Industry gets its power from hydroelectricity, and former peasants provide the labor.

Mt. Osorno, Chile
[*Chilean Consulate General, N.Y.*]

South of the nuclear area, Concepcion, Valdivia, Temuco, and other cities are local centers of urbanization and industrialization, surrounded by a rural countryside producing beef cattle, dairy products, wheat, Irish potatoes, apples, and timber. Farther south, in the fiord country, excellent timber is abundant. The cool ocean currents support an enormous fish population, a resource only partially exploited, although some canned fish is now exported. In extreme southern Chile, where the coolness of summer inhibits forest growth and promotes grasslands, millions of sheep are grazed. The recent discovery of petroleum in Chilean Tierra del Fuego initiated a rush of adventurers and settlers to the area. The southernmost city in the world, Puntas Arenas (Magallanes) grew to over 40,000. In addition to petroleum and sheep, this area also produces wool and furs.

Argentina held few attractions for the Spaniards who found that its sparsely populated plains lacked minerals. But the flat, open country offered a route from the Atlantic to Peru, from the Plata estuary to Lima, by way of the Parana-Paraguay river system. Following this path upstream, settlers reached the mouth of the Pilcomayo, where, on high ground and in the midst of a fairly dense population of agricultural Guarani Indians, they founded Asuncion, the first permanent settlement in the plains. Colonists then began arriving from the north, to settle at oasis sites along the western border of

the plains. Santiago del Estero (1553) and Tucuman (1564) were established by colonists from Bolivia, Mendoza (1561) was founded from Chile, and settlers spreading out from Asuncion founded in 1573 Cordoba and Santa Fe, and permanently established Buenos Aires, in 1581.

Cattle, horses, sheep, and goats were introduced by the first Europeans to reach the plains. Numbers of them escaped and survived to multiply amazingly in this highly favorable environment. The plains Indians were transformed into well-fed, fierce horsemen. The *gaucho* was born out of the vigorous life involved in chasing wild cattle. And the plains took on their prime colonial function: supplying Peru with mules, fodder, and cattle. This economy, however, did little to promote settlement, and the growth of Buenos Aires was stifled by the rule that all imports must come over the long Panama-Peru route. A change came with the establishment in 1776 of the viceroyalty of Buenos Aires, including present Argentina, Uruguay, Paraguay, and Bolivia. Trade barriers were removed and settlement encouraged, but these changes were made not so much to help the colonists as to provide Spain with a means to counter the Portuguese who had taken an interest in the area. After numerous conflicts, during which the Portuguese settlement of Colonia passed back and forth between Spanish and Portuguese hands, Spain finally gained full control of both banks of the Plata estuary.

The nuclear pattern for the whole region took shape. Its centers were Buenos Aires, Montevideo, Asuncion, and the western oasis towns. For each population cluster there was a largely self-contained economy. On both sides of the Plata estuary it was large ranches with little production of vegetable foods. In the oases and around Asuncion there was a stronger irrigation agriculture tradition. In general, there was little trade with the outside and rural population densities were low.

Transforming changes started in the middle of the nineteenth century, brought about by improved land and sea transportation, an apparently insatiable European urban market for food, and large-scale immigration that included Italians, Germans, British, and Spaniards. The grasslands promptly became exporters of meat, hides, and wool. The shipment of live animals gave way to chilled or frozen carcasses of fattened animals. Feed crops were necessary for the fattening of improved breeds, and the job of raising them was done by the immigrant peasants, who did not share the native disdain for agriculture. Gradually agriculture found a place, especially when it was discovered that the market for wheat and maize was equal to that for meat, hides, and wool. Fruits, vegetables, and dairy products found eager consumers in the cities.

The Pampa's rural landscape developed less along typical Spanish-American lines than along those of the agricultural interior of North America. There is a similar pattern of an intricate net of railroads, vast fields, farmsteads with a windbreak of trees, and grain elevators in shipping towns. There is a high degree of mechanization. The population is clearly European, not mestizo, and while its density is low, the concentration into cities is surprisingly large. In this small central core in the Pampa live two thirds of the country's population. To this core come sheep, wool, meat, gas, and petroleum from Patagonia; sugar from Tucuman; grapes and wine from Mendoza; yerba mate from Formosa on the Paraguayan border, and cotton and petroleum from the Chaco. All of the country's great cities and essentially all its industries are located in the Pampa. More than a quarter of Argentina's population live in four Pampa cities: Buenos Aires (3.8 million), Rosario (0.7), Cordoba (0.5), and La Plata (0.4). Many of the industries are concerned with processing for export the yield from farm and ranch, such as packing and canning meat, milling flour, weaving cotton textiles, making wines and beverages, and producing shoes and other leather goods. But in addition there is shipbuilding, metalworking, and the manufacture of glass, chemicals, paper, and furniture. Heavy industries are generally lacking because of the shortage of metallic ores and coal, and the remoteness of sources of hydroelectric power, but the national policy in the direction of diversity of industry may alter this picture.

Uruguay has had about the same sequence of development as the Pampa, and, like it, is racially European, and largely devoted to stock raising and wheat growing. Along the southern coast are vineyards and orchards, and in the Uruguay Valley, flax, rice, citrus fruits, and sugar cane are grown in addition to wheat. The dominating city is Montevideo, its million inhabitants accounting for a third of the country's total population. It is primarily a commercial center, but it also processes meat, wool, and hides, mills flour, manufactures textiles, and makes wines. Great industrial expansion seems unlikely in a country so little endowed with mineral resources and having Latin America's most thorough-going social legislation.

Paraguay is a more remote and less advanced extension of the Pampa landscape, but there are some major differences: the Paraguayan people are overwhelmingly mestizo, and there is an old tradition of agriculture. From the standpoint of arable land, climate, and vegetation resources, Paraguay is richly endowed, but it suffered a century of Indian revolts and wars with its neighbors, which left the country devastated. In the peace since 1933, attempts to reconstruct and repopulate the country have been handicapped by lack of transportation. Poverty, disease, and ignorance among the population are equaled in few other places in Latin America. Landless peasants work on large estates to produce a wide variety of food and commercial crops, such as maize, cotton, sugar cane, mandioca, yerba mate, peanuts, tobacco, and citrus fruits. But only 5 per cent of the cultivable land is farmed, and agriculture, like all other activities, centers around Asuncion. Much of the central part of the country, along the Paraguay Valley, is devoted to livestock grazing and the logging of quebracho trees from which tannin is derived. With its mineral resources left undeveloped, and lacking fuels and adequate transportation, such industry as Paraguay has is devoted to making a few goods for home consumption and to processing for export cotton, beef, hides, tobacco, and orange-leaf extract used in perfumes. High hopes are being pinned on the exploitation of Chaco petroleum, but this is unlikely to change the lot of the average Paraguayan.

Brazilian Highlands landscape, Terezopolis
[*J. Ronza*]

BRAZIL

With its 3.29 million square miles and 63 million inhabitants, Brazil is the giant country of Latin America, occupying half of South America and containing half the continent's population. Brazil shares a boundary with every other South American country except Ecuador and Chile, and within its vast territory it contains all the cultural diversity suggested by such widespread contacts. The population includes a large Negro element, and Indians living in a primitive state. Tropical, subtropical, and temperate crops are produced. There are large estates worked by landless laborers and small

Brazilian herdsmen
[*Consulate General of Brazil, N.Y.*]

farms worked by their owners, an old pastoral tradition, and great cities with expanding industries. But Brazil also has some qualities of its own, for example, its language is Portuguese rather than Spanish.

Brazil is a land of magnificent natural resources. A large proportion of its total area is usable for agriculture and grazing. Minerals and forests are both excellent and abundant. Yet diligent as the Brazilians are, many of the resources remain hardly touched, and only a quarter of the country is in agricultural production. The area of greatest utilization, densest population, and highest production is the Brazilian Highlands, the true Brazil of past and present. The Highlands, occupying about half the area of the country, are a plateau of irregular surface ranging in elevation from 1,000 to 3,000 feet, above which rise a few low ranges. Variations in elevation, exposure, and latitude are responsible for the wide range of climates and vegetation found within the Highland area. The northern coast is tropical rain forest, the northern interior is savanna, and the southern section is temperate forest land.

On the northeastern Highlands coast, around Salvador and Recife, there developed in the sixteenth century the system of commercial plantations involving Negro slaves, but to the south, in São Paulo, development followed a different course. Here the *Paulistas*, lacking both capital and experience needed in the commercial plantation system, became small farmers and herdsmen. Many roamed the interior looking for minerals, and for Indians to enslave, and incidently mixing with the Indians sufficiently to produce a new racial group of hardy, gaucho-like herdsmen who pioneered the new land and continue to populate the remoter interior of the plateau. The search for minerals was rewarded by a major discovery of gold in 1693, and diamonds a few years later. The center of activity was in the present state of Minas Gerais. To this region of riches came not only Paulistas but also Brazilians from the sugar area and hopefuls from many parts of the continent and the world. But as always, such mining booms came to an end. By the start of the nineteenth century many mines had been abandoned and population had decreased, but there remained a settled Minas Gerais and a Rio de Janeiro that had emerged as the most important of the many excellent Brazilian ports.

The state of São Paulo next entered enthusiastically into the coffee business, and soon captured world leadership in production, a ranking position still held by the southern Highlands, despite a new and growing rivalry with cotton for the land. The agricultural prosperity attracted European and Brazilian immigrants, the state became the most modernized section of Brazil, and its chief city, São Paulo, grew in size to where it could challenge the supremacy of Rio de Janeiro. In recent years Rio de Janeiro has been outstripped in both population and industry by São Paulo, and has lost its political function as capital to Brazilia, the new, planned city in the Highlands.

The system of plantation-coffee agriculture expanded northward into the sugar-cane region, and somewhat to the south into the temperate forest lands. In southernmost Brazil the pattern of occupance is different from that found elsewhere. In about 1825 a German colony was established there to ward off agressive moves by the Spanish. Germans are still a dominant element, although there are numerous Italians, Slavs, and others engaged in raising rice, manioc, maize, and other crops. The character of settlement in Rio Grande do Sul is typically European, the German areas being distinguished by Old World architecture, crops of rye and maize, and the production of hogs. Italian settlements are marked by vineyards. Everywhere the holdings are of modest size and are worked by the owners. To serve the area is Brazil's fifth largest city, Porto Alegre.

Outside the Brazilian Highlands lies the vast, sparsely settled Amazon drainage basin, where activities are mainly concerned with the gathering of wild products, such as Brazil nuts, timber, rubber, resins, castor beans, orchids, and fish. From 1850 to World War I, demand for rubber brought a spectacular boom to the Amazon. River ports, such as Manaus, Santarem, and Belem, grew enormously and even took on airs of urban sophistication. Malayan competition and plant diseases brought an end to prosperity.

More recent attempts to conduct plantation cultivation, sponsored by North American interests, have also ended in abandonment. Belem managed to survive, and is the one large urban center of the Amazon region.

The diverse present-day landscapes of Brazil follow the historic patterns: tropical plantations on the north coast of the Highlands, coffee and cotton estates in São Paulo; European-type farmsteads in the southern states; extensive grazing on the Highlands interior; and gathering in the Amazon forest. Mining, which has contributed more wealth than everything else combined, continues to yield gold, diamonds, iron, manganese, coal, chrome, tungsten, beryllium, and other minerals. Rather minor petroleum fields are being worked.

Imposed on these old patterns are the new developments of urbanization and industrialization. Brazil's six largest cities: São Paulo (3.2), Rio de Janeiro (2.9), Recife (0.7), Salvador (Bahia) (0.5), Porto Alegre (0.5), and Belo Horizonte (0.5), account for some 12 per cent of the country's total population, which is almost 40 per cent urban. This growth of great cities is a result of the rapid increase in industry. Manufacturing output is double the value of agriculture and grazing combined. Light industries are dominant, such as food-processing, textiles, clothing, paper, furniture, and small consumer goods, but heavy industry is represented in the new steel plants turning out both cast and rolled products.

The Guianas join Brazil on the north, and are three remnants of European empire in America: British Guiana (83,000 square miles and 540,000 inhabitants), Surinam or Dutch Guiana (55,400; 240,000), and French Guiana and Inini (65,000; 28,000). The effective territory of each country is a strip of tropical coast plain. Back of the plain rises the steep escarpment of the Guiana Highlands, over which numerous rivers plunge in rapids and waterfalls. The population of British Guiana and Surinam is dominantly East Indian, with a large group of mixed and pure Negroes, and a few Indians and Bush Negroes in the interior. French Guiana has a mixture of white and Negro peoples. The East Indians grow rice, and the Negroes work on large copper and other metals, and the forests. The situation in the Guianas confirms the opinion that in no case have European powers developed in tropical America a plan of utilization that is successful alike for capital, labor, and the land itself.

CONCLUSION

Latin America is "Latin" only in a limited sense. Racially much of the Cordilleran population is pure Indian, and the islands of the Caribbean and its borders are overwhelmingly Negroid. Nor is the cultural landscape dominantly European or "Latin." People living in isolated groups sprinkled over a vast area have developed a diversity of landscapes: the highland Indians of Guatemala, in contrast with the lowland tribes of Brazil; the African cultures of Haiti; Spanish colonial plantations of northeast Brazil and the herdsmen of the interior; miners and forest gatherers; the Vale of Chile and the Argentine Pampa; and finally, modern cities and growing industrialization. But this diversity is, in itself, a unifying characteristic, entitling Latin America to recognition as a distinct realm in the American division of the New World.

Panning for gold, Brazil
[*Consulate General of Brazil, N.Y.*]

plantations growing tropical food and export crops, such as sugar, coffee, cacao, coconuts, citrus fruits, yams, bananas, and root crops. Particularly important is the mining of bauxite in British and Dutch Guiana, but almost untouched are other resources, such as diamonds,

Index

CULTURE
WORLDS